TRANSLATIONS OF MATHEMATICAL MONOGRAPHS

VOLUME 21

CONSTRUCTIVE REAL NUMBERS AND CONSTRUCTIVE FUNCTION SPACES

BY

N. A. ŠANIN

american mathematical society
providence, rhode island
1968

КОНСТРУКТИВНЫЕ ВЕЩЕСТВЕННЫЕ ЧИСЛА И КОНСТРУКТИВНЫЕ ФУНКЦИОНАЛЬНЫЕ ПРОСТРАНСТВА

Н. А. ШАНИН

ТРУДЫ МАТЕМАТИЧЕСКОГО ИНСТИТУТА
имени В. А. СТЕКЛОВА
LXVII, 15–294

Издательство Академии Наук СССР
Москва 1962 Ленинград

Translated from the Russian by
E. Mendelson

Library of Congress Card Number 68—19437

Printed in the United States of America

TABLE OF CONTENTS

INTRODUCTION

0.1. This book is devoted to certain problems of constructive mathematical analysis.[1] The basic sections are Chapters II and III, which are devoted to the foundations of the theory of constructive function spaces. Information from the theory of constructive real numbers needed in these chapters is presented in the first chapter. The first chapter also contains other material: in it the logico-mathematical symbolism which we shall use is described and some problems of constructive mathematical logic are considered.

In the mathematical literature the adjective "constructive" is used in various senses. In the present work the adjective "constructive" will be used only in the following sense: the presence of this adjective in the term for a concept, the name of a method, the name of a branch of mathematics, etc. will signify that the indicated concept, method, branch of mathematics, etc. belongs to the constructive approach to mathematics.

The constructive approach to mathematics is characterized by the following features:[2] 1) in mathematical theories belonging to this approach, only constructive objects[3] figure as objects of study; 2) in the study of constructive

1) In this book the term "mathematical analysis" is used in the broad sense, covering the theory of functions of real variables, the theory of functions of complex variables, the theory of generalized functions, and functional analysis. The term "functional analysis" is also used in the broad sense covering the theory of metric, multimetric, normed, and multinormed spaces, the theory of functionals, operators, and equations in such spaces.

2) The author bases himself on the characterization of the constructive approach to mathematics given by A. A. Markov in lectures on the foundations of mathematics delivered at Leningrad University during the 1948–49 academic year. (Cf. also his paper "On constructive mathematics", published in this issue of Trudy Mat. Inst. Steklov.)

3) By constructive objects are meant objects which are the results of processes of construction realizable on the following basis: one assumes that the objects which figure in the given study as indecomposable initial objects are clearly described; one assumes given a list of rules of formation of new objects from previously constructed ones, which in the given study plays the role of a description of the admissable steps of constructive processes; one assumes that the processes of construction are carried out in discrete steps, where the choice of each succeeding step is arbitrary, within the limits determined by the list of already constructed objects and the set of those rules of formation of new objects which can actually be applied to already constructed objects. The constructive objects most used in mathematics are words in certain alphabets and lists of words in

objects one is permitted a certain idealization, the so-called *abstraction of potential realizability* (see [1]), but the use of the abstraction of actual infinity is completely forbidden; 3) in accordance with the type of objects of study and the abstraction of potential realizability as a meaningful basis for the construction of mathematical theories one takes the constructive interpretation of mathematical judgments (see [3]; a brief description of the fundamental principles of the constructive interpretation of judgments can be found in [4]).

In theories belonging to the constructive approach to mathematics the apparatus of logical deduction is the apparatus of constructive logic. This apparatus is developed in conformity with the constructive interpretation of mathematical judgments. The apparatus of logical deduction of constructive logic has essential differences from the apparatus of logical deduction of classical logic.

The term "constructive mathematics" will be understood in the following presentation as a synonym of the term "constructive approach to mathematics".

In accordance with the meaning taken above of the adjective "constructive", the term "constructive mathematical analysis" will be used here as a name for the approach to mathematical analysis which possesses the features mentioned above of the constructive approach to mathematics. In analogous senses we use the terms "constructive functional analysis", "constructive theory of sets", and other terms obtained by adding the adjective "constructive" or corresponding variations of this adjective to the names of various divisions of mathematics.

The constructive approach to mathematics arose only in the twentieth century. It differs essentially from the classical approach to mathematics.

To the classical approach to mathematics belong those mathematical theories in which the abstraction of actual infinity is used and in which the apparatus of classical logic 1) is employed as the apparatus of logical deduction. The term "classical mathematics" will be used in the following presentation as a synonym

certain alphabets (see [1]). We have not mentioned here algorithms and calculi, since algorithms and calculi of the customary types are given by means of lists of words. The consideration of lists of words in a given alphabet can be reduced, by a simple constructive method, to the consideration of words of a definite type in a suitably constructed alphabet. The same can be said about the study of constructive objects of other types occuring in mathematics (cf. [1] and [2]).

1) To classical logic belong those logical theories which follow in their main features a definite tradition stemming from Aristotle. The most important feature of these logical theories is that they have as one of their initial assumptions or as a consequence of their initial assumptions the law of excluded middle, formulated so as to be applicable to any proposition falling within the domain of the given logical theory.

of the term "classical approach to mathematics".

In this book the adjective "classical" will be used in the following sense: the presence of this adjective in the term for a concept, name of a method, name of a division of mathematics, etc. will signify that the corresponding concept, method, division of mathematics, etc. belongs to the classical approach to mathematics.

In accordance with this meaning of the adjective "classical", the term "classical mathematical analysis" will be used here as a name of the approach to mathematical analysis which has the features mentioned above of the classical approach to mathematics. In analogous senses we shall apply the terms "classical functional analysis", "classical theory of sets", and other terms obtained by adding the adjective "classical" or corresponding variations of this adjective to names of various divisions of mathematics.

It is necessary to emphasize that in works belonging to the classical approach to mathematics the adjective "constructive" is very often used in significantly wider senses than that characterized above. For example, the term "constructive theory of functions" used in classical mathematics is a name of a certain division of classical mathematics which, in the form in which it exists at the present time, cannot be placed within the scope of the constructive approach to mathematics. To avoid ambiguity we agree to call the above-mentioned "constructive theory of functions" the classical theory of approximate representation of functions. Assuming this convention, we are able to distinguish between the constructive theory of approximate representation of functions and the classical theory of the approximate representation of functions.

In works belonging to the classical approach to mathematics there often occur concepts, definitions, propositions, and proofs which are called by the authors of these papers constructive concepts, definitions, propositions, and proofs, while at the same time they do not satisfy some of the conditions necessary for including them in the constructive approach to mathematics. In all such cases the meaning of the term "constructive" differs from the meaning accepted in the present work.

0.2. The process of formulating the fundamental concepts of classical mathematical analysis began on a very unclear logical basis. In the works of Cauchy, Weierstrass, Dedekind, Cantor and other authors, the logical basis of mathematical analysis underwent a series of successive rigorizations and transformations. Of particular importance to the fate of this logical basis was the publication in the second half of the nineteenth century of the work of Dedekind and Cantor devoted to the foundations of the theory of sets and the theory of real numbers. In the papers of Dedekind and Cantor, as a basis of the definitions of many important concepts of mathematical analysis there was put in clear and sharp form the abstraction of actual infinity and the system of conceptual ideas arising from this abstraction.

The process of developing the theory of sets and the branches of mathematics based on it was at the same time a process of developing and making precise the methods of logical deduction on the basis of tradition and the fundamental principles of classical logic.

At the end of the nineteenth century the logical foundations of classical mathematical analysis were, in their principal features, clearly determined. Till the beginning of the twentieth century classical mathematical analysis was the unique and uniformly dominant approach to mathematical analysis.

At the beginning of the twentieth century L. E. J. Brouwer and H. Weyl examined certain theoretical aspects of the logical foundations of classical mathematics. Brouwer set forth detailed criticism of the abstraction of actual infinity and certain laws of classical logic (above all, the law of excluded middle).[1] Independently, Weyl criticized that use of the concepts "set" and "function" in which one ignored the problem concerning the method within the limits of which the sets and functions under consideration can be individually given. Weyl's criticism did not extend at first to the laws of classical logic. After becoming acquainted with Brouwer's criticism of classical logic, Weyl announced his agreement with this criticism.

Brouwer and Weyl did not limit themselves to criticism of classical mathematical analysis. They proposed their own construction of the foundations of mathematical analysis, starting from certain systems of idealizations and concepts which are essentially different from the idealizations and concepts lying at the basis of classical mathematical analysis. Weyl's theory [2] differs sharply from

1) Criticism of the abstraction of actual infinity was undertaken in the history of science even before Brouwer. However, Brouwer's criticism affects not only the abstraction of actual infinity but also classical logic, consisting of the theory of logical deduction (in the case of an infinite domain of objects of study) based on ideas stemming from the abstraction of actual infinity. Because of this, the criticism undertaken by Brouwer is essentially broader and more profound than the criticism expressed by his prodecessors.

2) See [5].

Brouwer's theory [1]. Each of these theories contains a host of very important ideas which exerted a great influence on later investigations and determined many features of contemporary constructive mathematical analysis.

The first important idea of Brouwer consisted in suggesting the construction of mathematical analysis and other divisions of mathmetics without use of the abstraction of actual infinity. The abstraction of potential realizability [2] was considered by Brouwer to be an admissable idealization. The second important idea of Brouwer reduces to the fact that, for mathematical theories redeveloped on the basis of the abstraction of potential realizability, a special logic, essentially different from the classical one, is necessary.

Weyl's most important idea consists in the plan for constructing mathematical analysis so that as objects of study occur only constructive objects which may be individually given within the scope of some clearly described symbolism. In Weyl's theory not only the term "rational number", but also the terms "set of rational numbers", "real number", "set of real numbers", "real function of a real variable" and others are connected with constructive objects admitting individual presentation by means of symbolic expressions of certain types.

The important ideas of Brouwer and Weyl mentioned above essentially determined the basic features of the constructive approach to mathematics. In addition to these main ideas, there is also in the papers of Brouwer and Weyl a host of important ideas of a more special character, which also had a great influence on the development of constructive mathematical analysis.

However, at the time when Brouwer and Weyl worked out their theories, mathematics still did not have at its disposal a fundamental concept which was formulated much later and without which it is impossible to find a satisfactory and fruitful way of reforming mathematical analysis on the basis of the general ideas of Brouwer and Weyl mentioned above. We have in mind here the precise concept of algorithm. Therefore it is not surprising that in the theories of Brouwer and

---

1) One can become familiar with the basic features of Brouwer's theory through the papers of H. Weyl, published in Russian in the collection [6], and through a book of A. Heyting [7]. *Translator's note.* Most of Brouwer's papers, in German and English, first appeared in Nederl. Akad. Wetensch. Proc. Ser. A. See Math. Reviews or Zbl. Math. for details.

2) The term "abstraction of potential realizability" was proposed by A. A. Markov. The meaning which Markov invests in this term (see [1]) is essentially identical with the meaning of the term "potential infinity", which had been used for a long time in the literature. Brouwer and Weyl used the term "potential infinity". In this paper the term "abstraction of potential realizability" will always be used.

Weyl the approaches to the construction of mathematical analysis on the basis of new ideas proposed by these authors possess a series of essential deficiences. Brouwer, in his theory, proceeds by introducing and systematically using a very obscure idea, "freely formed sequence". This idea is not compatible with the first feature of the constructive approach to mathematics (cf. §0.1).

The deficiencies in Weyl's theory have a completely different character. Weyl considers only constructive objects. But in the first place he applies to their study classical logic (as a result of which many propositions proved within the framework of Weyl's theory turn out to be refutable propositions in constructive mathematics), and secondly, the concept of constructive real number introduced by Weyl is such that there is no algorithm transforming any constructive real number x and any natural number n into a rational number such that the absolute value of the difference between this rational number and x is less than 2^{-n}. The latter fact casts doubt upon the advisability of using the concept of real number introduced by Weyl as the basis for the construction of constructive mathematical analysis. (Here it is assumed that the question of advisability is considered in close connection with the applications of mathematics.)

Neither Brouwer's theory nor Weyl's theory satisfied mathematicians. Completely new possibilities opened up when a precise concept of arithmetic algorithm (computable arithmetic function) was developed in mathematics. This happened in the middle of the thirties of this century. The enrichment of mathematics with the precise concept of arithmetic algorithm served as a starting point for fruitful investigation in a new direction by many authors. These investigations formed the beginning of a gradual formulation of the modern theory of constructive real numbers and constructive functions of a real variable.

The approach to mathematical analysis developed in this way, called constructive mathematical analysis, possesses those features which were enumerated above as the basic features of the constructive approach to mathematics. These basic features were determined to a considerable extent by a synthesis of the fundamental ideas of Brouwer and Weyl. A host of important ideas of Brouwer and Weyl having a more special character were also woven into the fabric of modern constructive mathematical analysis (in many cases, in considerably revised form). At the same time it is necessary to mention that modern constructive mathematical analysis differs considerably from the theories of Brouwer and Weyl. It is a new theory basing itself essentially on the precise concept of algorithm and on the theory of algorithms.

Constructive mathematical analysis arose only in the present century, and its modern structure began to be formed only in the thirties of this century. It still does not have a large literature, but has been intensively developed recently. Its basic idealization, its logical foundations, many essential features and details of its theory and also some of its theory as a whole differ essentially from the basic idealizations, logical foundations, corresponding features and details, and the corresponding theory of classical mathematical analysis.

0.3. Brouwer connects his criticism of classical mathematics with a philosophical viewpoint which has received the name "intuitionism". 1) Adherents to this viewpoint believe that the unique source of mathematics is the intuition, and the criterion of acceptability of mathematical concepts, constructions, and inferences is intuitive clarity. They ignore the fact that the root source of the formation of mathematical concepts, methods of mathematical constructions, and methods of inference is human practice and experience.

Certainly intuitionistic philosophy is in error. However, in the paper of Brouwer and Weyl, outside of the surface of intuitionistic philosophy one finds in many cases very valuable concrete observations and profound concrete analysis of the fundamental problems relating to the processes of forming mathematical abstractions and logical foundations of mathematics.

0.4. In connection with the problems of forming mathematical abstractions, Hilbert's paper [10] is of great interest. This paper contains an analysis of the abstraction of actual infinity, and it is emphasized that this abstraction is an idealization, not having support in experimental natural science.

The analysis of the processes of forming mathematical abstractions and logical foundations of mathematics, making more precise and adding to the ideas of Brouwer and Weyl, is being continued at the present time. Important work in this direction has been accomplished by A. A. Markov. In a series of lectures, and to some extent in published work (see [8], pp. 315–316 (transl. pp. 163–164)), Markov put forth a criticism of classical mathematics and an analysis of the properties of constructive mathematics on perfectly clear foundations. He starts out with an analysis of certain idealizations used in mathematics, and with an analysis of the connections between these idealizations and the experimental material of the natural sciences and everyday experience which are the initial sources of the

1) Weyl in some of his papers sympathetically presents the philosphical views of Brouwer and associates himself with them.

formation of these idealizations. Such an approach presented the opportunity of freeing oneself from the layers of intuitionistic philosophy, and of supplementing and making precise the valuable critical analysis of the foundations of classical mathematics which is in the papers of Brouwer and Weyl and the fundamental ideas of those prominent mathematicians who initiated the constructive approach to mathematics. Following this path, Markov gave a clear characterization of the constructive approach to mathematics.

0.5. In evaluting the possible role of constructive mathematical analysis in contemporary mathematics and its applications it is necessary to keep in mind the basic features of the criticism of classical mathematics which has been set forth by Brouwer, Weyl, Markov, and various other mathematicians.

Above all it is necessary to emphasize that in this criticism of classical mathematics the question does not concern some logical inconsistencies within classical mathematical analysis nor the omission of a consistency requirement, [1] but something else entirely. The question concerns the fact that the connection between real objects and the concepts involving the abstraction of actual infinity has, in many cases, a very indirect and vague character.

For the natural sciences, engineering, and other domains of human activity employing mathematics, it makes a difference to what extent the concepts and theorems of the applied mathematical theories are 'tangible', [2] i.e. correspond to real objects and connections among them. Particularly essential is the 'tangibility' of concepts when one considers some theorem about the existence of an object [3] of a certain type satisfying a given condition. If the concept

---

1) It is well known that the discovery, at a still early stage of development of the classical theory of sets, of logical contradictions in certain parts of this theory could have been eliminated without going outside the scope of classical mathematics and without revising its basic principles, by placing certain limitations on the methods of introducing concepts. We note that the consistency requirement is placed on mathematical theories by representatives of both the constructive and classical approach.

2) In this work we use quotation marks of two types. The quotation marks of the first type, already occuring above, "", are used for isolating terms and phrases in those cases where the term, phrase, or the abstract concept denoted by the term at the given place in the text figures as one of those objects which is being discussed in the sentence. Quotation marks of the second type, '', are used to isolate terms and phrases in those cases where the term or phrase is applied, at the given place in the text, not in its direct meaning but in a figurative sense.

3) Here and in the rest of this study, the term "object" is used in the wide sense, including both real objects and conceptual objects, i.e. idea, abstract concept, etc. In those cases where we have in mind only real objects, or only conceptual objects, we will apply the term "object" together with the corresponding adjective.

characterizing the type of object the existence of which is asserted by the theorem is based on very remote idealizations (i.e. on idealizations for which the connection between the concept and the real objects or processes turns out to be very indirect and vague or even, in general, not apparent), then, strictly speaking, we can not give a sufficiently clear coextensive interpretation of this theorem (and sometimes, none at all); in this case we do not have clear ideas permitting us to change the formulation of the theorem into some assertion about real objects stipulated by this formulation. This remark concerns not only existence theorems, but also all other theorems in which concepts based upon remote idealizations figure.

The use in classical mathematics of the abstraction of actual infinity and ideas and concepts arising from it lead to the result that many of the theorems of classical mathematics do not possess satisfactory (from the point of view connected with the experimental material of the natural and engineering sciences) 'tangibility'. This constitutes the main fact inducing criticism of the foundations of classical mathematics.

The formulation above concerning criticism of classical mathematics requires more precision and concreteness. To avoid overloading the Introduction with material which is not necessary for the comprehension of the basic contents of this work, more detailed consideration of the problem of criticism of classical mathematics is postponed to a special appendix to the paper. For the reading of this appendix no familiarity with any part of this book is required.

0.6. In constructive mathematics only constructive objects serve as objects of study. In addition, the investigation of constructive objects is carried out on the basis of constructive logic. The fundamental property of constructive objects, consisting in the fact that they are (by definition) potentially realizable as results of constructive processes, is one of the most important starting points of constructive logic. The abstraction of potential realizability, assumed in constructive mathematics, is a definite idealization and generates its own difficulties of interpretation. But this idealization is based on essentially less arbitrariness of our imagination than is the case for the abstraction of actual infinity, and the difficulty of interpretation generated by this idealization is of a simpler nature.

Keeping in mind the property of constructive mathematics just mentioned, one can say that the general direction of constructive mathematics consists in the construction of mathematical theories for which the path from abstract thought to real objects and connections among them and to experimental material is less indirect and more apparent than in the corresponding theories of classical mathematics.

0.7. In constructive mathematics the natural, whole and rational numbers are defined as groups of symbols of certain types, characterized by rules of construction (generating rules). Such definitions of natural, whole and rational numbers are carried over from classical mathematics. Sometimes in classical mathematics the terms "natural number", "whole number", and "rational number" are connected with certain abstract concepts, and the indicated constructive definitions are considered to be definitions of notations for these abstract concepts. But even in classical mathematics one starts most often from the constructive definitions of the indicated concepts. However, it is necessary to note that, in spite of the identical definitions of natural, whole and rational numbers in classical and constructive mathematics, the theory of natural, whole and rational numbers in constructive mathematics differs from the corresponding theory in classical mathematics. One can exhibit concrete propositions about natural numbers which are theorems of classical mathematics and at the same time false propositions (according to the constructive interpretation). One can also exhibit concrete proposition about natural numbers which are true propositions (according to the constructive interpretation) and yet their negations are theorems of classical mathematics (cf. [11]).

We remark that the examples which we have been discussing here are constructed in a quite complicated way. The elementary theorems about natural, whole and rational numbers (i.e. the theorems usually included in elementary courses in theoretical arithmetic) are common to both constructive and classical mathematics.

0.8. The problem as to which concept (or concepts) it is most advisable to choose as a constructive analogue (or constructive analogues) of the concept of real number used in classical mathematics was one of the chief problems at the first stage of development of constructive mathematical analysis. On comparing the concepts proposed by various authors as answers to this problem, it becomes clear that in certain cases the concepts compared lead to constructively similar theorems, while in other cases they lead to essentially different theorems.

As terms for these concepts which we have been discussing, in the literature one uses the terms "constructive real number", "computable real number", "definable real number", "computable and computably convergent sequence of rational numbers", "regularly convergent sequence of rational numbers", and various others.

In historical references given below to the definitions of these concepts we shall use as a term for the defined concepts only the term "constructive real number" (which we abbreviate CRN), independently of which term was introduced by the author of the given definition. In those cases where the source may be misunderstood, the term "CRN" will be supplemented by an indication of the author who proposed the given concept, or by some other clarification for the sake of precision. From what has been said it follows that the term "CRN" can have different meanings in different places in the historical references given below. In each place in the text the meaning of this term will be made precise by the accompanying text.

Certain concepts connected in the literature with the term "constructive real number" or the term "computable real number" are introduced by definitions of the following form. "A real number α (having in mind the concept of real number used in classical mathematics) is called a constructive (or computable) real number if there is a constructive object $\mathfrak{A}$ of such-and-such a type having such-and-such a relation to α." Concepts of this kind will not be considered here. They lie outside the scope of the constructive approach to mathematics, since they are based upon the nonconstructive concept of real number used in classical mathematics.

We note that in the mathematical literature there are a host of papers based on concepts of the kind just indicated. Concepts of this kind are introduced in papers employing this approach also with respect to functions, algebraic systems of various types, topological spaces, etc. This approach can be characterized as partially constructive. To this approach belong certain papers of S. Banach and S. Mazur, E. Specker, A. Grzegorczyk, V. A. Uspenskiĭ, D. Lacombe, D. Klaua, and various other authors. In papers with a partially constructive approach one usually goes beyond the scope of constructive logic (and the authors most often do not place upon themselves the task of adhering strictly to the logical methods of constructive logic), and therefore one loses that connection between proofs of theorems and solutions of constructive tasks which is one of the most essential features of the constructive approach to mathematics. Hence, generally speaking, papers belonging to the partial constructive approach have only an indirect relation to the constructive approach to mathematics, and also those theorems of a partially constructive approach which are formulated in terms of concepts of constructive mathematics are in need of a concrete analysis as to their provability within the scope of constructive mathematics.

We remark that some results found in papers with a partially constructive approach are such that one can easily exclude concepts of classical mathematics from the formulation of their results, and the proposition obtained after this exclusion can be proved within the scope of constructive mathematics. Some important results of constructive mathematical analysis entered constructive mathematics in just this way.

We shall now proceed to those concepts which connect the term "CRN" only with constructive objects and are formulated within the scope of the constructive approach to mathematics. Such concepts can be divided into three groups.

Concepts of the first group connect the term "CRN" with constructive objects of a certain type such that by means of definite algorithms one can extract from an individual representation of any concrete CRN, first, an algorithm giving a sequence of rational approximating values for the given CRN, [1)] and second, an algorithm which is a regulator of convergence in itself of the first algorithm, i.e. an algorithm computing for any natural number i the subscript beginning with which the absolute value of the difference between terms of the sequence of rational approximating values of the given CRN is less than 2^{-i}.

Concepts of the second group connect the term "CRN" with constructive objects of a certain type such that by means of a definite algorithm one can extract from the individual representation of any concrete CRN an algorithm giving a sequence of rational approximating values for the given CRN. In constrast with the concepts of the first group, it is not required here that there be an algorithm extracting from the individual representation of any CRN a regulator of convergence in itself of the sequence of rational approximating values of the given CRN. [2)]

1) One says that an algorithm ψ gives a sequence of rational approximating values for a given CNR x if, first, ψ transforms every natural number into a rational number, and second, one can construct an algorithm ω transforming every natural number into a natural number such that for any natural numbers i and k satisfying the condition $k \geq \omega(i)$ the absolute value of the difference between the numbers $\psi(k)$ and x is less than 2^{-i}. Here one assumes that certain arithmetic operations and an order relation are applicable to the given concept of CRN.

2) It is easily seen that one can always construct a regulator of convergence in itself of a sequence of rational approximating values of a given CRN if an algorithm ω, as described in the previous footnote, is initially given. However, it does not follow from this that a regulator of convergence can be constructed starting from only the given CRN.

The concepts of the third group, like the concepts of the first two groups, connect the term "CRN" with constructive objects of a certain type. However, the type of these objects is such that there cannot be an algorithm extracting from an individual representation of any CRN an algorithm giving a sequence of rational approximating values of the given CRN. A host of analogues (some very attractive) with the concept of real number used in classical mathematics serve as justification for the application in these cases of the term "CRN".

The historically first concept of CRN, proposed by Weyl (see [5]), belongs to the third group. In the same group belong the definitions of some other authors who followed in Weyl's path (see for example [12]). Concepts occuring in this third group are concepts of the constructive approach to mathematics and can serve as starting points for the construction of certain theories within the scope of this approach. However, the actual use of concrete real numbers in the natural sciences and engineering is essentially based on the possibility of extracting from an individual representation of a real number an algorithm giving a sequence of rational approximating values for it. Hence, if one deals with mathematics in connection with its applications and comes to the constructive approach to mathematics with this point of view, it is impossible to regard as definitive the use of concepts occuring in the third group. In any case, preference must be given to concepts occuring in the first two groups and to mathematical theories based on those concepts.

At the same time it is necessary to note that Weyl's theory anticipated many important properties of theories of CRN based on concepts of the first two groups, which arose at a much later date. Hence many results of these later theories which sound paradoxical in comparison with the theory of real numbers of classical mathematics and in many cases make use of essentially new ideas and completely different tools were not considered by mathematicians as unexpected. They underlined Weyl's pioneering role in the development of constructive mathematical analysis.

Concepts occuring in the third group are not dealt with here. Only some remarks connected with concepts from this group will be included in §8.4.

0.9. Now we shall briefly go into certain concepts which occur in the first and second groups. The precise concept of algorithm plays a role in the definitions of all the concepts discussed in this section. At the present time in mathematics one uses various precise concepts: concept of Turing machine; partial recursive function; arithmetization (associated with a fixed algorithm) of words in a given alphabet; the concept of normal algorithm introduced by Markov; and others, considered to be precise forms of the general descriptively defined concept of algorithm (see [1]).

The precise concepts which we have in mind here are interchangeable (in a definite sense), and each of them is considered at the present time as a mathematical concept which does not allow the construction of an example of a precise prescription which is subsumed under the general (descriptively defined) concept of algorithm and at the same time does not allow the construction of an equivalent algorithm of the given concrete type (see [1, Russian pp. 91–93]). The question as to which of these precise concepts of algorithm is to be taken as a basis for the concept of CRN is immaterial if we are concerned about the theoretical aspects of the given concept of CRN. From this standpoint, in the historical references given below concerning various concepts of CRN occuring in the first and second groups, we shall assume in the definitions of each concept of CRN that a choice is made of one of the precise concepts of algorithm (which one makes no difference), and when we are applying the term "algorithm" we shall mean an algorithm of the chosen type in a suitably selected and fixed alphabet.

As we have said, the first concept of CRN was introduced by Weyl. But this concept belongs in the third group. In the paper [13], A. M. Turing was the first to introduce a concept of CRN which belongs to the first group. [1)] The concept of CRN introduced by Turing in [13] can be defined in the following way. An algorithm ψ is called a constructive real number if ψ transforms every natural number into a rational number and one can construct an algorithm ϕ transforming 0 into some whole number, transforming every positive whole number k into a natural number $\phi(k)$ satisfying the condition $0 \leq \phi(k) \leq 9$, and such that, for any

1) Turing formulates the concept introduced by him in [13] in the following form: "A real number α (having in mind the concept of real number used in classical mathematics) is called a computable real number if there is a constructive object $\mathfrak{A}$ of such-and-such a type having such-and-such a relation to α". A concept introduced by such a definition belongs to a type which has been excluded from consideration in this paper. However, extracting from Turing's definition that part in which is given the characterization of the type of constructive objects by means of which individual representations of computable real numbers are realized (this characterization is not based on the concept of real number used in classical mathematics), we obtain a concept of CRN which belongs to the constructive approach to mathematics. It is just this latter concept which we shall have in mind when we use the expression "concept of CRN introduced by A. M. Turing in [13]". In the definition cited below of this concept there is also a divergence from Turing's initial definition in various technical details. But this divergence is completely immaterial from a theoretical standpoint.

natural number n

$$\psi(n)=\varphi(0)+\sum_{k=1}^{n}\varphi(k)\cdot 10^{-k}.$$

Right after publication of the paper [13], Turing criticized his first concept of CRN as insufficiently general [14]. As a criterion of sufficient generality of a concept of CRN Turing advanced the following. A concept of CRN can be recognized as sufficiently general only when the following proposition is valid: for any algorithms $\mathfrak{A}$ and $\mathfrak{B}$ transforming natural numbers into a rational numbers and such that for any natural number n

$$\mathfrak{A}(n)\leqslant\mathfrak{A}(n+1)<\mathfrak{B}(n+1)\leqslant\mathfrak{B}(n)$$

and

$$\mathfrak{B}(n)-\mathfrak{A}(n)<2^{-n},$$

one can construct a CRN x such that, for any natural number n

$$\mathfrak{A}(n)\leqslant x\leqslant\mathfrak{B}(n).$$

In [14] Turing stated that the concept of CRN proposed by him in [13] does not satisfy this criterion,[1)] and suggested a second concept of CRN. This second concept of CRN lies in the same group as the first concept (i.e. the first group).[2)] The concept of CRN introduced by Turing in [14] can be defined in the following way. An algorithm ψ is called a constructive real number if ψ transforms every natural number into a rational number and one can construct an algorithm θ transforming 0 into some whole number, transforming any positive whole number into one of the three whole numbers

$$-1,\ 0,\ 1$$

and such, for any natural number n

$$\psi(n)=\theta(0)+\sum_{k=1}^{n}\theta(k)\cdot 2^{k}\cdot 3^{-k}.$$

Turing states that a construction suggested by Brouwer of a special system of intervals on the real line was the conceptual source of this concept of CRN.

---

1) The concept of CRN introduced in [13] has still another lack of a fundamental character: there is no algorithm carrying out the addition of such CRN.

2) The remark in footnote on p. 14 concerning the concept of CRN introduced in [13] is true verbatim for the concept of CRN introduced in [14].

The second concept of CRN introduced by Turing satisfied the criterion of sufficient generality. It is completely satisfactory on the theoretical side, but inconvenient on the technical side.

In the rest of this study we shall be concerned only with those concepts of CRN which lies in the first or second group and satisfy the criterion of sufficient generality.

A. A. Markov in the paper [8] (see also [9]) introduced a very simply formulated concept of CRN, associated by him with the term "regularly convergent sequence of rational numbers". This concept can be defined in the following manner. An algorithm ψ is called a constructive real number if ψ transforms every natural number into a rational number, and for any natural numbers k and l

$$M(\psi(k+l)-\psi(k))\leqslant 2^{-k}.$$

Here M is a designation of the algorithm computing the absolute value (modulus) of rational numbers.

The concept of CRN introduced by Markov lies in the first group and satisfies the criterion of sufficient generality. Markov's concept of CRN and the second concept of CRN introduced by Turing (i.e. the concept of CRN introduced in [14]) lead to theories which are constructively similar. In this sense the two concepts of CRN being discussed here are interchangeable.

Markov's concept of CRN is very attractive because of its simplicity. However, in the details of construction of a theory of CRN based on this concept there arise many inconveniences of a technical nature.

In this book we shall take as a concept of CRN in the first group the concept of real FR-number (real duplex) defined in §3.5. The concept of real FR-number (real duplex) and Markov's concept of CRN lead to theories which are constructively similar. In this sense both concepts of CRN under discussion are interchangeable.

In addition to the concepts given above of CRN which lie in the first group there are in the literature still other concepts of CRN lying in the first group and satisfying the criterion of sufficient generality. We shall not formulate the definitions of these concepts, since the concept of real FR-number and each of these concepts lead to theories which are constructively similar.

In the paper [15], E. Specker inttoduced a concept of CRN lying in the second group. [1] This concept can be defined in the following way. An algorithm ψ is called a constructive real number if, first, ψ transforms every natural number into a rational number, and, second, an algorithm which is a regulator of convergence in itself of the algorithm ψ is potentially realizable.

Specker's concept of CRN is a constructive analogue of the concept of real number which was introduced by Méray (in 1869) and Cantor (in 1872) and has been one of the most frequently used concepts of real number in classical mathematics.

In this book we shall take as a concept of CRN in the second group the concept of real F-number defined in §3.5. The concept of real F-number differs in only technical details from the concept of CRN introduced by Specker in [15].

The existing theory of real numbers in classical mathematics, constructed on the basis of the concept of real number introduced by Méray and Cantor, can serve roughly for the construction of some parts of the theory of real F-numbers. However, in many essential points the analogy between the theories being discussed vanishes, and profound differences appear between them.

0.10. The accumlated experience in constructive mathematical analysis allows us to give a definite answer to the problem formulated at the beginning of §0.8. As a basis for the construction of a constructive mathematical analysis it is convenient to set two concepts of CRN: the first as a representative of the concepts occuring in the first group and satisfying the criterion of sufficient generality, and the second as a representative of the concepts occuring in the second group and satisfying the same criterion. We shall select as representatives the concept of real FR-number (real duplex) and the concept of real F-number, [2] respectively.

There is a definite connection between the concept of real FR-number and the concept of real F-number. This connection is weaker than mutual constructive similarity of the theories to which these concepts lead. However, this connection turns out to be sufficient to allow us to present certain parts of the theory of real F-numbers at the same time as the corresponding parts of the

---

1) E. Specker associates the concept introduced by this definition with the term "computable and computably convergent sequence of rational numbers". As for the concept associated by E. Specker with the term "computable real number", the remark made in the footnote on p. 14 is perfectly applicable to it.

2) The origin of the terms "real FR-numbers" and "real F-number" is connected with the fact that the letters F and R are, respectively, the first letters of the English terms "fundamental sequence" and "regulator of convergence".

theory of real FR-numbers. This connection also permits us, in the construction of various parts of the theory of real FR-numbers, to use as a rough orientation the corresponding classical mathematical theory of real numbers constructed on the basis of the concept of real number introduced by Méray and Cantor. However, as in the case of real F-numbers, in many essential points the analogy between the two theories vanishes and many profound differences between the theories appear.

From the point of view of computational mathematics real FR-numbers are more interesting objects than real F-numbers, since every real FR-number includes within itself essentially more information than the corresponding real F-number. Therefore, of principal importance in this book will be the real FR-numbers (real duplexes). However, there are certain problems for the consideration of which real F-numbers show themselves to be of most importance. Hence real F-numbers will also be dealt with in this book.

The basic facts from the theory of constructive real numbers, needed in Chapters II and III (which are devoted to constructive function spaces) will be presented in Chapter I.

0.11. In A. A. Markov's paper "On constructive functions" [8] (see also [9]), the concept of constructive function of a real variable is introduced. This concept is a constructive analogue of the concept of a real function of a real variable used in classical mathematics.

The central result of [8] can be formulated in the following way.

A constructive function of a real variable cannot have a constructive discontinuity at any point. (The notion of constructive discontinuity is formulated only with respect to those points at which the function is defined). 1)

This result of Markov's placed in doubt the possibility of using the concept of constructive function of a real variable as a basis for introducing into the constructive approach to mathematics those concepts which can be considered to be close analogues of the concepts of measurable function and integrable function introduced by Lebesgue.

Let us note that within classical theory of measurable and summable functions the consideration of the value of a function at isolated points essentially

---

1) G. S. Ceĭtin, in his paper [16] published in this issue of Trudy Mat. Inst. Steklov, carried Markov's result to its logical conclusion. He proved that any constructive function of a real variable is continuous (in the constructive sense) at every point at which it is defined.

loses meaning, since in this theory the equality of functions is defined in such a way that an arbitrary change of values of a function on a set of measure zero leads to a function equal to the original function. Of interest is only the average value (in various senses) on different intervals.

The concept of constructive function of a real variable introduced by Markov in [8] will occur only eposodically in this work. 1) At the center of attention will be those concepts of constructive mathematics which can be considered close analogues of the concepts of measurable function, function summable to the pth power (p is a positive real number), etc.

0.12. The method of completion of metric spaces, long and very fruitfully applied in topology and functional analysis, has a definite analogue in constructive mathematics. This analogue is based on the concept of algorithm. It provides the opportunity of introducing within the constructive approach to mathematics those concepts which are natural and close analogues of the concepts of measurable set, measurable function, summable function, function summable to the pth power (p is a positive real number), generalized function differentiable a given number of times (in the sense of S.L. Sobolev), absolutely continuous function, and others.

The constructive analogue of the method of completion of multimetric spaces provides the opportunity of introducing within the constructive approach to mathematics a natural and close analogue of the concept of generalized function in the sense of S. L. Sobolev and L. Schwartz. The same can be said of generalized functions of various other types considered in modern functional analysis.

It is generally known that the most important concrete function space studied in classical functional analysis are isometric to the completions of some of their own subspaces (chosen in suitable fashion), the elements of which have a sufficiently simple constructive representation. For example, the space of summable functions is isometric to the completion of the space of step functions with a finite number of steps, where the separation points between steps have rational abscissas, and the steps have rational ordinates (as metric one takes the integral of the absolute value of the difference of two given step functions). A second example: the space of absolutely continuous functions is isometric to the completion of the space of those polygonal functions for which the coordinates of

1) The papers [16, 17, 18, 19] of this issue of Trudy Mat. Inst. Steklov are devoted to the study of Markov's concept of constructive function of a real variable.

all vertices are rational numbers (as metric one takes the variation of difference of two given polygonal functions added to the absolute value of the difference of the values of the given functions at some fixed rational point).

Theorems of this kind established in classical mathematics can serve as initial points of orientation for the formulation within constructive mathematics of certain analogues of the concepts of classical mathematics mentioned above and various others. For example, by constructive summable functions it is natural to denote constructive objects of a definite type given by a constructively convergent-in-itself (with respect to the metric in the space of step functions mentioned above), algorithmically defined sequence of step functions of the type described above. Such constructive objects are not constructive functions of a real variable in the sense of Markov. They are constructive objects of another kind. It is natural to call constructive functions of a real variable in the sense of Markov constructive pointwise defined functions, and it is natural to call constructive summable functions and other analogous constructive objects, given by algorithmically defined sequences of constructively given functions of certain simple types satisfying certain conditions, constructive approximately defined functions.

Thus the search for constructive concepts analogous to the concept of function of a real variable used in many branches of classical mathematics [1] leads to the introduction of several different concepts in constructive mathematics, corresponding to the different applications of the concept of function of a real variable in classical mathematics. In addition to constructive pointwise defined functions and constructive approximately defined functions, also of interest are some other concepts of constructive mathematics which are also analogous in certain respects to the classical concept of function of a real variable and correspond to certain applications of this concept in classical mathematics. But in the following presentation we shall discuss only constructive pointwise defined functions and constructive approximately defined functions.

0.13. R. L. Goodstein, in the papers [20, 21] (see also [22]), established the foundations of the theory of constructive uniformly continuous functions and constructive functions uniformly differentiable a given number of times. [2]

---

1) We remark that the rise of the theory of generalized functions led, in classical mathematics also, to the introduction of approximately defined functions, which are not functions in the sense of the generally accepted definition. In constructive mathematics not only generalized functions but also measurable and summable functions are approximately defined functions.

2) Goodstein uses different terminology. We use here terminology borrowed from

Goodstein formulates and establishes his results within a certain logico-mathematical calculus, called by him the equation calculus, and underlines his desire to stay within the borders of this calculus. By means of the calculus used by Goodstein we can define only those arithmetic algorithms which are obtainable from the simplest primitive recursive functions by means of the schemas of substitution, primitive recursion, and simultaneous recursion on several variables. Every arithmetic algorithm definable in that calculus is a general recursive function, but not every general recursive function is definable in the calculus. Hence the concept of arithmetic algorithm used in Goodstein's theory is narrower than the concept of general recursive function.

If in all definitions, theorems and proofs of Goodstein's basic paper [20] we replace the partial concept of arithmetic algorithm used by him by the concept of general recursive function, if we replace references to Goodstein's calculus by references to the corresponding parts of the theory of general recursive functions, and if we preserve unchanged the rest of the text, then we obtain a theory completely embeddable within the constructive approach to mathematics, reproducing all of Goodstein's mathematical ideas, and at the same time corresponding to the modern general concept of everywhere-applicable arithmetic algorithm. 1) It is just this latter theory that we shall refer to in the sequel as Goodstein's theory.

In Goodstein's theory constructive uniformly continuous functions and constructive functions uniformly differentiable a given number of times are defined essentially as algorithmically given sequences of algorithmically given rational-valued functions of a rational variable, where these sequences are to satisfy certain conditions. 2) Goodstein's definition is not covered directly by the method of constructive completion of constructive metric spaces, but his approach is close to this method. As terms of constructive functional sequences Goodstein permits any algorithmically given rational-valued functions defined for all rational

---

classical mathematical analysis, which immediately indicates those concepts of classical analysis the analogues of which are the concepts of constructive analysis being considered.

1) This theory cannot be embedded within Goodstein's calculus. However, this fact does not serve as a good reason against the introduction into Goodstein's original theory of the changes suggested by the modern theory of algorithms and given above.

2) In the characterization given here of the concepts introduced by Goodstein, only the fundamental aspects of the definitions are reflected. Technical details of Goodstein's corresponding definitions are different; he considers algorithms applicable to pairs of objects: the first term of each pair is a natural number, and the second term is a rational number lying between two rational numbers giving the bounds of the domain of the function.

numbers in a given segment [1)] (this kind of approximating process is of definite interest !). But the set of such functions, first, does not form a subspace of a constructive function space, and second, is too extensive for us to take advantage of the completion process on some suitable metric. However, from Goodstein's results the possibility arises of transforming his definitions of constructive uniformly continuous functions and constructive functions uniformly differentiable a given number of times into definitions suitable for the method of constructive completion of constructive metric spaces, and we are able to repeat Goodstein's basic results on the basis of these new definitions.

There is another variant of Goodstein's theory. With respect to constructive pointwise defined functions of a real variable, in a perfectly natural way and by analogy with the corresponding definitions of classical mathematics, one can formulate definitions of constructive uniformly continuous functions and constructive functions uniformly differentiable a given number of times. The concept of constructive uniformly continuous pointwise defined functions and the corresponding concept of Goodstein's theory lead to theories which are constructively similar. The concept of constructive pointwise defined function uniformly differentiable a given number of times and the corresponding concept of Goodstein's theory also lead to constructively similar theories.

From what has been said above it follows that, on the basis of the concept of constructive pointwise defined function, one can construct a theory similar to Goodstein's theory. At the same time it is necessary to emphasize that in Goodstein's papers there appeared for the first time constructive approximately defined functions of a special type as independent objects of study in constructive mathematics.

In the sequel we shall not be concerned with Goodstein's theory, but we shall briefly go into models of this theory obtained by the method of constructive completion of constructive metric and normed spaces.

0.14. From what has been said in §0.12 it follows that the problem of

---

1) Such functions, considered as functions of a rational variable, can have constructive discontinuities at every point. As an example of such everywhere discontinuous functions we can use the function in the rational segment $[0,1]$ which at the points 0 and 1 is equal to zero and at every rational point a lying between 0 and 1 takes the value $1/n$, where n is the denominator of the fraction obtained after dividing the numerator and denominator of the fraction a by their greatest common divisor.

setting up a constructive analogue of the theory of measurable and summable functions and constructive analogues of various other function spaces can be solved quite simply in principle. In classical mathematics there is a great deal of material which can serve as a rough orientation in the construction of the corresponding theories of constructive mathematics. The same can be said about constructive analogues of the axiomatic theories of metric, normed (in particular, Hilbert), multimetric, and multinormed spaces. Consideration of the methods and achievements of topology and functional analysis shows that in these branches of classical mathematics the needed prerequisites for the development of corresponding axiomatic theories of constructive mathematics have already accumulated.

However, results in the literature on the theory of constructive real numbers, on various problems of constructive mathematical analysis, and results presented in this paper on the theory of constructive function spaces show that even in those cases where there are natural and close constructive analogues of concepts of classical mathematics simple replacement of the concepts of classical mathematics by the corresponding concepts of constructive mathematics in the theorems of classical mathematics far from always leads to true propositions of constructive mathematics.

About the results of such replacements of concepts one can say the following. In certain cases such replacements lead to true propositions of constructive mathematics. In other cases such replacements of concepts lead to propositions which are refutable in constructive mathematics [1)] but which at the same time admit changes in their formulation the results of which are propositions close in content to the original (but not equivalent to the original) and provable in constructive mathematics. For example, replacement of the concepts of classical mathematics by the corresponding concepts of constructive mathematics in Cauchy's theorem on the vanishing of every continuous function which has a change in sign, and in the theorems of Rolle, Lagrange and Taylor leads to propositions refutable in constructive mathematics. [2)] However, Goodstein found changes in formulation of these propositions the results of which are propositions close in content to the original and provable in constructive mathematics.

1) If some proposition, formulated in the language of constructive mathematics, is refutable in constructive mathematics, then the negation of this proposition is a theorem of constructive mathematics.

2) This fact has been established by G. S. Ceĭtin [17].

Finally, in certain cases, often of a fundamental nature, replacement of the concepts of classical mathematics by the corresponding concepts of constructive mathematics leads to propositions which are refutable in constructive mathematics and for which the search for true propositions of constructive mathematics close in content to the original does not lead to success. Cases of this kind are points of profound divergence between constructive and classical mathematics. A clear and very important example of this kind is the theorem of classical mathematics on the existence of a limit of any nondecreasing and bounded above sequence of real numbers.

In connection with what has been said above, it is necessary to emphasize that in classical mathematics the term "algorithm" is sometimes applied in a considerably wider sense than in constructive mathematics, and in many cases the description of the conceptual processes called algorithms in classical mathematics cannot be transformed into the kind of computing prescription with which the term "algorithm" is connected in constructive mathematics.

Not only in constructive but also in classical mathematics one formulates theorems on the existence of algorithms satisfying given conditions. However, in many cases it turns out that, after replacement in a theorem of this kind of the concepts of classical mathematics by the corresponding concepts of constructive mathematics and, in particular, after interpretation of the term "algorithm" in the sense that it has in constructive mathematics, one obtains refutable propositions of constructive mathematics. Hence in these cases it turns out that there can be no algorithm satisfying the corresponding condition. As an example of this kind one can cite the proposition, sometimes formulated as a theorem, on the existence of an algorithm for finding, for any continuous function having values of opposite sign at the ends of a given segment of the real line, those points at which the function vanishes.

Usually, as an algorithm for finding the desired points, one gives a description of a conceptual process each step of which consists in dividing in half the segment obtained at the preceding step, computing the value of the function at the point of division, and solving the problem as to whether the computed value of the function is zero. Upon an affirmative answer to this last problem the process stabilizes at this point of subdivision of the segment. Upon a negative answer, one proceeds to that one of the two halves of the segment considered at the given step on which the function changes sign, and the process continues in the same way.

Considering the steps of the conceptual process described here in reference to constructive analysis, we are compelled to find in it an essential gap: no method, formulable as a precise computational prescription (algorithm), is indicated which will permit us, for any constructive real number, to ascertain whether this number is equal to zero or different from zero. It is known that such an algorithm is impossible, and therefore the gap is not removable. Hence the whole conceptual process described above is not an algorithm in the sense in which the term "algorithm" is used in constructive mathematics.

Of course, the discovery of a nonremovable gap in the concrete conceptual process considered above does not prove that there can be no algorithm which, for any constructive continuous function having values of opposite sign at the ends of a given segment of the constructive real line, will find a constructive point at which the function vanishes. However, a proof of the impossibility of an algorithm possessing the indicated property is now known.[1)]

Our present knowledge does not give us any hope of the possibility of exhibiting a general method which will permit us to transform theorems of classical mathematical analysis into theorems of constructive mathematical analysis which can be considered as natural analogues of the original theorems of classical analysis. Thus there remains just one way to develop various parts of constructive mathematical analysis and constructive functional analysis. This way consists in a concrete, continuing search for theorems of constructive mathematics in which the theorems of classical mathematics can play a directing role only as first approximations.

0.15. We have already mentioned that in constructive mathematics constructive analogues of the concepts of (Lebesgue-) measurable set, (Lebesgue-) measurable function, function summable to the pth power (p is a positive real number) and a host of other concepts can be introduced on the basis of a constructive analogue of the method of completion of metric spaces. Constructive analogues of the measure of measurable sets and the Lebesgue integral can be introduced on the basis of a constructive analogue of the method of extending a function uniformly continuous on an everywhere dense subset of a metric space to the whole metric space. The theory obtained on the basis of such definitions resembles in certain respects the corresponding theory of classical mathematics, but in other respects is essentially different from the latter.

---

1) See G. S. Ceĭtin [17].

Chapter III of this paper is devoted to a description of constructive analogues of some concrete function spaces. In that chapter we describe, in particular, a constructive analogue of the Lebesgue integral and we establish a theory of the constructive analogue of the Lebesgue integral in constructive mathematics which is essentially different from the theory of the Lebesgue integral in classical mathematics.

The presentation of the material in Chapter III is based on some theorems of the axiomatic theory of constructive metric and constructive normed spaces. Chapter II is devoted to the axiomatic theory of constructive metric and normed spaces. In that chapter we touch upon only those problems of the axiomatic theory of constructive metric and normed spaces which are needed in Chapter III or which are closely connected with the material contained in Chapter III.

In Chapters II and III we also establish some essential differences between the theory of constructive Hilbert spaces and the theory of Hilbert spaces in classical mathematics.

A concise presentation of parts of the material contained in this paper has been published in [23,24], but here some problems are treated differently.

This paper reproduces in a somewhat altered and extended form the content of a lecture course on constructive mathematical analysis given by the author in the 1953–54 academic year at the Mathematics-Mechanics Faculty of Leningrad University.

0.16. Constructive mathematical analysis is based upon the theory of algorithms and constructive mathematical logic. The reader of this book should be familiar with the theory of normal algorithms to the extent of the first five chapters of A. A. Markov's monograph [1] and with the logico-mathematical languages of constructive mathematics and the constructive interpretation of mathematical propositions to the extent of the paper [3] of N. A. Šanin. Concepts and terminology introduced in [1] and [3] will be used below without explicit mention.

In this book we shall base ourselves on the concept of normal algorithm introduced by Markov in [1]. However, we shall not always give concrete algorithms in the form of normal algorithms. In all cases where an algorithm is introduced not in the form of a normal algorithm but in the form of precise prescriptions of other types, the construction of the corresponding normal algorithm is left to the reader.

It would be natural to consider the paper [3] as an introductory part of this book.

Logical deduction in constructive mathematics is often carried out by the method of "natural deduction". The theory of the method of natural deduction, for classical as well as constructive mathematics, was developed by G. Gentzen in the paper [25], familiarity with which will greatly facilitate the reading of this book.

In this work we shall use the logico-mathematical languages described in §§3 and 8 of [3]. In the exposition of constructive mathematical analysis the use of logico-mathematical languages is very convenient, since these languages permit us to clearly express the logical form of propositions, and, in particular, those aspects of the logical form of propositions which are of little importance in classical logic but of very great importance in constructive logic (for example, the existence of double negations). A series of supplements to the paper [3], concerned with logico-mathematical languages of constructive mathematics and the constructive interpretation of mathematical propositions, are included in §1 of this paper.

0.17. This book is divided into subsections denoted by pairs of natural numbers. In any such designation, the first number coincides with the number of the section, [1] while the second number indicates the ordinal number of the given subsection in the given section.

Theorems are denoted by triples of natural numbers. In any such designation the first two numbers denote that subsection of the book in which the given theorem is found, and the third number is the ordinal number of the given theorem in the given subsection.

Some lines of the text are furnished with numbers standing to the right of the indicated line and enclosed in parentheses. Within each subsection of the book the numbering of the selected lines is carried out independently of the numbering in other sections.

As references to theorems we shall write the complete designations of the theorems. In reference to any selected line we shall write only the number of the line, enclosed in parentheses, if that line occurs in the same subsection as the given reference, and we shall write the number of the subsection and the number of the line chosen in it, enclosed in parentheses, if the reference is to a different subsection.

Numbers in square brackets are references to the corresponding parts of the

---

1) In this connection the "Introduction" is considered to be §0.

bibliography. In certain cases we make more precise references to the literature, consisting of the indication of the number of section or page of the source. Every such amplification will be separated from the number of the corresponding source in the literature by a comma. References to different sources in the literature, placed in the same square brackets, will also be separated from each other by commas.

0.18. The author would like to direct the attention of the reader to the following fact. The term "set" is used in this book in precisely the same sense as in [3, §7], i.e. as a synonym of the expression "condition with one parameter". This concept of set has an important deficiency of a purely technical nature, consisting in the fact that, on the one hand, every one-parameter condition contains a free variable, the parameter of the given condition, and, and on the other hand, within a wider language intended for the formulation of propositions about sets, all occurrences of variables in words playing the role of concrete sets in the given proposition, must (for reasons of a semantic nature) be considered bound occurrences in such words.

The deficiency just mentioned can be eliminated by connecting the term "set" not directly with one-parameter conditions but with certain words which can be put into one-one correspondence with one-parameter formulas of the basic logico-mathematical language and such that in them is syntactically expressed the act of binding the parameters of the corresponding conditions. Certain authors (see for example [12, §10]) do just this.

This variant can be technically realized, for example, in the following way. We introduce a new quantifier, the symbol ꟼ, and by *sets* we mean words of the form $ꟼ\, \alpha\, \mathfrak{A}$, where $\mathfrak{A}$ is any one-parameter formula of the basic language and α is the parameter of this formula. The expression $ꟼ\, \alpha\, \mathfrak{A}$ is read "the set of those α which satisfy the condition $\mathfrak{A}$". This expression can also play the role of a proper name of the concrete concept characterized by the condition $\mathfrak{A}$. It is also convenient to introduce expressions of the form $ꟼ\, \alpha_1 \cdots \alpha_k \mathfrak{B}$, where k is a natural number greater than one, $\alpha_1, \cdots, \alpha_k$ are pairwise distinct variables, and $\mathfrak{B}$ is a formula such that the list of its parameters is contained in the list $\alpha_1, \cdots, \alpha_k$. The expression $ꟼ\, \alpha_1 \cdots \alpha_k \mathfrak{B}$ can play the role of a proper name of the concrete k-ary relation characterized by the condition $\mathfrak{B}$.

By means of the construction of certain superstructures on the basic logico-mathematical languages described in [3], one can introduce logico-mathematical languages which are sufficient for the purposes pursued in this book and are intended for those cases where, as objects of study, not only words in the given basic alphabets and algorithms over the given basic alphabets occur, but also sets characterized by one-parameter formulas in the given basic language. For such extended languages one can exhibit a method for the constructive interpretation of propositions which is a generalization of the method presented in [3] with respect to the basic logico-mathematical languages.

However, here such superstructures will not be described, and in those cases where it is necessary to consider sets the exposition is carried out in metamathematical style. In addition, we shall not use the concept of set characterized above as being introduced by a new quantifier ꟼ, but shall employ the concept of set borrowed from [3, §§7 and 8], which is less convenient from a technical standpoint. This stems from the tendency of the author not to extend the introductory part of this work, which, even without this, is sufficiently long and has only an auxiliary value with respect to the basic theme, and not to cause additional difficulty for the reader by divergence from the paper [3], which is assumed to be basically known. However, those readers who feel it more convenient to interpret the term "set" in the way described above have the opportunity of replacing part of the following text by a less clumsy text.

The exposition below also has the following property. The degree of detail in the proofs of theorems and descriptions of algorithms decreases with distance from the beginning of work. The possibility of certain constructions and proofs is only mentioned. In certain cases the author limits himself to a description of the required algorithm and leaves the construction to the reader. In all cases where we use the term "algorithm" we mean, in the final analysis, a normal algorithm in an appropriate alphabet. However, in many places in the text, the actual description of the algorithms is of an entirely different character (in such cases we assume that the reader, if he wishes, can himself find a way of constructing the corresponding normal algorithm).

All the properties of the exposition just mentioned stem from the tendency to avoid excessive awkwardness in the book.

CHAPTER I

CONSTRUCTIVE REAL NUMBERS

§1. DESCRIPTION OF THE NOTATION USED AND SOME DEFINITIONS

1.1. We shall introduce in turn certain alphabets, which are intended for use in building up constructive mathematical objects of various concrete types. The alphabets, which will be denoted by the expressions

$$Ч_0,\ Ч_1,\ Ч_2,\ Ч_3,\ Ч_4,\ Ч_5,\ \ldots,$$

will be called *basic alphabets*.

First of all we introduce the alphabets

$$\{0,\ |\},\qquad \{0,\ |,\ -\},\qquad \{0,\ |,\ -,\ /\}$$

and adopt the following notation:

$$Ч_0 \leftrightharpoons \{0,\ |\},\qquad Ч_1 \leftrightharpoons \{0,\ |,\ -\},\qquad Ч_2 \leftrightharpoons \{0,\ |,\ -,\ /\}.$$

Here and in the rest of the exposition the sign $\leftrightharpoons$ replaces the words "is introduced as notation for". If Σ is some symbol not occurring earlier in the text or some group of symbols not occurring earlier in the text, and Π is some group of symbols belonging to one of the types already introduced, then the expression

$$\Sigma \leftrightharpoons \Pi$$

is supposed to be read in the following way:

"Σ is introduced as a designation of the group of symbols Π".

The alphabet $Ч_0$ is called the *alphabet of natural numbers*, $Ч_1$ the *alphabet of integers*, and $Ч_2$ the *alphabet of rational numbers*. It is obvious that

$$Ч_0 \subset Ч_1 \subset Ч_2.$$

The alphabets to be associated with the designations $Ч_3,\ Ч_4,\ Ч_5, \cdots$ will be introduced later.

1.2. *Positive integers* are defined by the following generating rules: the word 0| is a positive integer; if K is a positive integer, then the word $K|$ is also a positive integer.

Natural numbers are defined by the following generating rules: the letter 0 is a natural number; if N is a natural number, then the word $N|$ is also a natural number.

Natural numbers will also be called *words of type* Н.

The choice made in this paper of the definitions of positive integers and natural numbers was motivated in [3], §3.3. Positive integers and natural numbers are words in the alphabet Ч_0.

As abbreviations of positive integers we shall often use the symbolism of the decimal number system: the words 0|, 0||, 0|||, 0||||, ··· will be denoted, respectively, by 1, 2, 3, 4, ··· .

Negative integers are defined by the following generating rules: if K is a positive integer, then the word $-K$ is a negative integer.

Integers are defined by the following generating rules: if K is a positive integer, then K is an integer; the letter 0 is an integer; if L is a negative integer, then L is an integer.

Integers will also be called *words of type* Ц.

Integers are words in the alphabet Ч_1.

Positive rational numbers are defined by the following generating rules: if K is a positive integer, then K is a positive rational number; if K_1 and K_2 are positive integers, then the word K_1/K_2 is a positive rational number.

Null rational numbers are defined by the following generating rules: the letter 0 is a null rational number; if K is a positive integer, then the word $0/K$ is a null rational number.

Negative rational numbers are defined by the following generating rules: if L is a negative integer, then L is a negative rational number; if L is a negative integer and K is a positive integer, then the word L/K is a negative rational number.

Rational numbers are defined by the following generating rules: if X is a positive rational number, then X is a rational number; if Y is a null rational number, then Y is a rational number; if Z is a negative rational number, then Z is a rational number.

It is obvious that rational numbers can be defined also by the following generating rules: if C is an integer, then C is a rational number; if C is an integer and K is a positive integer, then the word C/K is a rational number.

Rational numbers also will be called *words of type* p.

Rational numbers are words in the alphabet $Ч_2$.

Reduced rational numbers are defined by the following generating rules: if C is an integer, then C is a reduced rational number; if C is an integer and K is a positive integer different from 0| and the greatest common divisor of the integers C and K is equal to unity, then the word C/K is a reduced rational number.

Reduced rational numbers also will be called words of type $\overline{\mathrm{p}}$ (the expression $\overline{\mathrm{p}}$ will be considered as a single elementary symbol).

1.3. In the rest of the exposition we shall often make extensions of the list of alphabets to be used. But at each stage of the following exposition the list of basic alphabets used (see §1.1) will satisfy the conditions 1)–4) of [3], §3.4, and therefore every such list will determine a definite logico-matematical language of the type described in [3], §3. Any language of the type described in [3], §3 can serve as the basis for the introduction of various extensions of the languages described in [3], §8.

The symbolism and terminology of [3] will be used in what follows without explicit mention. In [3] the expressions $A_0, A_1, \cdots, A_h$ figure as designations of some alphabets satisfying certain conditions. The concrete form of the alphabets denoted by these expressions is there of no signfficance. In addition, in [3] the expressions $t_0, t_1, \cdots, t_h$ are designations of individual generic letters associated, respectively, with the alphabets $A_0, A_1, \cdots, A_h$, and the expressions $\lambda_0, \lambda_1, \cdots, \lambda_h$ are designations of functorial generic letters associated respectively with the alphabets $A_0, A_1, \cdots, A_h$.

In the present work, for the indicated expressions we shall completely preserve the meaning given to them in [3], and we shall use these expressions when we are concerned with any logico-mathematical language of one of the types described in [3]. However, in the present paper the content of the paper [3] will be applied mainly to certain concrete logico-mathematical languages, and, in the role of the alphabets $A_0, A_1, A_2, A_3, \cdots$, the alphabets $Ч_0, Ч_1, Ч_2, Ч_3, \cdots$, respectively, will usually occur.

As individual generic letters associated with the alphabets $Ч_0, Ч_1, Ч_2, Ч_3, \cdots$ we shall use the symbols $\mathrm{c}_0, \mathrm{c}_1, \mathrm{c}_2, \mathrm{c}_3, \ldots$ respectively, and, as functorial generic letters associated with the alphabets $Ч_0, Ч_1, Ч_2, Ч_3, \cdots$ we shall use the symbols

$$\Phi_0,\ \Phi_1,\ \Phi_2,\ \Phi_3,\ \cdots$$

respectively.

Each of the expressions

$$c_0,\ c_1,\ c_2,\ c_3,\ \ldots,\ \Phi_0,\ \Phi_1,\ \Phi_2,\ \Phi_3,\ \ldots$$

will be considered as a single elementary symbol (as one letter) of the logico-mathematical language.

In those cases where $Ч_0, Ч_1, \cdots$ play the role of the alphabets $A_0, A_1, \cdots$, respectively, the role of $t_0, t_1, \cdots$ will be played, respectively, by the letters $c_0, c_1, \cdots$, and the role of $\lambda_0, \lambda_1, \cdots$ by the letters $\Phi_0, \Phi_1, \cdots$, respectively.

The letters $c_0, c_1, \cdots$ and the letters $\Phi_0, \Phi_1, \cdots$ are generic basis letters (see [3], §8.2). Restricted generic letters ([3], §8.2) will be introduced in our exposition at the same time as the corresponding one-parameter formulas (basis sets).

We agree on the following notation for variables. If μ is any generic letter (it makes no difference whether it is a basis or restricted letter), then the variables

$$(\mu),\ (\mu\mu),\ (\mu\mu\mu),\ \ldots$$

will be denoted, respectively, by

$$\mu_1,\ \mu_2,\ \mu_3,\ \cdots$$

Individual basis variables

$$(c_i),\ (c_ic_i),\ (c_ic_ic_i),\ \cdots$$

will be denoted, respectively, by

$$c_{i,1},\ c_{i,2},\ c_{i,3},\ \cdots$$

and functorial basis variables

$$(\Phi_i),\ (\Phi_i\Phi_i),\ (\Phi_i\Phi_i\Phi_i),\ \cdots$$

will be denoted, respectively, by

$$\Phi_{i,1},\ \Phi_{i,2},\ \Phi_{i,3},\ \cdots$$

$(i = 0, 1, 2, 3, 4, 5, \cdots)$.

1.4. Let $A_0, \cdots, A_h$ be any list of alphabets satisfying conditions 1)–4) of [3], §3.4. The logico-mathematical language having this list of alphabets as its basis and described in [3], §3 will be denoted by the letter Я.

We introduce two operations on variables and on words composed of variables. The symbol $\sim$ will serve as a function sign for the first operation. The result of applying this operation is a natural number. The symbol $\backsim$ will serve as a function sign for the second operation. The result of applying this operation is a system of terms. We agree to write the result of applying the operations $\smile$ and $\frown$ to the initially given objects by placing the symbol $\smile$ under the word to which it is applied and the symbol $\frown$ over the word to which it is applied.

The operations $\smile$ and $\frown$ are defined in the following way. Let β be any variable. If β is a variable of type t_i, then we set:

$$\underset{\smile}{\beta} \circeq i, \qquad \overset{\frown}{\beta} \circeq \beta.$$

If β is a function variable, then we set:

$$\underset{\smile}{\beta} \circeq 0, \quad \overset{\frown}{\beta} \circeq \{\beta\}.$$

Let $\beta_1, \cdots, \beta_k$ be any variables and let V denote the word $\beta_1 \cdots \beta_k$. We set:

$$\underset{\smile}{V} \circeq \nu(\underset{\smile}{\beta_1}, \ldots, \underset{\smile}{\beta_k});$$

$$\overset{\frown}{V} \circeq \overset{\frown}{\beta_1}, \qquad \text{if} \quad k=1,$$

$$\overset{\frown}{V} \circeq \overset{\frown}{\beta_1} \square \overset{\frown}{\beta_2} \square \ldots \square \overset{\frown}{\beta_k}, \qquad \text{if} \quad k>1.$$

In accordance with the convention assumed in [3], §3.4, the expression $\nu(i_1, \cdots, i_k)$ denotes the subscript of the (unique) alphabet in the list of alphabets $\mathsf{A}_0, \mathsf{A}_1, \cdots, \mathsf{A}_h$ which is equal to the union of the alphabets $\mathsf{A}_{i_1}, \mathsf{A}_{i_2}, \cdots$ $\cdots, \mathsf{A}_{i_k}$.

We note that the operations $\smile$ and $\frown$ were used in [3] to define the algorithm for recognizing constructive problems (see [3],pp. 259–264 (transl. pp.140–145)). In what follows these operations will receive a new application.

1.5. Let $\mathfrak{C}$ be any formula of the type $[\beta_1 \cdots \beta_k]$, where $k \geq 1$ and $\beta_1, \cdots$ $\cdots, \beta_k$ are basis variables (see [3],p. 249 (transl. p. 130)).[1)] We introduce the notation:

$$V \rightleftharpoons \beta_1 \ldots \beta_k, \quad m \rightleftharpoons \underset{\smile}{V}.$$

Let H be some word in the alphabet A_0. One says of the algorithm $\langle H \rangle_m$ that it *verifies fulfillment of the condition expressed by the formula* $\mathfrak{C}$ if, first,

$$\widetilde{\forall}!\langle H\rangle_m(\overset{\frown}{V}) \tag{1}$$

and second[2)]

$$\widetilde{\forall}(\mathfrak{C} \equiv (\langle H\rangle_m(\overset{\frown}{V}) \mathrel{\dot{=}} \Lambda)). \tag{2}$$

---

1) In this section we assume that $\mathfrak{C}$ is a formula of the language $\mathfrak{A}$, and hence it has no parameters which are restricted variables. This condition is essential here.

2) The meaning of the symbol $\dot{=}$ is explained in [3],§3.5. In this work we shall also use the symbol $\dot{\neq}$. If Θ_1 and Θ_2 are any individual terms, then the expression $(\Theta_1 \dot{\neq} \Theta_2)$ will denote the formula

$$(!\Theta_1 \,\&\, !\Theta_2 \,\&\, \neg(\Theta_1 \simeq \Theta_2)).$$

One says of a formula $\mathfrak{C}$ that it *expresses an algorithmically verifiable condition* if one can construct some algorithm $\langle H\rangle_m$ verifying the fulfillment of the condition $\mathfrak{C}$. As a synonym for the term "algorithmically verifiable condition" there is sometimes used in the literature the term "recursive condition". The latter term was used when, as a concept intended as a standardization of the general concept of arithmetic algorithm, the concept of partial recursive function occurred almost exclusively.

Starting from the rules of the constructive reformulation of mathematical propositions one can prove the following proposition.

1.5.1. *A formula* $\mathfrak{C}$ *expresses an algorithemically verifiable condition if and only if*

$$\tilde{\forall}(\mathfrak{C} \vee \neg\mathfrak{C}).$$

If $\mathfrak{C}$ is a one-parameter formula and the parameter of this formula is an individual variable of type t_j, then $\widetilde{V} \,\overline{\overline{\circ}}\, \beta_1$, $m = j$, and formula (2) can be read as follows:

"the set $\mathfrak{C}$ is equal to the set $(\langle H\rangle_j(\beta_1) \doteq \Lambda)$"

(see [3], p. 294 (transl. p. 173)).

Let j be one of the natural numbers $0, \cdots, h$ and let $\mathfrak{M}$ be any set (any generated set) in the alphabet A_j. In this case, along with the terminology introduced above, one also uses the following terminology.

One says of an algorithm $\langle H\rangle_j$ (here H is any word in the alphabet A_0) that it *recognizes elements of the set (generated set)* $\mathfrak{M}$ *among all words of the alphabet* A_j if the algorithm $\langle H\rangle_j$ is applicable to every word in the alphabet A_j and the set (generated set) $\mathfrak{M}$ is equal to the set $(\langle H\rangle_j(c_{j,1}) \doteq \Lambda)$.

In ([3], §7) we formulated definitions of recursive sets in the alphabet A_j, recursively generated sets in the alphabet A_j, and recursively enumerable sets in the alphabet A_j. These definitions are results of a natural extension to words in the alphabet A_j of the corresponding definitions of E. L. Post, formulated by him with respect to natural numbers (see [26,27]). In the sequel, as synonyms of the terms "recursive set in the alphabet A_j", "recursively generated set in the alphabet A_j", and "recursively enumerable set in the alphabet A_j", we shall employ the corresponding terms "algorithmically solvable set in the alphabet A_j", "algorithmically solvable generated set in the alphabet A_j", and "algorithmically enumerable set in the alphabet A_j".

In the present work recursive functions are not used at all (they are mentioned only in some references of an historical and bibliographic nature), and therefore, in the sequel, we usually shall employ the second terminology.

The definitions of algorithmically solvable sets in the alphabet A_j and algorithmically solvable generated sets in the alphabet A_j can be formulated in the following manner.

A set (generated set) $\mathfrak{M}$ is called an *algorithmically solvable set* (respectively, *algorithmically solvable generated set*) *in the alphabet* A_j if one can potentially realize an algorithm $\langle H \rangle_j$ recognizing elements of the set (generated set) $\mathfrak{M}$ among all words in the alphabet A_j.

It is known that any generated set in the alphabet A_j is equal to some algorithmically enumerable set in A_j ([3], §7.7). It is also known that there are generated sets which are not algorithmically solvable generated sets ([3], §7.7). Hence it is important to notice that all the generated sets (the generated set of all positive integers, the generated set of all natural numbers, $\cdots$, the generated set of all reduced rational numbers) mentioned in §1.2 are algorithmically solvable generated sets.

1.6. It is not difficult to construct words P_0, P_1, Q, R_0, R_1, R_2, R_3, and R_4 in the alphabet $Ч_0$ such that:

a) the algorithm $\langle P_0 \rangle_0$ recognizes positive integers,[1] and therefore the generated set of all positive integers is equal to the set

$$(\langle P_0 \rangle_0 (c_{0,1}) \mathrel{\dot{=}} \Lambda); \tag{1}$$

b) the algorithm $\langle P_1 \rangle_0$ recognizes natural numbers, and therefore the generated set of all natural numbers is equal to the set

$$(\langle P_1 \rangle_0 (c_{0,1}) \mathrel{\dot{=}} \Lambda); \tag{2}$$

c) the algorithm $\langle Q \rangle_1$ recognizes integers, and therefore the generated set of all integers is equal to the set

$$(\langle Q \rangle_1 (c_{1,1}) \mathrel{\dot{=}} \Lambda); \tag{3}$$

d) the algorithm $\langle R_0 \rangle_2$ recognizes positive rational numbers, and therefore the generated set of all positive rational numbers is equal to the set

---

1) As P_0 one can take, for example, the transcription of the normal algorithm in the alphabet $Ч_0^{sa}$, defined by the schema

$$\begin{cases} 0\,\| \to 0\,| \\ 0\,| \to \cdot \end{cases}$$

$$(\langle R_0\rangle_2 (c_{2,1}) \mp \Lambda); \tag{4}$$

e) the algorithm $\langle R_1\rangle_2$ recognizes null rational numbers, and therefore the generated set of all null rational numbers is equal to the set

$$(\langle R_1\rangle_2 (c_{2,1}) \mp \Lambda); \tag{5}$$

f) the algorithm $\langle R_2\rangle_2$ recognizes negative rational numbers, and therefore the generated set of all negative numbers is equal to the set

$$(\langle R_2\rangle_2 (c_{2,1}) \mp \Lambda); \tag{6}$$

g) the algorithm $\langle R_3\rangle_2$ recognizes rational numbers, and therefore the generated set of all rational numbers is equal to the set

$$(\langle R_3\rangle_2 (c_{2,1}) \mp \Lambda); \tag{7}$$

h) the algorithm $\langle R_4\rangle_2$ recognizes reduced rational numbers, and therefore the generated set of all reduced rational numbers is equal to the set

$$(\langle R_4\rangle_2 (c_{2,1}) \mp \Lambda). \tag{8}$$

It is obvious that the word P_0 satisfying condition a) is not unique. However, we shall assume that, among all words satisfying condition a), some one word has been selected, and we shall assume that just this word is denoted by P_0. In an entirely analogous way, starting from conditions b)–h), we introduce, respectively, the notations P_1, Q, R_0, R_1, R_2, R_3, and R_4.

We agree to denote:

formula (1) by ($c_{0,1} \in$ pos. int),

formula (2) by ($c_{0,1} \in$ nat),

formula (3) by ($c_{1,1} \in$ int),

formula (4) by ($c_{2,1} \in$ pos. rat),

formula (5) by ($c_{2,1} \in$ null rat),

formula (6) by ($c_{2,1} \in$ neg. rat),

formula (7) by ($c_{2,1} \in$ rat),

formula (8) by ($c_{2,1} \in$ red. rat).

In this notation the symbol $\in$ occurs. We remark that it is used here as an abbreviation for certain logico-mathematical formula with precisely the same meaning with which the colon was used on pp. 295 and 305 in [3] (transl. pp. 175, 184). In this book the colon will occur as a symbol for the operation of division and will not be used (as a mathematical symbol) for any other purpose. The notation

$$(\alpha : \underline{\text{nat}}), \quad (\sigma : (\mu_1 \ldots \mu_k \rightarrow \mu_{k+1})_i),$$

introduced in [3] will not be carried over; instead of it we will use the notation

$$(\alpha \in \underline{\text{nat}}), \quad (\sigma \in (\mu_1 \ldots \mu_k \rightarrow \mu_{k+1})_i).$$

The symbol ∈ will be used not only as an abbreviation of certain logico-mathematical formulas but also for writing propositions about membership of letters in an alphabet (i.e. with the same meaning with which this symbol occurs in [1] and [3]). This does not lead to ambiguity, since in every case where the symbol ∈ is used it will be clear from the text in what sense the symbol is being used.

In §1.2 we agreed to call natural numbers words of type Н, integers words of type Ц, rational numbers words of type Р, and reduced rational numbers words of type $\overline{\text{Р}}$. The letters Н, Ц, Р, $\overline{\text{Р}}$ will be used as generic restricted letters, intended for the construction of restricted individual variables (see [3], §8.2), and, namely: variables of genus Н (i.e. the words (Н), (НН), (ННН), · · ·) called natural variables, variables of genus Ц (i.e. the words (Ц), (ЦЦ), (ЦЦЦ), · · ·) called *integer variables*, variables of genus Р (i.e. the words (Р), (РР), (РРР), · · ·) called *rational variables*, and variables of genus $\overline{\text{Р}}$ (i.e. the words ($\overline{\text{Р}}$), ($\overline{\text{РР}}$), ($\overline{\text{РРР}}$), · · ·). We shall consider the formulas (2), (3), (7), and (8), respectively, as characterizing formulas of the letters Н, Ц, Р, and $\overline{\text{Р}}$ (cf. [3], §8.2).

1.7. In presenting various branches of constructive mathematical analysis it is convenient to use, along with the basic logico-mathematical languages described in [3], §3, the extensions of the basic languages described in [3], §8.2. The introduction of restricted variables of various kinds (for example, natural variables, integer variables, rational variables, etc.), based on certain sets or generated sets, amounts to the introduction of corresponding extensions of the basic logico-mathematical language.

Above we introduced restricted variables of four concrete kinds: variables of types Н, Ц, Р, and $\overline{\text{Р}}$. In the sequel we shall introduce new (restricted) variables (individual and function).

The introduction of variables of a new kind is accompanied by presentation of some one-parameter formulas which play the role of characterizing formulas of the new restricted variables.[1)] By definition, as characterizing formulas of

1)A characterizing formula of a generic letter of certain restricted variables is called the characterizing formula of the restricted variables of the given type (see [3], p. 303 (transl. p. 181).

restricted variables of a given type one must use one-parameter basis formulas, i.e. one-parameter formulas in which restricted variables do not occur. However, in the sequel we shall sometimes give as characterizing formulas of newly introduced restricted variables one-parameter formulas which contain occurrences of previously introduced restricted variables. In every such case we shall assume that the characterizing formula of the newly introduced variables is the result of applying to the given formulas the algorithm $\mathfrak{c}$ described in [3], §8.7.

The algorithm $\mathfrak{c}$ transforms any formula $\mathfrak{F}$ of the language $\mathfrak{A}_\Sigma$ into a formula $\mathfrak{c}_\llcorner \mathfrak{F}_\lrcorner$ of the language $\mathfrak{A}$ called the *equivalent of the formula* $\mathfrak{F}$ *in the language* $\mathfrak{A}$. The algorithm $\mathfrak{c}$ will be called the *algorithm for eliminating restricted variables.*

1.8. To what was said in [3], §8.2 about extensions of basic languages it is necessary to make a few additions.

We shall consider any language $\mathfrak{A}_\Sigma$ of the type described in [3], §8.2. This language is an extension of the language $\mathfrak{A}$ (cf. §1.4), uniquely defined by the language $\mathfrak{A}$, a list of restricted generic letters and a list of basis formulas Σ. If the list Σ is empty (this case is not excluded!), then the language $\mathfrak{A}_\Sigma$ coincides with the language $\mathfrak{A}$.

We extend to all variables of the language $\mathfrak{A}_\Sigma$ and to words built up from these variables the operations $\smile$ and $\frown$ introduced in §1.4 for variables of the language $\mathfrak{A}$.

Let α be any variable of the language $\mathfrak{A}_\Sigma$ and let μ be the generic letter of this variable. We denote by i the index of the basic alphabet associated with the letter μ (see [3], p. 302 (transl. p. 180)). If α is an individual variable, then we set

$$\underset{\smile}{\alpha} \rightleftharpoons i, \quad \overset{\frown}{\alpha} \rightleftharpoons \alpha.$$

If α is a function variable, then we set

$$\underset{\smile}{\alpha} \rightleftharpoons 0, \quad \overset{\frown}{\alpha} \rightleftharpoons \{\alpha\}.$$

Let $\alpha_1, \cdots, \alpha_k$ be any variables and let S denote the word $\alpha_1 \cdots \alpha_k$. We set

$$\underset{\smile}{S} \rightleftharpoons \nu(\underset{\smile}{\alpha_1}, \ldots, \underset{\smile}{\alpha_k});$$

$$\overset{\frown}{S} \rightleftharpoons \overset{\frown}{\alpha_1}, \qquad \text{if} \quad k=1,$$

$$\overset{\frown}{S} \rightleftharpoons \overset{\frown}{\alpha_1} \square \overset{\frown}{\alpha_2} \square \ldots \square \overset{\frown}{\alpha_k}, \qquad \text{if} \quad k>1.$$

Let $\mathfrak{F}$ be any formula of type $[\alpha_1 \cdots \alpha_k]$, where $k \geq 1$. We impose no restrictions on the variables $\alpha_1, \cdots, \alpha_k$. In the list $\alpha_1, \cdots, \alpha_k$ different sorts of variables may occur: individual, function, basis, and restricted.

The formula $\mathfrak{F}$ will be considered as the transcription into the language $Я_\Sigma$ of the condition expressed by the basis formula $\mathrm{c}\llcorner\mathfrak{F}\lrcorner$(see [3], §8.7). We shall say that the formula $\mathfrak{F}$ *expresses an algorithmically verifiable condition* if the formula $\mathrm{c}\llcorner\mathfrak{F}\lrcorner$ expresses an algorithmically verifiable condition.

We shall say that a formula $\mathfrak{F}$ *expresses a condition algorithmically verifiable for admissible values of its parameters* if one can construct a word C in the alphabet A_0 such that, first,

$$\tilde{\forall}! \langle C \rangle_m (\widehat{S})$$

and second,

$$\tilde{\forall} (\mathfrak{F} \equiv (\langle C \rangle_m (\widehat{S}) \doteq \Lambda)).$$

Here $S \leftrightharpoons \alpha_1 \cdots \alpha_k$ and $m \leftrightharpoons \underset{\smile}{S}$.

Any closed formula expresses a proposition, not a condition. However, for the sake of uniform terminology, it is convenient to extend the terminology just adopted also to closed formulas.

We shall say that a closed formula $\mathfrak{F}$ *expresses a condition algorithmically verifiable for admissible values of its parameters* if one can construct a word C in the alphabet A_0 such that, first,

$$! \langle C \rangle_0 (\Lambda)$$

and second,

$$(\mathfrak{F} \equiv (\langle C \rangle_0 (\Lambda) \doteq \Lambda)).$$

Starting from the rules of the constructive reformulation of mathematical propositions, transcribed in the language $Я_\Sigma$, one can prove the following proposition.

1.8.1. *If a formula $\mathfrak{F}$ is such that the characterizing formulas of all restricted variables among its parameters are normal formulas, then $\mathfrak{F}$ expresses a condition algorithmically verifiable for all admissible values of its parameters if and only if*

$$\tilde{\forall} (\mathfrak{F} \vee \neg \mathfrak{F}).$$

The following proposition is also easily proved.

1.8.2. *If a formula $\mathfrak{F}$ is such that the characterizing formulas of all restricted variables among its parameters express algorithmically verifiable conditions, then the following two propositions are equivalent.*

a) *The formula $\mathfrak{F}$ expresses a condition algorithmically verifiable for admis-*

sible values of its parameters.

b) *The formula* $\mathfrak{F}$ *expresses an algorithmically verifiable condition.*

From 1.8.2 and the content of §1.6 we get

1.8.3. *If a formula* $\mathfrak{F}$ *is such that every restricted variable among its parameters is a variable of type* Н, *or type* Ц, *or type* Р, *or type* $\overline{\text{Р}}$, *then the sentences* a) *and* b) *of* 1.8.2 *are equivalent.*

If $\mathfrak{F}$ is a one-parameter formula and the parameter of this formula is a variable of type μ, then as a synonym of the expression "$\mathfrak{F}$ expresses a condition algorithmically verifiable for admissible values of its parameters", we shall use the expression "$\mathfrak{F}$ is an algorithmically solvable set of words of type μ". It is in this sense that in the sequel we shall understand the expressions "$\mathfrak{F}$ is an algorithmically solvable set of natural numbers", "$\mathfrak{F}$ is an algorithmically solvable set of rational numbers", etc.

1.9. Let $\mathfrak{F}$ and $\mathfrak{G}$ be arbitrary formulas of the language $Я_\Sigma$. One says that the formula $\mathfrak{F}$ is *equivalent to the formula* $\mathfrak{G}$ if

$$\tilde{\forall}(\mathfrak{F} \equiv \mathfrak{G}).$$

We note the following proposition.

1.9.1. *The formula* $\mathfrak{F}$ *is equivalent to the formula* $\mathfrak{G}$ *if and only if the basis formula* $\text{с}_\llcorner \mathfrak{F} \lrcorner$ *is equivalent to the basis formula* $\text{с}_\llcorner \mathfrak{G} \lrcorner$.

The proof of Proposition 1.9.1 is carried out without difficulty on the basis of the following lemma.

If $\mathfrak{A}$, $\mathfrak{B}$ *and* $\mathfrak{C}$ *are arbitrary basis formulas, then*

$$\tilde{\forall}.((\mathfrak{C} \supset (\mathfrak{A} \equiv \mathfrak{B})) \equiv ((\mathfrak{C} \,\&\, \mathfrak{A}) \equiv (\mathfrak{C} \,\&\, \mathfrak{B}))).$$

1.10. Now let us consider the problem of introducing terms for concepts and relational terms, as abbreviations of formulas of the language $Я_\Sigma$.

Let $\mathfrak{F}$ be any formula of the language $Я_\Sigma$ and let

$$\alpha_1, \cdots, \alpha_k$$

be the normal list of parameters of this formula. Assume here that $k \geq 1$.

Let us consider, to begin with, the case where $k = 1$. In this case $\mathfrak{F}$ expresses a one-place condition. If we associate some term with this condition, we obtain a definite concept. Let us suppose that as a term for the concept the symbol V has been chosen. We can now, according to the usual mathematical custom, use the concept V for abbreviating formulas of the language $\mathfrak{A}_{\Sigma}$. To this end, we introduce the expression

$$(\alpha_1 \in V),$$

which will be considered as a designation of the formula $\mathfrak{F}$:

$$(\alpha_1 \in V) \leftrightharpoons \mathfrak{F}.$$

The expression $(\alpha_1 \in V)$ is read: "α_1 is an object of type V".

Let T be any term similar to the variable α_1 (see [3], §§3.8, 8.2). We introduce the notation

$$(T \in V) \leftrightharpoons \mathbf{F}^{\alpha}_{T_\llcorner} \mathfrak{F}_\lrcorner$$

(see [3], §§3.9, 8.2). The expression $(T \in V)$ is read: "the value of the term T is an object of type V".

We also introduce the notation

$$(T \overset{+}{\in} V) \leftrightharpoons (!T \,\&\, (T \in V)).$$

Here, if T is a function term, then the expression $!T$ will be understood as a designation of the expression $!\Theta$, where Θ is an individual term such that

$$T \mathrel{\underset{\circ}{=}} \langle \mathrm{A}_j^{\mathrm{sa}} \omega \dot{\Theta} \rangle.$$

The individual term Θ and the basic alphabet A_j are determined uniquely by the word T.

The notation introduced in §1.6 for the formulas 1.6(1)–1.6(8) consists of designations of the form

$$(\alpha_1 \in V).$$

The symbols

pos. int, nat, int, pos. rat, neg. rat, rat, red. rat

are terms for concepts, characterized by the conditions 1.6(1)–1.6(8) respectively.

In the sequel we shall often use generic letters of basis and restricted variables as terms for concepts. If μ is any generic letter and T is any term, then the expression

$$(T \in \mu)$$

will denote the following: "the value of the term T is a word of type μ". In particular, the expression

$$(T \in c_i)$$

will denote the following: "the value of the term T is a word in the alphabet $Ч_i$".

Let us consider the case where $k \geq 2$. In that case $\mathfrak{F}$ expresses a k-ary condition. It can serve as a basis for the introduction of various k-ary relations. The number of pairwise nonequivalent relations which can be introduced on the basis of the condition $\mathfrak{F}$ does not exceed the number of permutations of k elements. We fix some enumeration without repetitions of all parameters of the formula $\mathfrak{F}$. If with the condition $\mathfrak{F}$ and the fixed enumeration of all parameters of the formula $\mathfrak{F}$ we associate some term, then we obtain a definite k-ary relation. Let us suppose that $\alpha_{i_1}, \cdots, \alpha_{i_k}$ is a list of all parameters of the formula $\mathfrak{F}$, written without repetition in a fixed order, and let us assume that the symbol W has been chosen as the relational term. Now, in the way customary in mathematics, we can use the relation W in abbreviations of formulas of the language Я_Σ. To this end, we introduce the expression

$$(\alpha_{i_1} \square \alpha_{i_2} \square \ldots \square \alpha_{i_k} \in W),$$

which will be considered as a designation of the formula $\mathfrak{F}$:

$$(\alpha_{i_1} \square \alpha_{i_2} \square \ldots \square \alpha_{i_k} \in W) \leftrightharpoons \mathfrak{F}.$$

The expression $(\alpha_{i_1} \square\ \alpha_{i_2} \square \cdots \square \alpha_{i_k} \in W)$ is read: "the objects $\alpha_{i_1}, \alpha_{i_2}, \cdots, \alpha_{i_k}$ are in the relation W".

Let $T_1, T_2, \cdots, T_k$ be a list of terms similar to the list of variables $\alpha_{i_1}, \alpha_{i_2}, \cdots, \alpha_{i_k}$ (see [3], pp. 250 and 304 (transl. pp. 131, 182)). We introduce the notation

$$(T_1 \square T_2 \square \ldots \square T_k \in W) \leftrightharpoons \mathbf{F}^{\alpha_{i_1}, \alpha_{i_2}, \ldots, \alpha_{i_k}}_{T_1, T_2, \ldots, T_k} \llcorner \mathfrak{F} \lrcorner .$$

The expression $(T_1 \square T_2 \square \cdots \square T_k \in W)$ is read: "the value of the term T_1, the value of the term $T_2, \cdots$, the value of the term T_k are in the relation W".

We also introduce the notation

$$(T_1 \square T_2 \square \ldots \square T_k \overset{+}{\in} W) \leftrightharpoons (!T_1 \,\&\, !T_2 \,\&\, \ldots \,\&\, !T_k \,\&\, (T_1 \square T_2 \square \ldots \square T_k \in W)).$$

In the case where $k = 2$, the following notation is also applied:

$$(\alpha_{i_1} W \alpha_{i_2}) \leftrightharpoons \mathfrak{F},$$

$$(T_1 W T_2) \leftrightharpoons \mathbf{F}^{\alpha_{i_1}, \alpha_{i_2}}_{T_1, T_2} \llcorner \mathfrak{F} \lrcorner,$$

$$(T_1 \overset{+}{W} T_2) \leftrightharpoons (!T_1 \,\&\, !T_2 \,\&\, (T_1 W T_2)).$$

In logic, concepts and relations are called *predicates*. Moreover, concepts are called *one-place predicates*, and two-place, three-place, etc., relations are called, respectively, *two-place, three-place*, etc., *predicates*.

A predicate Π is called an *algorithmically solvable predicate* if the condition expressed by the basis formula $\mathsf{c}_\llcorner \mathfrak{F}_\lrcorner$, where $\mathfrak{F}$ is the formula characterizing the predicate Π and c is the algorithm for eliminating restricted variables (see §1.7), is algorithmically verifiable. Algorithmically solvable predicates are also called *recursive predicates*.

1.11. Let $\mu_1, \cdots, \mu_k, \mu_{k+1}$ $(k \geq 1)$ be any list of generic individual letters. The indices of the basic alphabets associated with the generic letters $\mu_1, \cdots, \mu_k, \mu_{k+1}$ are denoted, respectively, by $r_1, \cdots, r_k, r_{k+1}$. Let A_i be any basic alphabet containing the union of the alphabets $A_{r_1}, \cdots, A_{r_k}, A_{r_{k+1}}$, and let σ be any function variable of type λ_i. We express by one-parameter formulas of the language $Я_\Sigma$ the following two conditions (containing σ as a parameter).

(*) "The algorithm σ is applicable to every word of the type $\mu_1 \cdots \mu_k$ and it transforms any word of type $\mu_1 \cdots \mu_k$ into a word of type μ_{k+1}."

(**) "The algorithm σ transforms every word of type $\mu_1 \cdots \mu_k$, to which it is applicable, into a word of type μ_{k+1}."

We form a list of individual variables

$$\alpha_1, \cdots, \alpha_k,$$

satisfying the following conditions: (1) the variables $\alpha_1, \cdots, \alpha_k$ are pairwise distinct, and (2) for every j $(j = 1, \cdots, k)$, α_j is a variable of type μ_j. We introduce the notation:

$$P \leftrightharpoons \alpha_1, \quad \text{if} \quad k = 1,$$

$$P \leftrightharpoons \alpha_1 \square \ldots \square \alpha_k, \quad \text{if} \quad k > 1,$$

$$\mathfrak{M} \leftrightharpoons (\langle I^i_{r_{k+1}} \rangle_i (\sigma(P)) = \Lambda).$$

Here $I^i_{r_{k+1}}$ denotes the transcription of the normal algorithm in the alphabet A_i^{sa}, defined by the abbreviated schema

$$\{\xi \rightarrow \qquad (\xi \in A_{r_{k+1}}).$$

The algorithm $\langle I^i_{r_{k+1}} \rangle_i$ is applicable to every word in the alphabet A_i^{sa}, and a word Q in this alphabet is transformed into the empty word if and only if Q is a word in the alphabet $A_{r_{k+1}}$. Thus, the algorithm $\langle I^i_{r_{k+1}} \rangle_i$ "recognizes" words in the alphabet $A_{r_{k+1}}$ among all the words in the alphabet A_i^{sa}.

If μ_{k+1} is a restricted generic letter, then we denote by $\mathfrak{R}$ the characterizing formula of the letter μ_{k+1} and by θ the parameter of the formula $\mathfrak{R}$. Finally, we introduce the notation

$$\mathfrak{F} \leftrightharpoons \forall \alpha_1 \ldots \alpha_k \mathfrak{M}, \qquad \text{if } \mu_{k+1} \text{ is a basis generic letter;}$$

$\mathfrak{F} \rightleftharpoons \forall\alpha_1 \ldots \alpha_k (\mathfrak{M} \& \mathbf{F}^{\theta}_{\sigma(P)} \llcorner \mathfrak{R} \lrcorner)$, if μ_{k+1} is a restricted generic letter;

$\mathfrak{G} \rightleftharpoons \forall\alpha_1 \ldots \alpha_k (!\,\sigma(\mathrm{P}) \supset \mathfrak{M})$, if μ_{k+1} is a basis generic letter;

$\mathfrak{G} \rightleftharpoons \forall\alpha_1 \ldots \alpha_k (!\,\sigma(P) \supset (\mathfrak{M} \& \mathbf{F}^{\theta}_{\sigma(P)} \llcorner \mathfrak{R} \lrcorner))$, if μ_{k+1} is a restricted generic letter.

The formula $\mathfrak{F}$ expresses the condition (*); we denote it by the expression

$$(\sigma \in (\mu_1 \ldots \mu_k \rightarrow \mu_{k+1})_i).$$

In accordance with this stipulation, the last designation has precisely the same meaning as the designation $(\sigma\colon (\mu_1 \cdots \mu_k \rightarrow \mu_{k+1})_i)$ introduced in [3], §8.3.

The formula $\mathfrak{G}$ expresses the condition (**); we denote it by the expression

$$(\sigma \in (\mu_1 \ldots \mu_k \dot{\rightarrow} \mu_{k+1})_i).$$

The expressions $(\mu_1 \cdots \mu_k \rightarrow \mu_{k+1})_i$ and $(\mu_1 \cdots \mu_k \dot{\rightarrow} \mu_{k+1})_i$ occurring in the notation just introduced are terms for the concepts characterized, respectively, by the conditions $\mathfrak{F}$ and $\mathfrak{G}$.

The expressions

$(\varphi \in (\mathrm{H} \rightarrow \mathrm{H})_0)$, where φ is a variable of type Φ_0,

$(\psi \in (\mathrm{H} \rightarrow \text{Ц})_1)$, where ψ is a variable of type Φ_1,

$(\chi \in (\mathrm{H} \rightarrow \mathrm{P})_2)$, where χ is a variable of type Φ_2,

will be read as follows:

"ϕ is a constructive sequence of natural numbers",

"ψ is a constructive sequence of integers",

"χ is a constructive sequence of rational numbers".

For brevity we shall omit the adjective "constructive" in front of the word "sequence". This will not lead to confusion, since in this book the term "sequence" will never be used in the sense connected with the term in classical mathematical analysis without special mention.

Sequences of natural numbers (i.e. functors satisfying the condition $(\phi \in (\mathrm{H} \rightarrow \mathrm{H})_0)$) will also be called *words of type f* or *functors of type f*, and we shall consider the letter f to be a restricted generic function letter, to be used for the construction of the restricted function variables

$$(f),\ (ff),\ (fff), \cdots .$$

On the basis of the convention accepted in §1.3, these variables will be denoted, respectively, by the expressions

$$f_1, f_2, f_3, \cdots$$

As a characterizing formula of the letter f the formula $(\phi_{0,1} \in (\mathrm{H} \to \mathrm{H})_0)$ will serve. It is easily seen that $\mathrm{c}_{\llcorner}(\phi_{0,1} \in (\mathrm{H} \to \mathrm{H})_0)_{\lrcorner}$ is a normal formula (cf. §1.7). Sequences of rational numbers (i.e. functors satisfying the condition $(\chi \in (\mathrm{H} \to \mathrm{p})_2)$) will be called *words of type* g or *functors of type* g, and we shall consider the letter g to be a restricted generic function letter, to be used for the construction of the restricted function variables

$$(g), (gg), (ggg), \cdots.$$

On the basis of the convention accepted in §1.3, these variables will be denoted, respectively, by the expressions

$$g_1, g_2, g_3, \cdots.$$

As a characterizing formula of the letter g the formula $(\phi_{2,1} \in (\mathrm{H} \to \mathrm{p})_2)$ will serve. It is easily seen that $\mathrm{c}_{\llcorner}(\phi_{2,1} \in (\mathrm{H} \to \mathrm{p})_2)_{\lrcorner}$ is a normal formula.

1.12. The two-place relation symbols

$$\underset{\mathrm{p}}{=}, \underset{\mathrm{p}}{\geqslant}, \underset{\mathrm{p}}{\leqslant}, \underset{\mathrm{p}}{\neq}, \underset{\mathrm{p}}{<}, \underset{\mathrm{p}}{>} \tag{1}$$

will be used, in application to rational numbers, in the same sense as the symbols $=, \geq, \leq, \neq, <, >$ are customarily used. The conditions characterizing these relations can be given by formulas of the form

$$(\langle H \rangle_2 (\mathrm{p}_1 \square \mathrm{p}_2) \mathrel{\dot{=}} \Lambda),$$

where J is a word in the alphabet Ч_0 such that

$$\forall \mathrm{c}_{2,1}\mathrm{c}_{2,2}! \langle H \rangle_2 (\mathrm{c}_{2,1} \square \mathrm{c}_{2,2}).$$

We have

$$\mathrm{c}_{\llcorner}(\langle H \rangle_2 (\mathrm{p}_1 \square \mathrm{p}_2) \mathrel{\dot{=}} \Lambda)_{\lrcorner} \mathrel{\overset{\circ}{=}} ((\mathrm{c}_{2,1} \in \mathrm{rat}) \& (\mathrm{c}_{2,2} \in \mathrm{rat}) \& (\langle H \rangle_2 (\mathrm{c}_{2,1} \square \mathrm{c}_{2,2}) \mathrel{\dot{=}} \Lambda)).$$

Hence the following proposition holds.

1.12.1. *Each of the predicates* (1) *is an algorithmically solvable predicate.*

Using 1.12.1, we can establish that all elementary properties of the relations (1), provable in classical arithmetic, can also be proved in constructive arithmetic. The properties which we have in mind here will be spelled out in the appropriate sections devoted to constructive real numbers.

Let W be any one of the symbols (1). On the basis of the convention accepted in §1. 10, the expression $(T_1 \square T_2 \in W)$ and the expression $(T_1 W T_2)$, where T_1 and T_2 are any individual terms, are to be accorded the same meaning: these two expressions denote one and the same formula. In accordance with established mathematical practice, we shall systematically use notation of the form $(T_1 W T_2)$.

In those cases where it is clear from the context that we are talking about relations between rational numbers, we shall use the symbols $=, \geq, \leq, \neq, <, >$ instead of the symbols (1).

We shall now agree on notation for the most common operations on rational numbers.

The symbols

$$M_p, \ +_p, \ -_p, \ \cdot_p, \ :_p, \ \Lambda_p, \ \max_p, \ \min_p \tag{2}$$

will be used in the sequel in the following senses.[1)]

M_p is a designation for the functor $\langle K_0 \rangle_2$, corresponding to the algorithm for constructing the absolute value (modulus) of a rational number.

$+_p$ is a designation of the functor $\langle K_1 \rangle_2$, corresponding to the algorithm for adding rational numbers. The algorithm $\langle K_1 \rangle_2$ transforms any system of rational numbers (i.e. any word of the form $R_1 \square R_2 \square \cdots \square R_j$, where $R_1, R_2, \cdots, R_j$ are rational numbers) into the sum of all the terms of the system.[2)]

$-_p$ is a designation of the functor $\langle K_2 \rangle_2$, corresponding to the algorithm for constructing the difference of rational numbers. The algorithm $\langle K_2 \rangle_2$ is chosen so that it transforms any pair of rational numbers into the result of subtracting the second term of the pair from the first term of the pair and it transforms any rational number R into the same rational number into which it transforms the pair $0 \square R$ (i.e. into the result of subtracting the rational number R from zero).

$\cdot_p$ is a designation of the functor $\langle K_3 \rangle_2$, corresponding to the algorithm for multiplying rational numbers. The algorithm $\langle K_3 \rangle_2$ transforms any system of

1) In the expression "$-_p$" a long line occurs, as opposed to the short line "-", which is a letter of the alphabet $Ч_2$.

2) Let μ be any restricted generic letter and let A_i be the alphabet associated with the letter μ (see [3], p. 302 (transl. p. 180)). *Systems of words of type* μ are defined by the following generating rules: any word of type μ is a system of words of type μ; if P and Q are systems of words of type μ, then the word $P \square Q$ is a system of words of type μ. Any two-termed system of words of type μ is called a *pair of words of type* μ.

rational numbers into the product of all terms of the system.

$:_{\mathrm{p}}$ is a designation of the functor $\langle K_4\rangle_2$, corresponding to the algorithm for dividing one rational number by another. The algorithm $\langle K_4\rangle_2$ is chosen so that, first, this algorithm transforms any pair of rational numbers in which the second term is not a null rational number into the result of dividing the first term of the pair by the second term of the pair, and second, if a pair of rational numbers is such that its second term is a null rational number, then the process of applying this algorithm to such a word does not terminate.

Λ_{p} is a designation of the functor $\langle K_5\rangle_2$, corresponding to the algorithm for raising a rational number to an integral power. The algorithm $\langle K_5\rangle_2$ is chosen so that, first, this algorithm transforms any word of the form $R \square C$, where R is a rational number and C is an integer and at least one of the words R and C is not a null rational number, into the result of raising R to the power with exponent C, and, second, if R is a null rational number, the process of applying the algorithm $\langle K_5\rangle_2$ to the word $R \square 0$ does not terminate.

$\max_{\mathrm{p}}$ is a designation of the functor $\langle K_6\rangle_2$, corresponding to the algorithm for selecting the largest rational number among the terms of any system of rational numbers.

$\min_{\mathrm{p}}$ is a designation of the functor $\langle K_7\rangle_2$, corresponding to the algorithm for selecting the least rational number among the terms of any system of rational numbers.

We shall assume that the algorithms $\langle K_0\rangle_2$, $\langle K_1\rangle_2$, $\langle K_2\rangle_2$, $\langle K_3\rangle_2$, $\langle K_4\rangle_2$, $\langle K_5\rangle_2$, $\langle K_6\rangle_2$, $\langle K_7\rangle_2$ are chosen so that the result of applying the algorithm M_{p} to any rational number, the results of applying the algorithms $+_{\mathrm{p}}$, $\cdot_{\mathrm{p}}$, $\max_{\mathrm{p}}$, $\min_{\mathrm{p}}$ to any system of rational numbers, the result of applying the algorithm $-_{\mathrm{p}}$ to any pair of rational numbers, and the results of applying the algorithms $:_{\mathrm{p}}$ and Λ_{p} to those pairs of rational numbers to which they are applicable, are reduced rational numbers.

Such a choice of the indicated algorithms is convenient in certain respects. In particular, sometimes we shall use the fact that the results of applying the algorithms $+_{\mathrm{p}}$, $\cdot_{\mathrm{p}}$, $\max_{\mathrm{p}}$, $\min_{\mathrm{p}}$ to any system of integers, the result of applying the algorithm $-_{\mathrm{p}}$ to any pair of integers, and the result of applying the algorithm $:_{\mathrm{p}}$ to any pair of integers in which the first term is divisible without remainder by the second term, are integers.

The words K_0, K_1, K_2, K_3, K_4, K_5, K_6, K_7 are suitable transcriptions of the constructed normal algorithms. These algorithms will be considered fixed.

Let $\Theta_1, \Theta_2, \cdots, \Theta_j$ $(j \geq 2)$ be any individual terms. In accordance with established mathematical practice we agree to denote the terms

$$\underset{\mathrm{p}}{+}(\Theta_1 \square \Theta_2 \square \ldots \square \Theta_j), \qquad \underset{\mathrm{p}}{-}(\Theta_1 \square \Theta_2), \qquad \underset{\mathrm{p}}{\cdot}(\Theta_1 \square \Theta_2 \square \cdots \square \Theta_j),$$
$$\underset{\mathrm{p}}{:}(\Theta_1 \square \Theta_2), \qquad \underset{\mathrm{p}}{\Lambda}(\Theta_1 \square \Theta_2)$$

by the expressions

$$(\Theta_1 \underset{\mathrm{p}}{+} \Theta_2 \underset{\mathrm{p}}{+} \ldots \underset{\mathrm{p}}{+} \Theta_j), \qquad (\Theta_1 \underset{\mathrm{p}}{-} \Theta_2), \qquad (\Theta_1 \underset{\mathrm{p}}{\cdot} \Theta_2 \underset{\mathrm{p}}{\cdot} \ldots \underset{\mathrm{p}}{\cdot} \Theta_j),$$
$$(\Theta_1 \underset{\mathrm{p}}{:} \Theta_2), \qquad \Theta_1^{\Theta_2}, \text{ respectively.}$$

We agree to denote the term $-_{\mathrm{p}}(\Theta)$, where Θ is any individual term, by the shorter expression $-_{\mathrm{p}}\Theta$, if the use of this abbreviation does not lead to ambiguity.

Remark. If R is a positive rational number, then

$$\underset{\mathrm{p}}{-} R \underset{\mathrm{p}}{=} \text{-} R, \qquad \underset{\mathrm{p}}{-} \text{-} R \underset{\mathrm{p}}{=} R.$$

(Here, "-" is a letter of the alphabet $Ч_2$.)

In those cases where it is clear from the context that we are talking about rational numbers, we shall use the symbols

$$M, \; +, \; -, \; \cdot, \; :, \; \Lambda, \; \max, \; \min.$$

instead of the symbols (2).

All elementary properties of the operations (2), provable in classical arithmetic, also can be proved in constructive arithmetic. The properties which we have in mind here will be spelled out in the appropriate sections devoted to constructive real numbers.

1.13. We shall consider some problems connected with the reading of logico-mathematical formulas.[1)]

Let $\mu_1, \cdots, \mu_k$ be generic letters, α_1 a variable of type $\mu_1, \cdots, \alpha_k$ a variable of type u_k and $\mathfrak{A}$ a logico-mathematical formula. The formula $\exists \alpha_1 \cdots \alpha_k \mathfrak{A}$ is read and contensively understood in the following way:

"Words α_1 of type $\mu_1, \cdots, \alpha_k$ of type μ_k are potentially realizable such that $\mathfrak{A}$ holds".

1) On the reading of logico-mathematical formulas, see [3].

For brevity of expression we agree to use the word "realizable" as a synonym for the expression "potentially realizable". As a second synonym of the expression "potentially realizable" we shall sometimes use the expression "one can construct".

In accordance with what has been said above, the formula $\neg\exists\alpha_1\cdots\alpha_k\mathfrak{A}$ is naturally read as follows:

"There cannot exist words α_1 of type $\mu_1, \cdots, \alpha_k$ of type μ_k such that $\mathfrak{A}$ holds".

We agree to read the formula $\neg\neg\exists\alpha_1\cdots\alpha_k\mathfrak{A}$ as follows:

"Words α_1 of type $\mu_1, \cdots, \alpha_k$ of type μ_k are quasirealizable such that $\mathfrak{A}$ holds".

In [3], §6.2 the symbol $\underset{\cdot}{\exists}$ was introduced and was called there the symbol of quasirealizability; it was agreed that the expression $\underset{\cdot}{\exists}\alpha_1\cdots\alpha_k\mathfrak{A}$ would be considered as a designation of the formula $\neg\forall\alpha_1\cdots\alpha_k\neg\mathfrak{A}$. The proposition

$$\tilde{\forall}(\underset{\cdot}{\exists}\alpha_1\ldots\alpha_k\mathfrak{A}\equiv\neg\neg\exists\alpha_1\ldots\alpha_k\mathfrak{A})$$

is valid.

We agree to read the formula $\neg\forall\alpha_1\cdots\alpha_k\neg\mathfrak{A}$ and its designation $\underset{\cdot}{\exists}\alpha_1\cdots\alpha_k\mathfrak{A}$ in precisely the same way as the formula $\neg\neg\exists\alpha_1\cdots\alpha_k\mathfrak{A}$.

Let $\mathfrak{A}_1, \mathfrak{A}_2, \cdots, \mathfrak{A}_n$ be arbitrary formulas. The formula

$$(\mathfrak{A}_1\vee\mathfrak{A}_2\vee\ldots\vee\mathfrak{A}_n)$$

is read: "$\mathfrak{A}_1$ or $\mathfrak{A}_2$ or $\cdots$ or $\mathfrak{A}_n$".

We agree to read the formula

$$\neg\neg(\mathfrak{A}_1\vee\mathfrak{A}_2\vee\ldots\vee\mathfrak{A}_n)$$

in the following way: "Either $\mathfrak{A}_1$ or $\mathfrak{A}_2$ or $\cdots$ or $\mathfrak{A}_n$". In ordinary discourse it is customary to consider the phrases "or" and "either $\cdots$ or" as synonyms. We shall not follow this tradition and we agree to use in the sequel the phrase "either $\cdots$ or" as a term for the logical connective expressed in terms of the logical connectives "or" and "not" in the manner indicated above. In view of this convention, the phrases "or" and "neither $\cdots$ or" will have different meanings in the sequel.

In [3], §6.2 we introduced the symbol $\underset{\cdot}{\vee}$, called there the symbol of quasidisjunction, and we made the convention that the expression $(\mathfrak{A}_1\underset{\cdot}{\vee}\mathfrak{A}_2\underset{\cdot}{\vee}\ldots\underset{\cdot}{\vee}\mathfrak{A}_n)$ would be considered as a designation of the formula

$$\neg(\neg\mathfrak{A}_1\&\neg\mathfrak{A}_2\&\ldots\&\neg\mathfrak{A}_n).$$

We then have the proposition:

$$\tilde{\forall}((\mathfrak{A}_1 \dot{\vee} \mathfrak{A}_2 \dot{\vee} \ldots \dot{\vee} \mathfrak{A}_n) \equiv \neg\neg(\mathfrak{A}_1 \vee \mathfrak{A}_2 \vee \ldots \vee \mathfrak{A}_n)).$$

We agree that the formula $\neg(\neg\mathfrak{A}_1 \& \neg\mathfrak{A}_2 \& \ldots \& \neg\mathfrak{A}_n)$ and its designation $(\mathfrak{A}_1 \dot{\vee} \mathfrak{A}_2 \dot{\vee} \ldots \dot{\vee} \mathfrak{A}_n)$ will be read in precisely the same way as the formula

$$\neg\neg(\mathfrak{A}_1 \vee \mathfrak{A}_2 \vee \ldots \vee \mathfrak{A}_n).$$

In the sequel we shall write propositions and conditions in various ways: sometimes by logico-mathematical formulas, sometimes by a mixture of ordinary language, of various elements of the logico-mathematical symbolism and of whole logico-mathematical formulas. We cite an example of an expression of the second type.

The proposition, expressed by the formula

$$\forall \mathrm{c}_{0,1} \exists \mathrm{H}_1 \mathrm{H}_2 \Phi_{2,1} (\mathfrak{A} \& (\forall \mathrm{p}_1 \mathfrak{B} \vee \exists \mathrm{c}_{0,2} \mathrm{H}_3 \mathfrak{C} \vee \neg \exists \mathrm{H}_4 \mathfrak{D})),$$

where $\mathfrak{A}$, $\mathfrak{B}$, $\mathfrak{C}$, $\mathfrak{D}$ are certain formulas, can also be written in the following way.

For any word $\mathrm{c}_{0,1}$ in the alphabet $\mathrm{Ч}_0$, natural numbers H_1, H_2 and an algorithm $\Phi_{2,1}$ in the alphabet $\mathrm{Ч}_2^{sa}$ are quasirealizable such that, first, $\mathfrak{A}$ holds, and second, at least one of the following three conditions is fulfilled:

1) $\forall \mathrm{p}_1 \mathfrak{B}$;

2) $\exists \mathrm{c}_{0,2} \mathrm{H}_3 \mathfrak{C}$;

3) $\neg \exists \mathrm{H}_4 \mathfrak{D}$.

In using such combined expressions, we shall tend to select, in each concrete case, the grammatical form of ordinary language such that one can without difficulty compose the corresponding formula which expresses by means of the logico-mathematical symbolism the whole text of the combined expression in its entirety. Such a choice of grammatical form is necessary because the rules of the constructive reinterpretation of propositions and conditions are formulated in [3] for propositions and conditions written by means of logico-mathematical formulas.

1.14. In this section we introduce some new notation and we agree on various ways of abbreviating clumsy symbolic expressions.

I. Above we agreed to:

a) denote natural variables, i.e. the words (Н), (НН), (ННН), $\cdots$, by H_1, H_2, H_3, $\cdots$, respectively;

b) denote integer variables, i.e. the words (Ц), (ЦЦ), (ЦЦЦ), $\cdots$, by $\mathrm{Ц}_1$, $\mathrm{Ц}_2$, $\mathrm{Ц}_3$, $\cdots$, respectively;

c) denote rational variables, i.e. the words (р), (рр), (ррр), $\cdots$, by p_1, p_2,

$\mathfrak{p}_3, \cdots$, respectively.

Now, for the first four natural variables, the first two integer variables, and the first four rational variables, which occur most often in the sequel, we introduce also the following briefer notation:

The letters k, l, m, n will denote, respectively, the natural variables (H), (HH), (HHH), (HHHH);

The letters v, w will denote, respectively, the integer variables (Ц), (ЦЦ);

The letters a, b, d, e will denote, respectively, the rational variables ($\mathfrak{p}$), ($\mathfrak{pp}$), ($\mathfrak{ppp}$), ($\mathfrak{pppp}$).

We cite two examples of the reading of symbolic expressions containing this notation and some of the notation introduced earlier.

The symbolic expression

$$\exists f_1 klm \forall n \text{H}_5 v\, (((f_1(n) \underset{\mathfrak{p}}{\cdot} v \underset{\mathfrak{p}}{\cdot} \text{H}_5) \in P) \,\&\, (f_1(\text{H}_5) \square k \square l \square m \in Q)),$$

where P is a term for a one-place predicate (term for a concept) and Q is a term for a four-place predicate (term for a four-place relation), is read as follows.

"A sequence of natural numbers f_1 and natural numbers k, l, m are potentially realizable such that, for any natural numbers n, H_5 and any integer v, the value of the term $(f_1(n) \underset{\mathfrak{p}}{\cdot} v \underset{\mathfrak{p}}{\cdot} \text{H}_5)$ possesses the property P and the values of the terms $f_1(\text{H}_5)$, k, l, m (arranged in the order in which the terms are written here) are in the relation Q".

The symbolic expression

$$\forall \mathfrak{p}_5 (\exists g_3 bd \forall \mathfrak{c}_{2,1} n \mathfrak{A} \supset \forall a \phi_{2,4} \neg \exists e f_9 \mathfrak{B}),$$

where $\mathfrak{A}$ and $\mathfrak{B}$ are logico-mathematical formulas, is read as follows.

"For any rational number $\mathfrak{p}_5$, the following holds: if a sequence g_3 of rational numbers and rational numbers b, d are potentially realizable such that, for any word $\mathfrak{c}_{2,1}$ in the alphabet Я_2 and any natural number n, the condition $\mathfrak{A}$ is fulfilled, then, for any rational number a and any algorithm $\phi_{2,4}$ in the alphabet Ч_2^{sa}, there cannot exist a rational number e and a sequence f_9 of natural numbers such that the condition $\mathfrak{B}$ is fulfilled".

In the sequel we shall often introduce syntactic variables (cf. [3], §3.1), the admissible values of which are any natural numbers or any natural numbers not exceeding some fixed natural number. Syntactic variables of this type already occurred in preceding sections. For example, as syntactic variables of this type we used the letter i at the end of §1.3, the letter j in §1.5, and the letters k and

n in §1.13.

As syntactic variables of the type just considered we shall use the letters i, j, k, l, m, n, and various other letters.

From what has been said above it follows that we shall use the letters k, l, m, n, first, as designations of certain natural variables, and, second, as syntactic variables. This situation does not lead to ambiguity since, in every concrete case it will be clear from the context what role the given letters are playing in the given place.

II. Let W be a symbol for any two-place relation and let $\Theta_1, \cdots, \Theta_i$, $\Theta'_1, \cdots, \Theta'_j$ be any individual terms. We introduce the notation

$$(\Theta_1, \ldots, \Theta_i W \Theta'_1, \ldots, \Theta'_j)$$
$$\leftrightharpoons ((\Theta_1 W \Theta'_1) \,\&\, (\Theta_2 W \Theta'_1) \,\&\, \ldots \,\&\, (\Theta_i W \Theta'_1)$$
$$\&\, (\Theta_1 W \Theta'_2) \,\&\, (\Theta_2 W \Theta'_2) \,\&\, \ldots \,\&\, (\Theta_i W \Theta'_2)$$
$$\cdots\cdots\cdots\cdots\cdots\cdots$$
$$\cdots\cdots\cdots\cdots\cdots\cdots$$
$$\&\, (\Theta_1 W \Theta'_j) \,\&\, (\Theta_2 W \Theta'_j) \,\&\, \ldots \,\&\, (\Theta_i W \Theta'_j)).$$

Examples. The expression $(l, m \geq f_1(k))$ denotes the formula $((l \geq f_1(k)) \,\&\, (m \geq f_1(k)))$; the expression $(b > 0, f_1(\mathrm{H}_5), g_1(n))$ denotes the formula $((b > 0) \,\&\, (b > f_1(\mathrm{H}_5)) \,\&\, (b > g_1(n)))$.

III. Let $W_1, W_2, \cdots, W_i$ be symbols for any two-place relations and let Θ_1, $\Theta_2, \cdots, \Theta_i, \Theta_{i+1}$ be any individual terms, we introduce the notation

$$(\Theta_1 W_1 \Theta_2 W_2 \ldots \Theta_i W_i \Theta_{i+1})$$
$$\leftrightharpoons ((\Theta_1 W_1 \Theta_2) \,\&\, (\Theta_2 W_2 \Theta_3) \,\&\, \ldots \,\&\, (\Theta_{i-1} W_{i-1} \Theta_i) \,\&\, (\Theta_i W_i \Theta_{i+1})).$$

Example. The expression $(f_1(5) < l = g_1(k+1) \leq (b + g_2(3)))$ denotes the formula

$$((f_1(5) < l) \,\&\, (l = g_1(k+1)) \,\&\, (g_1(k+1) \leqslant (b + g_2(3)))).$$

IV. Let $\mathfrak{A}_0, \mathfrak{A}_1, \cdots, \mathfrak{A}_{j-1}, \mathfrak{A}_j$ be any formulas. We construct the following lists of formulas:

First list	Second list	Third list	Fourth list
$(\mathfrak{A}_0 \supset \mathfrak{A}_1)$,	$\tilde{\forall}(\mathfrak{A}_0 \supset \mathfrak{A}_1)$,	$(\mathfrak{A}_0 \equiv \mathfrak{A}_1)$,	$\tilde{\forall}(\mathfrak{A}_0 \equiv \mathfrak{A}_1)$,
$(\mathfrak{A}_1 \supset \mathfrak{A}_2)$,	$\tilde{\forall}(\mathfrak{A}_1 \supset \mathfrak{A}_2)$,	$(\mathfrak{A}_1 \equiv \mathfrak{A}_2)$,	$\tilde{\forall}(\mathfrak{A}_1 \equiv \mathfrak{A}_2)$,
. . . . . .	. . . .	. . . . . .	. . . .
$(\mathfrak{A}_{j-2} \supset \mathfrak{A}_{j-1})$,	$\tilde{\forall}(\mathfrak{A}_{j-2} \supset \mathfrak{A}_{j-1})$,	$(\mathfrak{A}_{j-2} \equiv \mathfrak{A}_{j-1})$,	$\tilde{\forall}(\mathfrak{A}_{j-2} \equiv \mathfrak{A}_{j-1})$,
$(\mathfrak{A}_{j-1} \supset \mathfrak{A}_j)$;	$\tilde{\forall}(\mathfrak{A}_{j-1} \supset \mathfrak{A}_j)$;	$(\mathfrak{A}_{j-1} \equiv \mathfrak{A}_j)$;	$\tilde{\forall}(\mathfrak{A}_{j-1} \equiv \mathfrak{A}_j)$.

For these lists we agree to apply the following abbreviations:

Transcription of first list	Transcription of second list	Transcription of third list	Transcription of fourth list
$(\mathfrak{A}_0 \supset \mathfrak{A}_1)$,	$\tilde{\forall}(\mathfrak{A}_0 \supset \mathfrak{A}_1)$,	$(\mathfrak{A}_0 \equiv \mathfrak{A}_1)$,	$\tilde{\forall}(\mathfrak{A}_0 \equiv \mathfrak{A}_1)$,
$(\swarrow \supset \mathfrak{A}_2)$,	$\tilde{\forall}(\swarrow \supset \mathfrak{A}_2)$,	$(\swarrow \equiv \mathfrak{A}_2)$,	$\tilde{\forall}(\swarrow \equiv \mathfrak{A}_2)$,
. . . . . .	. . . .	. . . . . .	. . . . . .
$(\swarrow \supset \mathfrak{A}_{j-1})$,	$\tilde{\forall}(\swarrow \supset \mathfrak{A}_{j-1})$,	$(\swarrow \equiv \mathfrak{A}_{j-1})$,	$\tilde{\forall}(\swarrow \equiv \mathfrak{A}_{j-1})$,
$(\swarrow \supset \mathfrak{A}_j)$;	$\tilde{\forall}(\swarrow \supset \mathfrak{A}_j)$;	$(\swarrow = \mathfrak{A}_j)$;	$\tilde{\forall}(\swarrow \equiv \mathfrak{A}_j)$.

V. For a further reduction in the clumsiness of the logico-mathematical symbolism used, we introduce certain ways of abbreviating terms and formulas. First of all we formulate a series of auxiliary definitions.

Among the symbols introduced we choose certain symbols and to each chosen symbol we assign a natural number, called the *rank* of the given symbol. We shall assume that:

a) the symbol $\wedge_{\mathrm{p}}$ has rank 0;

b) the symbols $\cdot_{\mathrm{p}}$, $:_{\mathrm{p}}$ have rank 1;

c) the symbols $+_{\mathrm{p}}$, $-_{\mathrm{p}}$ have rank 2;

d) the symbols $\simeq$, $\doteq$, $\in$, $=_{\mathrm{p}}$, $\geq_{\mathrm{p}}$, $\leq_{\mathrm{p}}$, $\neq_{\mathrm{p}}$, $<_{\mathrm{p}}$, $>_{\mathrm{p}}$ have rank 3;

e) the symbol & has rank 4;

f) the symbol $\vee$ has rank 5;

g) the symbols $\supset$, $\equiv$ have rank 6.

In the remaining sections of this book we shall introduce a host of new symbols, and, for some of the symbols introduced, we shall also give (in suitable places of the accompanying text) their rank.

Any symbol for which the rank is defined will be called a *marked symbol.*

Terms, designations of terms, formulas and designations of formulas will be called *meaningful expressions.*

Let ξ be any marked symbol, and let $X * \xi * Y$ be any occurrence of the symbol ξ in a word C (see [1], Russian p. 26). We shall say that $X * \xi * Y$ is a *regular occurrence* if this occurrence is included in some occurrence in C of some meaningful expression, i.e. if one can construct words X_1, Z, W, Y_1 such that $X \doteq X_1 Z$, $Y \doteq W Y_1$, and $Z \xi W$ is a meaningful expression. We shall say that $X * \xi * Y$ is a *singular occurrence* if $X * \xi * Y$ is not a regular occurrence.

Every occurrence of any marked symbol in a meaningful expression is a regular occurrence. Hence if a word C is such that there is a singular occurrence in this word of some marked symbol, then C is not a meaningful expression. However, to reduce the clumsiness of our symbolism we shall introduce into our exposition and systematically use abbreviations of meaningful expressions, and, in words which will play this role, singular occurrences of marked symbols can occur

Below we shall define an algorithm for eliminating singular occurrences, to be used for the construction of meaningful expressions from their abbreviations, and, by means of this algorithm, we shall characterize those words which we shall consider abbreviations of meaningful expressions. As a preliminary, we formulate some auxiliary definitions.

Let C be any word, ξ a marked symbol, $X * \xi * Y$ an occurrence of ξ in C, and C_1 the word obtained by inserting in the word C the symbol "(" to the left of the occurrence $X * \xi * Y$ of the letter ξ and the symbol ")" to the right of this occurrence of the letter ξ (the left parenthesis "(" is placed between letters of the word C or in front of C, and the right parenthesis ")" is placed between letters of the word C or at the end of C). We denote by L that part of the word C_1 the first letter of which is the left parenthesis which has been inserted in C and the last letter of which is the right parenthesis placed in C. The parentheses inserted in C give a uniquely determined occurrence $U * L * V$ of the word L in the word C_1.

We shall say that C_1 is the *word derived from the word* C *with respect to the occurrence* $X * \xi * Y$ if the following conditions are fulfilled: (a) L is a meaningful expression; (b) for any shift to the left in the word C_1 of the symbol "(" which is the first symbol of the word LV and for any shift to the right in the word C_1 of the symbol ")" which is the last symbol of the word UL, and for any simultaneous shift of the indicated symbols on both sides, the word which is isolated by the new position of the shifted parentheses and includes these parentheses as bounding symbols is not a meaningful expression.

One can prove the following proposition.

If C_1 *is a word derived from the word* C *with respect to the occurrence* $X * \xi * Y$, *then every word derived from the word* C *with respect to* $X * \xi * Y$ *is graphically equal to the word* C_1.

Hence, either one can construct one and only one (with respect to graphical equality) word derived from C with respect to $X * \xi * Y$ or there is no such word.

The question as to which of these two possibilities is realized for a given word C and a given occurrence $X * \xi * Y$ is solved by successive examination of those words which can be obtained by inserting in the word C the symbol "(" to the left of the occurrence $X * \xi * Y$ of the letter ξ and the symbol ")" to the right of this occurrence of the letter ξ.

For each i $(i = 0, 1, 2, 3, 4, 5, 6)$, we denote by $\mathfrak{D}_i[C]$ the list of all singular occurrences in the word C of marked symbols of rank i. In forming the list $\mathfrak{D}_i[C]$ we shall write the respective occurrences in their natural order (i.e. in order of increasing length of their left wings). Now, from the lists $\mathfrak{D}_0[C]$, $\mathfrak{D}_1[C], \cdots, \mathfrak{D}_6[C]$ we form a single list of occurrences, writing first the list $\mathfrak{D}_0[C]$, then the list $\mathfrak{D}_1[C]$, etc., and, lastly, the list $\mathfrak{D}_6[C]$. The list of all singular occurrences in the word C obtained by this method will be denoted by $\mathfrak{D}[C]$.

We assume that there is at least one singular occurrence in the word C of some marked symbol. Under this assumption, we consider the following process. The singular occurrences in the list $\mathfrak{D}[C]$ will be considered one after the other in the order in which these occurrences stand in the list $\mathfrak{D}[C]$, and at each step we shall establish whether one can construct a word derived from the word C with respect to the singular occurrence being considered at the given step. If this process goes as far as the last term of the list $\mathfrak{D}[C]$, and at each step, including the last, the answer is negative, then we shall say that the word C does not allow a reduction in the number of singular occurrences. If the process proceeds to a step at which an affirmative answer is obtained, then we stop the process right after the first step with an affirmative answer and the word derived from C with respect to the singular occurrence at this step will be considered the result of the process just described and will be called the *principal word derived from the word* C.

The *algorithm for eliminating singular occurrences* is defined by the following prescription. Let C be a word containing at least one singular occurrence of a marked symbol. Each step in the process of applying the algorithm to this word consists of the construction of the principal word derived from the result of the immediately preceding step (we assume that the initial step of the process consists of writing the word C). We consider the process terminated when we have obtained a word having no singular occurrences of marked symbols or not allowing a reduction in the number of singular occurrences.

We shall make the following convention: if a word C contains at least one singular occurrence of a marked symbol, and we apply to C the algorithm for eliminating singular occurrences, the result of which is a meaningful expression R, then we shall consider the word C to be an abbreviation of the meaningful expression R.

For example, the word

$$(\neg\mathfrak{A}\vee\mathfrak{B}\supset\forall\text{ц}_1\neg\exists\text{н}_1\mathfrak{C}\,\&\,\text{p}_1\dotplus\Theta\dotplus\text{н}_2^{-3}\cdot\text{н}_1\leqslant\text{p}_2^5\,\&\,\exists\text{p}_3\mathfrak{D})\,\&\,\mathfrak{E},$$

where $\mathfrak{A}$, $\mathfrak{B}$, $\mathfrak{C}$, $\mathfrak{D}$, $\mathfrak{E}$ are certain formulas and Θ is some individual term, will be considered as an abbreviation of the meaningful expression

$$\underset{6}{(}\underset{5}{(}(\neg\mathfrak{A}\vee\mathfrak{B}\underset{5}{)}\supset\underset{4}{(}\forall\text{ц}_1\neg\exists\text{н}_1\mathfrak{C}\,\&\,\underset{3}{(}\underset{2}{(}\text{p}_1\dotplus\Theta\dotplus\underset{1}{(}\text{н}_2^{-3}\cdot\text{н}_1\underset{1}{)}\underset{2}{)}\leqslant\text{p}_2^5\underset{3}{)}\,\&\,\exists\text{p}_3\mathfrak{D})\underset{4}{)}\,\&\,\mathfrak{E}\underset{6}{)},$$

which denotes some formula. The natural numbers placed under all the parentheses except one left and one right parenthesis are not part of the structure of this meaningful expression. Each of the natural numbers standing under parentheses indicates the ordinal number of that step of the process of applying to the given word the algorithm for eliminating singular occurrences at which the parentheses above the given natural number appear.

If for some meaningful expression R one can exhibit different abbreviations, then we can use any of these, and even different abbreviations in various cases. It is natural to use only those abbreviations of the expression R from which one can restore R in a small number of steps. Hence we shall avoid using those abbreviations of the expression R which are obtained as a result of a very large number of admissible cancellations in R of left and right parentheses and we shall not always use that abbreviation which contains the smallest number of parentheses, in comparison with other abbreviations of the expression R.

If a meaningful expression R begins with the symbol "(" and ends with the symbol ")", then one of the abbreviations of R is a word R_1 obtained from R by cancelling the initial symbol "(" and the terminal symbol ")". If R is introduced into the exposition in isolation from other symbols of the logico-mathematical symbolism (i.e. not as a composite part of some other meaningful expression) then, on the basis of the accepted convention, we can use the word R_1 as an abbreviation of the meaningful expression R. We shall often take advantage of this opportunity.

Applying in suitable cases the method of abbreviating lists of formulas, introduced in Part IV of this section, we shall combine this method with the method just introduced for abbreviating meaningful expressions. In order to make this combination possible, we agree to regard every instance of the symbol "$\swarrow$" as a designation of some formula, and hence as a meaningful expression.

1.15. In the sequel we shall repeatedly use the following proposition.

1.15.1. *For any rational number* a,

$$\forall l\,(a < 2^{-l}) \supset (a \leqslant 0).$$

Proof. First we construct an algorithm $\mathfrak{D}$ in the alphabet Ч_2^{sa} such that

$$\forall a\,(a > 0 \supset \mathfrak{D}(a) \overset{+}{\in} \underline{\text{nat}}\ \&\ a \geqslant 2^{-\mathfrak{D}(a)}). \tag{1}$$

Let a be any rational number. Let us assume that

$$a > 0. \tag{2}$$

From (2) and (1) it follows that $\mathfrak{D}(a) \overset{+}{\in}$ nat and

$$a \geqslant 2^{-\mathfrak{D}(a)}. \tag{3}$$

Assume that

$$\forall l\,(a < 2^{-l}). \tag{4}$$

Then $(a < 2^{-\mathfrak{D}(a)})$, and therefore

$$\neg(a \geqslant 2^{-\mathfrak{D}(a)}) \tag{5}$$

Formulas (5) and (3) are incompatible. Hence

$$a > 0 \supset \neg\forall l\,(a < 2^{-l}).$$

By the rule of contraposition we obtain

$$\forall l\,(a < 2^{-l}) \supset \neg(a > 0).$$

Hence

$$\forall l\,(a < 2^{-l}) \supset (a \leqslant 0).$$

and Proposition 1.15.1 has been proved.

§2. SOME FACTS FROM THE THEORY OF ALGORITHMS AND CONSTRUCTIVE LOGIC

In this section we shall formulate some theorems from the theory of algorithms and constructive logic, in conjunction with the contents of the monograph [1] and the paper [3]. These theorems will be used many times in the sequel.

2.1. First of all, we mention the following theorem about the terms of the language $\mathfrak{A}$ (cf. §1.4).

2.1.1. *Let* Θ *be any individual term of the language* $\mathfrak{A}$ *and let* $\beta_1, \cdots, \beta_k$ *be the complete list of variables occurring in* Θ *and written, without repetition, in any order. Then one can construct a word* H *in the alphabet* A_0 *such that*

$$\tilde{\forall}(\langle H\rangle_m(\widetilde{V})\simeq\Theta). \tag{1}$$

Here

$$V\rightleftharpoons\beta_1\ldots\beta_k,\qquad m\rightleftharpoons\underset{\smile}{V}.$$

The proof of this theorem is carried out in the following way. Using the theorem on the union of algorithms [1], Russian p. 120 and the theorem on the reduction of algorithms [1], Russian p. 149, for each list of pairwise distinct basic alphabets $A_{i_1},\cdots,A_{i_l}$ one constructs an algorithm in the alphabet A_0^{sa} of type $(\underbrace{c_0\cdots c_0}_{l\text{ times}}\to c_0)_0$ transforming any word of the form $H_1\Box\cdots\Box H_l$, such that $H_1,\cdots,H_l$ are words in the alphabet A_0, into the transcription of the normal algorithm in the alphabet $A^{sa}_{\nu(i_1,\cdots,i_l)}$ equivalent with respect to $A_{\nu(i_1,\cdots,i_l)}$ to the union of the algorithm $\langle H_1\rangle_{i_1},\cdots,\langle H_l\rangle_{i_l}$. Further, using the theorem on the composition of algorithms [1], Russian p. 102 and the theorem on the reduction of algorithms, for every pair of basic alphabets A_i, A_j, we construct an algorithm in the alphabet A_0^{sa} of type $(c_0c_0\to c_0)_0$ transforming any word of the form $H_1\Box H_2$ such that H_1 and H_2 are words in the alphabet A_0 into the transcription of the normal algorithm in the alphabet $A^{sa}_{\nu(i,j)}$ equivalent with respect to $A_{\nu(i,j)}$ to the composition of the algorithms $\langle H_1\rangle_i$ and $\langle H_2\rangle_j$.

In addition, using the theorem on the universal algorithm [1], Russian p. 189, the theorem on the reduction of algorithms and some simple auxiliary algorithms, for each pair of basic alphabets A_i, A_j, for each triple of positive integers l, m, n, and for every pair of lists of positive integers $\tau_1,\cdots,\tau_m$ and $\sigma_1,\cdots,\sigma_n$ in which all terms do not exceed k, one constructs an algorithm $\mathfrak{C}$ in the alphabet A_0^{sa} of type $(c_0\to c_0)_0$ transforming any word H in the alphabet A_0 into a word $\mathfrak{C}(H)$ such that

$$\langle\langle H\rangle_i(X_{\tau_1}\Box\ldots\Box X_{\tau_m})\rangle_j(X_{\sigma_1}\Box\ldots\Box X_{\sigma_n})\simeq\langle\mathfrak{C}(H)\rangle_{\nu(i,j)}(X_1\Box\ldots\Box X_l),$$

for any words $X_1,\cdots,X_l$ in the alphabet $A_{\nu(i,j)}$.

With the aid of the indicated algorithms and some simple additional algorithms, Theorem 2.1.1 is proved without difficulty by the method of induction with respect to the generating rules for terms (see [3]). We shall not go into details.

The following theorem, 2.1.2, is a variant, formulated with respect to the concept of normal algorithm, of a theorem of S. C. Kleene about partial recursive functions.

2.1.2. *For any basic alphabet* A_j *containing the alphabet* A_0 *and for any natural numbers* k *and* l, *one can construct an algorithm* $\mathfrak{C}$ *in the alphabet* $\mathrm{A}_0^{\mathrm{sa}}$ *of type* $(\mathrm{c}_0 \to \mathrm{c}_0)_0$ *such that, first,*

$$\tilde{\forall}(\langle\mathfrak{G}(\alpha)\rangle_j(\beta_1\square\ldots\square\beta_k)\stackrel{+}{\in}\mathrm{c}_0) \tag{2}$$

and second,

$$\tilde{\forall}(\langle\alpha\rangle_j(\beta_1\square\ldots\square\beta_k\square\beta_{k+1}\square\ldots\square\beta_{k+l}) \simeq \langle\!\langle\mathfrak{G}(\alpha)\rangle_j(\beta_1\square\ldots\square\beta_k)\rangle_j(\beta_{k+1}\square\ldots\square\beta_{k+l})). \tag{3}$$

Here α *is a variable of type* c_0, *and* $\beta_1, \cdots, \beta_k, \beta_{k+1}, \cdots, \beta_{k+l}$ *are variables of type* c_j. *Moreover, the variables* $\alpha, \beta_1, \cdots, \beta_k, \beta_{k+1}, \cdots, \beta_{k+l}$ *are pairwise distinct. If* $l = 0$, *then we assume that the formula* (3) *has the form*

$$\tilde{\forall}(\langle\alpha\rangle_j(\beta_1\square\ldots\square\beta_k) \simeq \langle\!\langle\mathfrak{G}(\alpha)\rangle_j(\beta_1\square\ldots\square\beta_k)\rangle_j(\Lambda)). \tag{4}$$

With the help of an algorithm realizing a one-one correspondence between natural numbers and transcriptions of normal algorithms in the alphabet A_j, and with the help of an algorithm realizing a one-one correspondence between natural numbers and words in the alphabet A_j, one can derive Theorem 2.1.2 from the corresponding theorem of S. C. Kleene about partial recursive functions [28], §65, Theorem XXIII[1] and the results of V. K. Detlovs on the connection between partial recursive functions and normal algorithms [29], §2. In G. S. Ceĭtin's paper [16] there is proved, without use of the notion of partial recursive function, a proposition about normal algorithms (the first lemma of the second chapter) from which 2.1.2 immediately follows.

With the help of 2.1.2 one proves the following theorem, which is used repeatedly in the sequel.[2]

2.1.3. *Let* k *and* l *be any natural numbers and let* j_0, j_1, j_2 *be any natural numbers not exceeding* h *and such that the alphabets* A_{j_1} *and* A_{j_2} *are contained in the alphabet* A_{j_0}. *In addition, let*

$$\mathrm{A}_{i_1}, \ldots, \mathrm{A}_{i_k}, \mathrm{A}_{i_{k+1}}, \ldots, \mathrm{A}_{i_{k+l}}$$

be any list of basic alphabets such that: a) *each of the alphabets* $\mathrm{A}_{i_1}, \cdots, \mathrm{A}_{i_k}$ *is contained in the alphabet* A_{j_1} *and contains the alphabet* A_0, *and* b) *each of the alphabets* $\mathrm{A}_{i_{k+1}}, \cdots, \mathrm{A}_{i_{k+l}}$ *is contained in the alphabet* A_{j_2}. *From these initial conditions one can construct an algorithm* $\mathfrak{H}$ *in the alphabet* $\mathrm{A}_0^{\mathrm{sa}}$ *such*

---

1) This theorem is given in suitable form in [8].

2) The first time that Theorem 2.1.3 will be used will be in the proof of Theorem 4.4.1. Therefore acquaintance with 2.1.3 may be postponed until 4.4.1.

that, first,

$$\tilde{\forall}(\langle\mathfrak{H}(\alpha)\rangle_{j_1}(\gamma_1\square\ldots\square\gamma_k)\overset{+}{\in}c_0) \tag{5}$$

and second, for any word α *in the alphabet* A_0 *such that*

$$\forall\gamma_1\ldots\gamma_k\gamma_{k+1}\ldots\gamma_{k+l}(!\langle\alpha\rangle_{j_0}(\gamma_1\square\ldots\square\gamma_k\square\gamma_{k+1}\square\ldots\square\gamma_{k+l})$$
$$\supset\langle\alpha\rangle_{j_0}(\gamma_1\square\ldots\square\gamma_k\square\gamma_{k+1}\square\ldots\square\gamma_{k+l})\in c_{j_2}), \tag{6}$$

the proposition

$$\forall\gamma_1\ldots\gamma_k\gamma_{k+1}\ldots\gamma_{k+l}(\langle\alpha\rangle_{j_0}(\gamma_1\square\ldots\square\gamma_k\square\gamma_{k+1}\square\ldots\square\gamma_{k+l})$$
$$\simeq\langle\!\langle\mathfrak{H}(\alpha)\rangle_{j_1}(\gamma_1\square\ldots\square\gamma_k)\rangle_{j_2}(\gamma_{k+1}\square\ldots\square\gamma_{k+l})). \tag{7}$$

holds. Here α *is a variable of type* c_0, γ_1 *is a variable of type* $c_{i_1},\cdots,\gamma_k$ *is a variable of type* c_{i_k}, γ_{k+1} *is a variable of type* $c_{i_{k+1}},\cdots,\gamma_{k+l}$ *is a variable of type* $c_{i_{k+l}}$. *Moreover, the variables* $\alpha,\gamma_1,\cdots,\gamma_k,\gamma_{k+1},\cdots,\gamma_{k+l}$ *are pairwise distinct. If* $l=0$ *we assume that the formula* (7) *has the form*

$$\forall\gamma_1\ldots\gamma_k(\langle\alpha\rangle_{j_0}(\gamma_1\square\ldots\square\gamma_k)\simeq\langle\!\langle\mathfrak{H}(\alpha)\rangle_{j_1}(\gamma_1\square\ldots\square\gamma_k)\rangle_{j_2}(\Lambda)). \tag{8}$$

Theorem 2.1.3 will be proved if one can construct an algorithm $\mathfrak{H}$ in the alphabet A_0^{sa} such that, first,

$$\tilde{\forall}(\langle\mathfrak{H}(\alpha)\rangle_{j_1}(\varepsilon_1\square\ldots\square\varepsilon_k)\overset{+}{\in}c_0), \tag{9}$$

and second,

$$\tilde{\forall}(\langle P\rangle_{j_0}(\langle\alpha\rangle_{j_0}(\varepsilon_1\square\ldots\square\varepsilon_k\square\varepsilon_{k+1}\square\ldots\square\varepsilon_{k+l}))$$
$$\simeq\langle\!\langle\mathfrak{H}(\alpha)\rangle_{j_1}(\varepsilon_1\square\ldots\square\varepsilon_k)\rangle_{j_2}(\varepsilon_{k+1}\square\ldots\square\varepsilon_{k+l})), \tag{10}$$

where $\epsilon_1,\cdots,\epsilon_k$ are variables of type c_{j_1} and $\epsilon_{k+1},\cdots,\epsilon_{k+l}$ are variables of type c_{j_2} such that every term of the list

$$\alpha,\ \varepsilon_1,\ldots,\ \varepsilon_k,\ \varepsilon_{k+1},\ldots,\ \varepsilon_{k+l}$$

is different from all the other terms. The letter P will denote the transcription of the algorithm in the alphabet A_{j0}^{sa} defined by the abbreviated schema

$$\{\xi\rightarrow\quad(\xi\in A_{j_0}^{sa}\setminus A_{j_2}^{sa}).$$

This algorithm cancels from any word in the alphabet A_{j0}^{sa} all letters not belonging to the alphabet A_{j2}^{sa}.

We denote by $\mathfrak{R}$ the algorithm in the alphabet A_0^{sa} transforming any pair of words in the alphabet A_0 into the transcription of some algorithm in the alphabet A_{j0}^{sa} equivalent with respect to A_{j0}^{s} to the normal composition of the algorithms the transcriptions of which are the first and second terms, respectively, of the given pair of words. We have

$$\tilde{\forall}(\langle P\rangle_{j_0}(\langle\alpha\rangle_{j_0}(\beta_1\square\ldots\square\beta_k\square\beta_{k+1}\square\ldots\square\beta_{k+l}))$$
$$\simeq\langle\mathfrak{R}(\alpha\square P)\rangle_{j_0}(\beta_1\square\ldots\square\beta_k\square\beta_{k+1}\square\ldots\square\beta_{k+l})). \tag{11}$$

Here $\beta_1, \cdots, \beta_k, \beta_{k+1}, \cdots, \beta_{k+l}$ are variables of type c_{j_0} such that every term of the list

$$\alpha, \beta_1, \ldots, \beta_k, \beta_{k+1}, \ldots, \beta_{k+l}$$

is different from all the other terms.

For brevity, we introduce the notation

$$B_1 \leftrightharpoons \beta_1 \square \ldots \square \beta_k, \qquad B_2 \leftrightharpoons \beta_{k+1} \square \ldots \square \beta_{k+l},$$
$$E_1 \leftrightharpoons \varepsilon_1 \square \ldots \square \varepsilon_k, \qquad E_2 \leftrightharpoons \varepsilon_{k+1} \square \ldots \square \varepsilon_{k+l}.$$

On the basis of 2.1.2 one can construct an algorithm $\mathfrak{G}$ in the alphabet A_0^{sa} such that, first,

$$\tilde{\forall} (\langle \mathfrak{G} (\mathfrak{R} (\alpha \square P)) \rangle_{j_0} (B_1) \overset{+}{\in} c_0) \tag{12}$$

and second,

$$\tilde{\forall} (\langle \mathfrak{R} (\alpha \square P) \rangle_{j_0} (B_1 \square B_2) \simeq \langle\!\langle \mathfrak{G} (\mathfrak{R} (\alpha \square P)) \rangle_{j_0} (B_1) \rangle_{j_0} (B_2)). \tag{13}$$

We construct an algorithm $\mathfrak{T}$ in the alphabet A_0^{sa} such that

$$\forall \alpha (\mathfrak{T} (\alpha) \simeq \mathfrak{G} (\mathfrak{R} (\alpha \square P))). \tag{14}$$

From (11), (13), (14), and properties of the algorithm $\langle P \rangle_{j_0}$ it follows that

$$\tilde{\forall} (! \langle\!\langle \mathfrak{T} (\alpha) \rangle_{j_0} (B_1) \rangle_{j_0} (B_2) \supset \langle\!\langle \mathfrak{T} (\alpha) \rangle_{j_0} (B_1) \rangle_{j_0} (B_2) \in c_{j_2}). \tag{15}$$

The alphabets $A_{i_1}, \cdots, A_{i_k}$ are contained in A_{j_1} and the alphabets $A_{i_{k+1}}, \cdots, A_{i_{k+l}}$ are contained in A_{j_2}. Hence, on the basis of (12), (14), and (15), we have

$$\tilde{\forall} (\langle \mathfrak{T} (\alpha) \rangle_{j_0} (E_1) \overset{+}{\in} c_0), \tag{16}$$
$$\tilde{\forall} (! \langle\!\langle \mathfrak{T} (\alpha) \rangle_{j_0} (E_1) \rangle_{j_0} (E_2) \supset \langle\!\langle \mathfrak{T} (\alpha) \rangle_{j_0} (E_1) \rangle_{j_0} (E_2) \in c_{j_2}). \tag{17}$$

Let us denote by C the transcription of the algorithm in the alphabet A_{j0}^{sa} transforming the transcription of any algorithm in the alphabet A_{j0}^{sa} into the transcription of its translation into the alphabet A_{j2}^{sa}. This algorithm can be obtained easily on the basis of the definition of the translation of an algorithm (see [1], Russian p. 145). On the basis of (17) we have

$$\tilde{\forall} (\langle\!\langle \mathfrak{T} (\alpha) \rangle_{j_0} (E_1) \rangle_{j_0} (E_2) \simeq \langle\!\langle C \rangle_{j_0} (\langle \mathfrak{T} (\alpha) \rangle_{j_0} (E_1)) \rangle_{j_2} (E_1)). \tag{18}$$

In addition, we obtain

$$\tilde{\forall} (\langle C \rangle_{j_0} (\langle \mathfrak{T} (\alpha) \rangle_{j_0} (E_1)) \simeq \langle \mathfrak{R} (\mathfrak{T} (\alpha) \square C) \rangle_{j_0} (E_1)). \tag{19}$$

Let us denote by $\mathfrak{Z}$ the algorithm in the alphabet A_0^{sa} transforming the transcription of any algorithm in the alphabet A_{j0}^{sa} into the transcription of its translation into the alphabet A_{j1}^{sa}. On the basis of (16), (19) and the properties of the algorithm $\langle C \rangle_{j_0}$ we conclude that

$$\tilde{\forall} (\langle \mathfrak{R} (\mathfrak{T} (\alpha) \square C) \rangle_{j_0} (E_1) \simeq \langle \mathfrak{Z} (\mathfrak{R} (\mathfrak{T} (\alpha) \square C)) \rangle_{j_1} (E_1)).$$

Now we construct the algorithm $\mathfrak{H}$ in the alphabet A_0^{sa} such that

$$\forall \alpha (\mathfrak{H}(\alpha) \simeq \mathfrak{Z}(\mathfrak{R}(\mathfrak{T}(\alpha) \square C))).$$

It is easily seen that the algorithm $\mathfrak{H}$ satisfies the conditions (9) and (10). Theorem 2.1.3 has been proved.

2.2. In the theory of algorithms one introduces the operator of searching for the least natural number satisfying a given condition. This operator is called the $\boldsymbol{\mu}$-operator. (Here $\boldsymbol{\mu}$ is a semiboldface letter. It is necessary to distinguish it from the lightface letter μ occurring in Section 1.3 and in other sections to denote a certain generic letter of the logico-mathematical language.) The sort of conditions to which the $\boldsymbol{\mu}$-operator is applicable will be described below.

Let k be any natural number and let j be any natural number not exceeding h and such that the alphabet A_0 is contained in the alphabet A_j. Further, let $\mathrm{A}_{i_1}, \cdots, \mathrm{A}_{i_k}$ be any list of basic alphabets such that each of the alphabets $\mathrm{A}_{i_1}, \cdots, \mathrm{A}_{i_k}$ is contained in A_j. In addition, let $\mathfrak{A}$ be any normal algorithm in the alphabet A_j^{sa}. Let α be a variable of type H, β_1 a variable of type $\mathrm{c}_{i_1}, \cdots$ $\cdots$, β_k a variable of type c_{i_k}, such that each of the terms of the list $\alpha, \beta_1, \cdots$ $\cdots, \beta_k$ is different from all the remaining terms of the list. The expression

$$\boldsymbol{\mu}_\alpha (\mathfrak{A}(\beta_1 \square \ldots \square \beta_k \square \alpha) \doteq \Lambda)$$

is read as follows: "the least of those values of the variable α for which $\mathfrak{A}(\beta_1 \square \cdots \square \beta_k \square \alpha) \doteq \Lambda$". This expression is a designation of the term

$$\langle H \rangle_j (\beta_1 \square \ldots \square \beta_k),$$

where H is a word in the alphabet A_0 such that the normal algorithm $\langle H \rangle_j$ is equivalent with respect to the alphabet A_j^s to the algorithm $\mathfrak{B}$, the application of which to any word of the form

$$S_1 \square \ldots \square S_k,$$

where S_1 is a word in the alphabet $\mathrm{A}_{i_1}, \cdots$, S_k is a word in the alphabet A_{i_k}, is carried out in the following manner. First, we carry out the process of applyin the algorithm $\mathfrak{A}$ to the word $S_1 \square \cdots \square S_k \square 0$. If this process terminates and its result is the empty word, then, upon obtaining this result, the process of applyin the algorithm $\mathfrak{B}$ to the word $S_1 \square \cdots \square S_k$ also terminates and $\mathfrak{B}(S_1 \square \cdots \square S_k) \doteq$ If the process of applying $\mathfrak{A}$ to $S_1 \square \cdots \square S_k \square 0$ terminates and its result is a nonempty word, then we apply the algorithm $\mathfrak{A}$ to the word $S_1 \square \cdots \square S_k \square 0|$. If this process terminates and its result is the empty word, then, upon obtaining thi result, the process of applying the algorithm $\mathfrak{B}$ to the word $S_1 \square \cdots \square S_k$ also terminates and $\mathfrak{B}(S_1 \square \cdots \square S_k) \doteq 0|$. If the process of applying $\mathfrak{A}$ to $S_1 \square \cdots$

$\cdots \square S_k \square 0 |$ terminates and its result is a nonempty word, then we apply the algorithm $\mathfrak{A}$ to the word $S_1 \square \cdots \square S_k \square 0 \|$, etc.

If the words $S_1, \cdots, S_k$ are such that

$$\forall \alpha ! \mathfrak{A} (S_1 \square \ldots \square S_k \square \alpha),$$

then the algorithm $\mathfrak{B}$ is applicable to the word $S_1 \square \cdots \square S_k$ if and only if

$$\exists \alpha (\mathfrak{A} (S_1 \square \ldots \square S_k \square \alpha) \doteq \Lambda).$$

The algorithm $\mathfrak{B}$ is presented by means of a prescription satisfying the general descriptively defined concept of algorithm [1], but which is not a normal algorithm. A method of constructing a normal algorithm $\langle H \rangle_j$ equivalent to the algorithm $\mathfrak{B}$ with respect to A_j^s is indicated in V. K. Detlovs' paper [29], §5. In Detlovs' construction it is necessary to make certain changes of a technical character, determined by the following facts: 1) Detlovs' construction is carried out only for the case where $\mathfrak{A}$ is a normal algorithm over the alphabet of systems of natural numbers, and 2) in Detlovs' paper the term "natural number" is not understood in the same way as in this paper. (Detlovs, following Markov [1], defines a natural number as a word in the one-letter alphabet $\{ | \}$.) The necessary changes can be carried out without difficulty.

Let $\mathfrak{F}$ be a formula associated with the algorithm $\mathfrak{A}$ in the alphabet A_j^{sa} such that

$$\tilde{\forall} (\mathfrak{F} \equiv \mathfrak{A} (\beta_1 \square \ldots \square \beta_k \square \alpha) \doteq \Lambda).$$

The expression

$$\mu_\alpha \mathfrak{F}$$

will be considered to be a designation equivalent to the designation

$$\mu_\alpha (\mathfrak{A} (\beta_1 \square \ldots \square \beta_k \square \alpha) \doteq \Lambda).$$

2.3. In the theory of algorithms one constructs an algorithm Ω of type $(\mathrm{HH} \to \mathrm{H})_0$ such that, for the set determined by the one-parameter condition

$$\exists l (\Omega (k \square l) \doteq 0), \tag{1}$$

there is no algorithm of type $(\mathrm{H} \to \mathrm{H})_0$ distinguishing among all natural numbers those which belong to this set. In other words, one constructs an algorithm Ω of type $(\mathrm{HH} \to \mathrm{H})_0$ such that there is no algorithm ϕ of type $(\mathrm{H} \to \mathrm{H})_0$ satisfying the condition

$$\forall k (\varphi (k) \doteq 0 \equiv \exists l (\Omega (k \square l) \doteq 0)). \tag{2}$$

The algorithm Ω is the starting point for the construction of a series of examples of very fundamental significance in the constructive theory of sets and in constructive mathematical analysis.

A construction of the algorithm Ω in the form of a primitive recursive function can be found, for example, in S. C. Kleene [28], Russian p. 267, Theorem XII. The possibility of constructing a corresponding normal algorithm in the alphabet A_0^{sa} follows from the possibility of constructing the desired algorithm in the form of a primitive recursive function, by the results of Detlovs [29], §4 and the theorem of Markov on the reduction of normal algorithms.

The algorithm Ω can be constructed in other ways, close in fundamental character to Kleene's method (based on the use of a universal algorithm), but differing in details from that method. One of these ways proceeds in the following manner.

In Markov's monograph [1] there is constructed (with the aid of the universal algorithm) a normal algorithm $\mathfrak{B}_0$ in the alphabet A_0 satisfying the following condition: there is no normal algorithm over the alphabet A_0, applicable to every word in the alphabet A_0, and transforming into the empty word those and only those words in the alphabet A_0 to which the algorithm $\mathfrak{B}_0$ is applicable [1], Russian p. 197, Theorem 2.4. By means of an algorithm realizing a one-one correspondence between the set of all natural numbers and the set of all words in the alphabet A_0, one can construct, starting from $\mathfrak{B}_0$, an algorithm $\mathfrak{H}$ in the alphabet Ч_0^{sa} possessing the following property: there is no normal algorithm over the alphabet Ч_0, applicable to every natural number, and transforming into the empty word those and only those natural numbers to which the algorithm $\mathfrak{H}$ is applicable.

Basing oneself on the algorithm $\mathfrak{H}$, one can construct an algorithm Ω of type $(\text{НН} \to \text{Н})_0$ possessing the following property: for any natural numbers k and l, $\Omega(k \square l) \doteq 0$ if and only if the process of applying the normal algorithm $\mathfrak{H}$ to the natural number k terminates in not more than l steps. (The construction of the algorithm Ω, starting from the algorithm $\mathfrak{H}$, can be realized by a method similar to the method of constructing a universal algorithm.) The algorithm Ω is the desired one, since

$$\forall k (! \mathfrak{H}(k) \equiv \exists l (\Omega (k \square l) \doteq 0)).$$

S. C. Kleene proved the following proposition.[1]

For any algorithm $\mathfrak{A}$ *of type* $(\text{НН} \to \text{Н})_0$ *such that*

$$\exists k \exists l (\mathfrak{A}(k \square l) \doteq 0),$$

one can construct an algorithm $\mathfrak{P}$ *of type* $(\text{Н} \to \text{Н})_0$ *such that, for any natural*

---

1) Kleene formulates and proves his result with respect to the theory using the concept of partial recursive function as the precise concept of arithmetic algorithm. Here, Kleene's result is formulated with respect to the concept of normal algorithm. The possibility of such a translation follows from theorems of Detlovs [29].

number k,

$$\exists l(\mathfrak{A}(k\square l)\doteq 0)\equiv\exists l(k\doteq\mathfrak{P}(l))$$

[28], Russian p. 272, Theorem XIV.

The algorithm Ω which we discussed above is such that

$$\exists k\exists l(\Omega(k\square l)\doteq 0).$$

Hence one can construct an algorithm $\mathfrak{P}$ of type $(\mathrm{H}\rightarrow\mathrm{H})_0$ such that for any natural number k

$$\exists l(\Omega(k\square l)\doteq 0)\equiv\exists l(k=\mathfrak{P}(l)).$$

Hence the set (1) is the image of the set of natural numbers under the mapping $\mathfrak{P}$.

From what has been said above it follows that there can be no normal algorithm over the alphabet $Ч_0$ "distinguishing" among all natural numbers those natural numbers which are values of the arithmetic function $\mathfrak{P}$.

The algorithm $\mathfrak{P}$ can serve as a starting point for the construction of a host of interesting examples.

Using the concepts of algorithmically enumerable and algorithmically solvable sets (cf §1.5 and [3], §§7.4, 7.3), one can say that the set

$$\exists l(\Omega(k\square l)\doteq 0)$$

and the set

$$\exists l(k\doteq\mathfrak{P}(l))$$

which is equal to it, are examples of algorithmically enumerable sets which are not algorithmically solvable sets.

2.4. Let us consider some questions connected with the constructive reinterpretation of logico-mathematical formulas.

The constructive reinterpretation of logico-mathematical formulas containing bound occurrences of restricted variables is realized by the algorithm $\bar{\pi}_0$ described in [3], §§8.4–8.6. The algorithm $\bar{\pi}_0$ is the composition of two algorithms: the algorithm $\mathfrak{r}$ transforming any formula into an expanded formula (i.e. into a formula which does not contain bound occurrences of restricted variables), and the algorithm π_0 transforming any expanded formula into an expanded regular formula. The result of applying the algorithm $\bar{\pi}_0$ to any formula is a regular formula not containing bound occurrences of restricted variables. However, it often turns out to be convenient to replace this result by an equivalent formula containing bound occurrences of certain restricted variables.

Below we shall formulate a series of theorems establishing the admissibility of certain replacements of this kind.

2.4.1. *Let* $\mathfrak{A}$ *be a formula expressing a condition algorithmically verifiable for admissible values of its parameters. Let* $\mathfrak{B}$ *be any formula, and let* $\beta_1, \cdots, \beta_l$ *be pairwise distinct variables not occurring free in* $\mathfrak{A}$. *Then the formula*

$$(\mathfrak{A} \supset \exists \beta_1 \ldots \beta_l \mathfrak{B})$$

is equivalent to the formula

$$\exists \beta_1 \ldots \beta_l (\mathfrak{A} \supset \mathfrak{B}).$$

2.4.2. *Let* $\mathfrak{A}$ *be a normal formula and let* $\mathfrak{B}$ *be any formula. Let* $\beta_1, \cdots, \beta_l$ *be pairwise distinct variables, and let* $\alpha_1, \cdots, \alpha_k$ *be pairwise distinct variables not occurring free in the formula* $\exists \beta_1 \cdots \beta_l \mathfrak{B}$. *If every restricted variable occurring in the list* $\alpha_1, \cdots, \alpha_k$ *is such that its characterizing formula is a normal formula, then the formula*

$$(\exists \alpha_1 \ldots \alpha_k \mathfrak{A} \supset \exists \beta_1 \ldots \beta_k \mathfrak{B}) \tag{1}$$

is equivalent to the formula

$$\exists \sigma_1 \ldots \sigma_l \forall \alpha_1 \ldots \alpha_k (\mathfrak{A} \supset (\mathfrak{C}_1 \& \ldots \& \mathfrak{C}_l \& \mathfrak{D})).$$

Here $\sigma_1, \cdots, \sigma_l$ *are pairwise distinct variables such that for every* j $(j = 1, \cdots, l)$ *the variable* σ_j *is different from the variables* $\alpha_1, \cdots, \alpha_k$, *does not occur in the formula* (1), *and is a function variable of type* λn_j, *where* $n_j = \nu(\underbrace{\alpha_1 \ldots \alpha_k}, \underbrace{\beta_j})$. *We also used the notation*

$$\mathfrak{D} \leftrightharpoons \mathbf{F}^{\beta_1, \ldots, \beta_l}_{\Gamma_1, \ldots, \Gamma_l} \llcorner \mathfrak{B} \lrcorner,$$

$$\mathfrak{C}_j \leftrightharpoons (\Gamma_j \overset{+}{\in} \tau_j) \qquad (j = 1, \ldots, l),$$

where τ_j *is the generic letter of the variable* β_j, *and*

$$\Gamma_j \leftrightharpoons \sigma_j(\overbrace{\alpha_1 \ldots \alpha_k}), \qquad \text{if } \beta_j \text{ is an individual variable,}$$

$$\Gamma_j \leftrightharpoons \langle \sigma_j(\overbrace{\alpha_1 \ldots \alpha_k}) \rangle_{r_j}, \qquad \text{if } \beta_j \text{ is a function variable.}$$

In the last line, r_j *denotes the natural number such that the generic letter* λr_j *coincides with* τ_j *or is the characteristic generic letter of* τ_j.

2.4.3. *Let* $\mathfrak{B}$ *be any formula, and let* $\alpha_1, \cdots, \alpha_k, \beta_1, \cdots, \beta_l$ *be pairwise distinct variables. If every restricted variable occurring in the list* $\alpha_1, \cdots, \alpha_k$ *is such that its characterizing formula is a normal formula, then the formula*

$$\forall \alpha_1 \ldots \alpha_k \exists \beta_1 \ldots \beta_l \mathfrak{B} \tag{2}$$

is equivalent to the formula

$$\exists \sigma_1 \ldots \sigma_l \forall \alpha_1 \ldots \alpha_k (\mathfrak{C}_1 \& \ldots \& \mathfrak{C}_l \& \mathfrak{D}).$$

Here $\sigma_1, \cdots, \sigma_l$ *are pairwise distinct variables such that for each* j $(j = 1, \cdots, l)$ *the variable* σ_j *is different from the variables* $\alpha_1, \cdots, \alpha_k$, *does not occur in the formula* (2), *and is a function variable of type* λ_{n_j}, *where* $n_j = \nu(\underbrace{\alpha_1 \cdots \alpha_k}, \underbrace{\beta_j})$. *The letters* $\mathfrak{C}_1, \cdots, \mathfrak{C}_l$, $\mathfrak{D}$ *have here exactly the same meaning as in* 2.4.2.

We shall not carry out the proofs of 2.4.1–2.4.3 here, in view of the tedious transformations and constructions out of which these proofs are composed. We shall make only some remarks about the method of proof.

Theorem 2.4.1 asserts that two formulas of certain types are equivalent. We denote the formulas in question by $\mathfrak{F}$ and $\mathfrak{G}$. Applying to the formula

$$\tilde{\forall}(\mathfrak{F} \equiv \mathfrak{G}) \tag{3}$$

the algorithm $\overline{\pi}_0$, we exhibit a constructive problem which it is necessary to solve for the justification of proposition (3). This problem consists of the construction of algorithms satisfying a certain condition. The required algorithms can be constructed. In the construction of the desired algorithms the essential role is played by the algorithm verifying the fulfillment of the condition $\mathfrak{A}$ for admissible values of the parameters of the formula $\mathfrak{A}$ and by the theorem on the branching of normal algorithms [1], Russian p. 125.

The proofs of Theorems 2.4.2 and 2.4.3 are based on the same plan as the proof of Theorem 2.4.1. For the construction of the solution of the constructive problems exhibited by the constructive reformulation of Theorems 2.4.2 and 2.4.3, an essential role is played by Theorem 2.1.3.

2.5. We shall now go into the methods of proof of theorems of constructive mathematics.

Let $\mathfrak{F}$ be some closed formula which we suspect expresses a true proposition. One of the ways of proving the proposition $\mathfrak{F}$ consists of the following. To begin with, we apply to $\mathfrak{F}$ the algorithm $\overline{\pi}_0$ for the exhibition of constructive problems. This algorithm transforms $\mathfrak{F}$ into a regular formula $\overline{\pi}_0 \llcorner \mathfrak{F} \lrcorner$. If $\overline{\pi}_0 \llcorner \mathfrak{F} \lrcorner$ is a normal formula, then we undertake the search for a proof of the proposition $\overline{\pi}_0 \llcorner \mathfrak{F} \lrcorner$ within the borders of that part of constructive logic in which only normal formulas are considered. If $\overline{\pi}_0 \llcorner \mathfrak{F} \lrcorner$ is not a normal formula, then from the form of this formula we extract the formulation of a definite constructive problem. After this we undertake the search for a method of constructing constructive objects satisfying the condition which occurs in the formulation of a constructive problem.[1] This condition is expressed by a normal formula. The types and number of the constructive

1) The problem of choosing one of the terms of a conjunction among several terms reduces to the construction of a natural number satisfying a certain condition (cf. [3], p. 254, para. 3) (transl. p. 135)).

objects are determined by the formulation of the constructive problem. After giving the construction of certain constructive objects, which are suspected of satisfying the condition occurring in the formulation of the constructive problem, we begin a search for a proof of the proposition asserting that these constructive objects satisfy the indicated condition. Here we have in mind a proof within the scope of that part of constructive logic in which only normal formulas are considered.

The advantage of this way of proving the proposition consists of the fact that, proceeding according to this method, we obtain a clear representation of the constructive problem connected with the proposition to be proved. An important deficiency of this method consists of its great awkwardness, caused by the unwieldiness of the algorithm $\overline{\pi}_0$.

Another way of proving proposition $\mathfrak{F}$ consists of seeking a proof of $\mathfrak{F}$ within the scope of that part of constructive logic in which one deals with arbitrary formulas of the languages of constructive mathematics which we are using (including formulas containing the symbols $\exists$ and $\vee$).

The second way of proving propositions, if it succeeds, is usually very much briefer than the first, applied to the same proposition. This is explained by the fact that the process of justifying the admissibility of the rules of logical inference of constructive logic includes within itself, in a scattered form, the process of solving the constructive problem connected with the proposition to be proved.

We shall systematically use the second method of proving propositions. In those cases where it will be necessary or convenient for methodological considerations, we shall select the first method or combine the two methods.

The first method of proving propositions is illustrated in detail below in the example of Theorem 4.4.1. This theorem can be proved very much more briefly if one proceeds according to the second method.

In mathematics logical derivations are most often formulated as derivations from given hypotheses. In the paper [25], G. Gentzen made precise and formulated in sharp form a method of constructing logical derivations from given hypotheses. He formulated a definition of one system (sufficiently rich in its deductive possibilities) of rules of inference of constructive logic, which he called the *intuitionistic calculus of natural deduction* (abbreviated, the calculus NI).

Inferences in the calculus NI are written in the form of branching trees. But there is a variant of this calculus in which the inferences are written in a column, i.e. as logical inferences are usually written. In the paper [25] this variant is mentioned but is not described in detail. A formulation of this variant is obtained automatically from the formulation of the calculus NI if we use the concept of sequent introduced by G. Gentzen in [25], and if we interpret each sequent as a way of writing the dependence of the formulas standing in the succedent of the sequent on the premises standing in the antecedent of the sequent.[1)] If, to the act of introducing any assumption $\mathfrak{A}$, we associate the construction of the sequent $\mathfrak{A} \longrightarrow \mathfrak{A}$, and if to each rule of inference of the calculus NI, given by a rule of formation of conclusions from assumptions, we associate in a natural way a rule of transformation of sequents, then we obtain the description of a variant of the calculus NI in which inferences are written in a column.

In the sequel, when speaking about the intuitionistic calculus of natural deduction, we shall have in mind just this variant of the calculus. A formula $\mathfrak{A}$ is considered provable in this calculus if the sequent $\rightarrow \mathfrak{A}$ is provable in it.

In mathematics logical derivations based on hypotheses are usually formulated in an abbreviated form, and the concept of sequent is not used in a clear form. The greatest use of abbreviations consists of the following. First, after introducing some assumption $\mathfrak{A}$, it is not repeated as an assertion depending on the assumption $\mathfrak{A}$ (such a repetition would correspond to the introduction of the sequent $\mathfrak{A} \longrightarrow \mathfrak{A}$). Second, in the deduction process, one does not enumerate along with the result of an application of any rule of inference those assumptions on which this result depends (such an enumeration would correspond to the antecedent of the sequent), but the corresponding assumptions are only mentioned.

In the sequel we shall systematically use logical derivations from given hypotheses, and these derivations will be formulated as they are usually formulated in mathematics, i.e. in abbreviated form. In addition, finally, we shall use only those methods and rules of logical inference the admissibility of which can be justified within the frame of the constructive approach to mathematics.

A precise description and justification of the methods and rules of inference used below would lead beyong the scope of this paper. We remark also that the calculus NI and the equivalent calculi LI and LHI described in [25], pp. 190–193, 419–420 are insufficient for our purposes. These calculi are formulated with respect to a logico-mathematical language considerably simpler than the languages in this paper.

---

1). It suffices to consider only those sequents in which the succedent consists of one formula. When speaking of sequents in the following exposition, we shall have in mind sequents with one-termed succedents. The symbol of sequents $\rightarrow$ does not occur in the alphabet of formulas.

We shall use the rules of inference of constructive logic, adapted to the logico-mathematical languages used in this paper. Some of these rules of inference will be obtained by natural generalizations of the rules of inference of the calculus NI.

References made above to the calculus NI and to the concept of sequence are of a bibliographic nature. For the understanding of the remaining material of this paper, familiarity with the calculus NI and with the concept of sequent is not necessary.

We shall also use the rules of inference admissible in constructive mathematics but not occurring in simplest form in the calculus NI. Here, one must first of all refer to the rules of inference contained implicitly in the definitions of the algorithms π_0, π, $\mathfrak{r}$, and $\mathfrak{c}$ (see [3], §§4 and 8) in the form of descriptions of the various steps in the application of the algorithms. In addition, we shall use the rules for constructing true formulas indicated by A. A. Markov [9]. With respect to the language $\mathfrak{R}_\Sigma$ these rules can be formulated in the following way.

If $\mathfrak{A}$ is a formula of the language $\mathfrak{R}_\Sigma$, and S is a sequence of variables such that every variable occurring in S is either a basis variable or has as its characteristic set a nonempty algorithmically enumerable set, then the following formulas are true:

$$\tilde{\forall}(\forall S(\mathfrak{A} \vee \neg \mathfrak{A}) \supset (\neg\neg \exists S\mathfrak{A} \supset \exists S\mathfrak{A})), \tag{1}$$

$$\tilde{\forall}(\forall S(\mathfrak{A} \vee \neg \mathfrak{A}) \supset (\neg \forall S\mathfrak{A} \supset \exists S \neg \mathfrak{A})). \tag{2}$$

2.6. The rules of inference of constructive logic give us the opportunity to prove the following *stability law for formulas.*

2.6.1. *If* $\mathfrak{A}$, $\mathfrak{F}$, *and* $\mathfrak{G}$ *are any formulas and* $\mathfrak{B}$ *is a formula obtained as a result of substitution of the formula* $\mathfrak{G}$ *for certain (arbitrarily chosen) occurrences of the formula* $\mathfrak{F}$ *in the formula* $\mathfrak{A}$, *then the formula*

$$(\tilde{\forall}(\mathfrak{F} \equiv \mathfrak{G}) \supset (\mathfrak{A} \equiv \mathfrak{B}))$$

is provable, and therefore the rule of inference

$$\frac{(\mathfrak{F} \equiv \mathfrak{G})}{(\mathfrak{A} \equiv \mathfrak{B})}$$

is admissible.

The stability law for formulas will often be applied in the sequel. We shall also repeatedly use the fact that formulas of the following types are provable within the frame of constructive logic:

$$\tilde{\forall}(\forall S(\mathfrak{A} \,\&\, \mathfrak{B}) \equiv (\forall S\mathfrak{A} \,\&\, \forall S\mathfrak{B})), \tag{1}$$

$$\tilde{\forall}(\exists S(\mathfrak{A} \vee \mathfrak{B}) \equiv (\exists S\mathfrak{A} \vee \exists S\mathfrak{B})), \tag{2}$$

$$\tilde{\forall}(\neg \exists S\mathfrak{A} \equiv \forall S \neg \mathfrak{A}), \quad (3)$$

$$\tilde{\forall}((\mathfrak{A} \supset \mathfrak{B}) \supset (\neg \mathfrak{B} \supset \neg \mathfrak{A})), \quad (4)$$

$$\tilde{\forall}((\mathfrak{A} \supset \neg \mathfrak{B}) \equiv (\mathfrak{B} \supset \neg \mathfrak{A})), \quad \tilde{\forall}((\mathfrak{A} \supset \neg \mathfrak{B}) \equiv \neg (\mathfrak{A} \& \mathfrak{B})), \quad (5)$$

$$\tilde{\forall}(\neg (\mathfrak{A} \vee \mathfrak{B}) \equiv (\neg \mathfrak{A} \& \neg \mathfrak{B})), \quad (6)$$

$$\tilde{\forall}(\neg\neg (\mathfrak{A} \& \mathfrak{B}) \equiv (\neg\neg \mathfrak{A} \& \neg\neg \mathfrak{B})), \quad (7)$$

$$\tilde{\forall} \neg (\mathfrak{A} \& \neg \mathfrak{A}). \quad (8)$$

Here $\mathfrak{A}$ and $\mathfrak{B}$ are arbitrary formulas of the language $\mathfrak{A}_{\Sigma}$, and S is an arbitrary sequence of variables.

§3. CONSTRUCTIVE REAL NUMBERS

3.1. In this section we shall define the concepts of *real F-number* and *real FR-number* (*real duplex*), and we shall consider the problem of the connection between them. Brief historical references concerning these concepts were given in the Introduction (§§0.8–0.10).

As a basis for the concepts of real F-number and real FR-number (real duplex), the concept of *fundamental sequence of rational numbers* and the concept of *regulator of convergence in itself of a sequence of rational numbers* will be used. Both of these concepts are defined in the following section.

3.2. We shall say that the algorithm $\Phi_{2,1}$ is a *fundamental sequence of rational numbers* and also that it is a *sequence of rational numbers converging in itself*, and we shall write

$$(\Phi_{2,1} \in \underline{\text{fund. s. r. n.}}),$$

if, first,

$$\Phi_{2,1} \in (\text{H} \to \text{P})_2$$

and second,

$$\forall k \exists l \forall mn (m, n \geqslant l \supset M(\Phi_{2,1}(m) - \Phi_{2,1}(n)) < 2^{-k}). \quad (1)$$

The formula

$$\exists \Phi_{0,1}(\Phi_{0,1} \in (\text{H} \to \text{H})_0 \& \forall kmn (m, n \geqslant \Phi_{0,1}(k) \supset M(\Phi_{2,1}(m) - \Phi_{2,1}(n)) < 2^{-k})) \quad (2)$$

can be considered as a constructive reformation of the formula (1) (cf. 2.4.3). Using the restricted generic function letter f, introduced in §1.11, we construct the formula

$$\exists f_1 \forall kmn (m, n \geqslant f_1(k) \supset M(\Phi_{2,1}(m) - \Phi_{2,1}(n)) < 2^{-k}). \quad (3)$$

This formula is equivalent to formula (2), and hence formula (3) can also be considered as a constructive reformulation of formula (1).

We shall say that the algorithm $\Phi_{0,1}$ is a *regulator of convergence in itself of the algorithm* $\Phi_{2,1}$, and we shall write[1)]

$$(\Phi_{0,1}\ \underline{\text{reg. con.}}\ \Phi_{2,1}),$$

if, first,

$$\Phi_{0,1} \in (\text{H} \to \text{H})_0$$

and second,

$$\forall kmn\,(m,\ n \geqslant \Phi_{0,1}(k) \supset M(\Phi_{2,1}(m) - \Phi_{2,1}(n)) < 2^{-k}).$$

The following proposition is obvious.

3.2.1. *For any algorithm* $\Phi_{2,1}$,

$$\Phi_{2,1} \in \underline{\text{fund. s. r. n.}} \equiv \Phi_{2,1} \in (\text{H} \to \text{P})_2 \,\&\, \exists\, \Phi_{0,1}(\Phi_{0,1}\, \underline{\text{reg. con.}}\, \Phi_{2,1}). \tag{4}$$

3.3. We introduce a new elementary symbol $\Diamond$ and the notation

$$\text{Ч}_3 \rightleftharpoons \{0,\ |,\ \text{-},\ /,\ \Diamond\}.$$

The alphabet Ч_3 will be called the *alphabet of real numbers*.

By *real F-numbers* we mean, first, rational numbers, and second, words of the form $U\Diamond$, where U is a word in the alphabet Ч_0 such that the algorithm $\langle U \rangle_2$ is a fundamental sequence of rational numbers.

By *real FR-numbers* or *real duplexes* we mean, first, rational numbers, and second, words of the form $U \Diamond V$, where U and V are words in the alphabet Ч_0 such that the algorithm $\langle U \rangle_2$ is a sequence of rational numbers and the algorithm $\langle V \rangle_0$ is a regulator of convergence in itself of the algorithm $\langle U \rangle_2$.

3.4. The definitions formulated above of the concepts of real F-number and real FR-number (real duplex) lack precision. It is convenient to carry out the transition to the precise definitions with the aid of some auxiliary concepts and algorithms.

We shall say that the word $c_{3,1}$ is a *canonical word in the alphabet* Ч_3, and we shall write

$$(c_{3,1} \in \underline{\text{can}}_3),$$

1) We shall permit the use, instead of the term "regulator of convergence in itself of the algorithm $\Phi_{2,1}$", of the briefer term "regulator of convergence of the algorithm $\Phi_{2,1}$". This shorter term can lead to ambiguity if, along with regulators of convergence in itself, we considered regulators of convergence to a given constructive real number, defined in the natural way in the theory of limits. However, regulators of the second type will not be dealt with in this book.

if $c_{3,1}$ is a word in the alphabet $\{0, | ,\Diamond\}$ containing one and only one occurrence of the symbol $\Diamond$. Thus a canonical word in the alphabet $Ч_3$ is a word of the form $U \Diamond V$, where U and V are words in the alphabet $Ч_0$.

We shall say that the word $c_{3,1}$ is a *meaningful word in the alphabet* $Ч_3$, and we shall write

$$(c_{3,1} \in \underline{\mathrm{mean}}_3),$$

if $c_{3,1}$ is a rational number or a canonical word in the alphabet $Ч_3$.

Now we associate with each rational number a certain canonical word in the alphabet $Ч_3$. First of all, we construct and fix an algorithm τ in the alphabet $Ч_2^{sa}$ transforming any word P in the alphabet $Ч_2$ into the transcription of the normal algorithm in the alphabet $Ч_2^{sa}$ defined by the schema

$$\begin{cases} \xi \rightarrow & (\xi \in Ч_2) \\ \rightarrow \cdot P & \end{cases}.$$

For any words $c_{2,1}$ and $c_{2,2}$ in the alphabet $Ч_2$, we have

$$\langle\tau(c_{2,1})\rangle_2 (c_{2,2}) \doteqdot c_{2,1}.$$

In particular,

$$\forall p_1 H_1 (\langle\tau(p_1)\rangle_2 (H_1) \doteqdot p_1),$$

and thus for any p_1 the algorithm $\langle\tau(p_1)\rangle_2$ is an algorithm of type $(H \rightarrow p)_2$. We introduce another algorithm in the alphabet $Ч_0^{sa}$ defined by the schema

$$\begin{cases} \xi \rightarrow & (\xi \in Ч_0) \\ \rightarrow \cdot 0 & \end{cases}$$

We denote the transcription of this algorithm by Ъ. The algorithm $\langle Ъ \rangle_0$ transforms any natural number into 0, and hence it is an algorithm of type $(H \rightarrow H)_0$.

By the *duplex image of a rational number* a we mean the word

$$\tau(a) \Diamond Ъ.$$

We agree to denote the duplex image of a rational number a by $\hat{a}$. In other words,

$$\hat{a} \leftrightharpoons \tau(a) \Diamond Ъ. \tag{1}$$

Let Θ be any individual term. We introduce the notation

$$\hat{\Theta} \leftrightharpoons \tau(\Theta) \Diamond Ъ. \tag{2}$$

Now with each rational number we associate a certain canonical word in the alphabet $Ч_3$: the duplex image of the given rational number. One can construct an algorithm in the alphabet $Ч_3^{sa}$ distinguishing among all words in $Ч_3$ those words which are duplex images of rational numbers. One can also construct an algorithm which, for every word $c_{3,1}$ which is a duplex image of some rational number, constructs the (unique) rational number whose duplex image is $c_{3,1}$.

We construct and fix concrete algorithms $\overline{\text{lef}_3}$ and $\overline{\text{rig}_3}$ in the alphabet Ч_2^{sa} such that, for any word $c_{3,1}$, the following conditions are fulfilled.

1) If $c_{3,1}$ is a canonical word in Ч_3, then the algorithm $\overline{\text{lef}_3}(\overline{\text{rig}_3})$ transforms $c_{3,1}$ into the word which is the left (respectively, right) wing of the unique occurrence of the symbol $\diamondsuit$ in the word $c_{3,1}$; in other words, for any words $c_{0,1}$ and $c_{0,2}$ in the alphabet Ч_0, we have

$$\overline{\text{lef}_3}(c_{0,1}\diamondsuit c_{0,2}) \mathrel{\dot{=}} c_{0,1}, \qquad \overline{\text{rig}_3}(c_{0,1}\diamondsuit c_{0,2}) \mathrel{\dot{=}} c_{0,2};$$

2) If $c_{3,1}$ is a rational number, then the algorithm $\overline{\text{lef}_3}$ (algorithm $\overline{\text{rig}_3}$) transforms the word $c_{3,1}$ into the same word into which $\overline{\text{lef}_3}$ (respectively, $\overline{\text{rig}_3}$) transforms the duplex image of $c_{3,1}$; in other words, if $c_{3,1}$ is a rational number, then

$$\overline{\text{lef}_3}(c_{3,1}) \mathrel{\dot{=}} \overline{\text{lef}_3}(\hat{c}_{3,1}), \qquad \overline{\text{rig}_3}(c_{3,1}) \mathrel{\dot{=}} \overline{\text{rig}_3}(\hat{c}_{3,1});$$

3) If $c_{3,1}$ is neither a canonical word in the alphabet Ч_3 nor a rational number, then the algorithms $\overline{\text{lef}_3}$ and $\overline{\text{rig}_3}$ transform $c_{3,1}$ into the transcription of the normal algorithm defined by the schema

$$\{\rightarrow\ . \tag{3}$$

It is obvious that the process of applying the algorithm (3) to any word in the alphabet Ч_3 does not terminate.

Let H be any word in the alphabet Ч_3. We introduce the notation

$$\underset{\smile}{H} \leftrightharpoons \langle \overline{\text{lef}_3}(H)\rangle_2, \qquad \overleftrightarrow{H} \leftrightharpoons \langle \overline{\text{rig}_3}(H)\rangle_0.$$

The expression $\underset{\smile}{H}$ denotes an algorithm in the alphabet Ч_3^{sa} and $\overleftrightarrow{H}$ denotes an algorithm in the alphabet Ч_0^{sa}. Moreover, if H is not a meaningful word in the alphabet Ч_3, then the algorithms $\underset{\smile}{H}$ and $\overleftrightarrow{H}$ are not applicable to any word. If H is a rational number, then

$$\forall n(\underset{\smile}{H}(n) \mathrel{\dot{=}} H), \qquad \forall n(\overleftrightarrow{H}(n) \mathrel{\dot{=}} 0).$$

Let Θ be any individual term. We introduce the notation

$$\underset{\smile}{\Theta} \leftrightharpoons \langle \overline{\text{lef}_3}(\Theta)\rangle_2, \qquad \overleftrightarrow{\Theta} \leftrightharpoons \langle \overline{\text{rig}_3}(\Theta)\rangle_0.$$

This notation will be systematically used in the sequel.

We shall say that the word $c_{3,1}$ is a *one-sided canonical word in the alphabet* Ч_3, and we shall write

$$(c_{3,1} \in \underline{\text{one can}}_3),$$

if

$$c_{3,1} \in \underline{\text{can}}_3 \,\&\, \overline{\text{rig}_3}(c_{3,1}) \mathrel{\dot{=}} \Lambda.$$

Thus a one-sided canonical word in the alphabet Ч_3 is a word of the form

$U\diamondsuit$, where U is a word in the alphabet Ч_0.

We shall say that the word $c_{3,1}$ is a *one-sided meaningful word in the alphabet* Ч_3, and we shall write

$$(c_{3,1} \in \underline{\text{one mean}}_3),$$

if $c_{3,1}$ is a rational number or a one-sided canonical word in the alphabet Ч_3.

In the sequel we shall systematically use the following fact.

The predicates

$$\underline{\text{can}}_3, \quad \underline{\text{one can}}_3, \quad \underline{\text{mean}}_3, \quad \underline{\text{one mean}}_3$$

are algorithmically solvable predicates (see §1.10).

The algorithms corresponding to these predicates can be constructed without difficulty.

To each meaningful word in the alphabet Ч_3 we associate a certain one-sided meaningful word which we shall call the *principal part* of the given meaningful word. We construct and fix an algorithm $\overline{\text{prin}}_3$ in the alphabet Ч_3^{sa} (algorithm for isolating the principal part) such that, for any word $c_{3,1}$, the following conditions are fulfilled.

1) If $c_{3,1}$ is a canonical word in Ч_3, then the algorithm $\overline{\text{prin}}_3$ transforms $c_{3,1}$ into the one-sided word which is obtained by canceling all letters of the word $c_{3,1}$ standing to the right of the symbol $\diamondsuit$; in other words,

$$\overline{\text{prin}}_3(c_{3,1}) \underset{\cdot}{=} \overline{\text{lef}}_3(c_{3,1})\diamondsuit;$$

2) If $c_{3,1}$ is a rational number, then

$$\overline{\text{prin}}_3(c_{3,1}) \underset{\cdot}{=} c_{3,1};$$

3) If $c_{3,1}$ is not a meaningful word in Ч_3, then the algorithm $\overline{\text{prin}}_3$ is not applicable to $c_{3,1}$.

It is obvious that

$$\forall c_{3,1}(c_{3,1} \in \overline{\text{mean}}_3 \supset \overline{\text{lef}}_3(\overline{\text{prin}}_3(c_{3,1})) \underset{\cdot}{=} \overline{\text{lef}}_3(c_{3,1})).$$

3.5. Now we shall formulate the precise definitions of real F-numbers and real FR-numbers (real duplexes).

We shall say that a word $c_{3,1}$ is a *real* F*-number*, and we shall write

$$(c_{3,1} \in \underline{\text{real } F\text{-num}}),$$

if $c_{3,1}$ is a one-sided meaningful word in the alphabet Ч_3 and the algorithm $\underline{c_{3,1}}$ is a fundamental sequence of rational numbers.

The condition $(c_{3,1} \in \underline{\text{real } F\text{-num}}$ is expressed by the formula

$$c_{3,1} \in \underline{\text{one mean}}_3 \; \& \; \underline{c_{3,1}} \in (\text{н} \to \text{р})_2 \; \& \; \exists \phi_{0,1}(\phi_{0,1}\, \underline{\text{reg.con.}}\; \underline{c_{3,1}}). \qquad (1)$$

The condition $(c_{3,1} \in \underline{\text{one mean}}_3)$ is algorithmically verifiable; the conditions $(\underline{c_{3,1}} \in (H \to p)_2)$ and $(\Phi_{0,1}\ \underline{\text{reg. con.}}\ \underline{c_{3,1}})$ are expressed by normal formulas (see [3]). Hence the algorithm for exhibiting constructive problems transforms formula (1) into the completely regular formula

$$\exists\, \Phi_{0,1} (\Phi_{0,1}\ \underline{\text{reg. con.}^+}\ \underline{c_{3,1}}), \tag{2}$$

where

$$(\Phi_{0,1}\ \underline{\text{reg. con.}^+}\ \underline{c_{3,1}}) \leftrightharpoons (c_{3,1} \in \underline{\text{one mean}_3}\ \&\ \underline{c_{3,1}} \in (H \to p)_2\ \&\ \Phi_{0,1}\ \underline{\text{reg. con.}}\ \underline{c_{3,1}})$$

[3], §4.

Real F-numbers will also be called *words of type* B. The letter "B" will be considered in the sequel to be a restricted generic letter used for the construction of restricted individual variables

$$(\text{B}),\ (\text{BB}),\ (\text{BBB}),\ \ldots$$

In accordance with the convention accepted in §1.3, these variables will be denoted, respectively, by $B_1, B_2, B_3, \cdots$. The characterizing formula of these variables is the formula (1).

For the first three variables of type B we shall also introduce, in addition to the notation B_1, B_2, B_3, the following notation:

$$q \leftrightharpoons (\text{B}), \quad r \leftrightharpoons (\text{BB}), \quad s \leftrightharpoons (\text{BBB}).$$

It is obvious that every rational number is a real F-number.

If $c_{3,1}$ is a real F-number, then the algorithm $\underline{c_{3,1}}$ will be called the base of $c_{3,1}$.

3.6. We shall say that a word $c_{3,1}$ is a *real* FR-*number*, and we shall write

$$(c_{3,1} \in \underline{\text{real}\ \ FR\text{-num}}),$$

if $c_{3,1}$ is a meaningful word in the alphabet $Ч_3$, the algorithm $\underline{c_{3,1}}$ is a sequence of rational numbers, and the algorithm $\overline{c_{3,1}}$ is a regulator of convergence in itself of the algorithm $\underline{c_{3,1}}$.

Real FR-numbers will also be called *real duplexes*, and we shall use the expression

$$(c_{3,1} \in \underline{\text{real dup}})$$

as an equivalent of the expression $(c_{3,1} \in \underline{\text{real}\ FR\text{-num}})$.

The condition $(c_{3,1} \in \underline{\text{real dup}})$ is expressed by the normal formula

$$c_{3,1} \in \underline{\text{mean}_3}\ \&\ \underline{c_{3,1}} \in (H \to p)_2\ \&\ \overline{c_{3,1}}\ \underline{\text{reg. con.}}\ \underline{c_{3,1}}. \tag{1}$$

Real FR-numbers (real duplexes) will also be called *words of type* Д. The letter Д will be considered in the sequel as a restricted generic letter used for the construction of the restricted individual variables

$$(\text{д}),\ (\text{дд}),\ (\text{ддд}),\ \cdots$$

In accordance with the convention accepted in §1.3, these variables will be denoted, respectively, by $Д_1, Д_2, Д_3, \cdots,$ The characterizing formula of these variables is the formula (1).

For the first four variables of type $Д$ we introduce, in addition to the notation $Д_1, Д_2, Д_3, Д_4,$ the following notation:

$$x \leftrightharpoons (\text{д}),\quad y \leftrightharpoons (\text{дд}),\quad z \leftrightharpoons (\text{ддд}),\quad u \leftrightharpoons (\text{дддд}).$$

It is obvious that every rational number is a real FR-number (real duplex).

If $c_{3,1}$ is a real FR-number, then the algorithm $\underline{c_{3,1}}$ will be called the base of $c_{3,1}$.

We shall say that a word $c_{3,1}$ is a *constructive real number* if $c_{3,1}$ is a real F-number or a real FR-number.

For the sake of brevity we shall employ, instead of the terms "real F-number" and "real FR-number", the shorter terms "F-number" and "FR-number", respectively. This abbreviation of terms does not cause ambiguity since, in this book, complex F-numbers and complex FR-numbers (complex duplexes) are mentioned only in §8.5.

In addition, for the duration of this chapter, we shall use, instead of the term "real duplex", the shorter term "duplex". This convention will not be extended to later chapters, since in later chapters there will occur, in addition to real duplexes, measurable duplexes, duplexes summable to a given power, and duplexes of various other kinds.

3.7. The following propositions are obvious.

2.7.1. *A word* $c_{3,1}$ *is simultaneously an* F*-number and an* FR*-number (duplex) if and only if* $c_{3,1}$ *is a rational number.*

3.7.2. *If* $c_{3,1}$ *is a duplex, then the word* $\overline{\text{prin}_3}\,(c_{3,1})$ *is an* F*-number and the base of the* F*-number* $\overline{\text{prin}_3}\,(c_{3,1})$ *coincides with the base of the duplex* $c_{3,1}$.

Now we shall prove the following theorem.

3.7.3. $$\forall \text{в}_1 \exists \text{д}_1 (\overline{\text{prin}_3}(\text{д}_1) \doteqdot \text{в}_1). \qquad (1)$$

Proof. Applying to formula (1) the algorithm for eliminating restricted variables, we obtain the formula

$$\forall c_{3,1}\,(c_{3,1} \in \underline{\text{real } F\text{-num}} \supset \exists c_{3,2}\,(c_{3,2} \in \underline{\text{real dup}}\ \&\ \overline{\text{prin}_3}\,(c_{3,2}) \doteqdot c_{3,1})).$$

One can write the formula just obtained in the following way:

$$\forall c_{3,1}(\exists \Phi_{0,1}(\Phi_{0,1}\ \underline{\text{reg. con.}^{+}}\ \underset{\sqcup}{c_{3,1}}) \supset \exists c_{3,2}(c_{3,2} \in \underline{\text{real dup}} \;\&\; \overline{\text{prin}_3}(c_{3,2}) \mathrel{\overline{\overline{\cdot}}} c_{3,1})). \tag{2}$$

Carrying out the process of applying the algorithm for exhibiting constructive problems to the formula (2), we successively obtain the following formulas (3) and (4):

$$\forall c_{3,1}\exists \Phi_{3,1}\forall \Phi_{0,1}(\Phi_{0,1}\ \underline{\text{reg. con.}^{+}}\ \underset{\sqcup}{c_{3,1}} \supset \Phi_{3,1}(\{\Phi_{0,1}\}) \overset{+}{\in} c_3$$
$$\& \ \Phi_{3,1}(\{\Phi_{0,1}\}) \in \underline{\text{real dup}} \ \& \ \overline{\text{prin}_3}(\Phi_{3,1}(\{\Phi_{0,1}\})\mathrel{\overline{\overline{\cdot}}} c_{3,1}); \tag{3}$$

$$\exists \Phi_{3,2}\mathfrak{F}, \tag{4}$$

where

$$\mathfrak{F} \rightleftharpoons \forall c_{3,1}(\Phi_{3,2}(c_{3,1}) \overset{+}{\in} c_0 \,\&\, \forall \Phi_{0,1}(\Phi_{0,1}\ \underline{\text{reg.con.}^{+}}\ \underset{\sqcup}{c_{3,1}}$$
$$\supset \Theta \overset{+}{\in} c_3 \,\&\, \Theta \in \underline{\text{real dup}} \ \& \ \overline{\text{prin}_3}(\Theta) \mathrel{\overline{\overline{\cdot}}} c_{3,1})).$$

Here we have used the notation

$$\Theta \rightleftharpoons \langle \Phi_{3,2}(c_{3,1})\rangle_3(\{\Phi_{0,1}\}).$$

The formula (4) is a constructive reformulation of the formula (1).

Let us prove proposition (4). To do this, we solve the corresponding constructive problem, i.e. we construct an algorithm in the alphabet $Ч_3^{sa}$ satisfying the one-parameter condition $\mathfrak{F}$ (the variable $\Phi_{3,2}$ is the parameter of the formula $\mathfrak{F}$).

Let us denote by $\mathfrak{D}_1$ an algorithm in $Ч_3^{sa}$ defined by the abbreviated schema

$$\left\{\begin{array}{ll} \square\xi \to \square & (\xi \in Ч_3) \\ \square \to & \end{array}\right. ,$$

and by $\mathfrak{D}_2$ the algorithm in $Ч_3^{sa}$ defined by the schema

$$\{\ \square \to$$

It is obvious that, for any $c_{3,1}$ and $c_{3,2}$:

$$\mathfrak{D}_1(c_{3,1}\square c_{3,2}) \mathrel{\overline{\overline{\cdot}}} c_{3,1}, \qquad \mathfrak{D}_2(c_{3,1}\square c_{3,2}) \mathrel{\overline{\overline{\cdot}}} c_{3,1}c_{3,2}.$$

Let us denote by $\mathfrak{D}_3$ an algorithm in $Ч_3^{sa}$, applicable to every word in the alphabet $Ч_3^{s}$, and such that

$$\forall c_{3,1}c_{3,2}(\mathfrak{D}_3(c_{3,1}\square c_{3,2}) \mathrel{\overline{\overline{\cdot}}} \Lambda \equiv c_{3,1} \in \underline{\text{rat}}).$$

On the basis of the theorem about the ramified union of algorithms and the theorem on the reduction of algorithms [1], we construct an algorithm $\mathfrak{A}$ in $Ч_3^{sa}$

such that, for any $c_{3,1}$ and $c_{3,2}$,

$$\mathfrak{A}(c_{3,1}\square c_{3,2}) \simeq \begin{cases} \mathfrak{D}_1(c_{3,1}\square c_{3,2}), & \text{if} \quad \mathfrak{D}_3(c_{3,1}\square c_{3,2}) \doteq \Lambda, \\ \mathfrak{D}_2(c_{3,1}\square c_{3,2}), & \text{if} \quad \mathfrak{D}_3(c_{3,1}\square c_{3,2}) \not\doteq \Lambda. \end{cases}$$

According to 2.1.2, from the algorithm $\mathfrak{A}$ we can construct an algorithm $\mathfrak{B}$ in the alphabet Ч_3^{sa} such that, first,

$$\forall c_{3,1}(\mathfrak{B}(c_{3,1}) \overset{+}{\in} c_0)$$

and second,

$$\forall c_{3,1}c_{3,2}(\langle\mathfrak{B}(c_{3,1})\rangle_3(c_{3,2}) \simeq \mathfrak{A}(c_{3,1}\square c_{3,2})).$$

We introduce the notation

$$\mathfrak{F}^* \rightleftharpoons \mathbf{F}_{\mathfrak{B}}^{\phi_{3,2}} \llcorner\mathfrak{F}\lrcorner.$$

Let us prove the proposition expressed by the closed formula $\mathfrak{F}^*$. We introduce the notation

$$\begin{aligned} &\Theta^* \rightleftharpoons \langle\mathfrak{B}(c_{3,1})\rangle_3(\{\phi_{0,1}\}), \\ &\mathfrak{M} \rightleftharpoons \mathfrak{B}(c_{3,1}) \in c_0 \,\&\, \phi_{0,1}\, \underline{\text{reg. con}}\overset{+}{.}\, \underline{c_{3,1}}, \\ &\mathfrak{N} \rightleftharpoons \Theta^* \overset{+}{\in} c_3 \,\&\, \Theta^* \in \underline{\text{real dup}} \,\&\, \overline{\text{prin}}_3(\Theta^*) \doteq c_{3,1}, \\ &\widetilde{\mathfrak{F}} \rightleftharpoons \forall c_{3,1} \forall \phi_{0,1}(\mathfrak{M} \supset \mathfrak{N}). \end{aligned}$$

We have

$$\begin{aligned} \mathfrak{F}^* \,\overset{\circ}{=}\, &\forall c_{3,1}(\mathfrak{B}(c_{3,1}) \overset{+}{\in} c_0 \,\&\, \forall \phi_{0,1}(\phi_{0,1}\, \underline{\text{reg. con.}^+}\, \underline{c_{3,1}} \\ &\supset \Theta^* \overset{+}{\in} c_3 \,\&\, \Theta^* \in \underline{\text{real dup}} \,\&\, \overline{\text{prin}}_3(\Theta^*) \doteq c_{3,1})). \end{aligned}$$

It is obvious that

$$\mathfrak{F}^* \equiv \widetilde{\mathfrak{F}}.$$

Hence it suffices to prove the proposition $\widetilde{\mathfrak{F}}$.

Let us denote by $\mathfrak{R}$ the algorithm in the alphabet Ч_3^{sa}, applicable to every word in the alphabet Ч_3, and such that

$$\forall c_{3,1}(\mathfrak{R}(c_{3,1}) \doteq \Lambda \equiv c_{3,1} \in \underline{\text{rat}}).$$

From the applicability of the algorithm $\mathfrak{R}$ to every word in the alphabet Ч_3 it follows that

$$\begin{aligned} \widetilde{\mathfrak{F}} \equiv &\forall c_{3,1}(\mathfrak{R}(c_{3,1}) \doteq \Lambda \supset \forall \phi_{0,1}(\mathfrak{M} \supset \mathfrak{N})) \\ &\& \forall_{3,1}(\mathfrak{R}(c_{3,1}) \not\doteq \Lambda \supset \forall \phi_{0,1}(\mathfrak{M} \supset \mathfrak{N})). \end{aligned}$$

If a word $c_{3,1}$ is such that $\mathfrak{R}(c_{3,1}) \doteq \Lambda$, then

$$\forall \phi_{0,1}(\Theta^* \doteq c_{3,1})$$

and therefore $\Theta^* \in \underline{\text{rat}}$, $\overline{\text{prin}_3}(\Theta^*) \doteq \Theta^* \doteq c_{3,1}$, $\forall \Phi_{0,1}\mathfrak{N}$. Hence

$$\forall c_{3,1}(\mathfrak{R}(c_{3,1}) \doteq \Lambda \supset \forall \Phi_{0,1}(\mathfrak{M} \supset \mathfrak{N})).$$

If a word $c_{3,1}$ is such that $\mathfrak{R}(c_{3,1}) \not\doteq \Lambda$, then

$$\forall \Phi_{0,1}(\Theta^* \doteq c_{3,1}\{\Phi_{0,1}\})$$

and therefore

$$\forall \Phi_{0,1}(\Phi_{0,1}\,\underline{\text{reg.con.}^+}\,\underline{c_{3,1}} \supset c_{3,1} \in \underline{\text{one mean}_3} \,\&\, \Theta^* \in \underline{\text{real dup}}$$
$$\& \,\overline{\text{prin}_3}(\Theta^*) \doteq \overline{\text{prin}_3}(c_{3,1}\{\Phi_{0,1}\}) \doteq c_{3,1}).$$

Hence

$$\forall c_{3,1}(\mathfrak{R}(c_{3,1}) \not\doteq \Lambda \supset \forall \Phi_{0,1}(\mathfrak{M} \supset \mathfrak{N})).$$

Thus proposition $\widetilde{\mathfrak{F}}$ has been proved. Therefore proposition $\exists \Phi_{3,2}\mathfrak{F}$ has also been proved. Now we can assert that

$$\forall B_1 \exists Д_1(\overline{\text{prin}_3}(Д_1) \doteq B_1).$$

Fundamental remark. One cannot understand the theorem just proved as asserting that

$$\exists \Phi_{3,1} \forall B_1(\Phi_{3,1}(B_1) \overset{+}{\in} \underline{\text{real dup}} \,\&\, \overline{\text{prin}_3}(\Phi_{3,1}(B_1)) \doteq B_1), \tag{5}$$

which, by the algorithm for eliminating restricted variables and the algorithm for exhibiting constructive problems, is transformed in the assertion

$$\exists \Phi_{3,1} \forall c_{3,1}\Phi_{0,1}(\Phi_{0,1}\,\underline{\text{reg.con.}^+}\,\underline{c_{3,1}} \supset \Phi_{3,1}(c_{3,1}) \overset{+}{\in} \underline{\text{real dup}}$$
$$\& \,\overline{\text{prin}_3}(\Phi_{3,1}(c_{3,1})) \doteq c_{3,1}). \tag{6}$$

The formula which is a constructive reinterpretation of the condition ($c_{3,1} \in \underline{\text{real } F\text{-num}}$) begins with a quantifier of potential realizability, and therefore is not a normal formula. Hence Proposition 2.4.3 is not applicable to formula (1).

G. S. Ceĭtin [17] has disproved the assertion (5). He proved [17], (§3, Corollary 3 of Theorem 2) that there is no algorithm $\Phi_{3,1}$ satisfying the condition

$$\forall B_1(\Phi_{3,1}(B_1) \overset{+}{\in} \underline{\text{real dup}} \,\&\, \overline{\text{prin}_3}(\Phi_{3,1}(B_1)) \doteq B_1).$$

3.8. In this section we shall indicate a method of automatically obtaining (under certain conditions) theorems about F-numbers from theorems about duplexes, and conversely.

3.8.1. *Let* $\mathfrak{F}$ *be any formula,* α *any variable of type* B , *and* σ *any variable of type* Д *not occurring in the formula* $\mathfrak{F}$. *Then*

a) $\widetilde{\forall}(\forall\alpha\mathfrak{F} \equiv \forall\sigma\mathbf{F}^{\alpha}_{\text{prin}(\sigma)}\llcorner\mathfrak{F}\lrcorner)$;

b) $\widetilde{\forall}(\exists\alpha\mathfrak{F} \equiv \exists\sigma \mathbf{F}^{\alpha}_{\overline{\text{prin}_3}(\sigma)} \llcorner\mathfrak{F}\lrcorner)$.

Proof. We choose natural numbers i, j, k, l so that the variables $c_{3,i}$, $\Phi_{3,j}$, $c_{0,k}$, and $c_{3,l}$ do not occur in the formula $\mathfrak{F}$. For all values of the parameters of the formula $\forall\alpha\mathfrak{F}$, we have

$$\forall\alpha\mathfrak{F} \equiv \forall c_{3,i}\,(\exists\Phi_{0,j}\,(\Phi_{0,j}\,\underline{\text{reg.con.}^+}\,\underline{c_{3,i}}) \supset \mathbf{F}^{\alpha}_{c_{3,i}} \llcorner\mathfrak{F}\lrcorner)$$

$$\swarrow \quad \equiv \forall c_{3,i}\Phi_{0,j}\,(\Phi_{0,j}\,\underline{\text{reg.con.}^+}\,\underline{c_{3,i}} \supset \mathbf{F}^{\alpha}_{c_{3,i}} \llcorner\mathfrak{F}\lrcorner)$$

$$\swarrow \quad \equiv \forall c_{3,i}c_{0,k}(\langle c_{0,k}\rangle_0\,\underline{\text{reg.con.}^+}\,\underline{c_{3,i}} \supset \mathbf{F}^{\alpha}_{c_{3,i}} \llcorner\mathfrak{F}\lrcorner)$$

$$\swarrow \quad \equiv \forall c_{3,i}c_{0,k}(c_{3,i} \in \underline{\text{one mean}}_3\,\&\,\mathfrak{A}(c_{3,i}\,\square\,c_{0,k}) \in \underline{\text{real dup}} \supset \mathbf{F}^{\alpha}_{c_{3,i}} \llcorner\mathfrak{F}\lrcorner)$$

$$\swarrow \quad \equiv \forall c_{3,l}(c_{3,l} \in \underline{\text{mean}_3}\,\&\,\mathfrak{A}(\overline{\text{prin}_3}(c_{3,l})\,\square\,\overline{\text{rig}_3}(c_{3,l})) \in \underline{\text{real dup}}$$
$$\supset \mathbf{F}^{\alpha}_{\overline{\text{prin}_3}(c_{3,l})} \llcorner\mathfrak{F}\lrcorner)$$

$$\swarrow \quad \equiv \forall c_{3,l}(c_{3,l} \in \underline{\text{real dup}} \supset \mathbf{F}^{\alpha}_{\overline{\text{prin}_3}(c_{3,l})} \llcorner\mathfrak{F}\lrcorner)$$

$$\swarrow \quad \equiv \forall\sigma\,\mathbf{F}^{\alpha}_{\overline{\text{prin}_3}(\sigma)} \llcorner\mathfrak{F}\lrcorner,$$

where $\mathfrak{A}$ is the algorithm constructed in the proof of Theorem 3.7.3; in addition, we have

$$\exists\alpha\mathfrak{F} \equiv \exists c_{3,i}\,(\exists\Phi_{0,j}\,(\Phi_{0,j}\,\underline{\text{reg.con.}^+}\,\underline{c_{3,i}})\,\&\,\mathbf{F}^{\alpha}_{c_{3,i}} \llcorner\mathfrak{F}\lrcorner)$$

$$\swarrow \quad \equiv \exists c_{3,i}\Phi_{0,j}(\Phi_{0,j}\,\underline{\text{reg.con.}^+}\,\underline{c_{3,i}}\,\&\,\mathbf{F}^{\alpha}_{c_{3,i}} \llcorner\mathfrak{F}\lrcorner)$$

$$\swarrow \quad \equiv \exists c_{3,i}c_{0,k}\,(\langle c_{0,k}\rangle_0\,\underline{\text{reg.con.}^+}\,\underline{c_{3,i}}\,\&\,\mathbf{F}^{\alpha}_{c_{3,i}} \llcorner\mathfrak{F}\lrcorner)$$

$$\swarrow \quad \equiv \exists c_{3,i}c_{0,k}(c_{3,i} \in \underline{\text{one mean}}_3\,\&\,\mathfrak{A}(c_{3,i}\,\square\,c_{0,k}) \in \underline{\text{real dup}}\,\&\,\mathbf{F}^{\alpha}_{c_{3,i}} \llcorner\mathfrak{F}\lrcorner)$$

$$\swarrow \quad \equiv \exists c_{3,l}(c_{3,l} \in \underline{\text{mean}_3}\,\&\,\mathfrak{A}(\overline{\text{prin}_3}(c_{3,l})\,\square\,\overline{\text{rig}_3}(c_{3,l})) \in \underline{\text{real dup}}$$
$$\&\,\mathbf{F}^{\alpha}_{\overline{\text{prin}_3}(c_{3,l})} \llcorner\mathfrak{F}\lrcorner)$$

$$\swarrow \quad \equiv \exists c_{3,l}(c_{3,l} \in \underline{\text{real dup}}\,\&\,\mathbf{F}^{\alpha}_{\overline{\text{prin}_3}(c_{3,l})} \llcorner\mathfrak{F}\lrcorner)$$

$$\swarrow \quad \equiv \exists\sigma\mathbf{F}^{\alpha}_{\overline{\text{prin}_3}(\sigma)} \llcorner\mathfrak{F}\lrcorner.$$

Proposition 3.8.1 has been proved.

We say that formula $\mathfrak{F}$ is *primitive with respect to variables of type* B if there is no bound occurrence in the formula $\mathfrak{F}$ of variables of type B. We say that a formula $\mathfrak{G}$ is *semiprimitive with respect to variables of type* B if

$$\mathfrak{G} \rightleftharpoons KS_0 \alpha_1 S_1 \cdots \alpha_i S_i \mathfrak{F}, \tag{1}$$

where K is a quantifier, $i \geq 1$, and $\alpha_1, \cdots, \alpha_i$ are variables of type B; and for every $j(1 \leq j \leq i)$ the word S_j represents either the empty word or a string of variables not containing variables of type B, and $\mathfrak{F}$ is a formula which is primitive with respect to variables of type B.

If a formula $\mathfrak{G}$ is such that (1) holds, then by the *adjoint formula* of $\mathfrak{G}$ we will mean the formula

$$KS_0\sigma_1 S_1 \cdots \sigma_i S_i \mathbf{F} \frac{\alpha_1 \cdots \alpha_i}{\overline{\text{prin}_3(\sigma_1)}, \cdots, \overline{\text{prin}_3(\sigma_i)}} \llcorner \mathfrak{F} \lrcorner,$$

where $\sigma_1, \cdots, \sigma_i$ are respectively the first, $\cdots$, ith variables among the variables of type Д not appearing in $\mathfrak{G}$.

By the *algorithm of adjoint formulas* we mean the algorithm transforming any formula $\mathfrak{P}$ in the following way. If no formula semiprimitive with respect to variables of type B occurs in $\mathfrak{P}$, then the operation of the algorithm terminates at the 0th step and has formula $\mathfrak{P}$ as its result. If at least one formula semiprimitive with respect to variables of type B occurs in $\mathfrak{P}$, then we seek among all occurrences in $\mathfrak{P}$ of formulas semiprimitive with respect to variables of type B the first such occurrence and we substitute for this first occurrence the formula adjoint to the basis of this first occurrence (see [1], Russian p. 26). The formula so obtained we denote by $\mathfrak{P}_1$. We transform the formula $\mathfrak{P}_1$ exactly the same way as the formula $\mathfrak{P}$, etc. We consider the process terminated when we obtain a formula primitive with respect to variables of type B.

The formula which is the result of applying the algorithm of adjoint formulas to the formula $\mathfrak{P}$ will be called the adjoint formula of $\mathfrak{P}$.

It is easily seen that the following lemma is true.

3.8.2. *If $\mathfrak{P}$ is any formula and $\mathfrak{Q}$ is the adjoint formula of $\mathfrak{P}$, then*

1) *no variable of type* B *occurs bound*[1] *in the formula $\mathfrak{Q}$;*

2) *the normal list of parameters* (*see* [3], §3.6) *of the formula $\mathfrak{Q}$ is identical with the normal list of parameters of the formula $\mathfrak{P}$; in particular, if $\mathfrak{P}$ is a closed*

1) One says that an individual variable τ occurs bound in a formula $\mathfrak{H}$ if there is at least one bound occurrence of τ in $\mathfrak{H}$.

formula, then $\mathfrak{Q}$ *is also a closed formula.*

From 3.8.1, 3.8.2, and the stability law 2.6.1, the following theorem follows immediately.

3.8.3. a) *If* $\mathfrak{P}$ *is any formula and* $\mathfrak{Q}$ *is the adjoint formula of* $\mathfrak{P}$, *then*

$$\tilde{\forall}(\mathfrak{P} \equiv \mathfrak{Q}).$$

b) *If* $\mathfrak{P}$ *is any closed formula and* $\mathfrak{Q}$ *is the adjoint formula of* $\mathfrak{P}$, *then* $\mathfrak{Q}$ *is a closed formula not containing variables of type* B, *and*

$$\mathfrak{P} \equiv \mathfrak{Q}.$$

In the sequel we shall often use this theorem for automatically obtaining theorems about F-numbers from certain theorems about duplexes.

3.9. A central role in the sequel will be played by the concept of FR-number (duplex), and the concept of F-number will play a secondary role. This assignment of roles is connected with the following facts.

The condition characterizing the concept of duplex is expressed by a normal formula. Hence if some word in the alphabet $Ч_3$ is presented and we assume that it is a duplex, then for the justification of this assumption it suffices to produce a proof of a certain proposition not containing the logical connectives $\exists$ and $\vee$.

The situation is different with the concept of F-number. The constructive reinterpretation of the condition characterizing the concept of F-number is given by a formula of the form $\exists \phi_{0,1} \mathfrak{N}$, where $\mathfrak{N}$ is a normal formula (see §3.5). Therefore, if some word H in the alphabet $Ч_3$ is presented and we assume that it is an F-number, then for the justification of this assumption it is necessary, first of all, to solve a constructive problem: to find by means of a creative search an algorithm in the alphabet $Ч_0^{sa}$ satisfying the condition $\mathbf{F}_H^{c}{}^{3,1} \ulcorner \mathfrak{N} \urcorner$, or at least to find a method for a potentially realizable construction of such an algorithm. Thus the logical structure of the condition characterizing F-numbers is fundamentally more complicated than the logical structure of the condition characterizing duplexes.

Now we shall compare duplexes and F-numbers from the point of view of computational mathematics, i.e. we consider them as the initially given objects for the application of various algorithms.

Every word which is a duplex contains within itself a definite F-number and very important additional information — a transcription of a regulator of convergence in itself of the sequence of rational numbers corresponding to this F-number.

On the other hand, when it is asserted about some word $c_{3,1}$ that it is an F-number, then it is assumed that there is information about one of the regulators of convergence in itself of the sequence of rational numbers corresponding to the given F-number. But this information is not contained in the word $c_{3,1}$. Thus any duplex is significantly richer in information than the F-number which is the principal part of the given duplex. This fact is very important, since in many cases it turns out that an algorithm transforming duplexes into duplexes and possessing a given property is potentially realizable, but an algorithm transforming F-numbers into F-numbers and possessing an analogous property is impossible.

Thus considerations of a logical nature and considerations connected with computational mathematics induce us to choose as the basic concept of the theory of constructive real numbers the concept of duplex and not the concept of F-number. At the same time it is necessary to mention that the concept of F-number is also of some interest. Because of the theorems proved in §3.8, there is no necessity to present the theory of F-numbers independently. To obtain many theorems about F-numbers one can use Theorem 3.8.3 and the opportunity it offers of translating statements about duplexes into statements about F-numbers. To make this translation simple, it is convenient (when possible) to formulate the definitions of certain predicates first for F-numbers and then to extend them to duplexes by using the algorithm $\overline{\text{prin}}_3$. In the sequel we shall use (when possible) this method of defining predicates.

§4. ORDER RELATIONS BETWEEN CONSTRUCTIVE REAL NUMBERS

4.1. We shall say that an *F-number r is equal to an F-number s*, and we shall write $(r =_{\text{B}} s)$, if

$$\forall k \exists l \forall m (m \geqslant l \supset M(\underset{\sim}{s}(m) - \underset{\sim}{r}(m)) < 2^{-k}). \tag{1}$$

We shall say that an *F-number r majorizes an F-number s*, and we shall write $(r \geq_{\text{B}} s)$, if

$$\forall k \exists l \forall m (m \geqslant l \supset \underset{\sim}{s}(m) - \underset{\sim}{r}(m) < 2^{-k}). \tag{2}$$

We shall say that an *F-number r is majorized by an F-number s*, and we shall write $(r \leq_{\text{B}} s)$, if

$$\forall k \exists l \forall m (m \geqslant l \supset \underset{\sim}{r}(m) - \underset{\sim}{s}(m) < 2^{-k}). \tag{3}$$

We shall say that an *F-number r is different from an F-number s*, and we shall write $(r \neq_{\text{B}} s)$, if

$$\exists kl \forall m (m \geqslant l \supset M(\underset{\sim}{s}(m) - \underset{\sim}{r}(m)) \geqslant 2^{-k}). \tag{4}$$

We shall say that an *F-number r is less than an F-number s*, and we shall write $(r <_B s)$, if

$$\exists kl \forall m (m \geqslant l \supset \underset{\sim}{s}(m) - \underset{\sim}{r}(m) \geqslant 2^{-k}). \tag{5}$$

We shall say that an *F-number r is greater than an F-number s*, and we shall write $(r >_B s)$, if

$$\exists kl \forall m (m \geqslant l \supset \underset{\sim}{r}(m) - \underset{\sim}{s}(m) \geqslant 2^{-k}). \tag{6}$$

Remark. These definitions remain meaningful if, instead of F-numbers r and s, we substitute arbitrary words $c_{3,1}$ and $c_{3,2}$ in the alphabet $Ч_3$ such that $\underline{c_{3,1}} \in (\mathrm{H} \to \mathrm{D})_2$ and $\underline{c_{3,2}} \in (\mathrm{H} \to \mathrm{D})_2$. This extension of the definitions formulated above turns out to be convenient in dealing with certain concepts which are generalizations of the concept of F-number.

All the definitions formulated just now imitate corresponding definitions of the theory of Méray and Cantor. The essential difference from the Méray–Cantor theory consists in the fact that, in the theory of constructive real numbers, it is necessary to understand conditions (1)–(6) in accordance with the principles of the constructive interpretation of mathematical propositions and conditions.

Formulas (4), (5), and (6) are completely regular formulas and the constructive problems connected with conditions (4), (5), and (6) are immediately clear from the form of these conditions.

Formulas (1), (2), and (3) are not regular formulas. Applying to them the algorithm for exhibiting constructive problems and using 2.4.3, we obtain the formulas

$$\exists \Phi_{0,1} (\Phi_{0,1} \in (\mathrm{H} \to \mathrm{H})_0 \mathbin{\&} \forall km (m \geqslant \Phi_{0,1}(k) \supset M(\underset{\sim}{s}(m) - \underset{\sim}{r}(m)) < 2^{-k})), \tag{1a}$$

$$\exists \Phi_{0,1} (\Phi_{0,1} \in (\mathrm{H} \to \mathrm{H})_0 \mathbin{\&} \forall km (m \geqslant \Phi_{0,1}(k) \supset \underset{\sim}{s}(m) - \underset{\sim}{r}(m) < 2^{-k})), \tag{2a}$$

$$\exists \Phi_{0,1} (\Phi_{0,1} \in (\mathrm{H} \to \mathrm{H})_0 \mathbin{\&} \forall km (m \geqslant \Phi_{0,1}(k) \supset \underset{\sim}{r}(m) - \underset{\sim}{s}(m) < 2^{-k})). \tag{3a}$$

These formulas can be considered constructive reformulations of the formulas (1), (2), and (3), respectively. Using the restricted variable f introduced in §1.11, we construct the formulas

$$\exists f_1 \forall km (m \geqslant f_1(k) \supset M(\underset{\sim}{s}(m) - \underset{\sim}{r}(m)) < 2^{-k}), \tag{1b}$$

$$\exists f_1 \forall km (m \geqslant f_1(k) \supset \underset{\sim}{s}(m) - \underset{\sim}{r}(m) < 2^{-k}), \tag{2b}$$

$$\exists f_1 \forall km (m \geqslant f_1(k) \supset \underset{\sim}{r}(m) - \underset{\sim}{s}(m) < 2^{-k}). \tag{3b}$$

The formulas (1b), (2b), and (3b) are equivalent, respectively, to the formulas (1a), (2a), and (3a), and one can also consider them constructive reformulations of the formulas (1), (2), and (3), respectively.

The following propositions are obvious.

4.1.1. *For any F-numbers r and s,*

$$r \underset{\mathrm{B}}{\leqslant} s \equiv s \underset{\mathrm{B}}{\geqslant} r, \qquad r \underset{\mathrm{B}}{>} s \equiv s \underset{\mathrm{B}}{<} r.$$

4.1.2. *For any rational numbers* a *and* b,

$$a \underset{\mathrm{B}}{=} b \equiv a \underset{\mathrm{p}}{=} b, \qquad a \underset{\mathrm{B}}{\geqslant} b \equiv a \underset{\mathrm{p}}{\geqslant} b, \qquad a \underset{\mathrm{B}}{\leqslant} b \equiv a \underset{\mathrm{p}}{\leqslant} b,$$

$$a \underset{\mathrm{B}}{\neq} b \equiv a \underset{\mathrm{p}}{\neq} b, \qquad a \underset{\mathrm{B}}{<} b \equiv a \underset{\mathrm{p}}{<} b, \qquad a \underset{\mathrm{B}}{>} b \equiv a \underset{\mathrm{p}}{>} b.$$

4.2. Now we shall extend the relations $=_{\mathrm{B}}, \geq_{\mathrm{B}}, \leq_{\mathrm{B}}, \neq_{\mathrm{B}}, <_{\mathrm{B}}, >_{\mathrm{B}}$ to duplexes. The extension will be carried out in such a way that the conditions characterizing the relations between duplexes introduced below will be obtained from the conditions characterizing these relations between F-numbers by substituting variables of type Д for free occurrences of variables of type В. Thus, for the relations between duplexes introduced below, we can, without risk of ambiguity, use the same notation which was assigned to the corresponding relations between F-numbers.

Let W be one of the symbols $=_{\mathrm{B}}, \geq_{\mathrm{B}}, \leq_{\mathrm{B}}, \neq_{\mathrm{B}}, <_{\mathrm{B}}, >_{\mathrm{B}}$. We shall say that a *duplex x is in the relation W to the duplex y*, and we shall write (xWy), if $(\overline{\mathrm{prin}_3}(x)\ W\ \overline{\mathrm{prin}_3}(y))$.

We extend the reading of the formulas $(r =_{\mathrm{B}} s)$, $(r \geq_{\mathrm{B}} s)$, $(r \leq_{\mathrm{B}} s)$, $(r \neq_{\mathrm{B}} s)$, $(r <_{\mathrm{B}} s)$, $(r >_{\mathrm{B}} s)$ to the formulas $(x =_{\mathrm{B}} y)$, $(x \geq_{\mathrm{B}} y)$, $(x \leq_{\mathrm{B}} y)$, $(x \neq_{\mathrm{B}} y)$, $(x <_{\mathrm{B}} y)$, $(x >_{\mathrm{B}} y)$, respectively.

Generalizing the definitions introduced above with respect to any two words $\mathrm{c}_{3,1}$ and $\mathrm{c}_{3,2}$ in the alphabet Ч$_3$ such that $\underline{\mathrm{c}_{3,1}} \in (\mathrm{H} \rightarrow \mathrm{p})_2$ and $\underline{\mathrm{c}_{3,2}} \in (\mathrm{H} \rightarrow \mathrm{p})_2$, we agree to write $(\mathrm{c}_{3,1}\ W\ \mathrm{c}_{3,2})$, if $(\overline{\mathrm{prin}_3}(\mathrm{c}_{3,1})\ W\ \overline{\mathrm{prin}_3}(\mathrm{c}_{3,2}))$ (cf. the remark in §4.1).

From the obvious proposition

$$\forall xm\ (\underline{\overline{\mathrm{prin}_3}(x)}(m) \underset{\mathrm{p}}{=} \underline{x}(m))$$

and from the contents of §4.1, the following propositions 4.2.1–4.2.6 are direct consequences.

4.2.1. *The condition* $(x =_{\mathrm{B}} y)$ *is characterized by each of the formulas*

$$\forall k \exists l \forall m (m \geqslant l \supset M(\underline{y}(m) - \underline{x}(m)) < 2^{-k}), \tag{1}$$

$$\exists \phi_{0,1} (\phi_{0,1} \in (\text{н} \to \text{н})_0 \,\&\, \forall km (m \geqslant \phi_{0,1}(k) \supset M(\underline{y}(m) - \underline{x}(m)) < 2^{-k})), \tag{1a}$$

$$\exists f_1 \forall km (m \geqslant f_1(k) \supset M(\underline{y}(m) - \underline{x}(m)) < 2^{-k}). \tag{1b}$$

4.2.2. *The condition* $(x \geq_B y)$ *is characterized by each of the formulas*

$$\forall k \exists l \forall m (m \geqslant l \supset \underline{y}(m) - \underline{x}(m) < 2^{-k}), \tag{2}$$

$$\exists \phi_{0,1} (\phi_{0,1} \in (\text{н} \to \text{н})_0 \,\&\, \forall km (m \geqslant \phi_{0,1}(k) \supset \underline{y}(m) - \underline{x}(m) < 2^{-k})), \tag{2a}$$

$$\exists f_1 \forall km (m \geqslant f_1(k) \supset \underline{y}(m) - \underline{x}(m) < 2^{-k}). \tag{2b}$$

4.2.3. *The condition* $(x \leq_B y)$ *is characterized by each of the formulas*

$$\forall k \exists l \forall m (m \geqslant l \supset \underline{x}(m) - \underline{y}(m) < 2^{-k}), \tag{3}$$

$$\exists \phi_{0,1} (\phi_{0,1} \in (\text{н} \to \text{н})_0 \,\&\, \forall km (m \geqslant \phi_{0,1}(k) \supset \underline{x}(m) - \underline{y}(m) < 2^{-k})), \tag{3a}$$

$$\exists f_1 \forall km (m \geqslant f_1(k) \supset \underline{x}(m) - \underline{y}(m) < 2^{-k}). \tag{3b}$$

4.2.4. *The condition* $(x \neq_B y)$ *is characterized by the formula*

$$\exists kl \forall m (m \geqslant l \supset M(\underline{y}(m) - \underline{x}(m)) \geqslant 2^{-k}). \tag{4}$$

4.2.5. *The condition* $(x <_B y)$ *is characterized by the formula*

$$\exists kl \forall m (m \geqslant l \supset \underline{y}(m) - \underline{x}(m) \geqslant 2^{-k}). \tag{5}$$

4.2.6. *The condition* $(x >_B y)$ *is characterized by the formula*

$$\exists kl \forall m (m \geqslant l \supset \underline{x}(m) - \underline{y}(m) \geqslant 2^{-k}). \tag{6}$$

The following proposition is also obvious.

4.2.7. *For any duplexes* x *and* y,

$$x \underset{B}{\leqslant} y \equiv y \underset{B}{\geqslant} x, \qquad x \underset{B}{>} y \equiv y \underset{B}{<} x.$$

4.3. We shall assign to the symbols $=_B$, $\geq_B$, $\leq_B$, $\neq_B$, $<_B$, $>_B$ the rank 3.

To simplify the writing of formulas we shall permit replacement of these symbols by the symbols $=$, $\geq$, $\leq$, $\neq$, $<$, $>$, respectively, in those places in formulas and in the text where such a replacement does not lead to ambiguity.

Replacing in any formula some occurrence of the symbol $=_B$ by the symbol $=$, we obtain an abbreviation of the original formula. It can turn out that possible values of the terms to the left and to the right of the occurrence of the symbol $=$ arising from this replacement are words in the alphabet Ч$_2$ (one can be led to this conclusion, for example, by considering the structure of the indicated terms). In this case we can also interpret the symbol $=_B$ and as an abbreviation of the symbol $=_\text{Ч}$ (see §1.12). However, on the basis of the result formulated in

4.1.2, the two interpretations of the symbol $=$ lead to equivalent formulas. If these two formulas can be considered in the given context as mutually interchangeable, then the replacement of the symbol $=_B$ by the symbol $=$ does not lead to ambiguity. The same thing can be repeated with respect to the symbols $\geq_B$, $\leq_B$, $\neq_B$, $<_B$, $>_B$.

4.4. The following theorem will play an important role in the sequel.

4.4.1. *For any duplexes x and y,*

$$(x=y)\equiv\forall n(M(\underline{y}(\overline{y}(n+1))-\underline{x}(\overline{x}(n+1)))\leqslant 2^{-n}), \tag{a}$$

$$(x\geqslant y)\equiv\forall n(\underline{y}(\overline{y}(n+1))-\underline{x}(\overline{x}(n+1))\leqslant 2^{-n}), \tag{b}$$

$$(x\leqslant y)\equiv\forall n(\underline{x}(\overline{x}(n+1))-\underline{y}(\overline{y}(n+1))\leqslant 2^{-n}), \tag{c}$$

$$(x\neq y)\equiv\exists n(M(\underline{y}(\overline{y}(n+1))-\underline{x}(\overline{x}(n+1)))>2^{-n}), \tag{d}$$

$$(x<y)\equiv\exists n(\underline{y}(\overline{y}(n+1))-\underline{x}(\overline{x}(n+1))>2^{-n}), \tag{e}$$

$$(x>y)\equiv\exists n(\underline{x}(\overline{x}(n+1))-\underline{y}(\overline{y}(n+1))>2^{-n}). \tag{f}$$

For the sake of brevity we introduce an algorithm $\mathfrak{L}$ in the alphabet $Ч_3^{sa}$ such that, for any words $c_{3,1}$, $c_{3,2}$ and $c_{0,1}$, the condition

$$\mathfrak{L}(c_{3,1}\square c_{3,2}\square c_{0,1})\simeq\underline{c_{3,2}}(\overline{c_{3,2}}(c_{0,1}+1))-\underline{c_{3,1}}(\overline{c_{3,1}}(c_{0,1}+1)).$$

is fulfilled.

Let us denote by $\mathfrak{L}^*$ the normal composition of the algorithms $\mathfrak{L}$ and M_p, constructed as an algorithm in the alphabet $Ч_3^{sa}$. We have

$$\forall xyn(\mathfrak{L}(x\square y\square n)\doteq\underline{y}(\overline{y}(n+1))-\underline{x}(\overline{x}(n+1))),$$

$$\forall xyn(\mathfrak{L}^*(x\square y\square n)\doteq\underset{p}{M}(\underline{y}(\overline{y}(n+1))-\underline{x}(\overline{x}(n+1)))).$$

Using $\mathfrak{L}$ and $\mathfrak{L}^*$, we can rewrite 4.4.1 in the following form:

$$\forall xy((x=y)\equiv\forall n(\mathfrak{L}^*(x\square y\square n)\leqslant 2^{-n})), \tag{1}$$

$$\forall xy((x\geqslant y)\equiv\forall n(\mathfrak{L}(x\square y\square n)\leqslant 2^{-n})), \tag{2}$$

$$\forall xy((x\leqslant y)\equiv\forall n(\mathfrak{L}(y\square x\square n)\leqslant 2^{-n})), \tag{3}$$

$$\forall xy((x\neq y)\equiv\exists n(\mathfrak{L}^*(x\square y\square n)>2^{-n})), \tag{4}$$

$$\forall xy((x<y)\equiv\exists n(\mathfrak{L}(x\square y\square n)>2^{-n})), \tag{5}$$

$$\forall xy((x>y)\equiv\exists n(\mathfrak{L}(y\square x\square n)>2^{-n})). \tag{6}$$

Proof of Theorem 4.4.1. Let us prove assertion (1). One can give a rather short proof of assertion (1), using from the very beginning methods of logical inference of constructive logic. However, we shall construct the proof in a different way. First we apply to (1) the algorithm for exhibiting constructive problems and we formulate in a precise way the constructive problem which it is necessary to solve for the justification of assertion (1). Then we construct a certain algorithm $\mathfrak{Z}$ and we prove that $\mathfrak{Z}$ is a solution of the constructive problem connected with assertion (1). The proof of this last assertion will be carried out by means of methods of logical inference taken from only that part of the theory of logical inference in which one deals with formulas not containing the logical connectives $\exists$ and $\vee$.

The proof of assertion (1) presented below contains a good illustration of the theory of the construction interpretation of mathematical propositions and can also serve as an example of a certain method of proving theorems of constructive mathematical analysis.

The carrying out of the constructive reformulation of formula (1) leads sucessively to the following formulas (7), (8), (9), (10):

$$\forall xy\,((\exists f_1 \mathfrak{M} \supset \mathfrak{N})\,\&\,(\mathfrak{N} \supset \exists f_1 \mathfrak{M})), \tag{7}$$

where

$$\mathfrak{M} \leftrightharpoons \forall km\,(m \geqslant f_1(k) \supset M(\underline{y}(m) - \underline{x}(m)) < 2^{-k}),$$
$$\mathfrak{N} \leftrightharpoons \forall n\,(\mathfrak{L}^*(x \,\square\, y \,\square\, n) \leqslant 2^{-n});$$
$$\forall xy\,(\forall f_1(\mathfrak{M} \supset \mathfrak{N})\,\&\,\exists \phi_{0,1}(\mathfrak{N} \supset \mathfrak{K})), \tag{8}$$

where

$$\mathfrak{K} \leftrightharpoons \phi_{0,1}(\Lambda) \overset{!}{\in} \mathrm{c}_0 \,\&\, \langle \phi_{0,1}(\Lambda) \rangle_0 \in (\mathrm{H} \to \mathrm{H})_0 \,\&\, \mathbf{F}^{f_1}_{\langle \phi_{0,1}(\Lambda) \rangle_0} \llcorner \mathfrak{M} \lrcorner;$$
$$\forall xy \exists \phi_{0,1}(\forall f_1(\mathfrak{M} \supset \mathfrak{N})\,\&\,(\mathfrak{N} \supset \mathfrak{K})); \tag{9}$$
$$\exists \phi_{3,1} \mathfrak{F}, \tag{10}$$

where

$$\mathfrak{F} \leftrightharpoons \forall xy\,(\phi_{3,1}(x \,\square\, y) \overset{+}{\in} \mathrm{c}_0 \,\&\, \forall f_1(\mathfrak{M} \supset \mathfrak{N})\,\&\,(\mathfrak{N} \supset \mathbf{F}^{\phi_{0,1}}_{\langle \phi_{3,1}(x \square y) \rangle_0} \llcorner \mathfrak{K} \lrcorner)).$$

Formula (10) is the result of the constructive reformulation of formula (1). Hence for the proof of (1) it is necessary to construct an algorithm in the alphabet Ч_3^{sa} satisfying condition $\mathfrak{F}$.

Let us construct, first of all, an algorithm $\mathfrak{P}$ in the alphabet Ч_3^{sa} such that

$$\forall \mathrm{c}_{3,1}\,\mathrm{c}_{3,2}\,\mathrm{c}_{0,1}\,(\mathfrak{P}(\mathrm{c}_{3,1} \,\square\, \mathrm{c}_{3,2} \,\square\, \mathrm{c}_{0,1}) \simeq \max(\overline{\mathrm{c}_{3,1}}(\mathrm{c}_{0,1} \dotplus 2) \,\square\, \overline{\mathrm{c}_{3,2}}(\mathrm{c}_{0,1} \dotplus 2))) \tag{11}$$

(cf. 2.1.1). Further, basing ourselves on 2.1.3 and (11), we construct, starting from $\mathfrak{P}$, an algorithm $\mathfrak{Q}$ in the alphabet Ч_3^{sa} such that, first,

$$\forall \mathrm{c}_{3,1}\,\mathrm{c}_{3,2}\,(\mathfrak{Q}(\mathrm{c}_{3,1} \,\square\, \mathrm{c}_{3,2}) \overset{+}{\in} \mathrm{c}_0) \tag{12}$$

and second

$$\forall \mathrm{c}_{3,1}\mathrm{c}_{3,2}\mathrm{c}_{0,1}(\langle\mathfrak{Q}(\mathrm{c}_{3,1}\square\mathrm{c}_{3,2})\rangle_0(\mathrm{c}_{0,1})\simeq\mathfrak{P}(\mathrm{c}_{3,1}\square\mathrm{c}_{3,2}\square\mathrm{c}_{0,1})). \tag{13}$$

Basing ourselves on 2.1.3 and (12), we construct, starting from $\mathfrak{Q}$, an algorithm $\mathfrak{Z}$ in the alphabet $Ч_3^{sa}$ such that, first,

$$\forall \mathrm{c}_{3,1}\mathrm{c}_{3,2}(\mathfrak{Z}(\mathrm{c}_{3,1}\square\mathrm{c}_{3,2})\overset{+}{\in}\mathrm{c}_0) \tag{14}$$

and second,

$$\forall \mathrm{c}_{3,1}\mathrm{c}_{3,2}(\langle\mathfrak{Z}(\mathrm{c}_{3,1}\square\mathrm{c}_{3,2})\rangle_0(\Lambda)\simeq\mathfrak{Q}(\mathrm{c}_{3,1}\square\mathrm{c}_{3,2})). \tag{15}$$

We shall prove that the algorithm $\mathfrak{Z}$ satisfies condition $\mathfrak{F}$. In other words, we shall prove that

$$\mathbf{F}_{\mathfrak{Z}}^{\Phi_{3,1}}\llcorner\mathfrak{F}\lrcorner. \tag{16}$$

Formula (16) does not contain the symbols $\exists$ and $\vee$. It is equivalent to the conjunction of the following formulas (17)–(21):

$$\forall xy(\mathfrak{Z}(x\square y)\in\mathrm{c}_0), \tag{17}$$

$$\forall xyf_1(\mathfrak{M}\supset\mathfrak{N}), \tag{18}$$

$$\forall xy(\mathfrak{N}\supset\langle\mathfrak{Z}(x\square y)\rangle_0(\Lambda)\overset{\scriptscriptstyle F}{\in}\mathrm{c}_0), \tag{19}$$

$$\forall xy(\mathfrak{N}\supset\langle\langle\mathfrak{Z}(x\square y)\rangle_0(\Lambda)\rangle_0\in(\mathrm{H}\to\mathrm{H}_0)), \tag{20}$$

$$\forall xy(\mathfrak{N}\supset\forall km(m\geqslant\langle\langle\mathfrak{Z}(x\square y)\rangle_0(\Lambda)\rangle_0(k)\supset M(\underline{y}(m)-\underline{x}(m))<2^{-k})). \tag{21}$$

Formula (17) follows from (14).

Let us prove (18). Let x and y be arbitrary duplexes and f_1 any algorithm of type $(\mathrm{H}\to\mathrm{H})_0$. Assume that

$$\forall km(m\geqslant f_1(k)\supset M(\underline{y}(m)-\underline{x}(m))<2^{-k}). \tag{22}$$

We shall prove that, under the given assumptions,

$$\forall n(\mathfrak{L}^*(x\square y\square n)\leqslant 2^{-n}). \tag{23}$$

Let n and l be any natural numbers. We introduce the notation

$$\Theta\leftrightharpoons\max(f_1(l)\square\overline{x}(n+1)\square\overline{y}(n+1)).$$

We have

$$\Theta\geqslant f_1(l),\quad \Theta\geqslant\overline{x}(n+1),\quad \Theta\geqslant\overline{y}(n+1). \tag{24}$$

From (24) and (22) it follows that

$$\mathfrak{L}^*(x\square y\square n)\leqslant M(\underline{y}(\overline{y}(n+1))-\underline{y}(\Theta))+M(\underline{y}(\Theta)-\underline{x}(\Theta))$$
$$+M(\underline{x}(\Theta)-\underline{x}(\overline{x}(n+1)))<2^{-(n+1)}+2^{-l}+2^{-(n+1)}=2^{-n}+2^{-l}.$$

Therefore

$$\forall nl(\mathfrak{L}^*(x\square y\square n)<2^{-n}+2^{-l}),$$

$$\forall nl(\mathfrak{L}^*(x\square y\square n)-2^{-n}<2^{-l}). \tag{25}$$

Applying to (25) Theorem 1.15.1, we obtain

$$\forall n(\mathfrak{L}^*(x \square y \square n) - 2^{-n} \leqslant 0).$$

Hence (23) holds. Proposition (18) has been proved.

From (12) and (15) it follows that

$$\forall xy(\langle 3(x \square y)\rangle_0(\Lambda) \stackrel{+}{\in} c_0).$$

Hence (19) holds.

From (11), (13) and (15) it follows that

$$\forall xyk(\langle\langle 3(x \square y)\rangle_0(\Lambda)\rangle_0(k) \stackrel{+}{\in} \underline{\text{nat}}).$$

Hence

$$\forall xy(\langle\langle 3(x \square y)\rangle_0(\Lambda)\rangle_0 \in (\text{H} \to \text{H})_0).$$

From this, proposition (20) follows.

Let us prove proposition (21). From (13) and (15) it follows that formula (21) is equivalent to the formula

$$\forall xy(\mathfrak{N} \supset \forall km(m \geqslant \mathfrak{P}(x \square y \square k) \supset M(\underline{y}(m) - \underline{x}(m)) < 2^{-k})). \quad (26)$$

This formula in turn is equivalent to

$$\forall xykm(\mathfrak{N} \supset (m \geqslant \mathfrak{P}(x \square y \square k) \supset M(\underline{y}(m) - \underline{x}(m)) < 2^{-k})). \quad (27)$$

Let x and y be any duplexes, and k and m any natural numbers. Assume that

$$\forall n(\mathfrak{L}^*(x \square y \square n) \leqslant 2^{-n}) \quad (28)$$

and

$$m \geqslant \mathfrak{P}(x \square y \square k). \quad (29)$$

Let us prove that, under the given assumptions,

$$M(\underline{y}(m) - \underline{x}(m)) < 2^{-k}. \quad (30)$$

From (29) and (11) it follows that

$$m \geqslant \overline{x}(k+2), \qquad m \geqslant \overline{y}(k+2). \quad (31)$$

From (31) and (28) it follows that

$$M(\underline{y}(m) - \underline{x}(m)) \leqslant M(\underline{y}(m) - \underline{y}(\overline{y}(k+2)))$$
$$+ M(\underline{y}(\overline{y}(k+2)) - \underline{x}(\overline{x}(k+2))) + M(\underline{x}(\overline{x}(k+2)) - \underline{x}(m)) < 2^{-(k+2)}$$
$$+ 2^{-(k+1)} + 2^{-(k+2)} = 2^{-k}.$$

Hence (30) holds. Proposition (27) has been proved. From (27), (21) follows.

Thus the proof of proposition (16) has been completed. Hence proposition (10) has been proved, and, at the same time, proposition (1).

If in the proof of proposition (1) we replace the formula $(x = y)$ by the formula

$(x \geq y)$, cancel all occurrences of the functor M and replace the functor $\mathfrak{L}^*$ by the functor $\mathfrak{L}$ at all places where $\mathfrak{L}^*$ occurs, we obtain a proof of proposition (2).

Proposition (3) follows from 4.2.7 and proposition (2).

Let us prove proposition (4). We begin the proof by applying to formula (4) the algorithm for exhibiting constructive problems.

Choosing this method of proof, we are guided by the same considerations of a methodological nature as for the choice of the method of proof of proposition (1).

The process of constructive reformulation of formula (4) produces in succession the following formulas (32)–(35):

$$\forall xy\,((\exists\, kl\, \mathfrak{B} \supset \exists\, n\, \mathfrak{W})\,\&\,(\exists\, n\, \mathfrak{W} \supset \exists\, kl\, \mathfrak{B})), \tag{32}$$

where

$$\mathfrak{B} \leftrightharpoons \forall m\,(m \geqslant l \supset M(\underline{y}(m) - \underline{x}(m)) \geqslant 2^{-k}),$$
$$\mathfrak{W} \leftrightharpoons (\mathfrak{L}^*(x \,\Box\, y \,\Box\, n) > 2^{-n});$$
$$\forall xy\,(\exists\, \Phi_{0,1}\, \mathfrak{A}\,\&\,\exists\, \Phi_{0,2}\Phi_{0,3}\, \mathfrak{R}), \tag{33}$$

where

$$\mathfrak{A} \leftrightharpoons \forall\, kl\,(\mathfrak{B} \supset \Phi_{0,1}(k \,\Box\, l) \overset{+}{\in} \underline{\text{nat}}\,\&\,\mathbf{F}^{n}_{\Phi_{0,1}(k\Box l)\llcorner}\mathfrak{W}_{\lrcorner}),$$
$$\mathfrak{R} \leftrightharpoons \forall\, n\,(\mathfrak{W} \supset \Phi_{0,2}(n) \overset{+}{\in} \underline{\text{nat}}\,\&\,\Phi_{0,3}(n) \overset{+}{\in} \underline{\text{nat}}\,\&\,\mathbf{F}^{k,\ \ l}_{\Phi_{0,2}(n),\ \Phi_{0,3}(n)\llcorner}\mathfrak{B}_{\lrcorner});$$
$$\forall\, xy\, \exists\, \Phi_{0,1}\Phi_{0,2}\Phi_{0,3}(\mathfrak{A}\,\&\,\mathfrak{R}); \tag{34}$$
$$\exists\, \Phi_{3,1}\Phi_{3,2}\Phi_{3,3}\, \mathfrak{T}, \tag{35}$$

where

$$\mathfrak{T} \leftrightharpoons \forall\, xy\,(\Phi_{3,1}(x \,\Box\, y) \overset{+}{\in} c_0\,\&\,\Phi_{3,2}(x \,\Box\, y) \overset{+}{\in} c_0\,\&\,\Phi_{3,3}(x \,\Box\, y) \overset{+}{\in} c_0$$
$$\&\,\mathbf{F}^{\Phi_{0,1},\ \ \Phi_{0,2},\ \ \Phi_{0,3}}_{\langle \Phi_{3,1}(x\Box y)\rangle_0,\ \langle \Phi_{3,2}(x\Box y)\rangle_0,\ \langle \Phi_{3,3}(x\Box y)\rangle_0\llcorner}(\mathfrak{A}\,\&\,\mathfrak{R})_{\lrcorner}).$$

Formula (35) is the result of the constructive reformulation of formula (4). Hence for a proof of (4) it is necessary to construct three algorithms in the alphabet Ч_3^{sa} satisfying condition $\mathfrak{T}$ (condition $\mathfrak{T}$ has three parameters: $\Phi_{3,1}$, $\Phi_{3,2}$, $\Phi_{3,3}$).

First of all, let us construct an algorithm $\mathfrak{P}_1$ in the alphabet Ч_3^{sa} such that

$$\forall c_{3,1}c_{3,2}c_{0,1}c_{0,2}\,(\mathfrak{P}_1(c_{3,1} \,\Box\, c_{3,2} \,\Box\, c_{0,1} \,\Box\, c_{0,2}) \simeq c_{0,1} + 1), \tag{36}$$

and, basing ourselves on 2.1.3, we construct, starting from $\mathfrak{P}_1$, an algorithm $\mathfrak{Q}_1$ in the alphabet Ч_3^{sa} such that, first,

$$\forall\, c_{3,1}c_{3,2}\,(\mathfrak{Q}_1(c_{3,1} \,\Box\, c_{3,2}) \overset{+}{\in} c_0) \tag{37}$$

and second,

$$\forall \mathfrak{c}_{3,1} \mathfrak{c}_{3,2} (\langle \mathfrak{Q}_1 (\mathfrak{c}_{3,1} \square \mathfrak{c}_{3,2}) \rangle_0 (\mathfrak{c}_{0,1} \square \mathfrak{c}_{0,2}) \simeq \mathfrak{P}_1 (\mathfrak{c}_{3,1} \square \mathfrak{c}_{3,2} \square \mathfrak{c}_{0,1} \square \mathfrak{c}_{0,2})). \quad (38)$$

Further, we construct an algorithm $\mathfrak{D}$ in the alphabet $Ч_2^{sa}$ such that

$$\forall a (a > 0 \supset \mathfrak{D}(a) \overset{+}{\in} \underline{\mathrm{nat}} \;\&\; a \geqslant 2^{-\mathfrak{D}(a)}). \quad (39)$$

We construct an algorithm $\mathfrak{P}_2$ in the alphabet $Ч_3^{sa}$ such that

$$\forall \mathfrak{c}_{3,1} \mathfrak{c}_{3,2} \mathfrak{c}_{0,1} (\mathfrak{P}_2 (\mathfrak{c}_{3,1} \square \mathfrak{c}_{3,2} \square \mathfrak{c}_{0,1}) \simeq \mathfrak{D}(\mathfrak{L}^* (\mathfrak{c}_{3,1} \square \mathfrak{c}_{3,2} \square \mathfrak{c}_{0,1}) - 2^{-\mathfrak{c}_{0,1}})). \quad (40)$$

From (39) and (40) it follows that

$$\forall xyn (\mathfrak{L}^* (x \square y \square n) > 2^{-n} \supset \mathfrak{P}_2 (x \square y \square n) \overset{+}{\in} \underline{\mathrm{nat}}$$
$$\& \; \mathfrak{L}^* (x \square y \square n) \geqslant 2^{-n} + 2^{-\mathfrak{P}_2 (x \square y \square n)}). \quad (41)$$

Basing ourselves on 2.1.3 and (40), we construct, starting from $\mathfrak{P}_2$, an algorithm $\mathfrak{Q}_2$ in the alphabet $Ч_3^{sa}$ such that, first,

$$\forall \mathfrak{c}_{3,1} \mathfrak{c}_{3,2} (\mathfrak{Q}_2 (\mathfrak{c}_{3,1} \square \mathfrak{c}_{3,2}) \overset{+}{\in} \mathfrak{c}_0) \quad (42)$$

and second,

$$\forall \mathfrak{c}_{3,1} \mathfrak{c}_{3,2} \mathfrak{c}_{0,1} (\langle \mathfrak{Q}_2 (\mathfrak{c}_{3,1} \square \mathfrak{c}_{3,2}) \rangle_0 (\mathfrak{c}_{0,1}) \simeq \mathfrak{P}_2 (\mathfrak{c}_{3,1} \square \mathfrak{c}_{3,2} \square \mathfrak{c}_{0,1})). \quad (43)$$

In addition, we construct an algorithm $\mathfrak{P}_3$ in the alphabet $Ч_3^{sa}$ such that

$$\forall \mathfrak{c}_{3,1} \mathfrak{c}_{3,2} \mathfrak{c}_{0,1} (\mathfrak{P}_3 (\mathfrak{c}_{3,1} \square \mathfrak{c}_{3,2} \square \mathfrak{c}_{0,1})$$
$$\simeq \max (\overline{\mathfrak{c}_{3,1}} (\mathfrak{c}_{0,1} + 1) \square \overline{\mathfrak{c}_{3,2}} (\mathfrak{c}_{0,1} + 1))). \quad (44)$$

Basing ourselves on 2.1.3 and (44), we construct, starting from $\mathfrak{P}_3$, an algorithm $\mathfrak{Q}_3$ in the alphabet $Ч_3^{sa}$ such that, first,

$$\forall \mathfrak{c}_{3,1} \mathfrak{c}_{3,2} (\mathfrak{Q}_3 (\mathfrak{c}_{3,1} \square \mathfrak{c}_{3,2}) \overset{+}{\in} \mathfrak{c}_0) \quad (45)$$

and second,

$$\forall \mathfrak{c}_{3,1} \mathfrak{c}_{3,2} \mathfrak{c}_{0,1} (\langle \mathfrak{Q}_3 (\mathfrak{c}_{3,1} \square \mathfrak{c}_{3,2}) \rangle_0 (\mathfrak{c}_{0,1}) \simeq \mathfrak{P}_3 (\mathfrak{c}_{3,1} \square \mathfrak{c}_{3,2} \square \mathfrak{c}_{0,1})). \quad (46)$$

Let us prove that the three algorithms $\mathfrak{Q}_1$, $\mathfrak{Q}_2$, $\mathfrak{Q}_3$ form a solution of the constructive problem in which we are interested. In other words, let us prove that

$$\mathbf{F}^{\Phi_{3,1}, \Phi_{3,2}, \Phi_{3,3}}_{\mathfrak{Q}_1, \mathfrak{Q}_2, \mathfrak{Q}_3} \llcorner \mathfrak{T} \lrcorner. \quad (47)$$

Formula (47) does not contain the symbols $\exists$ and $\vee$. It is equivalent to the conjunction of the following formulas (48)–(55):

$$\forall xy (\mathfrak{Q}_1 (x \square y) \overset{+}{\in} \mathfrak{c}_0), \quad (48)$$
$$\forall xy (\mathfrak{Q}_2 (x \square y) \overset{+}{\in} \mathfrak{c}_0), \quad (49)$$
$$\forall xy (\mathfrak{Q}_3 (x \square y) \overset{+}{\in} \mathfrak{c}_0), \quad (50)$$
$$\forall xykl (\mathfrak{B} \supset \Gamma_1 \overset{+}{\in} \underline{\mathrm{nat}}), \quad (51)$$
$$\forall xykl (\mathfrak{B} \supset \mathfrak{L}^* (x \square y \square \Gamma_1) > 2^{-\Gamma_1}), \quad (52)$$

$$\forall xyn\,(\mathfrak{W} \supset \Gamma_2 \overset{+}{\in} \underline{\text{nat}}), \qquad (53)$$

$$\forall xyn\,(\mathfrak{W} \supset \Gamma_3 \overset{+}{\in} \underline{\text{nat}}), \qquad (54)$$

$$\forall xyn\,(\mathfrak{W} \supset \forall m\,(m \geqslant \Gamma_3 \supset M(\underline{y}(m) - \underline{x}(m)) \geqslant 2^{-\Gamma_2})). \qquad (55)$$

Here we have used the notation

$$\Gamma_1 \leftrightharpoons \langle \mathfrak{Q}_1 (x \,\square\, y)\rangle_0 (k \,\square\, l), \quad \Gamma_2 \leftrightharpoons \langle \mathfrak{Q}_2 (x \,\square\, y)\rangle_0 (n), \quad \Gamma_3 \leftrightharpoons \langle \mathfrak{Q}_3 (x \,\square\, y)\rangle_0 (n).$$

Formulas (48), (49), (50) follow, respectively, from (37), (42), (45).

From (36) and (38) it follows that

$$\forall xykl\,(\Gamma_1 \overset{+}{\in} \underline{\text{nat}}).$$

Hence (51) holds.

Let us prove (52). Assume x and y are any duplexes, and k and l are any natural numbers. Further, assume that

$$\forall m\,(m \geqslant l \supset M(\underline{y}(m) - \underline{x}(m)) \geqslant 2^{-k}). \qquad (56)$$

Let us prove that, under the given assumptions,

$$\mathfrak{L}^* (x \,\square\, y \,\square\, \Gamma_1) > 2^{-\Gamma_1}. \qquad (57)$$

From (36) and (38) it follows that $\Gamma_1 \doteq k+1$. Hence formula (57) is equivalent to the formula

$$M(\underline{y}(\overline{y}(k+2)) - \underline{x}(\overline{x}(k+2))) > 2^{-(k+1)}. \qquad (58)$$

Thus it remains to prove (58).

We introduce an algorithm $\mathfrak{S}$ in the alphabet $Ч_2^{sa}$, applicable to any word in the alphabet $Ч_2$ and such that

$$\forall c_{2,1}\,(\mathfrak{S}(c_{2,1}) \doteq \Lambda \equiv c_{2,1} \in \underline{\text{pos. rat.}}). \qquad (59)$$

It is obvious that

$$\forall c_{2,1}\,(\mathfrak{S}(c_{2,1}) \neq \Lambda \,\&\, c_{2,1} \in \underline{\text{rat}} \,\&\, c_{2,1} \neq 0 \supset c_{2,1} < 0). \qquad (60)$$

We introduce the notation

$$T \leftrightharpoons \max(\overline{x}(k+2) \,\square\, \overline{y}(k+2) \,\square\, l).$$

We have

$$T \geqslant \overline{x}(k+2), \quad T \geqslant \overline{y}(k+2), \quad T \geqslant l. \qquad (61)$$

From (56) and (61) it follows that

$$M(\underline{y}(T) - \underline{x}(T)) \geqslant 2^{-k}. \qquad (62)$$

Hence

$$\underline{y}(T) - \underline{x}(T) \neq 0. \qquad (63)$$

Let us assume that

$$\mathfrak{S}(\underline{y}(T)-\underline{x}(T)) \doteq \Lambda. \tag{64}$$

Then

$$\underline{y}(T)-\underline{x}(T)>0. \tag{65}$$

In addition, on the basis of (61), (65), and (62) we have

$$\underline{y}(\bar{y}(k+2))-\underline{x}(\bar{x}(k+2)) = \underline{y}(\bar{y}(k+2))-\underline{y}(T)+\underline{y}(T)-\underline{x}(T)$$
$$+\underline{x}(T)-\underline{x}(\bar{x}(k+2))>-2^{-(k+2)}+2^{-k}-2^{-(k+2)}=2^{-(k+1)}.$$

Hence

$$\mathfrak{S}(\underline{y}(T)-\underline{x}(T)) \doteq \Lambda \supset M(\underline{y}(\bar{y}(k+2))-\underline{x}(\bar{x}(k+2)))>2^{-(k+1)}. \tag{66}$$

Now let us assume that

$$\mathfrak{S}(\underline{y}(\mathrm{T})-\underline{x}(\mathrm{T})) \not\doteq \Lambda.$$

On the basis of (63) and (60) we conclude that

$$\underline{y}(T)-\underline{x}(T)<0. \tag{67}$$

In addition, on the basis of (61), (62), and (67), we have

$$\underline{x}(\bar{x}(k+2))-\underline{y}(\bar{y}(k+2)) = \underline{x}(\bar{x}(k+2))-\underline{x}(T)+\underline{x}(T)-\underline{y}(T)$$
$$+\underline{y}(T)-\underline{y}(\bar{y}(k+2))>-2^{-(k+2)}+2^{-k}-2^{-(k+2)}=2^{-(k+1)},$$
$$M(\underline{y}(\bar{y}(k+2))-\underline{x}(\bar{x}(k+2)))=\underline{x}(\bar{x}(k+2))-\underline{y}(\bar{y}(k+2)).$$

Hence

$$\mathfrak{S}(\underline{y}(T)-\underline{x}(T)) \not\doteq \Lambda \supset M(\underline{y}(\bar{y}(k+2))-\underline{x}(\bar{x}(k+2)))>2^{-(k+1)}. \tag{68}$$

From (66), (68), and the applicability of the algorithm $\mathfrak{S}$ to every word in the alphabet $Ч_2$, (58) follows. Hence (57) holds. Proposition (52) has been proved.

Formula (53) follows from (41) and (43).

From (44) and (46) it follows that $\forall xyn\ (\Gamma_3 \overset{+}{\in} \underline{\mathrm{nat}})$. Hence (54) holds.

Let us prove proposition (55). Let x and y be arbitrary duplexes and let n be any natural number such that

$$\mathfrak{L}^*(x \,\square\, y \,\square\, n)>2^{-n}. \tag{69}$$

Further, let n be any natural number such that

$$m \geqslant \Gamma_3. \tag{70}$$

Let us prove that, under the given assumptions,

$$M(\underline{y}(m)-\underline{x}(m)) \geqslant 2^{-\Gamma_2}. \tag{71}$$

From (44) and (46) it follows that

$$\Gamma_3 \doteq \max(\bar{x}(n+1) \,\square\, \bar{y}(n+1)).$$

Hence

$$m \geqslant \bar{x}(n+1), \quad m \geqslant \bar{y}(n+1). \tag{72}$$

From (69), (41) and (43) it follows that

$$\mathfrak{L}^*(x \square y \square n) \geqslant 2^{-n} + 2^{-\Gamma_2}. \tag{73}$$

Let us assume that

$$\mathfrak{S}(\underline{y}(\overline{y}(n+1)) - \underline{x}(\overline{x}(n+1))) \doteq \Lambda.$$

Then

$$\underline{y}(\overline{y}(n+1)) - \underline{x}(\overline{x}(n+1)) > 0. \tag{74}$$

In addition, on the basis of (72)–(74) we conclude that

$$\underline{y}(m) - \underline{x}(m) = \underline{y}(m) - \underline{y}(\overline{y}(n+1)) + \underline{y}(\overline{y}(n+1)) - \underline{x}(\overline{x}(n+1)) \\ + \underline{x}(\overline{x}(n+1)) - \underline{x}(m) > -2^{-(n+1)} + 2^{-n} + 2^{-\Gamma_2} - 2^{-(n+1)} = 2^{-\Gamma_2}.$$

Hence

$$\mathfrak{S}(\underline{y}(\overline{y}(n+1)) - \underline{x}(\overline{x}(n+1))) \doteq \Lambda \supset M(\underline{y}(m) - \underline{x}(m)) \geqslant 2^{-\Gamma_2}. \tag{75}$$

Let us assume that

$$\mathfrak{S}(\underline{y}(\overline{y}(n+1)) - \underline{x}(\overline{x}(n+1))) \not\doteq \Lambda.$$

On the basis of (73) and (60) we conclude that

$$\underline{y}(\overline{y}(n+1)) - \underline{x}(\overline{x}(n+1)) < 0. \tag{76}$$

On the basis of (72), (73) and (76), we have

$$\underline{x}(m) - \underline{y}(m) = \underline{x}(m) - \underline{x}(\overline{x}(n+1)) + \underline{x}(\overline{x}(n+1)) - \underline{y}(\overline{y}(n+1)) \\ + \underline{y}(\overline{y}(n+1)) - \underline{y}(m) > -2^{-(n+1)} + 2^{-n} + 2^{-\Gamma_2} - 2^{-(n+1)} = 2^{-\Gamma_2},$$

$$M(\underline{y}(m) - \underline{x}(m)) = \underline{x}(m) - \underline{y}(m).$$

Hence

$$\mathfrak{S}(\underline{y}(\overline{y}(n+1)) - \underline{x}(\overline{x}(n+1))) \not\doteq \Lambda \supset M(\underline{y}(m) - \underline{x}(m)) \geqslant 2^{-\Gamma_2}. \tag{77}$$

From (75), (77), and the applicability of the algorithm $\mathfrak{S}$ to every word in the alphabet $Ч_2$, (71) follows. Proposition (55) has been proved.

Thus, the proof of proposition (4) is complete.

If in the proof of proposition (4) we replace the formula $(x \neq y)$ by the formula $(x < y)$, cancel all occurrences of the functor M, replace the functor $\mathfrak{L}^*$ by the functor $\mathfrak{L}$ at all places where $\mathfrak{L}^*$ occurs, and replace all places in the proof in which the algorithm $\mathfrak{S}$ figures or in which reference is made to this algorithm by by the corresponding obvious arguments without reference to $\mathfrak{S}$, then we obtain a proof of proposition (5).

Proposition (6) follows from 4.2.7 and proposition (5).

Theorem 4.4.1 has been proved.

Remark. We construct algorithms $\mathfrak{L}_1$ and $\mathfrak{L}_1^*$ in the alphabet $Ч_3^{sa}$ such that

$$\forall xyn(\mathfrak{L}_1(x\,\square\,y\,\square\,n) \mathrel{\dot{=}} \underline{y}(H) - \underline{x}(H)),$$
$$\forall xyn(\mathfrak{L}_1^*(x\,\square\,y\,\square\,n) \mathrel{\dot{=}} M(\mathfrak{L}_1(x\,\square\,y\,\square\,n))),$$

where

$$H \leftrightharpoons \max(n\,\square\,\overline{x}(n+1)\,\square\,\overline{y}(n+1)).$$

We replace in the fomulas (1)–(6) the symbol $\mathfrak{L}$ by the symbol $\mathfrak{L}_1$ and the symbol $\mathfrak{L}^*$ by the symbol $\mathfrak{L}_1^*$. All propositions obtained as a result of this replacement can be proved. They form a modification of Theorem 4.4.1 which will sometimes be more convenient to apply than 4.4.1.

Now we introduce some algorithms needed for the formulation of the following theorems.

1) We construct an algorithm $\mathfrak{P}$ in the alphabet $Ч_3^{sa}$ such that

$$\forall xyk(\mathfrak{P}(x\,\square\,y\,\square\,k) \simeq \max(\overline{x}(k+2)\,\square\,\overline{y}(k+2))). \tag{78}$$

It is obvious that

$$\forall xyk(\mathfrak{P}(x\,\square\,y\,\square\,k) \overset{+}{\in} \underline{\text{nat}}). \tag{79}$$

2) We construct an algorithm $\mathfrak{D}$ in the alphabet $Ч_2^{sa}$ such that

$$\forall a(a > 0 \supset \mathfrak{D}(a) \overset{+}{\in} \text{nat} \;\&\; a \geqslant 2^{-\mathfrak{D}(a)}). \tag{80}$$

3) We construct algorithms Δ, Δ_1, and Δ_2 in the alphabet $Ч_3^{sa}$ such that

$$\forall xy(\Delta(x\,\square\,y) \simeq \mu_n(\mathfrak{L}^*(x\,\square\,y\,\square\,n) > 2^{-n})), \tag{81}$$
$$\forall xy(\Delta_1(x\,\square\,y) \simeq \mu_n(\mathfrak{L}(x\,\square\,y\,\square\,n) > 2^{-n})), \tag{82}$$
$$\forall xy(\Delta_2(x\,\square\,y) \simeq \mu_n(\mathfrak{L}(y\,\square\,x\,\square\,n) > 2^{-n})). \tag{83}$$

It is obvious that

$$\forall xy(!\Delta(x\,\square\,y) \equiv \exists n(\mathfrak{L}^*(x\,\square\,y\,\square\,n) > 2^{-n})), \tag{84}$$
$$\forall xy(!\Delta_1(x\,\square\,y) \equiv \exists n(\mathfrak{L}(x\,\square\,y\,\square\,n) > 2^{-n})), \tag{85}$$
$$\forall xy(!\Delta_2(x\,\square\,y) \equiv \exists n(\mathfrak{L}(y\,\square\,x\,\square\,n) > 2^{-n})) \tag{86}$$

and

$$\forall xy(!\Delta(x\,\square\,y) \supset \Delta(x\,\square\,y) \in \underline{\text{nat}} \;\&\; \mathfrak{L}^*(x\,\square\,y\,\square\,\Delta(x\,\square\,y)) > 2^{-\Delta(x\square y)}), \tag{87}$$
$$\forall xy(!\Delta_1(x\,\square\,y) \supset \Delta_1(x\,\square\,y) \in \underline{\text{nat}} \;\&\; \mathfrak{L}(x\,\square\,y\,\square\,\Delta_1(x\,\square\,y)) > 2^{-\Delta_1(x\square y)}), \tag{88}$$
$$\forall xy(!\Delta_2(x\,\square\,y) \supset \Delta_2(x\,\square\,y) \in \underline{\text{nat}} \;\&\; \mathfrak{L}(y\,\square\,x\,\square\,\Delta_2(x\,\square\,y)) > 2^{-\Delta_2(x\square y)}). \tag{89}$$

4) We construct algorithms $\mathfrak{X}$, $\mathfrak{X}_1$, and $\mathfrak{X}_2$ in the alphabet $Ч_3^{sa}$ such that

$$\forall xy(\mathfrak{X}(x\,\square\,y) \simeq \mathfrak{D}(\mathfrak{L}^*(x\,\square\,y\,\square\,\Delta(x\,\square\,y)) - 2^{-\Delta(x\square y)})), \tag{90}$$
$$\forall xy(\mathfrak{X}_1(x\,\square\,y) \simeq \mathfrak{D}(\mathfrak{L}(x\,\square\,y\,\square\,\Delta_1(x\,\square\,y)) - 2^{-\Delta_1(x\square y)})), \tag{91}$$
$$\forall xy(\mathfrak{X}_2(x\,\square\,y) \simeq \mathfrak{D}(\mathfrak{L}(y\,\square\,x\,\square\,\Delta_2(x\,\square\,y)) - 2^{-\Delta_2(x\square y)})). \tag{92}$$

It is obvious that

$$\forall xy(!\mathfrak{X}(x\square y)\equiv !\Delta(x\square y)), \qquad \forall xy(!\mathfrak{X}(x\square y)\supset \mathfrak{X}(x\square y)\in \underline{\text{nat}}), \tag{93}$$
$$\forall xy(!\mathfrak{X}_1(x\square y)\equiv !\Delta_1(x\square y)), \qquad \forall xy(!\mathfrak{X}_1(x\square y)\supset \mathfrak{X}_1(x\square y)\in \underline{\text{nat}}), \tag{94}$$
$$\forall xy(!\mathfrak{X}_2(x\square y)\equiv !\Delta_2(x\square y)), \qquad \forall xy(!\mathfrak{X}_2(x\square y)\supset \mathfrak{X}_2(x\square y)\in \underline{\text{nat}}). \tag{95}$$

5) We construct algorithms $\mathfrak{Y}$, $\mathfrak{Y}_1$, and $\mathfrak{Y}_2$ in the alphabet Ч_3^{sa} such that

$$\forall xy(\mathfrak{Y}(x\square y)\simeq \max(\bar{x}(\Delta(x\square y)+1)\square \bar{y}(\Delta(x\square y)+1))), \tag{96}$$
$$\forall xy(\mathfrak{Y}_1(x\square y)\simeq \max(\bar{x}(\Delta_1(x\square y)+1)\square \bar{y}(\Delta_1(x\square y)+1))), \tag{97}$$
$$\forall xy(\mathfrak{Y}_2(x\square y)\simeq \max(\bar{x}(\Delta_2(x\square y)+1)\square \bar{y}(\Delta_2(x\square y)+1))). \tag{98}$$

It is obvious that

$$\forall xy(!\mathfrak{Y}(x\square y)\equiv !\Delta(x\square y)), \qquad \forall xy(!\mathfrak{Y}(x\square y)\supset \mathfrak{Y}(x\square y)\in \underline{\text{nat}}), \tag{99}$$
$$\forall xy(!\mathfrak{Y}_1(x\square y)\equiv !\Delta_1(x\square y)), \qquad \forall xy(!\mathfrak{Y}_1(x\square y)\supset \mathfrak{Y}_1(x\square y)\in \underline{\text{nat}}), \tag{100}$$
$$\forall xy(!\mathfrak{Y}_2(x\square y)\equiv !\Delta_2(x\square y)), \qquad \forall xy(!\mathfrak{Y}_2(x\square y)\supset \mathfrak{Y}_2(x\square y)\in \underline{\text{nat}}). \tag{101}$$

6) We construct an algorithm Ω in the alphabet Ч_2^{sa} such that

$$\forall a((a>0\supset \Omega(a)\doteq 0|)\,\&\,(a\leqslant 0\supset \Omega(a)\doteq 0\|)). \tag{102}$$

From (102) it follows that

$$\forall a(\Omega(a)\doteq 0|\equiv a>0), \qquad \forall a(\Omega(a)\doteq 0\|\equiv a\leqslant 0). \tag{103}$$

7) We construct an algorithm $\mathfrak{C}$ in the alphabet Ч_3^{sa} such that

$$\forall xy(\mathfrak{C}(x\square y)\simeq \Omega(\mathfrak{L}(x\square y\square \Delta(x\square y)))). \tag{104}$$

It is obvious that

$$\forall xy(!\mathfrak{C}(x\square y)\equiv !\Delta(x\square y)), \tag{105}$$
$$\forall xy(!\mathfrak{C}(x\square y)\supset \mathfrak{C}(x\square y)\in \underline{\text{nat}}\,\&\,0|\leqslant \mathfrak{C}(x\square y)\leqslant 0\|). \tag{106}$$

The algorithms $\mathfrak{P}$ and $\mathfrak{D}$ figured in the proof of Theorem 4.4.1.

The concrete algorithms $\mathfrak{P}, \mathfrak{X}, \mathfrak{Y}, \mathfrak{X}_1, \mathfrak{Y}_1, \mathfrak{X}_2, \mathfrak{Y}_2$ just introduced allow us to formulate the following theorem.

4.4.2. *For any duplexes x and y,*

$$(x=y)\equiv \forall km(m\geqslant \mathfrak{P}(x\square y\square k)\supset M(\underline{y}(m)-\underline{x}(m))<2^{-k}), \tag{107}$$
$$(x\geqslant y)\equiv \forall km(m\geqslant \mathfrak{P}(x\square y\square k)\supset \underline{y}(m)-\underline{x}(m)<2^{-k}), \tag{108}$$
$$(x\leqslant y)\equiv \forall km(m\geqslant \mathfrak{P}(x\square y\square k)\supset \underline{x}(m)-\underline{y}(m)<2^{-k}), \tag{109}$$
$$(x\neq y)\equiv !\mathfrak{X}(x\square y)\,\&\,!\mathfrak{Y}(x\square y)\,\&\,\forall m(m\geqslant \mathfrak{Y}(x\square y)$$
$$\supset M(\underline{y}(m)-\underline{x}(m))\geqslant 2^{-\mathfrak{X}(x\square y)}), \tag{110}$$

$$(x < y) \equiv !\,\mathfrak{X}_1(x \square y) \,\&\, !\,\mathfrak{Y}_1(x \square y) \,\&\, \forall m\,(m \geqslant \mathfrak{Y}_1(x \square y) \supset \underline{y}(m) - \underline{x}(m) \geqslant 2^{-\mathfrak{X}_1(x \square y)}), \tag{111}$$

$$(x > y) \equiv !\,\mathfrak{X}_2(x \square y) \,\&\, !\,\mathfrak{Y}_2(x \square y) \,\&\, \forall m\,(m \geqslant \mathfrak{Y}_2(x \square y) \supset \underline{x}(m) - \underline{y}(m) \geqslant 2^{-\mathfrak{X}_2(x \square y)}). \tag{112}$$

Proof. We shall refer to the proof of Theorem 4.4.1. From (1), (11)–(15) and (21) it follows that

$$\forall xy\,((x = y) \supset \forall km\,(m \geqslant \mathfrak{P}(x \square y \square k) \supset M(\underline{y}(m) - \underline{x}(m)) < 2^{-k})). \tag{113}$$

Now we shall prove that

$$\forall xy\,(\forall km\,(m \geqslant \mathfrak{P}(x \square y \square k) \supset M(\underline{y}(m) - \underline{x}(m)) < 2^{-k}) \supset \forall n\,(\mathfrak{L}^*(x \square y \square n) \leqslant 2^{-n})). \tag{114}$$

Let us use the algorithm $\mathfrak{Q}$ introduced in the proof of Theorem 4.4.1.

From (11)–(13) it follows that

$$\forall xyk\,(\langle \mathfrak{Q}(x \square y)\rangle_0(k) \simeq \mathfrak{P}(x \square y \square k)), \tag{115}$$

$$\forall xy\,(\langle \mathfrak{Q}(x \square y)\rangle_0 \overset{+}{\in} (\text{H} \to \text{H})_0). \tag{116}$$

From (116) and from proposition (18), which was established in the course of the proof of Theorem 4.4.1, it follows that

$$\forall xy \mathbf{F}^{f_1}_{\langle \mathfrak{Q}(x \square y)\rangle_0 \text{L}}(\mathfrak{M} \supset \mathfrak{N})_{\text{J}}. \tag{117}$$

From (117) and (115), (114) follows.

From (113), (114), and (1), (107) follows.

The proof of proposition (108) is analogous to the proof of (107).

Proposition (109) follows from 4.2.7, proposition (108), and the obvious assertion

$$\forall xyk\,(\mathfrak{P}(y \square x \square k) \doteq \mathfrak{P}(x \square y \square k)).$$

Let us prove proposition (110). From (4), (84), (93) and (99) it follows that

$$\forall xy\,((x \neq y) \equiv !\,\mathfrak{X}(x \square y)), \quad \forall xy\,((x \neq y) \equiv !\,\mathfrak{Y}(x \square y)). \tag{118}$$

We shall prove that

$$\forall xy\,((x \neq y) \supset \forall m\,(m \geqslant \mathfrak{Y}(x \square y) \supset M(\underline{y}(m) - \underline{x}(m)) \geqslant 2^{-\mathfrak{X}(x \square y)})). \tag{119}$$

We shall start from proposition (55), established in the course of the proof of Theorem 4.4.1. From (55), (43), (40), (46) and (44) it follows that

$$\forall xyn\,(\mathfrak{W} \supset \forall m\,(m \geqslant \tilde{\Gamma}_3 \supset M(\underline{g}(m) - \underline{x}(m)) \geqslant 2^{-\tilde{\Gamma}_2})), \tag{120}$$

where

$$\tilde{\Gamma}_2 \rightleftharpoons \mathfrak{D}(\mathfrak{L}^*(x \square y \square n) - 2^{-n}), \tag{121}$$

$$\tilde{\Gamma}_3 \rightleftharpoons \max(\overline{x}(n+1) \square \overline{y}(n+1)). \tag{122}$$

From (120) it follows that

$$\forall xy\,(!\,\Delta\,(x\,\square\,y) \supset \mathbf{F}^{n}_{\Delta(x\square y)\llcorner}\mathfrak{H}_{\lrcorner}), \tag{123}$$

where

$$\mathfrak{H} \leftrightharpoons (\mathfrak{W} \supset \forall m\,(m \geqslant \tilde{\Gamma}_3 \supset M(\underline{y}\,(m) - \underline{x}\,(m)) \geqslant 2^{-\tilde{\Gamma}_2})).$$

We have

$$\mathbf{F}^{n}_{\Delta(x\square y)\llcorner}\mathfrak{W}_{\lrcorner} \mathrel{\underline{\underline{\circ}}} (\mathfrak{L}^{*}\,(x\,\square\,y\,\square\,\Delta\,(x\,\square\,y)) > 2^{-\Delta(x\square y)}).$$

In addition, from (121), (90), (122) and (96) it follows that[1)]

$$\forall xy\,(\mathbf{F}^{n}_{\Delta(x\square y)\llcorner}\Gamma_{2\lrcorner} \simeq \mathfrak{X}\,(x\,\square\,y)),$$
$$\forall xy\,(\mathbf{F}^{n}_{\Delta(x\square y)\llcorner}\Gamma_{3\lrcorner} \simeq \mathfrak{Y}\,(x\,\square\,y)).$$

Hence

$$\forall xy\,(!\,\Delta\,(x\,\square\,y) \supset (\mathfrak{L}^{*}\,(x\,\square\,y\,\square\,\Delta\,(x\,\square\,y)) > 2^{-\Delta(x\square y)}$$
$$\supset \forall m\,(m \geqslant \mathfrak{Y}\,(x\,\square\,y) \supset M(\underline{y}\,(m) - \underline{x}\,(m)) \geqslant 2^{-\mathfrak{X}(x\square y)}))). \tag{124}$$

In addition, from (4) and (81) it follows that

$$\forall xy\,((x \neq y) \supset !\,\Delta\,(x\,\square\,y)\,\&\,\mathfrak{L}^{*}\,(x\,\square\,y\,\square\,\Delta\,(x\,\square\,y)) > 2^{-\Delta(x\square y)}). \tag{125}$$

From (125) and (124), (119) follows.

From (118) and (119), proposition (110) follows.

The proof of proposition (111) is analogous to the proof of (110).

Proposition (112) follows from 4.2.7, proposition (111), and the obvious assertion

$$\forall xy\,(\mathfrak{X}_2\,(x\,\square\,y) \simeq \mathfrak{X}_1\,(y\,\square\,x)\,\&\,\mathfrak{Y}_2\,(x\,\square\,y) \simeq \mathfrak{Y}_1\,(y\,\square\,x)).$$

Theorem 4.4.2 has been proved.

Theorem 4.4.2 establishes a very important fundamental fact, namely that the predicates $=_B$, $\geq_B$, $\leq_B$, $\neq_B$, $<_B$, $>_B$, applied to duplexes, can be characterized by normal formulas. We note that the formulas by means of which these predicates are characterized according to their definitions are not normal formulas.

The role in the sequel of the algorithm $\mathfrak{C}$ introduced before Theorem 4.4.2 is

---

1) The operation of substituting given terms for free occurrences of given variables, described in [3], §3.9, is defined with respect to formulas. In this book it will also be applied to terms. If $\alpha_1, \cdots, \alpha_k$ is a list of variables and $T_1, \cdots, T_k$ is a list of terms similar to the list of variables $\alpha_1, \cdots, \alpha_k$, then we agree that the application of the operation $\mathbf{F}^{\alpha_1, \ldots, \alpha_k}_{T_1, \ldots, T_k}$ to an arbitrary term H consists in the simultaneous replacement of all occurrences in H of the variables α_1 by the term $T_1, \cdots, \alpha_k$ by the term T_k.

determined by the following theorem.

4.4.3. *For any duplexes x and y*

$$(x \neq y) \supset \mathfrak{C}(x \,\square\, y) \overset{+}{\in} \underline{\mathrm{nat}} \,\&\, 0| \leqslant \mathfrak{C}(x \,\square\, y) \leqslant 0\| \\ \&\, (\mathfrak{C}(x \,\square\, y) \underset{\cdot}{=} 0| \supset x < y) \,\&\, (\mathfrak{C}(x \,\square\, y) \underset{\cdot}{=} 0\| \supset x > y). \tag{126}$$

Proof. From (4), (84), (105) and (106) it follows that

$$\forall xy\,((x \neq y) \supset \mathfrak{C}(x \,\square\, y) \overset{+}{\in} \underline{\mathrm{nat}} \,\&\, 0| \leqslant \mathfrak{C}(x \,\square\, y) \leqslant 0\|).$$

Hence for a proof of (126) it suffices to show that

$$\forall xy\,((x \neq y) \supset (\mathfrak{C}(x \,\square\, y) \underset{\cdot}{=} 0| \supset x < y) \,\&\, (\mathfrak{C}(x \,\square\, y) \underset{\cdot}{=} 0\| \supset x > y)). \tag{127}$$

Let x and y be any duplexes. Assume that $(x \neq y)$. Then, on the basis of (4), (84) and (87), we have, first,

$$\Delta(x \,\square\, y) \overset{+}{\in} \underline{\mathrm{nat}} \tag{128}$$

and second,

$$\mathfrak{L}^*(x \,\square\, y \,\square\, \Delta(x \,\square\, y)) > 2^{-\Delta(x \square y)}. \tag{129}$$

From (128) it follows that

$$\mathfrak{L}(x \,\square\, y \,\square\, \Delta(x \,\square\, y)) \overset{+}{\in} \underline{\mathrm{rat}}. \tag{130}$$

Assume $\mathfrak{C}(x \square y) \underset{\cdot}{=} 0|$. From (104) and (103) it follows that

$$\mathfrak{L}(x \,\square\, y \,\square\, \Delta(x \,\square\, y)) > 0. \tag{131}$$

Hence

$$\mathfrak{L}^*(x \,\square\, y \,\square\, \Delta(x \,\square\, y)) \underset{\cdot}{=} \mathfrak{L}(x \,\square\, y \,\square\, \Delta(x \,\square\, y)). \tag{132}$$

From (129) and (132) it follows that

$$\mathfrak{L}(x \,\square\, y \,\square\, \Delta(x \,\square\, y)) > 2^{-\Delta(x \square y)}.$$

Hence

$$\exists n\,(\mathfrak{L}(x \,\square\, y \,\square\, n) > 2^{-n}). \tag{133}$$

Therefore

$$\mathfrak{C}(x \,\square\, y) \underset{\cdot}{=} 0| \supset (x < y). \tag{134}$$

Assume $\mathfrak{C}(x \square y) \underset{\cdot}{=} 0\|$. From (104) and (103) it follows that

$$\mathfrak{L}(x \,\square\, y \,\square\, \Delta(x \,\square\, y)) \leqslant 0.$$

We have

$$\forall n\,(\mathfrak{L}(y \,\square\, x \,\square\, n) = -\mathfrak{L}(x \,\square\, y \,\square\, n)).$$

Hence

$$\mathfrak{L}(y \,\square\, x \,\square\, \Delta(x \,\square\, y)) \geqslant 0,$$

$$\mathfrak{L}^*(x \,\square\, y \,\square\, \Delta(x \,\square\, y)) = \mathfrak{L}(y \,\square\, x \,\square\, \Delta(x \,\square\, y)). \tag{135}$$

From (129) and (135) it follows that

$$\mathfrak{L}(y \,\square\, x \,\square\, \Delta(x \,\square\, y)) > 2^{-\Delta(x \square y)}.$$

Hence

$$\exists n\,(\mathfrak{L}(y \,\square\, x \,\square\, n) > 2^{-n}).$$

Therefore

$$\mathfrak{C}(x \square y) \mathrel{\dot{=}} 0 \,\|\, \supset (x > y). \tag{136}$$

From (134) and (136), (127) follows. Theorem 4.4.3 has been proved.

Theorem 4.4.3 asserts that the algorithm $\mathfrak{C}$ "distinguishes" among all pairs of duplexes satisfying the condition

"first term of the pair is different from the second term"

those pairs of duplexes which satisfy the condition

"first term of the pair is less than the second term",

and those pairs of duplexes which satisfy the condition

"first term of the pair is greater than the second term".

4.5. We establish now some logical connections among the relations $=_B$, $\geq_B$, $\leq_B$, $\neq_B$, $<_B$, $>_B$. First we formulate a series of auxiliary propositions.

We have

$$\forall xyn\,(\mathfrak{L}(x \square y \square n) \overset{+}{\in} \text{rat}). \tag{1}$$

Using (1), one can easily establish that the constructive problem exhibited by the constructive reformulation of the assertion

$$\forall xyn\,(\mathfrak{L}(x \square y \square n) \geqslant 0 \vee \mathfrak{L}(x \square y \square n) \leqslant 0). \tag{2}$$

is solvable. Hence proposition (2) is true.

In addition, we have

$$\forall xyn\,(\mathfrak{L}^*(x \square y \square n) \mathrel{\dot{=}} M(\mathfrak{L}(x \square y \square n))), \tag{3}$$

$$\forall xyn\,(\mathfrak{L}(y \square x \square n) \mathrel{\dot{=}} -\mathfrak{L}(x \square y \square n)), \tag{4}$$

$$\forall xyn\,(\mathfrak{L}(x \square y \square n) \geqslant 0 \equiv \mathfrak{L}^*(x \square y \square n) \mathrel{\dot{=}} \mathfrak{L}(x \square y \square n)), \tag{5}$$

$$\forall xyn\,(\mathfrak{L}(x \square y \square n) \leqslant 0 \equiv \mathfrak{L}^*(x \square y \square n) \mathrel{\dot{=}} \mathfrak{L}(y \square x \square n)). \tag{6}$$

From (2), (5), and (6), it follows that

$$\forall xyn\,(\mathfrak{L}^*(x \square y \square n) \leqslant 2^{-n} \equiv \mathfrak{L}(x \square y \square n) \leqslant 2^{-n} \,\&\, \mathfrak{L}(y \square x \square n) \leqslant 2^{-n}), \tag{7}$$

$$\forall xyn\,(\mathfrak{L}^*(x \square y \square n) > 2^{-n} \equiv \mathfrak{L}(x \square y \square n) > 2^{-n} \vee \mathfrak{L}(y \square x \square n) > 2^{-n}). \tag{8}$$

Now we form the following list of formulas:

$$\left.\begin{array}{ll} \mathfrak{L}^*(x \square y \square n) \leqslant 2^{-n}, & \mathfrak{L}^*(x \square y \square n) > 2^{-n}, \\ \mathfrak{L}(x \square y \square n) \leqslant 2^{-n}, & \mathfrak{L}(x \square y \square n) > 2^{-n}, \\ \mathfrak{L}(y \square x \square n) \leqslant 2^{-n}, & \mathfrak{L}(y \square x \square n) > 2^{-n}. \end{array}\right\} \tag{9}$$

Let $\mathfrak{A}$ be any formula of the list (9) and let $\mathfrak{B}$ be the formula of the list (9) which stands in the same row as the formula $\mathfrak{A}$. From (1), (3) and (4) it follows that

$$\forall xyn(\neg\mathfrak{A} \equiv \mathfrak{B}). \tag{10}$$

Further, from (1), (3) and (4) it follows that

$$\forall xyn(\mathfrak{A} \vee \neg\mathfrak{A}). \tag{11}$$

On the basis of (11), (10) and §2.5 (2), we can conclude that

$$\forall xy(\neg\forall n\mathfrak{A} \equiv \exists n\mathfrak{B}). \tag{12}$$

The propositions indicated above will be used in the proof of Theorem 4.5.1, which characterizes the basic logical connections among the relations $=_B$, $\geq_B$, $\leq_B$, $\neq_B$, $<_B$, $>_B$.

4.5.1. *For any duplexes x and y,*

$x \neq y \equiv x < y \vee x > y,$	(13)	$x = y \equiv x \geqslant y \,\&\, x \leqslant y,$	(22)
$x < y \equiv x \leqslant y \,\&\, x \neq y,$	(14)	$x > y \vee x = y \supset x \geqslant y,$	(23)
$x > y \equiv x \geqslant y \,\&\, x \neq y,$	(15)	$x < y \vee x = y \supset x \leqslant y,$	(24)
$\neg(x \neq y) \equiv x = y,$	(16)	$\neg(x = y) \equiv x \neq y,$	(25)
$\neg(x < y) \equiv x \geqslant y,$	(17)	$\neg(x \geqslant y) \equiv x < y,$	(26)
$\neg(x > y) \equiv x \leqslant y,$	(18)	$\neg(x \leqslant y) \equiv x > y,$	(27)
$\neg\neg(x \neq y) \equiv x \neq y,$	(19)	$\neg\neg(x = y) \equiv x = y,$	(28)
$\neg\neg(x < y) \equiv x < y,$	(20)	$\neg\neg(x \geqslant y) \equiv x \geqslant y,$	(29)
$\neg\neg(x > y) \equiv x > y,$	(21)	$\neg\neg(x \leqslant y) \equiv x \leqslant y,$	(30)

$$x \geqslant y \equiv \neg\neg(x > y \vee x = y), \tag{31}$$

$$x \leqslant y \equiv \neg\neg(x < y \vee x = y), \tag{32}$$

$\neg(x \neq y \,\&\, x = y),$	(33)	$\neg\neg(x = y \vee x \neq y),$	(38)
$\neg(x < y \,\&\, x \geqslant y),$	(34)	$\neg\neg(x \geqslant y \vee x < y),$	(39)
$\neg(x > y \,\&\, x \leqslant y),$	(35)	$\neg\neg(x \leqslant y \vee x > y),$	(40)
$\neg(x \neq y \,\&\, x \geqslant y \,\&\, x \leqslant y),$	(36)	$\neg\neg(x = y \vee x < y \vee x > y),$	(41)
$\neg(x < y \,\&\, x > y),$	(37)	$\neg\neg(x \geqslant y \vee x \leqslant y).$	(42)

Proof. Let x and y be arbitrary duplexes. Proposition (13) follows from 4.4.1 and propositions (8) and §2.6 (2). Proposition (22) follows from 4.4.1 and propositions (7) and §2.6 (1). Propositions (16), (17), and (18) follow from 4.4.1 and proposition §2.6 (3). Propositions (25), (26), and (27) follow from 4.4.1 and proposition (12). Propositions (19), (20), (21), (28), (29), and (30) follow from (16), (17), (18), (25), (26), (27). Propositions (33), (34), and (35) follow from (16), (17),

(18), (25), (26), (27). Propositions (33), (34), and (35) follow, respectively, from (16), (17), and (18), and from §2.6 (8). Proposition (36) follows from (33) and (22). Propositions (38)–(41) follow, respectively, from (33)–(36), and proposition §2.6 (6). It remains to prove propositions (14), (15), (23), (24), (31), (32), (37), and (42). First, we prove the propositions

$$x > y \supset x \geqslant y, \tag{43}$$
$$x < y \supset x \leqslant y, \tag{44}$$
$$x = y \supset x \geqslant y, \tag{45}$$
$$x = y \supset x \leqslant y. \tag{46}$$

On the basis of 4.4.1, formula (43) is equivalent to the formula

$$\exists n (\mathfrak{L}(y \square x \square n) > 2^{-n}) \supset \forall k (\mathfrak{L}(x \square y \square k) \leqslant 2^{-k}). \tag{47}$$

Formula (47) is equivalent to the formula

$$\forall nk (\mathfrak{L}(y \square x \square n) > 2^{-n} \supset \mathfrak{L}(x \square y \square k) \leqslant 2^{-k}). \tag{48}$$

Let n and k be arbitrary natural numbers, and assume that

$$\mathfrak{L}(y \square x \square n) > 2^{-n}.$$

Then on the basis of (4) we have

$$\mathfrak{L}(x \square y \square n) < -2^{-n}. \tag{49}$$

In addition, from (49) it follows that

$$\begin{aligned}\mathfrak{L}(x \square y \square k) &= \underline{y}(\overline{y}(k+1)) - \underline{y}(\overline{y}(n+1)) + \mathfrak{L}(x \square y \square n) \\ &+ \underline{x}(\overline{x}(n+1)) - \underline{x}(\overline{x}(k+1)) < 2^{-\min(k+1 \square n+1)} - 2^{-n} \\ &+ 2^{-\min(k+1 \square n+1)} = 2^{-\min(k \square n)} - 2^{-n} \leqslant 2^{-k}.\end{aligned}$$

Hence $\mathfrak{L}(x \square y \square k) \leq 2^{-k}$. Proposition (48), and therefore proposition (43), have been proved. Proposition (44) follows from (43) and 4.2.7.

On the basis of 4.4.1, formula (45) is equivalent to the formula

$$\forall n (\mathfrak{L}^*(x \square y \square n) \leqslant 2^{-n}) \supset \forall n (\mathfrak{L}(x \square y \square n) \leqslant 2^{-n}).$$

This formula is a consequence of the obvious assertion

$$\forall n (\mathfrak{L}(x \square y \square n) \leqslant \mathfrak{L}^*(x \square y \square n)).$$

Hence proposition (45) is proved. Proposition (46) follows from (45) and 4.2.7.

From (43) and (45), (23) follows, and, from (44) and (46), (24) follows.

On the basis of (13), (44) and (18) we have

$$\begin{aligned} x \leqslant y \,\&\, x \neq y &\equiv x \leqslant y \,\&\, (x < y \vee x > y) \\ \swarrow \quad &\equiv (x \leqslant y \,\&\, x < y) \vee (x \leqslant y \,\&\, x > y) \\ \swarrow \quad &\equiv x < y \vee (\neg(x > y) \,\&\, x > y) \\ \swarrow \quad &\equiv x < y. \end{aligned}$$

Proposition (14) has been proved. From (14) and 4.2.7, (15) follows.

On the basis of (17), (14), (18) and (25) we have

$$
\begin{aligned}
x \geqslant y &\equiv \neg(x < y)\\
\swarrow \quad &\equiv \neg(x \leqslant y \,\&\, x \neq y)\\
\swarrow \quad &\equiv \neg(\neg(x > y) \,\&\, \neg(x = y))\\
\swarrow \quad &\equiv \neg\neg(x > y \vee x = y).
\end{aligned}
$$

Proposition (31) has been proved. From (31) and 4.2.7, (32) follows.

Proposition (37) is proved in the following manner. From (43) it follows that

$$x < y \,\&\, x > y \supset x < y \,\&\, x \geqslant y.$$

From this formula, by the rule of contraposition (§2.6 (4)), we obtain

$$\neg(x < y \,\&\, x \geqslant y) \supset \neg(x < y \,\&\, x > y). \qquad (50)$$

(37) follows from (34) and (50). Proposition (42) follows from (26), (27), and (37).

Theorem 4.5.1 has been proved.

In connection with propositions (23), (31), (24), and (32), the problem arises as to the truth of the assertions

$$\forall xy\,(x \geqslant y \supset x > y \vee x = y), \qquad (51)$$

$$\forall xy\,(x \leqslant y \supset x < y \vee x = y). \qquad (52)$$

In addition, in connection with propositions (38)–(42), the problem arises as to the truth of the assertions

$$\forall xy\,(x = y \vee x \neq y), \qquad (53)$$

$$\forall xy\,(x \geqslant y \vee x < y), \qquad (54)$$

$$\forall xy\,(x \leqslant y \vee x > y), \qquad (55)$$

$$\forall xy\,(x = y \vee x < y \vee x > y), \qquad (56)$$

$$\forall xy\,(x \geqslant y \vee x \leqslant y). \qquad (57)$$

Special cases of assertions (51)–(57) are, respectively, the following assertions (58)–(64):

$$\forall x\,(x \geqslant 0 \supset x > 0 \vee x = 0), \qquad (58)$$

$$\forall x\,(x \leqslant 0 \supset x < 0 \vee x = 0), \qquad (59)$$

$$\forall x\,(x = 0 \vee x \neq 0), \qquad (60)$$

$$\forall x\,(x \geqslant 0 \vee x < 0), \qquad (61)$$

$$\forall x\,(x \leqslant 0 \vee x > 0), \qquad (62)$$

$$\forall x\,(x = 0 \vee x < 0 \vee x > 0), \qquad (63)$$

$$\forall x\,(x \geqslant 0 \vee x \leqslant 0). \qquad (64)$$

The results of applying to formulas (58)–(64) the algorithm of the constructive reformulation of mathematical propositions are assertions about the potential realizability of algorithms satisfying certain conditions. For example, the process of applying the algorithm of constructive reformulation to the formula (64) leads, first, to the formula[1)]

$$\forall x \exists l (0| \leqslant l \leqslant 0|| \,\&\, (l \doteq 0| \supset x \geqslant 0) \,\&\, (l \doteq 0|| \supset x \leqslant 0)),$$

and then to the formula

$$\exists \phi_{3,1} \mathfrak{A}, \tag{65}$$

where

$$\mathfrak{A} \rightleftharpoons \forall x (\phi_{3,1}(x) \mathrel{\dot{\in}} \underline{\text{nat}} \,\&\, 0| \leqslant \phi_{3,1}(x) \leqslant 0||$$
$$\& (\phi_{3,1}(x) \doteq 0| \supset x \geqslant 0) \,\&\, (\phi_{3,1}(x) \doteq 0|| \supset x \leqslant 0)).$$

In [17] G. S. Ceĭtin has proved that there can be no algorithm satisfying condition $\mathfrak{A}$. Hence the proposition

$$\neg \forall x (x \geqslant 0 \vee x \leqslant 0) \tag{66}$$

is true. On the basis of (66), 4.5.1, and (43)–(46), it is easy to prove (see [17], §2) the following propositions (67)–(72):

$$\neg \forall x (x \geqslant 0 \supset x > 0 \vee x = 0), \tag{67}$$
$$\neg \forall x (x \leqslant 0 \supset x < 0 \vee x = 0), \tag{68}$$
$$\neg \forall x (x = 0 \vee x \neq 0), \tag{69}$$
$$\neg \forall x (x \geqslant 0 \vee x < 0), \tag{70}$$
$$\neg \forall x (x \leqslant 0 \vee x > 0), \tag{71}$$
$$\neg \forall x (x = 0 \vee x < 0 \vee x > 0). \tag{72}$$

Each of the propositions (67)–(72) is an assertion about the impossibility of an algorithm satisfying a certain condition.

Remark. Propositions (67)–(72) can be proved another way, without using (66). First, as obvious corollaries of the theorem of A. A. Markov on the impossibility of a constructive discontinuity of a constructive function ([8], p. 345 (transl. p. 192)), we obtain propositions (69) and (72), and then, on the basis of (69) and the properties of certain arithmetic operations on duplexes introduced below in §6, we establish (70), (71), (67), and (68).

From (66)–(72) the following propositions (73)–(79), respectively, are consequences:

1) For the constructive reformulation of formula (64), we can assume (on the basis of 4.4.1) that, instead of the formulas $(x \geq 0)$ and $(x \leq 0)$ we have substituted in (64) the normal formulas $\forall n (\mathfrak{L}(x \square 0 \square n) \leqslant 2^{-n})$ and $\forall n (\mathfrak{L}(0 \square x \square n) \leqslant 2^{-n})$.

$$\neg\forall xy(x \geqslant y \vee x \leqslant y), \tag{73}$$
$$\neg\forall xy(x \geqslant y \supset x > y \vee x = y), \tag{74}$$
$$\neg\forall xy(x \leqslant y \supset x < y \vee x = y), \tag{75}$$
$$\neg\forall xy(x = y \vee x \neq y), \tag{76}$$
$$\neg\forall xy(x \geqslant y \vee x < y), \tag{77}$$
$$\neg\forall xy(x \leqslant y \vee x > y), \tag{78}$$
$$\neg\forall xy(x = y \vee x < y \vee x > y). \tag{79}$$

These propositions are the negations of the propositions (57), (51)–(56).

Proposition (66) is an example of assertions of the form

$$\neg\forall x(x \geqslant H \vee x \leqslant H), \tag{80}$$

where H is a concrete duplex. The subtraction operation on duplexes, defined below in §6, permits us to establish the equivalence of any assertion of the form (80) to proposition (66). Hence the proposition

$$\forall y \neg\forall x(x \geqslant y \vee x \leqslant y) \tag{81}$$

is true.

On the basis of (81), 4.5.1, and (43)–(46), the following propositions (82)–(87) are easily proved.

$$\forall y \neg\forall x(x \geqslant y \supset x > y \vee x = y), \tag{82}$$
$$\forall y \neg\forall x(x \leqslant y \supset x < y \vee x = y), \tag{83}$$
$$\forall y \neg\forall x(x = y \vee x \neq y), \tag{84}$$
$$\forall y \neg\forall x(x \geqslant y \vee x < y), \tag{85}$$
$$\forall y \neg\forall x(x \leqslant y \vee x > y), \tag{86}$$
$$\forall y \neg\forall x(x = y \vee x < y \vee x > y). \tag{87}$$

Propositions (73)–(79) and (81)–(87) testify to the existence of significant differences between the theory of the relations $=_B$, $\geq_B$, $\leq_B$, $\neq_B$, $<_B$, $>_B$ in constructive mathematics and the theory of the corresponding relations in classical mathematics.

In classical mathematics one reads the symbols $\geq$ and $\leq$, respectively, by the phrases "greater than or equal" and "less than or equal". From what has been said above it follows that in the theory of constructive real numbers such a reading of the symbols $\geq$ and $\leq$ can lead to confusion of a fundamental character and is therefore inadmissible. It is natural to read the formulas $(x \geq y)$ and $(x \leq y)$, respectively, in the following way: "the duplex x majorizes the duplex y"

and "the duplex x is majorized by the duplex y". At the same time, on the basis of propositions (31) and (32) and the convention accepted in §1.13, the symbols $\geq$ and $\leq$ can be read, respectively, by the phrases "either greater than or equal" and "either less than or equal".

We remark that in applications to rational numbers the same reading of the symbols $\geq$ and $\leq$ as in classical mathematics is possible, since

$$\forall ab\,(a \geqslant b \equiv a > b \vee a = b),$$
$$\forall ab\,(a \leqslant b \equiv a < b \vee a = b).$$

We note also that

$$\forall ab\,(a = b \vee a \neq b), \qquad \forall ab\,(a \geqslant b \vee a < b),$$
$$\forall ab\,(a \leqslant b \vee a > b), \qquad \forall ab\,(a = b \vee a < b \vee a > b),$$
$$\forall ab\,(a \geqslant b \vee a \leqslant b).$$

In connection with propositions (74) and (75), it is important to emphasize that the assertion

$$\forall xy\,(x \neq y \supset x < y \vee x > y) \tag{88}$$

is correct, since it is a corollary of proposition (13). The proof of proposition (13) by means of the rules of logical inference of constructive logic was carried out above. We can extend it to a proof of proposition (88). We cite here another proof of (88), based on Theorem 4.4.3.

On the basis of 4.4.1 and propositions (25)–(27) one can assume that in formula (88), instead of $(x \neq y)$, $(x < y)$ and $(x > y)$, we have substituted, respectively, the normal formulas

$$\neg\forall n\,(\mathfrak{L}^*(x \square y \square n) \leqslant 2^{-n}), \qquad \neg\forall n\,(\mathfrak{L}(x \square y \square n) \leqslant 2^{-n}),$$
$$\neg\forall n\,(\mathfrak{L}(y \square x \square n) \leqslant 2^{-n}).$$

The process of constructive reformulation of formula (88) leads in succession to the following formulas:

$$\forall xy\,(x \neq y \supset \exists l\,(0| \leqslant l \leqslant 0\| \,\&\, (l \mathrel{\dot{=}} 0| \supset x < y) \,\&\, (l \mathrel{\dot{=}} 0\| \supset x > y))),$$
$$\forall xy \exists \phi_{0,1}\,(x \neq y \supset \phi_{0,1}(\Lambda) \overset{+}{\in} \underline{\text{nat}} \,\&\, 0| \leqslant \phi_{0,1}(\Lambda) \leqslant 0\|$$
$$\&\, (\phi_{0,1}(\Lambda) \mathrel{\dot{=}} 0| \supset x < y) \,\&\, (\phi_{0,1}(\Lambda) \mathrel{\dot{=}} 0\| \supset x > y)),$$
$$\exists \phi_{3,1} \forall xy\,(\phi_{3,1}(x \square y) \overset{+}{\in} c_0 \,\&\, (x \neq y \supset \mathfrak{M})), \tag{89}$$

where

$$\mathfrak{M} \rightleftharpoons \langle \phi_{3,1}(x \square y) \rangle_0(\Lambda) \overset{+}{\in} \underline{\text{nat}} \,\&\, 0| \leqslant \langle \phi_{3,1}(x \square y) \rangle_0(\Lambda) \leqslant 0\|$$
$$\&\, (\langle \phi_{3,1}(x \square y) \rangle_0(\Lambda) \mathrel{\dot{=}} 0| \supset x < y) \,\&\, (\langle \phi_{3,1}(x \square y) \rangle_0(\Lambda) \mathrel{\dot{=}} 0\| \supset x > y).$$

From 2.1.1 it follows that formula (89) is equivalent to the formula

$$\exists \Phi_{3,2} \mathfrak{T}, \tag{90}$$

where

$$\mathfrak{T} \rightleftharpoons \forall xy (x \neq y \supset \Phi_{3,2}(x \square y) \dot{\in} \underline{\text{nat}} \,\&\, 0| \leqslant \Phi_{3,2}(x \square y) \leqslant 0\| \\ \& (\Phi_{3,2}(x \square y) \dot{=} 0| \supset x < y) \,\&\, (\Phi_{3,2}(x \square y) \dot{=} 0\| \supset x > y)).$$

Theorem 4.4.3 asserts that the algorithm $\mathfrak{C}$ satisfies the condition $\mathfrak{T}$. Proposition (90) has been proved. Hence (88) is also proved.

4.6. The following two theorems are easily established.

4.6.1. $$\forall x (x \dot{W}_1 x),$$

where W_1 *is any of the symbols* $=, \geq, \leq$;

$$\forall xy (x W_2 y \supset y W_2 x),$$

where W_2 *is any of the symbols* $=, \neq$; *and*

$$\forall xyz (x W_3 y \,\&\, y W_3 z \supset x W_3 z),$$

where W_3 *is any of the symbols* $=, \geq, \leq, <, >$.

In other words, the relations $=, \geq, \leq$ are reflexive, the relations $=, \neq$ are symmetric, and the relations $=, \geq, \leq, <, >$ are transitive.

4.6.2. $$\forall xyzu (z = x \,\&\, u = y \supset (x W y \equiv z W u)),$$

where W *is any of the symbols* $=, \geq, \leq, \neq, <, >$.

4.7. We replace in Theorem 4.5.1 the word "duplex" by the expression "*F*-number" and we replace the variables x and y by the variables r and s, respectively. We make the same replacement in propositions (73)–(79) and (81)–(87). In Theorems 4.6.1 and 4.6.2 we replace the variables x, y, z, u by the variables B_1, B_2, B_3, B_4, respectively.

All the propositions resulting from these replacements are true assertions about *F*-numbers.

In fact, if W is any of the symbols $=, \geq, \leq, \neq, <, >$, then

$$\forall xy (x W y \equiv \overline{\text{prin}_3(x)\, W\, \text{prin}_3(y)})$$

(cf. §4.2). It remains to quote 3.8.3.

4.8. For the proof of certain propositions formulated in the next part it is necessary to establish a supplement to Theorem 4.4.1. This supplement is Theorem 4.8.1, formulated below.

If x is an arbitrary duplex and y is a duplex which is a rational number, then, of course, each of assertions (a)–(e) of Theorem 4.4.1 holds. At the same time the following theorem also holds.

4.8.1. *For any duplex x and rational number a,*

$$(x = a) \equiv \forall k (M(a - \underline{x}(\bar{x}(k+1))) \leqslant 2^{-(k+1)}), \tag{a}$$

$$(x \geqslant a) \equiv \forall k (a - \underline{x}(\bar{x}(k+1)) \leqslant 2^{-(k+1)}), \tag{b}$$

$$(x \leqslant a) \equiv \forall k (\underline{x}(\bar{x}(k+1)) - a \leqslant 2^{-(k+1)}), \tag{c}$$

$$(x \neq a) \equiv \exists k (M(a - \underline{x}(\bar{x}(k+1))) > 2^{-(k+1)}), \tag{ }$$

$$(x < a) \equiv \exists k (a - \underline{x}(\bar{x}(k+1)) > 2^{-(k+1)}), \tag{e}$$

$$(x > a) \equiv \exists k (\underline{x}(\bar{x}(k+1)) - a > 2^{-(k+1)}). \tag{f}$$

Using the algorithms $\mathfrak{L}$ and $\mathfrak{L}^*$ introduced above in §4.4, and noting that

$$\forall ak (\underline{a}(\bar{a}(k)) \doteq a),$$

we can rewrite 4.8.1 in the form

$$\forall xa ((x = a) \equiv \forall k (\mathfrak{L}^*(x \square a \square k) \leqslant 2^{-(k+1)})), \tag{1}$$

$$\forall xa ((x \geqslant a) \equiv \forall k (\mathfrak{L}(x \square a \square k) \leqslant 2^{-(k+1)})), \tag{2}$$

$$\forall xa ((x \leqslant a) \equiv \forall k (\mathfrak{L}(a \square x \square k) \leqslant 2^{-(k+1)})), \tag{3}$$

$$\forall xa ((x \neq a) \equiv \exists k (\mathfrak{L}^*(x \square a \square k) > 2^{-(k+1)})), \tag{4}$$

$$\forall xa ((x < a) \equiv \exists k (\mathfrak{L}(x \square a \square k) > 2^{-(k+1)})), \tag{5}$$

$$\forall xa ((x > a) \equiv \exists k (\mathfrak{L}(a \square x \square k) > 2^{-(k+1)})). \tag{6}$$

Proof. First we prove assertion (5).

Let us construct an algorithm Γ in the alphabet $Ч_3^{sa}$ such that

$$\forall xak (\Gamma(x \square a \square k) \simeq \mu_m (\mathfrak{L}(x \square a \square k) - 2^{-(k+1)} \geqslant 2^{-m})).$$

We have

$$\forall xak (\mathfrak{L}(x \square a \square k) > 2^{-(k+1)} \supset \Gamma(x \square a \square k) \overset{+}{\in} \underline{\text{nat}}).$$

Let x be any duplex and a any rational number. In addition, assume that

$$\exists k (\mathfrak{L}(x \square a \square k) > 2^{-(k+1)}),$$

and let k be any natural number satisfying the condition

$$\mathfrak{L}(x \square a \square k) > 2^{-(k+1)}.$$

We introduce the notation

$$B \rightleftharpoons \Gamma(x \square a \square k).$$

Under the assumptions made above, we have

$$B \overset{+}{\in} \underline{\text{nat}}, \qquad \mathfrak{L}(x \square a \square k) \geqslant 2^{-(k+1)} + 2^{-B},$$

$$\mathfrak{L}(x \square a \square B + k) = a - \underline{x}(\bar{x}(k+1)) + \underline{x}(\bar{x}(k+1)) - \underline{x}(\bar{x}(B+k+1))$$

$$> 2^{-(k+1)} + 2^{-B} - 2^{-(k+1)} = 2^{-B} \geqslant 2^{-(B+k)},$$

$$\mathfrak{L}(x \square a \square B + k) > 2^{-(B+k)}.$$

Hence

$$\exists n(\mathfrak{L}(x\,\square\, a\,\square\, n)>2^{-n}).$$

We have proved the proposition.

$$\forall xa(\exists k(\mathfrak{L}(x\,\square\, a\,\square\, k)>2^{-(k+1)})\supset \exists n(\mathfrak{L}(x\,\square\, a\,\square\, n)>2^{-n})). \tag{7}$$

The proposition

$$\forall xa(\exists n(\mathfrak{L}(x\,\square\, a\,\square\, n)>2^{-n})\supset \exists k(\mathfrak{L}(x\,\square\, a\,\square\, k)>2^{-(k+1)})) \tag{8}$$

is obvious. (5) follows from (7) and (8).

The proof of proposition (6) is analogous to the proof of (5).

Proposition (4) follows from (5), (6), §4.5 (13), and §2.6 (2).

Propositions (1), (2), and (3) are consequences, respectively, of (4) and §4.5 (16), of (5) and §4.5 (17), and of (6) and §4.5 (18).

Theorem 4.8.1 has been proved.

4.9. In concluding this section we note three more theorems, connected with the relation $\leq$.

4.9.1. *If the duplexes x and y are such that*

$$\exists m\forall l(l\geqslant m\supset y\leqslant \underline{x}(l)),$$

then $y\leq x$.

4.9.2. *If the duplexes x and z are such that*

$$\exists m\forall l(l\geqslant m\supset \underline{x}(l)\leqslant z),$$

then $x\leq z$.

Theorems 4.9.1 and 4.9.2 are easily derived from the definition of the relation $\leq$. The following theorem 4.9.3, which is often applied in the sequel, is a consequence of 4.9.1 and 4.9.2.

4.9.3. *For any duplex x and any natural number k,*

$$\underline{x}(\overline{x}(k))-2^{-k}\leqslant x\leqslant \underline{x}(\overline{x}(k))+2^{-k}.$$

Proof. Let x be a duplex and k a natural number. For any l such that $l\geq \overline{x}(k)$, we have

$$M(\underline{x}(l)-\underline{x}(\overline{x}(k)))<2^{-k}.$$

Hence, if $l\geq \overline{x}(k)$, then

$$\underline{x}(\overline{x}(k))-2^{-k}<\underline{x}(l)<\underline{x}(\overline{x}(k))+2^{-k}.$$

Reference to §4.5 (43)–(44), 4.9.1 and 4.9.2 completes the proof of the theorem.

§5. SOME SPECIAL MAPPINGS OF DUPLEXES

5.1. In this section we shall introduce algorithms γ_- and γ_+ mapping any duplex x into duplexes $\gamma_-(x)$ and $\gamma_+(x)$, equal to the duplex x and such that

$$\forall k(\underline{\gamma_-(x)}(k) \leqslant x \leqslant \underline{\gamma_+(x)}(k)).$$

We construct the algorithm γ_- in the alphabet $Ч_3^{sa}$ such that

$$\forall x(\gamma_-(x) \overset{+}{\in} \underline{\text{can}}_3), \tag{1}$$

$$\forall xk(\underline{\gamma_-(x)}(k) \doteq \underline{x}(\bar{x}(k+1)) - 2^{-(k+1)}), \tag{2}$$

$$\forall xk(\overline{\gamma_-(x)}(k) \doteq k). \tag{3}$$

We construct the algorithm γ_+ in the alphabet $Ч_3^{sa}$ such that

$$\forall x(\gamma_+(x) \overset{+}{\in} \underline{\text{can}}_3), \tag{4}$$

$$\forall xk(\underline{\gamma_+(x)}(k) \doteq \underline{x}(\bar{x}(k+1)) + 2^{-(k+1)}), \tag{5}$$

$$\forall xk(\overline{\gamma_+(x)}(k) \doteq k). \tag{6}$$

The construction of the algorithms γ_- and γ_+ can be realized in the following manner. First we construct algorithms $\mathfrak{A}_-$ and $\mathfrak{A}_+$ in the alphabet $Ч_3^{sa}$ such that

$$\forall c_{3,1}c_{0,1}(\mathfrak{A}_-(c_{3,1} \square c_{0,1}) \simeq \underline{c_{3,1}}(\overline{c_{3,1}}(c_{0,1}+1)) - 2^{-(c_{0,1}+1)}),$$

$$\forall c_{3,1}c_{0,1}(\mathfrak{A}_+(c_{3,1} \square c_{0,1}) \simeq \underline{c_{3,1}}(\overline{c_{3,1}}(c_{0,1}+1)) + 2^{-(c_{0,1}+1)}).$$

Now (basing ourselves on 2.1.3 and starting from the algorithms $\mathfrak{A}_-$ and $\mathfrak{A}_+$) we construct algorithms $\mathfrak{B}_-$ and $\mathfrak{B}_+$ in the alphabet $Ч_3^{sa}$ such that

$$\forall c_{3,1}(\mathfrak{B}_-(c_{3,1}) \overset{+}{\in} c_0),$$
$$\forall c_{3,1}c_{0,1}(\langle\mathfrak{B}_-(c_{3,1})\rangle_2(c_{0,1}) \simeq \mathfrak{A}_-(c_{3,1} \square c_{0,1})),$$
$$\forall c_{3,1}(\mathfrak{B}_+(c_{3,1}) \overset{+}{\in} c_0),$$
$$\forall c_{3,1}c_{0,1}(\langle\mathfrak{B}_+(c_{3,1})\rangle_2(c_{0,1}) \simeq \mathfrak{A}_+(c_{3,1} \square c_{0,1})).$$

Further, we denote by E the transcription of the algorithm in the alphabet $Ч_0^{sa}$ defined by the schema

$$\{ \rightarrow \cdot,$$

and we denote by $\mathfrak{C}$ the algorithm in the alphabet $Ч_3^{sa}$ transforming any word in the alphabet $Ч_3$ into the word E. Applying the theorems on union and reduction of algorithms [1] to the pair of algorithms $\mathfrak{B}_-$, $\mathfrak{C}$ and to the pair of algorithms

$\mathfrak{B}_+$, $\mathfrak{C}$, we obtain algorithms γ_- and γ_+ in the alphabet $Ч_3^{sa}$ such that

$$\forall c_{3,1}(\gamma_-(c_{3,1}) \simeq \mathfrak{B}_-(c_{3,1}) \diamond \mathfrak{C}(c_{3,1})),$$
$$\forall c_{3,1}(\gamma_+(c_{3,1}) \simeq \mathfrak{B}_+(c_{3,1}) \diamond \mathfrak{C}(c_{3,1})).$$

It is obvious that the algorithm γ_- possesses properties (1)–(3) and algorithm γ_+ possesses properties (4)–(6).

5.1.1. *For any duplex x, the canonical words $\gamma_-(x)$ and $\gamma_+(x)$ are duplexes.*

Proof. Let x be any duplex and let k, m, n be any natural numbers. In addition, assume that $m, n, \geq k$. Then

$$M(\underline{\gamma_-(x)}(m) - \underline{\gamma_-(x)}(n)) = M(\underline{x}(\bar{x}(m+1)) - \underline{x}(\bar{x}(n+1))$$
$$+ 2^{-(n+1)} - 2^{-(m+1)}) \leqslant M(\underline{x}(\bar{x}(m+1)) - \underline{x}(\bar{x}(n+1)))$$
$$+ M(2^{-(n+1)} - 2^{-(m+1)}) < 2^{-(\min(m \square n)+1)} + 2^{-(\min(m \square n)+1)} = 2^{-\min(m \square n)} \leqslant 2^{-k}.$$

Hence

$$\forall xkmn(m, n \geqslant \overline{\gamma_-(x)}(k) \supset M(\underline{\gamma_-(x)}(m) - \underline{\gamma_-(x)}(n)) < 2^{-k}).$$

Analogously one proves that

$$\forall xkmn(m, n \geqslant \overline{\gamma_+(x)}(k) \supset M(\underline{\gamma_+(x)}(m) - \underline{\gamma_+(x)}(n)) < 2^{-k}).$$

Proposition 5.1.1 has been proved.

Now we shall prove the following auxiliary proposition.

5.1.2. *For any duplex x,*

$$\forall km(m \geqslant \bar{x}(k+1) \supset \underline{\gamma_-(x)}(k) < \underline{x}(m) < \underline{\gamma_-(x)}(k) + 2^{-k}), \tag{7}$$

$$\forall km(m \geqslant \max(\bar{x}(k+1) \square k) \supset M(\underline{\gamma_-(x)}(m) - \underline{x}(m)) < 2^{-k}), \tag{8}$$

$$\forall km(m \geqslant \bar{x}(k+1) \supset \underline{\gamma_+(x)}(k) - 2^{-k} < \underline{x}(m) < \underline{\gamma_+(x)}(k)), \tag{9}$$

$$\forall km(m \geqslant \max(\bar{x}(k+1) \square k) \supset M(\underline{\gamma_+(x)}(m) - \underline{x}(m)) < 2^{-k}). \tag{10}$$

Proof. Let x be any duplex and let k and m be any natural numbers. In addition, assume that $m \geq \bar{x}(k+1)$. Then

$$\underline{\gamma_-(x)}(k)-\underline{x}(m)=\underline{x}(\bar{x}(k+1))-\underline{x}(m)-2^{-(k+1)}<2^{-(k+1)}-2^{-(k+1)}=0,$$

$$\underline{x}(m)-(\underline{\gamma_-(x)}(k)+2^{-k})=\underline{x}(m)-\underline{x}(\bar{x}(k+1))+2^{-(k+1)}-2^{-k}$$

$$<2^{-(k+1)}-2^{-(k+1)}=0.$$

Hence

$$\underline{\gamma_-(x)}(k)<\underline{x}(m)<\underline{\gamma_-(x)}(k)+2^{-k}.$$

Proposition (7) has been proved.

Let x be any duplex and let k and m be any natural numbers. In addition, assume that

$$m\geqslant \max(\bar{x}(k+1)\,\square\, k).$$

Then $m \geq \bar{x}(k+1)$, $m \geq k$. Hence

$$M(\underline{\gamma_-(x)}(m)-\underline{x}(m))=M(\underline{x}(\bar{x}(m+1))-\underline{x}(m)-2^{-(m+1)})$$

$$\leqslant M(\underline{x}(\bar{x}(m+1))-\underline{x}(m))+2^{-(m+1)}<2^{-(\min(m\,\square\, k)+1)}$$

$$+2^{-(m+1)}=2^{-(k+1)}+2^{-(m+1)}\leqslant 2^{-k}.$$

Therefore

$$M(\underline{\gamma_-(x)}(m)-\underline{x}(m))<2^{-k}.$$

Proposition (8) has been proved.

The proof of proposition (9) is analogous to the proof of (7). The proof of proposition (10) is analogous to the proof of (8).

The following Theorem 5.1.3 states those properties of the algorithms γ_- and γ_+ which determine the role of these algorithms in the sequel.

5.1.3. *For any duplex* x,

$$\gamma_-(x)=\gamma_+(x)=x, \tag{11}$$

$$\forall k(\underline{\gamma_-(x)}(k)\leqslant x\leqslant \underline{\gamma_+(x)}(k)), \tag{12}$$

$$\forall k(\underline{\gamma_+(x)}(k)-\underline{\gamma_-(x)}(k)=2^{-k}). \tag{13}$$

Proof. Let x be any duplex and k any natural number. From (8) it follows that

$$\forall m(m\geqslant \max(\bar{x}(k+1)\,\square\, k)\supset M(\underline{\gamma_-(x)}(m)-\underline{x}(m))<2^{-k}).$$

Hence

$$\exists l \forall m (m \geqslant l \supset M(\underline{\gamma_-(x)}(m) - \underline{x}(m)) < 2^{-k}).$$

Therefore $\gamma_-(x) = x$. From (10) it follows that

$$\exists l \forall m (m \geqslant l \supset M(\underline{\gamma_+(x)}(m) - \underline{x}(m)) < 2^{-k}).$$

Hence $\gamma_+(x) = x$. Proposition (11) has been proved.

Further, introducing the same assumptions as above, we can conclude, on the basis of (7), that

$$\forall m (m \geqslant \overline{x}(k+1) \supset \underline{\gamma_-(x)}(k) - \underline{x}(m) < 0).$$

Let n be any natural number. We have

$$\forall m (m \geqslant \overline{x}(k+1) \supset \underline{\gamma_-(x)}(k) - \underline{x}(m) < 2^{-n}).$$

Hence[1)]

$$\exists l \forall m (m \geqslant l \supset \underline{\widehat{\underline{\gamma_-(x)}(k)}}(m) - \underline{x}(m) < 2^{-n}).$$

Therefore

$$\underline{\gamma_-(x)}(k) \leqslant x.$$

On the basis of (9) we prove in an analogous way that

$$x \leqslant \underline{\gamma_+(x)}(k).$$

Finally, directly from the definitions of γ_- and γ_+ we conclude that

$$\underline{\gamma_+(x)}(k) - \underline{\gamma_-(x)}(k) = 2^{-k}.$$

Theorem 5.1.3 has been proved.

5.2. Now we note that

$$\forall xyn (\mathfrak{L}(x \square y \square n) - 2^{-n} = \underline{\gamma_-(y)}(n) - \underline{\gamma_+(x)}(n)), \tag{1}$$

$$\forall xan (\mathfrak{L}(x \square a \square n) - 2^{-(n+1)} = a - \underline{\gamma_+(x)}(n)), \tag{2}$$

$$\forall xan (\mathfrak{L}(a \square x \square n) - 2^{-(n+1)} = \underline{\gamma_-(x)}(n) - a). \tag{3}$$

From §4.5 (7)–(8), 4.4.1 and (1) the next theorem follows immediately.

5.2.1. *For any duplexes* x *and* y,

---

1) In accordance with the convention made in §3.4, the expression $\widehat{\underline{\gamma_-(x)}(k)}$ denotes the duplex image of the rational number $\underline{\gamma_-(x)}(k)$.

$$(x=y)\equiv\forall n(\underline{\gamma_+(x)}(n)\geqslant\underline{\gamma_-(y)}(n)\,\&\,\underline{\gamma_-(x)}(n)\leqslant\underline{\gamma_+(y)}(n)),$$

$$(x\geqslant y)\equiv\forall n(\underline{\gamma_+(x)}(n)\geqslant\underline{\gamma_-(y)}(n)),$$

$$(x\leqslant y)\equiv\forall n(\underline{\gamma_-(x)}(n)\leqslant\underline{\gamma_+(y)}(n)),$$

$$(x\neq y)\equiv\exists n(\underline{\gamma_+(x)}(n)<\underline{\gamma_-(y)}(n)\vee\underline{\gamma_-(x)}(n)>\underline{\gamma_+(x)}(n)),$$

$$(x<y)\equiv\exists n(\underline{\gamma_+(x)}(n)<\gamma_-(y)(n)),$$

$$(x>y)\equiv\exists n(\underline{\gamma_-(x)}(n)>\underline{\gamma_+(y)}(n)).$$

From §4.5 (7)–(8), 4.8.1, (2) and (3) the next theorem immediately follows.

5.2.2. *For any duplex x and rational number a,*

$$(x=a)\equiv\forall n(\underline{\gamma_+(x)}(n)\geqslant a\,\&\,\underline{\gamma_-(x)}(n)\leqslant a),$$

$$(x\geqslant a)\equiv\forall n(\underline{\gamma_+(x)}(n)\geqslant a),$$

$$(x\leqslant a)\equiv\forall n(\underline{\gamma_-(x)}(n)\leqslant a),$$

$$(x\neq a)\equiv\exists n(\underline{\gamma_+(x)}(n)<a\vee\underline{\gamma_-(x)}(n)>a),$$

$$(x<a)\equiv\exists n(\underline{\gamma_+(x)}(n)<a),$$

$$(x>a)\equiv\exists n(\underline{\gamma_-(x)}(n)>a).$$

5.3. Next we introduce algorithms $\gamma_\uparrow$ and $\gamma_\downarrow$ transforming any duplex x into duplexes $\gamma_\uparrow(x)$ and $\gamma_\downarrow(x)$, respectively, which are equal to the duplex x and such that

$$\forall k(\underline{\gamma_\uparrow(x)}(k+1)\geqslant\underline{\gamma_\uparrow(x)}(k)),$$

$$\forall k(\underline{\gamma_\downarrow(x)}(k+1)\leqslant\underline{\gamma_\downarrow(x)}(k)).$$

We construct the algorithm $\gamma_\uparrow$ in the alphabet $Ч_3^{sa}$ such that

$$\forall x(\gamma_\uparrow(x)\overset{+}{\in}\underline{\text{can}}_3),$$

$$\forall xk(\underline{\gamma_\uparrow(x)}(k)\doteq\max(\underline{\gamma_-(x)}(0)\,\square\ldots\square\,\underline{\gamma_-(x)}(k))),\tag{1}$$

$$\forall xk(\overline{\gamma_\uparrow(x)}(k)\doteq k).$$

We construct the algorithm $\gamma_\downarrow$ in the alphabet $Ч_3^{sa}$ such that

$$\forall x\,(\gamma_\downarrow(x)\ \overset{+}{\in}\ \underline{\mathrm{can}}_3),$$

$$\forall xk\,(\underline{\gamma_\downarrow(x)}(k) \doteq \min(\underline{\gamma_+(x)}(0)\,\square \ldots \square\, \underline{\gamma_+(x)}(k))), \tag{2}$$

$$\forall xk\left(\overline{\gamma_\downarrow(x)}(k) \doteq k\right).$$

The construction of the algorithms $\gamma_\uparrow$ and $\gamma_\downarrow$ can be carried out in the following manner. First we construct algorithms $\mathfrak{M}_\uparrow$ and $\mathfrak{M}_\downarrow$ in the alphabet $Ч_3^{sa}$ such that

$$\forall c_{3,1}\,(\mathfrak{M}_\uparrow(c_{3,1}\square 0) \simeq \underline{\gamma_-(c_{3,1})}(0)),$$

$$\forall c_{3,1}k\,(\mathfrak{M}_\uparrow(c_{3,1}\square k+1) \simeq \max(\mathfrak{M}_\uparrow(c_{3,1}\square k)\square \underline{\gamma_-(c_{3,1})}(k+1))),$$

$$\forall c_{3,1}\,(\mathfrak{M}_\downarrow(c_{3,1}\square 0) \simeq \gamma_+(c_{3,1})(0)),$$

$$\forall c_{3,1}k\,(\mathfrak{M}_\downarrow(c_{3,1}\square k+1) \simeq \min(\mathfrak{M}_\downarrow(c_{3,1}\square k)\square \underline{\gamma_+(c_{3,1})}(k+1))).$$

The algorithms $\mathfrak{M}_\uparrow$ and $\mathfrak{M}_\downarrow$ can be constructed by the method by means of which V. K. Detlovs, in [29], constructed a normal algorithm corresponding to the schema of recursion with respect to the last argument.

The next part of the process of constructing algorithms $\gamma_\uparrow$ and $\gamma_\downarrow$ is completely analogous to the part of the process of constructing algorithms γ_- and γ_+ which follows the construction of the algorithm $\mathfrak{A}_-$ and $\mathfrak{A}_+$. Only now, instead of $\mathfrak{A}_-$ and $\mathfrak{A}_+$, we use the algorithms $\mathfrak{M}_\uparrow$ and $\mathfrak{M}_\downarrow$, respectively.

Let us prove the following auxiliary proposition.

5.3.1.
$$\forall xkl\,(\underline{\gamma_-(x)}(l) - \underline{\gamma_\uparrow(x)}(k) < 2^{-k}), \tag{3}$$

$$\forall xkl\,(\underline{\gamma_\downarrow(x)}(k) - \underline{\gamma_+(x)}(l) < 2^{-k}). \tag{4}$$

Proof. Let x be any duplex, and k and l any natural numbers. We consider two cases.

Case 1: $\underline{\gamma_-(x)}(l) \le_{\mathrm{p}} \underline{\gamma_\uparrow(x)}(k)$. In this case

$$\underline{\gamma_-(x)}(l) - \underline{\gamma_\uparrow(x)}(k) \leqslant 0 < 2^{-k}.$$

Case 2: $\underline{\gamma_-(x)}(l) >_{\mathrm{p}} \underline{\gamma_\uparrow(x)}(k)$. From (1) it follows that $l > k$ and $\underline{\gamma_\uparrow(x)}(k) \ge \underline{\gamma_-(x)}(k)$. From these inequalities and from 5.1 (3) it follows that

$$\underline{\gamma_-(x)}(l)-\underline{\gamma_\uparrow(x)}(k)\leqslant\underline{\gamma_-(x)}(l)-\underline{\gamma_-(x)}(k)<2^{-k}.$$

Now we note that

$$\forall xkl\,(\underline{\gamma_-(x)}(l)\underset{\mathrm{p}}{\leqslant}\underline{\gamma_\uparrow(x)}(k)\vee\underline{\gamma_-(x)}(l)\underset{\mathrm{p}}{>}\underline{\gamma_\uparrow(x)}(k)).$$

Hence (3) holds.

The proof of proposition (4) is analogous to the proof of (3).

Now let us prove the following proposition.

5.3.2. *For any duplex x, the canonical words $\gamma_\uparrow(x)$ and $\gamma_\downarrow(x)$ are duplexes.*

Proof. Let x be any duplex, and k, m, n any natural numbers. In addition, assume that $m, n \geq k$. We introduce the notation

$$R \rightleftharpoons \underline{\gamma_\uparrow(x)}(m)-\underline{\gamma_\uparrow(x)}(n).$$

We consider three cases:

Case 1: $R =_{\mathrm{p}} 0$. In this case

$$M(R)=0<2^{-k}.$$

Case 2: $R >_{\mathrm{p}} 0$. In this case

$$\underline{\gamma_\uparrow(x)}(m)>\underline{\gamma_\uparrow(x)}(n)\geqslant\underline{\gamma_\uparrow(x)}(k).$$

On the basis of (1) we can find l such that $0 \leq l \leq m$ and

$$\underline{\gamma_\uparrow(x)}(m)=\underline{\gamma_-(x)}(l).$$

We introduce the notation

$$C \rightleftharpoons \mu_l(\underline{\gamma_\uparrow(x)}(m)=\underline{\gamma_-(x)}(l)).$$

On the basis of 5.3.1 we have

$$M(R)=R=\underline{\gamma_-(x)}(C)-\underline{\gamma_\uparrow(x)}(n)$$

$$\leqslant\underline{\gamma_-(x)}(C)-\underline{\gamma_\uparrow(x)}(k)<2^{-k}.$$

Case 3: $R <_{\mathrm{p}} 0$. We introduce the notation

$$Q \rightleftharpoons \underline{\gamma_\uparrow(x)}(n)-\underline{\gamma_\uparrow(x)}(m).$$

We have

$$Q\underset{\mathrm{p}}{>}0, \qquad M(R)=Q.$$

The rest of the argument in this case is obtained as a result of replacing in the argument for the preceding case the letters R, m, n by the letters Q, n, m, respectively. We obtain the result

$$M(R)=M(Q)<2^{-k}.$$

Now we note that

$$\forall xmn\,(R \underset{\mathrm{p}}{=} 0 \lor R \underset{\mathrm{p}}{>} 0 \lor R \underset{\mathrm{p}}{<} 0).$$

Hence

$$\forall xkmn\,(m,\, n \geqslant \overline{\gamma_{\uparrow}(x)}(k) \supset M(R)<2^{-k}).$$

We have proved that for any duplex x the canonical word $\gamma_{\uparrow}(x)$ is a duplex.

One proves in an analogous way that for any duplex x the canonical word $\gamma_{\downarrow}(x)$ is a duplex.

The following theorem 5.3.3 states those properties of the algorithms $\gamma_{\uparrow}$ and $\gamma_{\downarrow}$ which determine the role of these algorithms in the sequel.

5.3.3. *For any duplex* x,

$$\gamma_{\uparrow}(x)=\gamma_{\downarrow}(x)=x, \tag{5}$$

$$\forall k\,(\underline{\gamma_{\uparrow}(x)}(k) \leqslant x \leqslant \underline{\gamma_{\downarrow}(x)}(k)), \tag{6}$$

$$\forall k\,(\underline{\gamma_{\downarrow}(x)}(k) - \underline{\gamma_{\downarrow}(x)}(k) \leqslant 2^{-k}), \tag{7}$$

$$\forall kl\,(k \geqslant l \supset \underline{\gamma_{\uparrow}(x)}(k) \geqslant \underline{\gamma_{\uparrow}(x)}(l)), \tag{8}$$

$$\forall kl\,(k \geqslant l \supset \underline{\gamma_{\downarrow}(x)}(k) \leqslant \underline{\gamma_{\downarrow}(x)}(l)). \tag{9}$$

Proof. We construct algorithms $\delta_{\uparrow}$ and $\delta_{\downarrow}$ in the alphabet $Ч_3^{\text{sa}}$ such that

$$\forall xk\,(\delta_{\downarrow}(x \square k) \simeq \mu_l(\underline{\gamma_{\uparrow}(x)}(k) = \underline{\gamma_{-}(x)}(l))), \tag{10}$$

$$\forall xk\,(\delta_{\downarrow}(x \square k) \simeq \mu_l(\underline{\gamma_{\downarrow}(x)}(k) = \underline{\gamma_{+}(x)}(l))). \tag{11}$$

It is obvious that

$$\forall xk\,(\delta_{\uparrow}(x \square k) \overset{+}{\in} \underline{\mathrm{nat}} \,\&\, 0 \leqslant \delta_{\uparrow}(x \square k) \leqslant k),$$

$$\forall xk\,(\delta_{\downarrow}(x \square k) \overset{+}{\in} \underline{\mathrm{nat}} \,\&\, 0 \leqslant \delta_{\downarrow}(x \square k) \leqslant k).$$

In addition, from (1), (10), (2), (11), and 5.1.3 it follows that

$$\forall xk\,(\underline{\gamma_{-}(x)}(k) \leqslant \underline{\gamma_{\uparrow}(x)}(k) = \underline{\gamma_{-}(x)}(\delta_{\uparrow}(x \square k)) \leqslant x), \tag{12}$$

$$\forall xk\,(\underline{\gamma_{+}(x)}(k) \geqslant \underline{\gamma_{\downarrow}(x)}(k) = \underline{\gamma_{+}(x)}(\delta_{\downarrow}(x \square k)) \geqslant x). \tag{13}$$

From (12), (13) and 5.1.3 propositions (5), (6), and (7) follow. Propositions (8) and (9) are consequences of (1) and (2).

The next theorem is a direct consequence of Theorem 5.3.3.

5.3.4. *For any duplex x, duplexes y and z are potentially realizable such that*

$$y = z = x,$$
$$\forall k (\underline{y}(k) \leqslant x \leqslant \underline{z}(k)),$$
$$\forall k (\underline{z}(k) - \underline{y}(k) \leqslant 2^{-k}),$$
$$\forall kl (k \geqslant l \supset \underline{y}(k) \geqslant \underline{y}(l)),$$
$$\forall kl (k \geqslant l \supset \underline{z}(k) \leqslant \underline{z}(l)).$$

The next theorem is a consequence of 5.3.4.

5.3.5. *For any F-number q, F-numbers r and s are potentially realizable such that*

$$r = s = q,$$
$$\forall k (\underline{r}(k) \leqslant q \leqslant \underline{s}(k)),$$
$$\forall k (\underline{s}(k) - \underline{r}(k) \leqslant 2^{-k}),$$
$$\forall kl (k \geqslant l \supset \underline{r}(k) \geqslant \underline{r}(l)),$$
$$\forall kl (k \geqslant l \supset \underline{s}(k) \leqslant \underline{s}(l)).$$

In fact, if by means of the algorithm for adjoint formulas described in §3.8 we construct the proposition adjoint to 5.3.5, and if we use the fact that

$$\forall yk (\underbrace{\overline{\mathrm{prin}_3(y)}(k)}\, \underset{\mathrm{P}}{=} \underline{y}(k)),$$

then we obtain proposition 5.3.4. For the proof of 5.3.5 we need only quote 3.8.3 and 5.3.4.

§6. BASIC OPERATIONS ON CONSTRUCTIVE REAL NUMBERS

6.1. In this section we shall define the following operations on duplexes: the operation of constructing the absolute value (modulus), the operation of constructing the maximum, the operation of constructing the minimum, the operations of addition, subtraction, multiplication, division, and raising to an integral power. Each of these algorithms is an algorithm in the alphabet $Ч_3^{sa}$. The enumerated operations will be denoted, respectively, by

$$\underset{\mathrm{B}}{M},\ \underset{\mathrm{B}}{\max},\ \underset{\mathrm{B}}{\min},\ \underset{\mathrm{B}}{+},\ \underset{\mathrm{B}}{-},\ \underset{\mathrm{B}}{\cdot},\ \underset{\mathrm{B}}{:},\ \underset{\mathrm{B}}{\wedge}.$$

For the construction of these operations we shall use an algorithm $\mathfrak{R}$ in the alphabet Ч_3^{sa}, applicable to any word in the alphabet Ч_3^{s} and such that, for any words $c_{3,1}$ and $c_{3,2}$,

$$\mathfrak{R}(c_{3,1}) \mathrel{\dot{=}} \Lambda \equiv c_{3,1} \in \underline{\text{rat}},$$

$$\mathfrak{R}(c_{3,1} \square c_{3,2}) \mathrel{\dot{=}} \Lambda \equiv c_{3,1} \in \underline{\text{rat}} \mathbin{\&} c_{3,2} \in \underline{\text{rat}}.$$

The algorithm $\mathfrak{R}$ distinguishes the rational numbers among all words in the alphabet Ч_3 and pairs of rational numbers among all pairs of words in the alphabet Ч_3.

Construction of the operation M_{B}. We construct algorithms $\mathfrak{A}_0$ and $\mathfrak{B}_0$ in the alphabet Ч_3^{sa} such that, for all admissible values of the variables,

$$\mathfrak{A}_0(x) \mathrel{\dot{\in}} c_0, \qquad \mathfrak{B}_0(x) \mathrel{\dot{\in}} c_0,$$

$$\langle \mathfrak{A}_0(x) \rangle_2 (k) \simeq \underset{\mathrm{P}}{M}(\underline{x}(k)),$$

$$\langle \mathfrak{B}_0(x) \rangle_0 (k) \simeq \overline{x}(k).$$

The construction of the algorithms $\mathfrak{A}_0$ and $\mathfrak{B}_0$ satisfying the indicated conditions can be carried out in the following way. First of all, on the basis of 2.1.1, we construct algorithms $\mathfrak{P}$ and $\mathfrak{Q}$ in the alphabet Ч_3^{sa} such that, for all admissible values of the variables,

$$\mathfrak{P}(c_{3,1} \square c_{0,1}) \simeq \underset{\mathrm{P}}{M}(\underline{c_{3,1}}(c_{0,1})),$$

$$\mathfrak{Q}(c_{3,1} \square c_{0,1}) \simeq \overline{c_{3,1}}(c_{0,1}).$$

On the basis of 2.1.3 we can construct algorithms $\mathfrak{A}_0$ and $\mathfrak{B}_0$ in the alphabet Ч_3^{sa} such that, for all admissible values of the variables,

$$\mathfrak{A}_0(c_{3,1}) \mathrel{\dot{\in}} c_0, \qquad \mathfrak{B}_0(c_{3,1}) \mathrel{\dot{\in}} c_0,$$

$$\langle \mathfrak{A}_0(c_{3,1}) \rangle_2 (c_{0,1}) \simeq \mathfrak{P}(c_{3,1} \square c_{0,1}),$$

$$\langle \mathfrak{B}_0(c_{3,1}) \rangle_0 (c_{0,1}) \simeq \mathfrak{Q}(c_{3,1} \square c_{0,1}).$$

The algorithms $\mathfrak{A}_0$ and $\mathfrak{B}_0$ are the desired ones.

Let x be any duplex, i any natural number, and k and l any natural numbers such that $k, l \geq \overline{x}(i)$. We introduce the notation

$$\mathfrak{M}_0 \rightleftharpoons \langle \mathfrak{A}_0(x) \rangle_2, \qquad \mathfrak{N}_0 \rightleftharpoons \langle \mathfrak{B}_0(x) \rangle_0.$$

We have

$$\mathfrak{M}_0(i) \overset{+}{\in} \underline{\text{rat}}, \quad \mathfrak{N}_0(i) \overset{+}{\in} \underline{\text{nat}},$$

$$\underset{\text{p}}{M}(\mathfrak{M}_0(k) - \mathfrak{M}_0(l)) \leqslant \underset{\text{p}}{M}(\underline{x}(k) - \underline{x}(l)) < 2^{-i}.$$

Hence $\mathfrak{M}_0 \in (\text{H} \rightarrow \text{P})_2$, $\mathfrak{N}_0 \in (\text{H} \rightarrow \text{H})_0$, and $\mathfrak{N}_0$ is a regulator of convergence of the algorithm $\mathfrak{M}_0$. Therefore the word

$$\mathfrak{A}_0(x) \diamondsuit \mathfrak{B}_0(x)$$

is a duplex.

Using theorems on the union, branching, and reduction of algorithms [1], we construct an algorithm M_{B} in the alphabet $Ч_3^{\text{sa}}$ such that, for any duplex x,

$$\mathfrak{R}(x) \mathrel{\dot{=}} \Lambda \supset \underset{\text{B}}{M}(x) \mathrel{\dot{\simeq}} \underset{\text{p}}{M}(x),$$

$$\mathfrak{R}(x) \mathrel{\dot{\neq}} \Lambda \supset \underset{\text{B}}{M}(x) \simeq \mathfrak{A}_0(x) \diamondsuit \mathfrak{B}_0(x).$$

We have

$$\forall x (\underset{\text{B}}{M}(x) \overset{+}{\in} \underline{\text{real dup}}),$$

$$\forall a \, (\underset{\text{B}}{M}(a) \mathrel{\dot{=}} \underset{\text{p}}{M}(a) \,\&\, \underset{\text{B}}{M}(a) \overset{+}{\in} \underline{\text{red. rat}}).$$

In what follows we shall often use, instead of the notation M_{B} (as well as instead of M_{p}) the briefer notation M, if the use of such an abbreviation does not lead to ambiguity.

Construction of the operations $\max_{\text{B}}$, $\min_{\text{B}}$, $+_{\text{B}}$, $-_{\text{B}}$. We construct algorithms $\mathfrak{A}_1$, $\mathfrak{A}_2$, $\mathfrak{A}_3$, $\mathfrak{A}_4$, and $\mathfrak{B}_*$ in the alphabet $Ч_3^{\text{sa}}$ such that, for all admissible values of the variables,

$$\mathfrak{A}_j(x \square y) \overset{+}{\in} \text{c}_0 \qquad (j = 1, 2, 3, 4),$$

$$\mathfrak{B}_*(x \square y) \overset{+}{\in} \text{c}_0,$$

$$\langle \mathfrak{A}_1(x \square y) \rangle_2(k) \simeq \underset{\text{p}}{\max}(\underline{x}(k) \square \underline{y}(k)),$$

$$\langle \mathfrak{A}_2(x \square y) \rangle_2(k) \simeq \underset{\text{p}}{\min}(\underline{x}(k) \square \underline{y}(k)),$$

$$\langle \mathfrak{A}_3(x \square y) \rangle_2(k) \simeq \underline{x}(k) \underset{\text{p}}{+} \underline{y}(k),$$

$$\langle \mathfrak{A}_4(x \square y) \rangle_2(k) \simeq \underline{x}(k) \underset{\text{p}}{-} \underline{y}(k),$$

$$\langle \mathfrak{B}_*(x \square y) \rangle_0(k) \simeq \underset{\text{p}}{\max}(\overline{x}(k \underset{\text{p}}{+} 1) \square \overline{y}(k \underset{\text{p}}{+} 1)).$$

The method of constructing algorithms $\mathfrak{A}_1$, $\mathfrak{A}_2$, $\mathfrak{A}_3$, $\mathfrak{A}_4$, and $\mathfrak{B}_*$ is similar to the method of constructing the algorithms $\mathfrak{A}_0$ and $\mathfrak{B}_0$. Let x and y be any duplexes, i any natural number, and k and l any natural numbers such that

$$k,\ l \geqslant \max_{\mathrm{p}}(\overline{x}(i+1)\square\overline{y}(i+1)).$$

We introduce the notation

$$\mathfrak{M}_j \rightleftharpoons \langle \mathfrak{A}_i(x\square y)\rangle_2 \qquad (j=1,\ 2,\ 3,\ 4),$$
$$\mathfrak{N}_* \rightleftharpoons \langle \mathfrak{B}_*(x\square y)\rangle_0, \qquad I \rightleftharpoons \langle \mathfrak{B}_*(x\square y)\rangle_0(i).$$

We have

$$\mathfrak{M}_j(i) \overset{+}{\in} \underline{\text{rat}} \qquad (j=1,\ 2,\ 3,\ 4), \tag{1}$$
$$\mathfrak{N}_*(i) \overset{+}{\in} \underline{\text{nat}}, \tag{2}$$
$$M(\mathfrak{M}_1(k)-\mathfrak{M}_1(l)) \leqslant M(\mathfrak{M}_1(k)-\mathfrak{M}_1(I)) + M(\mathfrak{M}_1(I)-\mathfrak{M}_1(l)). \tag{3}$$

Since $l,\ k,\ l \geq \overline{x}(i+1)$ and $I,\ k,\ l \geq \overline{y}(i+1)$, we have

$$\underline{x}(I)-2^{-(i+1)} < \underline{x}(k) < \underline{x}(I)+2^{-(i+1)},$$
$$\underline{y}(I)-2^{-(i+1)} < \underline{y}(k) < \underline{y}(I)+2^{-(i+1)},$$
$$\underline{x}(I)-2^{-(i+1)} < \underline{x}(l) < \underline{x}(I)+2^{-(i+1)},$$
$$\underline{y}(I)-2^{-(i+1)} < \underline{y}(l) < \underline{y}(I)+2^{-(i+1)}.$$

From this we obtain

$$\mathfrak{M}_1(I)-2^{-(i+1)} < \mathfrak{M}_1(k) < \mathfrak{M}_1(I)+2^{-(i+1)},$$
$$\mathfrak{M}_1(I)-2^{-(i+1)} < \mathfrak{M}_1(l) < \mathfrak{M}_1(I)+2^{-(i+1)}.$$

Hence

$$M(\mathfrak{M}_1(k)-\mathfrak{M}_1(I)) < 2^{-(i+1)}, \tag{4}$$
$$M(\mathfrak{M}_1(l)-\mathfrak{M}_1(I)) < 2^{-(i+1)}. \tag{5}$$

From (3), (4), and (5), we obtain

$$M(\mathfrak{M}_1(k)-\mathfrak{M}_1(l)) < 2^{-i}. \tag{6}$$

One proves in a similar way that

$$M(\mathfrak{M}_2(k)-\mathfrak{M}_2(l)) < 2^{-i}. \tag{7}$$

In addition, we have

$$M(\mathfrak{M}_3(k)-\mathfrak{M}_3(l)) = M((\underline{x}(k)+\underline{y}(k))-(\underline{x}(l)+\underline{y}(l)))$$
$$\leqslant M(\underline{x}(k)-\underline{x}(l)) + M(\underline{y}(k)-\underline{y}(l)) < 2^{-(i+1)}+2^{-(i+1)} = 2^{-i}.$$

Hence

$$M(\mathfrak{M}_3(k) - \mathfrak{M}_3(l)) < 2^{-i}. \tag{8}$$

One proves in a similar way that

$$M(\mathfrak{M}_4(k) - \mathfrak{M}_4(l)) < 2^{-i}. \tag{9}$$

From (1), (2), (6), (7), (8), and (9), it follows that $\mathfrak{M}_j \in (\mathrm{H} \to \mathrm{P})_2$ $(j = 1, 2, 3, 4)$, $\mathfrak{N}_* \in (\mathrm{H} \to \mathrm{H})_0$, and $\mathfrak{N}_*$ is a regulator of convergence in itself of the algorithms $\mathfrak{M}_1$, $\mathfrak{M}_2$, $\mathfrak{M}_3$, $\mathfrak{M}_4$. Hence the words

$$\mathfrak{A}_1(x \square y) \diamond \mathfrak{B}_*(x \square y), \qquad \mathfrak{A}_2(x \square y) \diamond \mathfrak{B}_*(x \square y),$$
$$\mathfrak{A}_3(x \square y) \diamond \mathfrak{B}_*(x \square y), \qquad \mathfrak{A}_4(x \square y) \diamond \mathfrak{B}_*(x \square y)$$

are duplexes.

Using theorems on the union, branching, and reduction of algorithms [1], we construct algorithms $\max_{B,0}$, $\min_{B,0}$, $+_{B,0}$, $-_{B,0}$ in the alphabet $\mathrm{Ч}_3^{sa}$ such that, for any duplexes x and y,

$$\mathfrak{R}(x \square y) = \Lambda \supset \underset{\mathrm{B}}{\max}_0(x \square y) \simeq \underset{\mathrm{P}}{\max}(x \square y),$$

$$\mathfrak{R}(x \square y) \neq \Lambda \supset \underset{\mathrm{B}}{\max}_0(x \square y) \simeq \mathfrak{A}_1(x \square y) \diamond \mathfrak{B}_*(x \square y),$$

$$\mathfrak{R}(x \square y) = \Lambda \supset \underset{\mathrm{B}}{\min}_0(x \square y) \simeq \underset{\mathrm{P}}{\min}(x \square y),$$

$$\mathfrak{R}(x \square y) \neq \Lambda \supset \underset{\mathrm{B}}{\min}_0(x \square y) \simeq \mathfrak{A}_2(x \square y) \diamond \mathfrak{B}_*(x \square y),$$

$$\mathfrak{R}(x \square y) = \Lambda \supset \underset{\mathrm{B}}{+}_0(x \square y) \simeq \underset{\mathrm{P}}{+}(x \square y),$$

$$\mathfrak{R}(x \square y) \neq \Lambda \supset \underset{\mathrm{B}}{+}_0(x \square y) \simeq \mathfrak{A}_3(x \square y) \diamond \mathfrak{B}_*(x \square y),$$

$$\mathfrak{R}(x \square y) = \Lambda \supset \underset{\mathrm{B}}{-}_0(x \square y) \simeq \underset{\mathrm{P}}{-}(x \square y),$$

$$\mathfrak{R}(x \square y) \neq \Lambda \supset \underset{\mathrm{B}}{-}_0(x \square y) \simeq \mathfrak{A}_4(x \square y) \diamond \mathfrak{B}_*(x \square y),$$

$$\underset{\mathrm{B}}{-}_0(y) \simeq \underset{\mathrm{B}}{-}_0(0 \square y).$$

It is not difficult to establish the following lemma.

6.1.1. *Let* A *be some alphabet not containing the symbol* $\square$, *and let* $\mathfrak{A}$ *be some normal algorithm over the alphabet* A^s. *One can construct a normal algorithm* $\mathfrak{B}$ *over the alphabet* A^s *such that, for any natural number* j *not less than three* *and for any words* $S_1, S_2, \cdots, S_j$ *in the alphabet* A,

$$\mathfrak{B}(S_1 \square S_2) \simeq \mathfrak{A}(S_1 \square S_2),$$

$$\mathfrak{B}(S_1 \square S_2 \square \ldots \square S_{j-1} \square S_j) \simeq \mathfrak{A}(\mathfrak{B}(S_1 \square S_2 \square \ldots \square S_{j-1}) \square S_j).$$

Let $\delta_{B,0}$ be any of the algorithms $\max_{B,0}$, $\min_{B,0}$, $+_{B,0}$, $-_{B,0}$. Applying 6.1.1 to the case where $Ч_3$ plays the role of the alphabet A and $\delta_{B,0}$ plays the role of the algorithm $\mathfrak{A}$ and then applying the theorem on the reduction of algorithms, we obtain an algorithm in the alphabet $Ч_3^{sa}$ which is a generalization of the operation $\delta_{B,0}$ to all systems of duplexes. We can denote this algorithm by the expression obtained from the designation of the algorithm $\delta_{B,0}$ by removing from this designation the subscript "0".

We obtain algorithms

$$\max_B, \min_B, +_B, -_B.$$

If δ is any of the expressions max, min, +, −, and $j \geq 2$, then

$$\tilde{\forall}(\delta_B(\text{д}_1 \square \ldots \square \text{д}_j) \stackrel{+}{\in} \underline{\text{real dup}}),$$

$$\tilde{\forall}(\delta_B(\text{p}_1 \square \ldots \square \text{p}_j) \mathrel{\dot{=}} \delta_P(\text{p}_1 \square \ldots \square \text{p}_j) \,\&\, \delta_B(\text{p}_1 \square \ldots \square \text{p}_j) \stackrel{+}{\in} \underline{\text{red. rat}}).$$

Let $\Theta_1, \Theta_2, \cdots, \Theta_j$ ($j \geq 2$) be any individual terms. In accordance with established mathematical practice we agree to denote the terms

$$+_B(\Theta_1 \square \Theta_2 \square \ldots \square \Theta_j), \quad -_B(\Theta_1 \square \Theta_2 \square \ldots \square \Theta_j)$$

by the expressions

$$(\Theta_1 +_B \Theta_2 +_B \ldots +_B \Theta_j), \quad (\Theta_1 -_B \Theta_2 -_B \ldots -_B \Theta_j).$$

respectively.

We agree to denote the term $-_B(\Theta)$, where Θ is any individual term, by the briefer expression $-_B\Theta$, if the use of this abbreviation does not lead to ambiguity.

In using abbreviations of terms and formulas we shall assume that the symbols $+_B$ and $-_B$ have rank 2 (cf. §1.14, V).

In what follows we shall often use, instead of the notation $\max_B$, $\min_B$, $+_B$, $-_B$ (just as instead of the notation $\max_P$, $\min_P$, $+_P$, $-_P$) the shorter notation max, min, +, −, if the use of such abbreviated notation does not lead to ambiguity.

Construction of the operation $\cdot_B$. We construct algorithms $\mathfrak{A}_5$ and $\mathfrak{B}_5$ in the alphabet $Ч_3^{sa}$ such that, for all admissible values of the variables,

$$\mathfrak{A}_5(x \square y) \overset{+}{\in} \mathrm{c}_0, \qquad \mathfrak{B}_5(x \square y) \overset{+}{\in} \mathrm{c}_0,$$

$$\langle \mathfrak{A}_5(x \square y)\rangle_2(k) \simeq \underline{x}(k) \underset{\mathrm{p}}{\cdot} \underline{y}(k),$$

$$\langle \mathfrak{B}_5(x \square y)\rangle_2(k) \simeq \max(\overline{x}(0) \square \overline{y}(0) \square \overline{x}(k+1+D) \square \overline{y}(k+1+D)),$$

where

$$D \rightleftharpoons \mu_i(\max(M(\underline{x}(\overline{x}(0)))+1 \square M(\underline{y}(\overline{y}(0)))+1) \leqslant 2^i).$$

The letter μ denotes the operator for searching for the least natural number satisfying a given condition (cf. §2.2).

The method of constructing algorithms $\mathfrak{A}_5$ and $\mathfrak{B}_5$ is similar to the method of constructing algorithms $\mathfrak{A}_0$ and $\mathfrak{B}_0$. Let x and y be any duplexes, i any natural number, and k and l any natural numbers such that

$$k,\ l \geqslant \langle \mathfrak{B}_5(x \square y)\rangle_0(i).$$

We introduce the notation

$$\mathfrak{M}_5 \rightleftharpoons \langle \mathfrak{A}_5(x \square y)\rangle_2, \qquad \mathfrak{N}_5 \rightleftharpoons \langle \mathfrak{B}_5(x \square y)\rangle_0.$$

We have

$$\mathfrak{M}_5(i) \overset{+}{\in} \underline{\mathrm{rat}}, \qquad \mathfrak{N}_5(i) \overset{+}{\in} \underline{\mathrm{nat}}, \tag{10}$$

$$M(\mathfrak{M}_5(k) - \mathfrak{M}_5(l)) = M(\underline{x}(k) \underset{\mathrm{p}}{\cdot} \underline{y}(k) - \underline{x}(l) \underset{\mathrm{p}}{\cdot} \underline{y}(l))$$

$$\leqslant M(\underline{x}(k)) \underset{\mathrm{p}}{\cdot} M(\underline{y}(k) + \underline{y}(l)) + M(\underline{y}(l)) \underset{\mathrm{p}}{\cdot} M(\underline{x}(k) - \underline{x}(l)). \tag{11}$$

In addition,

$$\forall m(m \geqslant \overline{x}(0) \supset M(\underline{x}(m) - \underline{x}(\overline{x}(0))) < 2^{-0}).$$

Since $k \geq \overline{x}(0)$, we have

$$M(\underline{x}(k) - \underline{x}(\overline{x}(0))) < 1.$$

Hence

$$M(\underline{x}(k)) < M(\underline{x}(\overline{x}(0))) + 1 \leqslant 2^D. \tag{12}$$

Similarly we obtain

$$M(\underline{y}(l)) < 2^D. \tag{13}$$

In addition, since $k, l \geq \overline{x}(i+1+D)$, and $k, l \geq \overline{y}(i+1+D)$, we have

$$M(\underline{x}(k) - \underline{x}(l)) < 2^{-(i+1+D)}, \qquad M(\underline{y}(k) - \underline{y}(l)) < 2^{-(i+1+D)}. \tag{14}$$

From (11) and (14) it follows that

$$M(\mathfrak{M}_5(k) - \mathfrak{M}_5(l)) < 2^D \underset{\mathrm{p}}{\cdot} 2^{-(i+1+D)} + 2^D \underset{\mathrm{p}}{\cdot} 2^{-(i+1+D)} = 2^{-i}. \tag{15}$$

From (10) and (15) it follows that $\mathfrak{M}_5 \in (\text{H} \to \text{P})_2$, $\mathfrak{N}_5 \in (\text{H} \to \text{H})_0$, and $\mathfrak{N}_5$ is a regulator of convergence in itself of the algorithm $\mathfrak{M}_5$. Hence the word $\mathfrak{A}_5(x \square y) \diamondsuit \mathfrak{B}_5(x \square y)$ is a duplex.

Using theorems on union branching, and reduction of algorithms [1], we construct an algorithm $\cdot_{\text{B},0}$ in the alphabet Ч_3^{sa} such that, for any duplexes x and y,

$$\mathfrak{R}(x \square y) \mathrel{\overline{\overline{\cdot}}} \Lambda \supset \underset{\text{B}}{\cdot_0}(x \square y) \simeq \underset{\text{P}}{\cdot}(x \square y),$$

$$\mathfrak{R}(x \square y) \not\mathrel{\overline{\overline{\cdot}}} \Lambda \supset \underset{\text{B}}{\cdot_0}(x \square y) \simeq \mathfrak{A}_5(x \square y) \diamondsuit \mathfrak{B}_5(x \square y).$$

Applying Lemma 6.1.1 to the case where Ч_3 plays the role of the alphabet A and $\cdot_{\text{B},0}$ plays the role of the algorithm $\mathfrak{A}$, and then applying the theorem on reduction of algorithms, we obtain an algorithm in the alphabet Ч_3^{sa} (denoted by $\cdot_{\text{B}}$) such that, for any natural number j not less than three and for any duplexes $Д_1, \cdots, Д_j$,

$$\underset{\text{B}}{\cdot}(Д_1 \square Д_2) \simeq \underset{\text{B}}{\cdot_0}(Д_1 \square Д_2),$$

$$\underset{\text{B}}{\cdot}(Д_1 \square Д_2 \square \ldots \square Д_{j-1} \square Д_j) \simeq \underset{\text{B}}{\cdot_0}(\underset{\text{B}}{\cdot}(Д_1 \square Д_2 \square \ldots \square Д_{j-1}) \square Д_j).$$

If $j \geq 2$ we have

$$\tilde{\forall}(\underset{\text{B}}{\cdot}(Д_1 \square Д_2 \square \ldots \square Д_j) \stackrel{+}{\in} \underline{\text{real dup}}),$$

$$\tilde{\forall}(\underset{\text{B}}{\cdot}(\text{p}_1 \square \text{p}_2 \square \ldots \square \text{p}_j) \mathrel{\overline{\overline{\cdot}}} \underset{\text{P}}{\cdot}(\text{p}_1 \square \text{p}_2 \square \ldots \text{p}_j) \,\&\, \underset{\text{B}}{\cdot}(\text{p}_1 \square \text{p}_2 \square \ldots \square \text{p}_j) \stackrel{+}{\in} \underline{\text{red. rat}}).$$

Let $\Theta_1, \Theta_2, \cdots, \Theta_j$ ($j \geq 2$) be any individual terms. In accordance with established mathematical practice we agree to denote the term

$$\underset{\text{B}}{\cdot}(\Theta_1 \square \Theta_2 \square \ldots \square \Theta_j)$$

by the expression

$$(\Theta_1 \underset{\text{B}}{\cdot} \Theta_2 \underset{\text{B}}{\cdot} \ldots \underset{\text{B}}{\cdot} \Theta_j).$$

In using abbreviations of terms and formulas we shall assume that the symbol $\cdot_{\text{B}}$ has rank 1.

In what follows we shall often use, instead of the notation $\cdot_{\text{B}}$ (just as instead of the notation $\cdot_{\text{P}}$) the shorter notation ".", if the use of this abbreviation does not lead to ambiguity.

Construction of the operation $:_{\mathrm{B}}$. In §4.4 algorithms $\mathfrak{X}$ and $\mathfrak{Y}$ in the alphabet $Ч_3^{sa}$ were constructed such that, for any duplexes x and y,

$$(x \neq y) \equiv !\,\mathfrak{X}(x \square y) \,\&\, !\,\mathfrak{Y}(x \square y) \,\&\, \forall m\,(m \geqslant \mathfrak{Y}(x \square y) \\ \supset M(\underline{y}(m) - \underline{x}(m)) \geqslant 2^{-\mathfrak{X}(x \square y)})$$

(cf. 4.4.2). Now we construct algorithms $\overline{\mathfrak{X}}$ and $\overline{\mathfrak{Y}}$ in the alphabet $Ч_3^{sa}$ such that

$$\forall y\,(\overline{\mathfrak{X}}(y) \simeq \mathfrak{X}(y \square 0)), \quad \forall y\,(\overline{\mathfrak{Y}}(y) \simeq \mathfrak{Y}(y \square 0)).$$

For any duplex y we have

$$(y \neq 0) \equiv !\,\overline{\mathfrak{X}}(y) \,\&\, !\,\overline{\mathfrak{Y}}(y) \,\&\, \forall m\,(m \geqslant \overline{\mathfrak{Y}}(y) \supset M(\underline{y}(m)) \geqslant 2^{-\overline{\mathfrak{X}}(y)}). \quad (16)$$

Now we construct algorithms $\mathfrak{A}_6$ and $\mathfrak{B}_6$ in the alphabet $Ч_3^{sa}$ such that, for any admissible values of the variables,

$$\mathfrak{A}_6(x \square y) \overset{+}{\in} c_0, \qquad \mathfrak{B}_6(x \square y) \overset{+}{\in} c_0,$$

$$\langle \mathfrak{A}_6(x \square y) \rangle_2 (k) \simeq \underline{x}(k) :_{\mathrm{p}} \underline{y}(k), \qquad \text{if} \quad \underline{y}(k) \neq 0,$$

$$\langle \mathfrak{A}_6(x \square y) \rangle_2 (k) \simeq 0, \qquad \text{if} \quad \underline{y}(k) = 0,$$

$$\langle \mathfrak{B}_6(x \square y) \rangle_2 (k) \simeq \max(\overline{\mathfrak{Y}}(y) \square \overline{x}(0) \square \overline{y}(0) \square \overline{x}(H) \square \overline{y}(H)),$$

where

$$H \leftrightharpoons k + 1 + D + 2 \cdot \overline{\mathfrak{X}}(y).$$

The letter D denotes the same term as in the definition of the operation $\cdot_{\mathrm{B}}$.

Now we construct an algorithm $\mathfrak{B}_6^*$ in the alphabet $Ч_3^{sa}$ such that, for all admissible values of the variables,

$$!\,\mathfrak{B}_6^*(x \square y) \equiv !\,\overline{\mathfrak{X}}(y), \quad (17)$$

$$!\,\mathfrak{B}_6^*(x \square y) \supset \mathfrak{B}_6^*(x \square y) \doteqdot \mathfrak{B}_6(x \square y). \quad (18)$$

[We note that $\forall y\,(!\,\overline{\mathfrak{X}}(y) \equiv y \neq_{\mathrm{B}} 0)$]. The algorithm $\mathfrak{B}_6^*$ can be constructed, for example, in the following manner.. We denote by $\mathfrak{H}$ the composition of three algorithms: the algorithm transforming any word of the form $C_1 \square C_2$, where C_1 and C_2 are words in the alphabet $Ч_3$, into the word C_2, the algorithm $\overline{\mathfrak{X}}$, and the algorithm transforming any word in the alphabet $Ч_3^{s}$ into the empty word. On the basis of the theorem on the union of algorithms [1] we can construct an algorithm $\mathfrak{G}$ over the alphabet $Ч_3^s$ such that, for any words $c_{3,1}$ and $c_{3,2}$,

$$\mathfrak{G}(c_{3,1} \square c_{3,2}) \simeq \mathfrak{B}_6(c_{3,1} \square c_{3,2})\, \mathfrak{H}(c_{3,1} \square c_{3,2}).$$

Applying to $\mathfrak{G}$ the theorem on reduction of algorithms, we obtain the desired algorithm $\mathfrak{B}_6^*$.

The algorithm $\mathfrak{B}_6^*$ is introduced instead of the algorithm $\mathfrak{B}_6$ in order that the operation of division of duplexes be a constructive function in the sense of A. A. Markov (cf. §6.3. below).

Let x be any duplex, y a duplex different from 0, i any natural number, and k and l natural numbers such that

$$k,\ l \geqslant \langle \mathfrak{B}_6^*(x \square y) \rangle_0 (i). \tag{19}$$

We introduce the notation

$$\mathfrak{M}_6 \leftrightharpoons \langle \mathfrak{A}_6(x \square y) \rangle_2, \quad \mathfrak{N}_6 \leftrightharpoons \langle \mathfrak{B}_6^*(x \square y) \rangle_0.$$

We have

$$\mathfrak{M}_6(i) \overset{+}{\in} \underline{\text{rat}}, \quad \mathfrak{N}_6(i) \overset{+}{\in} \underline{\text{nat}}. \tag{20}$$

In addition, it follows from (19) that

$$k,\ l \geqslant \overline{\mathfrak{Y}}(y). \tag{21}$$

From (21) and (16) it follows that

$$\underline{y}(k) \neq 0, \quad \underline{y}(l) \neq 0. \tag{22}$$

Further, in view of (21) and (22), we obtain

$$M(\mathfrak{M}_6(k) - \mathfrak{M}_6(l)) = M(((\underline{x}(k) \cdot \underline{y}(l) - \underline{x}(k) \cdot \underline{y}(k)) + (\underline{x}(k) \cdot \underline{y}(k) - \underline{x}(l) \cdot \underline{y}(k))) \underset{p}{:} (\underline{y}(k) \cdot \underline{y}(l)))$$

$$\leqslant (M(\underline{x}(k)) \cdot M(\underline{y}(l) - \underline{y}(k)) + M(\underline{y}(k)) \cdot M(\underline{x}(k) - \underline{x}(l))) \overset{p}{:} M(\underline{y}(k) \cdot \underline{y}(l))$$

$$< (2^D \cdot 2^{-(i+1+D+2\cdot\mathfrak{X}(y))} + 2^D \cdot 2^{-(i+1+D+2\cdot\mathfrak{X}(y))}) \underset{p}{:} 2^{-2\cdot\overline{\mathfrak{X}}(y)} = 2^{-i}.$$

Hence

$$M(\mathfrak{M}_6(k) - \mathfrak{M}_6(l)) < 2^{-i}. \tag{23}$$

From (20) and (23) it follows that $\mathfrak{M}_6 \in (\text{H} \to \text{P})_2$, $\mathfrak{N}_6 \in (\text{H} \to \text{H})_0$, and $\mathfrak{N}_6$ is a regulator of convergence in itself of the algorithm $\mathfrak{M}_6$.

From what has been said above, it follows that if $y \neq 0$, then the word

$$\mathfrak{A}_6(x \square y) \lozenge \mathfrak{B}_6^*(x \square y)$$

is a duplex.

Using the theorems on the union, branching, and reduction of algorithms [1], we construct an algorithm $:_{\text{B}}$ in the alphabet $Ч_3^{sa}$ such that, for any duplexes x and y,

$$\mathfrak{R}(x\,\Box\, y) \doteq \Lambda \supset \underset{\text{B}}{:}(x\,\Box\, y) \simeq \underset{\text{P}}{:}(x\,\Box\, y),$$

$$\mathfrak{R}(x\,\Box\, y) \not\doteq \Lambda \supset \underset{\text{B}}{:}(x\,\Box\, y) \simeq \mathfrak{A}_6(x\,\Box\, y) \diamond \mathfrak{B}_6^*(x\,\Box\, y).$$

From (17) and the properties of the algorithm $:_{\text{P}}$, it follows that

$$\forall xy\,(!\underset{\text{B}}{:}(x\,\Box\, y) \equiv y \underset{\text{B}}{\neq} 0).$$

In addition we have

$$\forall xy\,(y \underset{\text{B}}{\neq} 0 \supset \underset{\text{B}}{:}(x\,\Box\, y) \overset{+}{\in} \underline{\text{ real dup }}),$$

$$\forall ab\,(\underset{\text{B}}{:}(a\,\Box\, b) \simeq \underset{\text{P}}{:}(a\,\Box\, b)\,\&\,(b \underset{\text{P}}{\neq} 0 \supset \underset{\text{B}}{:}(a\,\Box\, b) \overset{+}{\in} \underline{\text{ red. rat }})).$$

Let Θ_1 and Θ_2 be any individual terms. In accordance with established mathematical practice, we agree to denote the term

$$\underset{\text{B}}{:}(\Theta_1\,\Box\,\Theta_2)$$

by the expression

$$(\Theta_1 \underset{\text{B}}{:} \Theta_2).$$

In using abbreviations of terms and formulas we shall assume that the symbol $:_{\text{B}}$ has rank 1.

In the sequel we shall often use, instead of the notation $:_{\text{B}}$ (just as instead of the notation $:_{\text{P}}$) the shorter notation ":", if the use of such an abbreviation does not lead to ambiguity.

Construction of the operation $\wedge_{\text{B}}$. First we introduce some auxiliary algorithms.

We construct the composition of the algorithm $\overline{\mathfrak{X}}$, introduced above in this section, and the algorithm transforming any word in the alphabet $Ч_3^{sa}$ into the word $0|$. We denote the translation of this composition into the alphabet $Ч_3^{sa}$ by σ_0. For any duplex x we have

$$!\sigma_0(x) \equiv x \underset{\text{B}}{\neq} 0,$$

$$!\sigma_0(x) \supset \sigma_0(x) \doteq 0|.$$

We construct an algorithm σ_1 in the alphabet $Ч_3^{sa}$ such that, for any duplex x and any positive integer n,

$$\sigma_1(x\,\square\,0|) \doteq x,$$

$$\sigma_1(x\,\square\,n+1) \doteq \sigma_1(x\,\square\,n)\cdot x.$$

The algorithm σ_1 can be constructed by the method presented in [29], §4.

We construct an algorithm σ_2 in the alphabet $Ч_3^{sa}$ such that, for any duplex x and any positive integer n,

$$\sigma_2(x\,\square\,-n) \simeq 1 : \sigma_1(x\,\square\,n).$$

Using theorems on the branching and reduction of algorithms, we construct an algorithm $\mathcal{A}_B$ in the alphabet $Ч_3^{sa}$ such that, for any duplex x and any integer v,

$$\mathfrak{R}(x) \doteq \Lambda \supset \underset{B}{\mathcal{A}}(x\,\square\,v) \simeq \underset{p}{\mathcal{A}}(x\,\square\,v),$$

$$\mathfrak{R}(x) \not\doteq \Lambda\ \&\ v = 0 \supset \underset{B}{\mathcal{A}}(x\,\square\,v) \simeq \sigma_0(x),$$

$$\mathfrak{R}(x) \not\doteq \Lambda\ \&\ v > 0 \supset \underset{B}{\mathcal{A}}(x\,\square\,v) \simeq \sigma_1(x\,\square\,v),$$

$$\mathfrak{R}(x) \not\doteq \Lambda\ \&\ v < 0 \supset \underset{B}{\mathcal{A}}(x\,\square\,v) \simeq \sigma_2(x\,\square\,v).$$

One can prove that

$$\forall xv\,(!\,\underset{B}{\mathcal{A}}(x\,\square\,v) \equiv x \underset{B}{\neq} 0 \vee v \underset{p}{>} 0).$$

In addition, we have

$$\forall xv\,(x \underset{B}{\neq} 0 \vee v \underset{p}{>} 0 \supset \underset{B}{\mathcal{A}}(x\,\square\,v)\ \overset{+}{\in}\ \underline{\text{real dup}}\,),$$

$$\forall av\,(\underset{B}{\mathcal{A}}(a\,\square\,v) \simeq \underset{p}{\mathcal{A}}(a\,\square\,v)\ \&\ (a \neq 0 \vee v > 0 \supset \underset{B}{\mathcal{A}}(a\,\square\,v)\ \overset{+}{\in}\ \underline{\text{red. rat}}\,)).$$

Let Θ_1 and Θ_2 be any individual terms. In accordance with established mathematical practice, we agree to denote the term

$$\underset{B}{\mathcal{A}}(\Theta_1\,\square\,\Theta_2) \tag{24}$$

by the expression

$$\Theta_1^{\Theta_2}.$$

As a second designation of the term (24), we shall use the expression

$$(\Theta_1 \underset{B}{\mathcal{A}} \Theta_2).$$

In using abbreviations of terms and formulas we shall assume that the symbol $\mathcal{A}_B$ has rank 0.

In the sequel we shall often use, instead of the notation $\mathcal{N}_{\mathrm{B}}$ (just as instead of the notation $\mathcal{N}_{\mathrm{p}}$), the shorter notation $\mathcal{N}$, if the use of this abbreviation does not lead to ambiguity.

6.2. We now introduce the operation of raising the absolute value of a duplex to a rational power. This operation will be denoted by $\mathcal{N}^*_{\mathrm{B}}$.

First we introduce some auxiliary algorithms.

We construct algorithms τ, τ_1, and τ_2 in the alphabet Ч_3^{sa}, applicable to every rational number and such that, for any rational number a: 1) $\tau(a)$ is the reduced rational number equal to a, 2) if $\tau(a)$ is an integer then $\tau_1(a) \doteq \tau(a)$ and $\tau_2(a) \doteq 0|$, 3) if $\tau(a)$ has the form v/k, where v is an integer and k is a positive integer, then $\tau_1(a) = v$ and $\tau_2(a) \doteq k$.

We construct an algorithm ζ in the alphabet Ч_3^{sa} such that, for any rational number a and any natural number n,

$$\zeta(a\square n) \simeq \mu_j(a < (j+1)^n)$$

(cf. §2.2). If $a \geq 0$ and $n > 0$, then $\zeta(a \square n)$ is the integral part of the nth power of a.

We construct an algorithm θ in the alphabet Ч_3^{sa} such that, for any rational numbers a and b and for any natural number n,

$$\theta(a\square b\square n) \simeq \mu_j((b+2^{-j})^n \leqslant a).$$

It is obvious that for any admissible values of the variables

$$0<n\,\&\,0\leqslant b\,\&\,b^n<a \supset \theta(a\square b\square n)\,\dot{\in}\,\underline{\mathrm{nat}}.$$

We construct an algorithm χ in the alphabet Ч_3^{sa} such that, for any rational number a and any natural numbers n and i,

$$\chi(a\square n\square 0) \simeq \zeta(a\square n),$$

$$\chi(a\square n\square i+1) \simeq \begin{cases} \chi(a\square n\square i), & \text{if } \chi(a\square n\square i)^n = a, \\ \chi(a\square n\square i)+2^{-T}, & \text{if } \chi(a\square n\square i)^n < a, \end{cases}$$

where $T \leftrightharpoons \theta(a\square\chi(a\square n\square i)\square n)$.

It is easily seen that, if $b \geq a \geq 0$ and $n > 0$, then

$$0 \leqslant \chi(a\square n\square i) \leqslant \chi(a\square n\square i+1), \quad \chi(a\square n\square i) \leqslant \chi(b\square n\square i), \tag{1}$$

$$\chi(a\square n\square i)^n \leqslant a, \quad (\chi(a\square n\square i)+2^{-i})^n > a \tag{2}$$

In addition, if $a \geq 0$, $n > 0$, and $k, l \geq i$, then

$$M(\chi(a\square n\square k)-\chi(a\square n\square l)) < 2^{-i}. \tag{3}$$

It is also easy to see that, if $a \geq 0$, $n > 0$, and m is an arbitrary positive integer, then

$$\chi(a \square n \square i) \simeq \chi(a^m \square m \cdot n \square i). \tag{4}$$

We construct an algorithm ψ in the alphabet Ч_3^{sa} such that, for any rational number a and natural numbers m, n, and i,

$$\psi(a \square m/n \square i) \simeq \chi(M(a)^m \square n \square i). \tag{5}$$

Let x be any duplex, and m and n natural numbers such that $m > 0$ and $n > 0$|. Further, let k and l be any natural numbers. We introduce the notation

$$A_{k,l} \leftrightharpoons \psi(\underline{x}(k) \square m/n \square l),$$
$$B_k \leftrightharpoons M(\underline{x}(k)),$$
$$C \leftrightharpoons m/n \cdot (M(\underline{x}(\overline{x}(0))) + 2)^{m-1},$$
$$D \leftrightharpoons \mu_j (C \leqslant 2^j).$$

Let i be any natural number and

$$E \leftrightharpoons \max(i + 2 \square \overline{x}(0) \square \overline{x}(D + n \cdot (i + 2))). \tag{6}$$

Let us prove the following proposition:

$$k,\ l \geqslant E \supset M(A_{k,k} - A_{l,l}) < 2^{-i}. \tag{7}$$

Assume that

$$k,\ l \geqslant E. \tag{8}$$

We have

$$M(A_{k,k} - A_{l,l}) \leqslant M(A_{k,k} - A_{k,l}) + M(A_{k,l} - A_{l,l}).$$

From (8) and (6) it follows that

$$k,\ l \geqslant i + 2. \tag{9}$$

From (9), (5), and (3), it follows that

$$M(A_{k,k} - A_{k,l}) < 2^{-(i+2)}. \tag{10}$$

In addition, from (2) and (5) it follows that

$$A_{k,l}^n \leqslant B_k^m, \tag{11}$$

$$(A_{k,l} + 2^{-l})^n > B_k^m, \tag{12}$$

$$A_{l,l}^n \leqslant B_l^m, \tag{13}$$

$$(A_{l,l} + 2^{-l})^n > B_l^m. \tag{14}$$

B_k and B_l are rational numbers. Therefore

$$(B_k \geqslant B_l) \vee (B_l \geqslant B_k). \tag{15}$$

Let us suppose that $B_k \geq B_l$. We introduce the notation

$$\eta \rightleftharpoons B_k - B_l, \quad t \rightleftharpoons A_{k,i} - A_{l,i}.$$

We have

$$\eta \geqslant 0. \tag{16}$$

From (16) and (1) it follows that

$$t \geqslant 0. \tag{17}$$

From (11) we obtain

$$(A_{l,i} + t)^n \leqslant (B_l + \eta)^m. \tag{18}$$

From (9) and (14) we obtain

$$(A_{l,i} + 2^{-(i+2)})^n > B_l^m. \tag{19}$$

From (18) and (19) it follows that

$$(A_{l,i} + t)^n - (A_{l,i} + 2^{-(i+2)})^n \leqslant (B_l + \eta)^m - B_l^m. \tag{20}$$

We denote the left side of formula (20) by P and the right side by Q. We have

$$P = (t - 2^{-(i+2)}) \cdot ((A_{l,i} + t)^{n-1} + (A_{l,i} + t)^{n-2} \cdot (A_{l,i} + 2^{-(i+2)}) + \dots$$
$$\dots + (A_{l,i} + 2^{-(i+2)})^{n-1}).$$

We consider two cases.

1) $t \leq 2^{-(i+2)}$. In this case $t < 2^{-(i+1)}$.

2) $t > 2^{-(i+2)}$. In this case

$$P > (t - 2^{-(i+2)}) \cdot (A_{l,i} + 2^{-(i+2)})^{n-1} \cdot n \geqslant (t - 2^{-(i+2)}) \cdot 2^{-(i+2) \cdot (n-1)} \cdot n,$$

$$Q = \eta \cdot ((B_l + \eta)^{m-1} + (B_l + \eta)^{m-2} \cdot B_l + \dots + B_l^{m-1}) \leqslant \eta \cdot (B_l + \eta)^{m-1} \cdot m.$$

Hence

$$(t - 2^{-(i+2)}) \cdot 2^{-(i+2) \cdot (n-1)} \cdot n < \eta \cdot (B_l + \eta)^{m-1} \cdot m,$$

$$t < 2^{-(i+2)} + \eta \cdot (B_l + \eta)^{m-1} \cdot m / n \cdot 2^{(i+2) \cdot (n-1)}. \tag{21}$$

From (8) it follows that

$$M(\underline{x}(l) - \underline{x}(\bar{x}(0))) < 2^{-0},$$

$$M(\underline{x}(l)) < M(\underline{x}(\bar{x}(0))) + 1,$$

$$B_l < M(\underline{x}(\bar{x}(0))) + 1.$$

In addition, from (8) it follows that

$$\eta = M(\underline{x}(k)) - M(\underline{x}(l)) \leqslant M(\underline{x}(k) - \underline{x}(l)) < 2^{-(D + n \cdot (i+2))}. \tag{23}$$

From (22) and (23) it follows that

$$B_l + \eta < B_l + 1 < M(\underline{x}(\bar{x}(0))) + 2,$$

$$(B_l + \eta)^{m-1} \cdot m/n < (M(\underline{x}(\bar{x}(0))) + 2)^{m-1} \cdot m/n \leqslant 2^D. \tag{24}$$

From (21), (24), and (23) it follows that

$$t < 2^{-(i+2)} + \eta \cdot 2^D \cdot 2^{(i+2)\cdot(n-1)} < 2^{-(i+2)} + 2^{-(i+2)} = 2^{-(i+1)}.$$

Hence in case 2), just as in case 1), we have

$$0 \leqslant t < 2^{-(i+1)}. \tag{25}$$

Since t and $2^{-(i+2)}$ are rational numbers, we have

$$(t \leqslant 2^{-(i+2)}) \vee (t > 2^{-(i+2)}).$$

Hence

$$0 \leqslant A_{k,l} - A_{l,l} < 2^{-(i+1)}. \tag{26}$$

If $B_l \geq B_k$, then by the same method as was used for the assumption $B_k \geq B_l$ we arrive (basing ourselves on (13) and (12) instead of (11) and (14)) at the inequality

$$0 \leqslant A_{l,l} - A_{k,l} < 2^{-(i+1)}. \tag{27}$$

From (26), (27), and (15) it follows that

$$M(A_{k,l} - A_{l,l}) < 2^{-(i+1)}. \tag{28}$$

From (10) and (28) it follows that

$$M(A_{k,k} - A_{l,l}) < 2^{-(i+2)} + 2^{-(i+1)} < 2^{-i}.$$

Proposition (7) has been proved.

Now we construct algorithms $\mathfrak{A}_7$ and $\mathfrak{B}_7$ in the alphabet $Ч_3^{sa}$ such that, for all admissible values of the variables,

$$\mathfrak{A}_7(x \,\square\, b) \overset{+}{\in} c_0, \quad \mathfrak{B}_7(x \,\square\, b) \overset{+}{\in} c_0,$$

$$\langle \mathfrak{A}_7(x \,\square\, b) \rangle_2 (i) \simeq \psi(\underline{x}(i) \,\square\, \tau_1(b)/\tau_2(b) \,\square\, i),$$

$$\langle \mathfrak{B}_7(x \,\square\, b) \rangle_0 (i) \simeq \max(i + 2 \,\square\, \bar{x}(0) \,\square\, \bar{x}(R + \tau_2(b) \cdot (i+2))),$$

where

$$R \leftrightharpoons \mu_j (b \cdot (M(\underline{x}(\bar{x}(0))) + 2)^{\tau_1(b)-1} \leqslant 2^j).$$

Using theorems on the union, branching and reduction of algorithms, we construct an algorithm $\mathcal{A}^*_{\mathrm{B}}$ in the alphabet $Ч_3^{sa}$ such that, for any duplex x and any rational number b,

$$\tau_2(b) = 0 \,|\supset \mathcal{A}^*_{\mathrm{B}}(x \,\square\, b) \simeq \mathcal{A}_{\mathrm{B}}(M(x) \,\square\, \tau_1(b)),$$

$$\tau_2(b) > 0 | \& \tau_1(b) > 0 \supset \underset{B}{\varLambda^*}(x \square b) \simeq \mathfrak{A}_7(x \square b) \diamond \mathfrak{B}_7(x \square b),$$

$$\tau_2(b) > 0 | \& \tau_1(b) < 0 \supset \underset{B}{\varLambda^*}(x \square b) \simeq \mathfrak{A}_7(x^{-1} \square - b) \diamond \mathfrak{B}_7(x^{-1} \square - b).$$

One can prove that

$$\forall xb\,(!\, \underset{B}{\varLambda^*}(x \square b) \equiv x \underset{B}{\neq} 0 \vee b \underset{P}{>} 0).$$

In addition, on the basis of (7), we have

$$\forall xb\,(x \underset{B}{\neq} 0 \vee b \underset{P}{>} 0 \supset \underset{B}{\varLambda^*}(x \square b) \overset{+}{\in} \underline{\text{real dup}}\,).$$

We note also that

$$\forall xv\,(x \underset{B}{\neq} 0 \vee v \underset{P}{>} 0 \supset \underset{B}{\varLambda^*}(x \square v) \overset{+}{=} \underset{B}{\varLambda}(M(x) \square v)).$$

The algorithm $\varLambda^*_B$ is the operation of raising the absolute value of a duplex to a rational power. Starting from this algorithm, one can define in a natural way the operation of raising the absolute value of a duplex to a duplex power. But we shall not describe here the construction of the appropriate algorithm.

Let Θ_1 and Θ_2 be any individual terms. We agree to denote the term

$$\underset{B}{\varLambda^*}(\Theta_1 \square \Theta_2)$$

by the expression

$$\underset{B}{M}(\Theta_1)^{\Theta_2}.$$

As a second designation of the term $\varLambda^*_B(\Theta_1 \square \Theta_2)$, we shall use the expression

$$(\Theta_1 \underset{B}{\varLambda^*} \Theta_2).$$

In using abbreviations of terms and formulas, we shall assume that the symbol $\varLambda^*_B$ has rank 0.

In the sequel we shall often use, instead of the notation $\varLambda^*_B$, the shorter notation $\varLambda^*$, if the use of this abbreviation does not lead to ambiguity.

6.3. One of the basic concepts of classical mathematical analysis is the well-known concept of a real function of a real variable.[1] A constructive analogue of this concept was introduced by A. A. Markov in [8]. This concept can be defined in the following way.

A normal algorithm $\Phi_{3,1}$ in the alphabet Ч_3^{sa} is called a function of type $(\text{Д} \dot{\rightarrow} \text{Д})$[2] if, first, $\Phi_{3,1}$ is an algorithm of type $(\text{Д} \dot{\rightarrow} \text{Д})_3$ (see §1.11), i.e.

1) This concept is a special case of the concept of a mapping of one set into another.
2) Markov uses the term "constructive function of a real variable".

$$\forall x(!\,\Phi_{3,1}(x) \supset \Phi_{3,1}(x) \in \underline{\text{real dup}}),$$

and second,

$$\forall xy(!\,\Phi_{3,1}(x) \,\&\, x \underset{\text{В}}{=} y \supset !\,\Phi_{3,1}(y) \,\&\, \Phi_{3,1}(y) \underset{\text{В}}{=} \Phi_{3,1}(x)).$$

If an algorithm $\Phi_{3,1}$ is a function of type $(\text{Д} \dot{\to} \text{Д})$ and $\forall x!\,\Phi_{3,1}(x)$, then we shall say that $\Phi_{3,1}$ is a function of type $(\text{Д} \dot{\to} \text{Д})$.

Let $\mu_1, \cdots, \mu_k, \mu_{k+1}$ $(k \geq 1)$ be a list of generic individual letters such that for each i $(i = 1, \cdots, k, k+1)$ the letter μ_i is one of the generic letters Н, Ц, Р, Д, В. A normal algorithm $\Phi_{3,1}$ in the alphabet Ч_3^{sa} is a function of type $(\mu_1 \cdots \mu_k \dot{\to} \mu_{k+1})$ if, first, $\Phi_{3,1}$ is an algorithm of type $(\mu_1 \cdots \mu_k \dot{\to} \mu_{k+1})_3$ (§1.11), and second,

$$\tilde{\forall}\,(!\,\Phi_{3,1}(\alpha_1 \Box \ldots \Box \alpha_k) \,\&\, \alpha_1 \underset{\mu_1}{=} \beta_1 \,\&\, \ldots \,\&\, \alpha_k \underset{\mu_k}{=} \beta_k$$

$$\supset !\,\Phi_{3,1}(\beta_1 \Box \ldots \Box \beta_k) \,\&\, \Phi_{3,1}(\beta_1 \Box \ldots \Box \beta_k) \underset{\mu_{k+1}}{=} \Phi_{3,1}(\alpha_1 \Box \ldots \Box \alpha_k)).$$

Here $\alpha_1, \cdots, \alpha_k, \beta_1, \cdots, \beta_k$ are pairwise distinct variables such that α_1 and β_1 are variables of type $\mu_1, \cdots, \alpha_k$ and β_k are variables of type μ_k. Here and below, the expressions $=_{\text{Н}}$ and $=_{\text{Ц}}$ must be interpreted as the symbol $=_{\text{Р}}$, and the expression $=_{\text{Д}}$ must be interpreted as the symbol $=_{\text{В}}$.

If an algorithm $\Phi_{3,1}$ is a function of type $(\mu_1 \cdots \mu_k \dot{\to} \mu_{k+1})$ and $\forall \alpha_1 \cdots \cdots \alpha_k!\,\Phi_{3,1}(\alpha_1 \Box \cdots \Box \alpha_k)$ [here α_1 is a variable of type $\mu_1, \cdots, \alpha_k$ is a variable of type μ_k], then we shall say that $\Phi_{3,1}$ is a function of type $(\mu_1 \cdots \mu_k \to \mu_{k+1})$.

If μ_{k+1} is one of the letters Н, Ц, Р, Д, then the process of constructive reformulation of the conditions

$$\Phi_{3,1} \in (\mu_1 \ldots \mu_k \dot{\to} \mu_{k+1})_3, \qquad \Phi_{3,1} \in (\mu_1 \ldots \mu_k \to \mu_{k+1})_3 \tag{1}$$

leads to normal formulas. If μ_{k+1} is the letter "В", then the process of constructive reformulation of the condition (1) leads to formulas beginning with a quantifier of potential realizability. Let us find, for example, the constructive reformulation of the conditions

$$\Phi_{3,1} \in (\text{В} \dot{\to} \text{В})_3, \qquad \Phi_{3,1} \in (\text{В} \to \text{В})_3.$$

The condition

$$\Phi_{3,1} \in (\text{В} \dot{\to} \text{В})_3 \tag{2}$$

has the form

$$\forall r\,(!\,\Phi_{3,1}(r) \supset \Phi_{3,1}(r) \in \underline{\text{real } F\text{-num}}). \tag{3}$$

Applying to (3) the algorithm for eliminating restricted variables c (see §1.7) and reformulating the term "$\underline{\text{real } F\text{-num}}$", we arrive at the formula

$$\forall c_{3,1}(c_{3,1} \in \underline{\text{one mean}}_3 \,\&\, \underset{\sqcup}{c_{3,1}} \in (\text{H} \to \text{p})_2$$

$$\&\exists \phi_{0,1}\,(\phi_{0,1}\,\underline{\text{reg. con.}}\,\underset{\sqcup}{c_{3,1}}) \,\&\, !\,\phi_{3,1}(c_{3,1}) \supset \phi_{3,1}(c_{3,1}) \in \underline{\text{one mean}}_3$$

$$\&\underset{\sqcup}{\phi_{3,1}(c_{3,1})} \in (\text{H} \to \text{p})_2 \,\&\, \exists \phi_{0,2}(\phi_{0,2}\,\underline{\text{reg. con.}}\,\underset{\sqcup}{\phi_{3,1}(c_{3,1})})). \tag{4}$$

Applying to (4) the algorithm for exhibiting constructive problems, we arrive at the formula

$$\exists \phi_{3,2}\forall c_{3,1}(\phi_{3,2}(c_{3,1}) \overset{+}{\in} c_0 \,\&\, \forall \phi_{0,1}(\mathfrak{M} \,\&\, !\,\phi_{3,1}(c_{3,1}) \supset \mathfrak{N}$$

$$\&\, \langle\phi_{3,2}(c_{3,1})\rangle_0(\{\phi_{0,1}\}) \overset{+}{\in} c_0 \,\&\, \langle\langle\phi_{3,2}(c_{3,1})\rangle_0(\{\phi_{0,1}\})\rangle_0\,\underline{\text{reg. con.}}\,\underset{\sqcup}{\phi_{3,1}(c_{3,1})})), \tag{5}$$

where

$$\mathfrak{M} \rightleftharpoons c_{3,1} \in \underline{\text{one mean}}_3 \,\&\, \underset{\sqcup}{c_{3,1}} \in (\text{H} \to \text{p})_2 \,\&\, \phi_{0,1}\,\underline{\text{reg. con.}}\,\underset{\sqcup}{c_{3,1}},$$

$$\mathfrak{N} \rightleftharpoons \phi_{3,1}(c_{3,1}) \in \underline{\text{one mean}}_3 \,\&\, \underset{\sqcup}{\phi_{3,1}(c_{3,1})} \in (\text{H} \to \text{p})_2.$$

Applying 2.1.1 and 2.1.3, we conclude that the formula (5) is equivalent to the formula

$$\exists \phi_{3,3}\mathfrak{U}, \tag{6}$$

where

$$\mathfrak{U} \rightleftharpoons \forall c_{3,1}\phi_{0,1}(\mathfrak{M} \,\&\, !\,\phi_{3,1}(c_{3,1}) \supset \mathfrak{N} \,\&\, \phi_{3,3}(c_{3,1} \square \{\phi_{0,1}\}) \overset{+}{\in} c_0$$

$$\&\, \langle\phi_{3,3}(c_{3,1} \square \{\phi_{0,1}\})\rangle_0\,\underline{\text{reg. con.}}\,\underset{\sqcup}{\phi_{3,1}(c_{3,1})}).$$

Formula (6) can be considered as the constructive reformulation of condition (2).

By the same method, one can prove that, as a constructive reformulation of the condition

$$\phi_{3,1} \in (\text{B} \to \text{B})_3 \tag{7}$$

one can use the formula

$$\exists \phi_{3,3}\mathfrak{B}, \tag{8}$$

where

$$\mathfrak{B} \rightleftharpoons \forall c_{3,1}\phi_{0,1}(\mathfrak{M} \supset !\,\phi_{3,1}(c_{3,1}) \,\&\, \mathfrak{N} \,\&\, \phi_{3,3}(c_{3,1} \square \{\phi_{0,1}\}) \overset{+}{\in} c_0 \,\&$$

$$\&\, \langle\phi_{3,3}(c_{3,1} \square \{\phi_{0,1}\})\rangle_0\,\underline{\text{reg. con.}}\,\underset{\sqcup}{\phi_{3,1}(c_{3,1})}).$$

We say that an algorithm $\phi_{3,2}$ is a *covering algorithm* for the algorithm $\phi_{3,1}$, and we shall write $(\Phi_{3,2}\ \underline{\text{cov}}\ \Phi_{3,1})$ if, first,

$$\forall c_{3,1}\Phi_{0,1}(\mathfrak{M} \supset (!\,\Phi_{3,2}(c_{3,1}\{\Phi_{0,1}\}) \equiv !\,\Phi_{3,1}(c_{3,1}))),$$

and second,

$$\forall c_{3,1}\Phi_{0,1}(\mathfrak{M}\ \&\ !\,\Phi_{3,1}(c_{3,1}) \supset \mathfrak{K}),$$

where

$$\mathfrak{K} \leftrightharpoons \Phi_{3,1}(c_{3,1}) \mathrel{\bar{=}} \overline{\text{prin}}_3(\Phi_{3,2}(c_{3,1}\{\Phi_{0,1}\}))\ \&\ \overline{\Phi_{3,2}(c_{3,1}\{\Phi_{0,1}\})}\ \underline{\text{reg. con.}}\ \underline{\Phi_{3,1}(c_{3,1})}.$$

The following theorem holds.

6.3.1.

a) $\forall\Phi_{3,1}(\Phi_{3,1} \in (\text{в} \dashrightarrow \text{в})_3 \equiv \exists\Phi_{3,2}(\Phi_{3,2} \in (\text{д} \dashrightarrow \text{д})_3\ \&\ \Phi_{3,2}\ \underline{\text{cov}}\ \Phi_{3,1}))$.

b) $\forall\Phi_{3,1}(\Phi_{3,1} \in (\text{в} \to \text{в})_3 \equiv \exists\Phi_{3,2}(\Phi_{3,2} \in (\text{д} \to \text{д})_3\ \&\ \Phi_{3,2}\ \underline{\text{cov}}\ \Phi_{3,1})$.

Proof. Let $\Phi_{3,1}$ be an algorithm such that

$$\Phi_{3,1} \in (\text{в} \dashrightarrow \text{в})_3.$$

Then on the basis of what has been said above

$$\exists\Phi_{3,3}\mathfrak{U}.$$

Let $\Phi_{3,3}$ be an algorithm such that $\mathfrak{U}$ holds .

One can construct an algorithm $\Phi_{3,2}$ such that

$$\forall c_{3,2}(\Phi_{3,2}(c_{3,2}) \simeq \Phi_{3,1}(\overline{\text{prin}}_3(c_{3,2}))\ \Phi_{3,3}(\overline{\text{prin}}_3(c_{3,2}) \square\ \overline{\text{rig}}_3(c_{3,2}))).$$

It is easy to verify that $\Phi_{3,2} \in (\text{Д} \dashrightarrow \text{Д})_3$ and $\Phi_{3,2}\ \underline{\text{cov}}\ \Phi_{3,1}$. Hence

$$\exists\Phi_{3,2}(\Phi_{3,2} \in (\text{д} \dashrightarrow \text{д})_3\ \&\ \Phi_{3,2}\ \underline{\text{cov}}\ \Phi_{3,1}).$$

Therefore

$$\forall\Phi_{3,1}(\Phi_{3,1} \in (\text{в} \dashrightarrow \text{в})_3 \supset \exists\Phi_{3,2}(\Phi_{3,2} \in (\text{д} \dashrightarrow \text{д})_3\ \&\ \Phi_{3,2}\ \underline{\text{cov}}\ \Phi_{3,1})). \tag{9}$$

Assume that $\Phi_{3,1}$ is an algorithm such that

$$\exists\Phi_{3,2}(\Phi_{3,2} \in (\text{д} \dashrightarrow \text{д})_3\ \&\ \Phi_{3,2}\ \underline{\text{cov}}\ \Phi_{3,1}).$$

Let $\Phi_{3,2}$ be an algorithm such that

$$\Phi_{3,2} \in (\text{д} \dashrightarrow \text{д})_3\ \&\ \Phi_{3,2}\ \underline{\text{cov}}\ \Phi_{3,1}.$$

One can construct an algorithm $\Phi_{3,3}$ such that

$$\forall c_{3,1}c_{0,1}(\Phi_{3,3}(c_{3,1} \square c_{0,1}) \simeq \overline{\text{rig}}_3(\Phi_{3,2}(c_{3,1}c_{0,1}))).$$

It is easy to check that $\Phi_{3,3}$ satisfies condition $\mathfrak{U}$. Hence $\Phi_{3,1} \in (\text{В} \dashrightarrow \text{В})$. We have proved that

$$\forall\Phi_{3,1}(\exists\Phi_{3,2}(\Phi_{3,2} \in (\text{д} \dashrightarrow \text{д})_3\ \&\ \Phi_{3,2}\ \underline{\text{cov}}\ \Phi_{3,1}) \supset \Phi_{3,1} \in (\text{в} \dashrightarrow \text{в})_3). \tag{10}$$

From (9) and (10) proposition a) follows. Proposition b) is proved in similar fashion.

Remark 1. Since the constructive reformulation of condition (2) begins with the symbol $\exists$, proposition (9) does not justify us in asserting that there is an algorithm which, for the transcription of any algorithm of type $(\text{В} \dashrightarrow \text{В})_3$, constructs the transcription of an algorithm of type $(\text{Д} \dashrightarrow \text{Д})_3$ which is a covering for the given algorithm.

In the proof given above of proposition (9), one of the initially given objects for the construction of the algorithm $\Phi_{3,2}$ is an algorithm $\Phi_{3,3}$ satisfying condition $\mathfrak{U}$.

Remark 2. If, in the formulation of Theorem 6.3.1, we replace the expressions $\dot{\Phi}_{3,1} \in (\text{В} \dashrightarrow \text{В})_3$, $\dot{\Phi}_{3,2} \in (\text{Д} \dashrightarrow \text{Д})_3$, $\Phi_{3,1} \in (\text{В} \rightarrow \text{В})_3$, $\dot{\Phi}_{3,2} \in (\text{Д} \rightarrow \text{Д})_3$, by the expressions "$\Phi_{3,1}$ is a function of type $(\text{В} \dashrightarrow \text{В})$", "$\dot{\Phi}_{3,2}$ is a function of type $(\text{Д} \dashrightarrow \text{Д})$", "$\Phi_{3,1}$ is a function of type $(\text{В} \rightarrow \text{В})$", "$\dot{\Phi}_{3,2}$ is a function of type $(\text{Д} \rightarrow \text{Д})$", respectively, then we obtain a true assertion.

Now we shall return to the consideration of the operations

$$\underset{\text{В}}{M},\ \underset{\text{В}}{\max},\ \underset{\text{В}}{\min},\ \underset{\text{В}}{+},\ \underset{\text{В}}{-},\ \underset{\text{В}}{\cdot},\ \underset{\text{В}}{:},\ \underset{\text{В}}{\Lambda},\ \underset{\text{В}}{\Lambda^*}.$$

One can prove the following theorem.

6.3.2. a) *The operation* $M_{\text{В}}$ *is a function of type* $(\text{Д} \rightarrow \text{Д})$. b) *For any natural number n, the operations* $\max_{\text{В}}$, $\min_{\text{В}}$, $+_{\text{В}}$, $-_{\text{В}}$, *and* $\cdot_{\text{В}}$ *are functions of type* $(\underbrace{\text{Д}\cdots\text{Д}}_{n \text{ times}} \rightarrow \text{Д})$. *The operation* $:_{\text{В}}$ *is a function of type* $(\text{ДД} \dashrightarrow \text{Д})$. c) *The operation* $\Lambda_{\text{В}}$ *is a function of type* $(\text{ДЦ} \dashrightarrow \text{Д})$. d) *The operation* $\Lambda^*_{\text{В}}$ *is a function of type* $(\text{ДР} \dashrightarrow \text{Д})$.

Let $\mathfrak{F}$ be a one-parameter formula, the parameter of which is a variable of type μ, where μ is one of the generic letters Р, Д, В. We shall say that $\mathfrak{F}$ is a faithful set of words of type μ if

$$\forall \alpha\beta (\mathfrak{F} \,\&\, \beta \underset{\mu}{=} \alpha \supset \mathbf{F}^{\alpha}_{\beta\llcorner}\mathfrak{F}\lrcorner),$$

where α is the parameter of the formula $\mathfrak{F}$ and β is a variable of type μ which is different from α.

The following proposition is obvious.

6.3.3. *If* $\mathfrak{A}$ *is a function of type* $(\mu \dashrightarrow \mu)$, *where* μ *is one of the generic letters* Р, Д, В, *then the set given by the formula* $!\,\mathfrak{A}$ *is a faithful set of words of type* μ.

The following proposition is also obvious.

6.3.4. *If μ is one of the generic letters* Ƿ, Д, B, *and if* $\mathfrak{F}$ *and* $\mathfrak{G}$ *are faithful sets of words of type* μ, *then the union, intersection, and difference of the sets* $\mathfrak{F}$ *and* $\mathfrak{G}$ *are faithful sets of words of type* μ.[1)]

6.4. We shall now enumerate (without proof) some properties of the operations introduced in §§6.1 and 6.2.

6.4.1. *The operations* $\max_{\text{B}}$ *and* $\min_{\text{B}}$ *are associative and commutative. In addition, for any natural number j not less than two and any natural number i not exceeding j,*

$$\tilde{\forall}(\max(Д_1 \square Д_2 \square \ldots \square Д_j) \geqslant Д_i),$$

$$\tilde{\forall}(Д_{j+1} \geqslant Д_1 \mathbin{\&} Д_{j+1} \geqslant Д_2 \mathbin{\&} \ldots \mathbin{\&} Д_{j+1} \geqslant Д_j \supset Д_{j+1} \geqslant \max(Д_1 \square Д_2 \square \ldots \square Д_j)),$$

$$\tilde{\forall}(\min(Д_1 \square Д_2 \square \ldots \square Д_j) \leqslant Д_i),$$

$$\tilde{\forall}(Д_{j+1} \leqslant Д_1 \mathbin{\&} Д_{j+1} \leqslant Д_2 \mathbin{\&} \ldots \mathbin{\&} Д_{j+1} \leqslant Д_j \supset Д_{j+1} \leqslant \min(Д_1 \square Д_2 \square \ldots \square Д_j)),$$

$$\tilde{\forall}(Д_{j+1} > Д_1 \mathbin{\&} Д_{j+1} > Д_2 \mathbin{\&} \ldots \mathbin{\&} Д_{j+1} > Д_j \supset Д_{j+1} > \max(Д_1 \square Д_2 \square \ldots \square Д_j)),$$

$$\tilde{\forall}(Д_{j+1} < Д_1 \mathbin{\&} Д_{j+1} < Д_2 \mathbin{\&} \ldots \mathbin{\&} Д_{j+1} < Д_j \supset Д_{j+1} < \min(Д_1 \square Д_2 \square \ldots \square Д_j)),$$

$$\tilde{\forall}(\max(Д_1 \square \ldots \square Д_j) = -\min(-Д_1 \square \ldots \square -Д_j)),$$

$$\tilde{\forall}(\min(Д_1 \square \ldots \square Д_j) = -\max(-Д_1 \square \ldots \square -Д_j)).$$

6.4.2. *For any duplexes x and y,*

$$x \geqslant y \equiv \max(x \square y) = x, \qquad x \leqslant y \equiv \max(x \square y) = y, \tag{1}$$

$$x \geqslant y \equiv \min(x \square y) = y, \qquad x \leqslant y \equiv \min(x \square y) = x, \tag{2}$$

$$\neg\neg(\max(x \square y) = x \vee \max(x \square y) = y),$$

$$\neg\neg(\min(x \square y) = x \vee \min(x \square y) = y).$$

As an immediate consequence of §4.5 (73), (1) and (2), we have the following proposition.

6.4.3.

$$\neg\forall xy(\max(x \square y) = x \vee \max(x \square y) = y),$$

$$\neg\forall xy(\min(x \square y) = x \vee \min(x \square y) = y).$$

Proposition 6.4.3 indicates the existence of an important difference between the properties of the operations $\max_{\text{B}}$ and $\min_{\text{B}}$, on the one hand, and the pro-

---

1) If the parameter of the formula $\mathfrak{F}$ coincides with the parameter of the formula $\mathfrak{G}$, then the union, intersection, and difference of the sets $\mathfrak{F}$ and $\mathfrak{G}$ are given, respectively, by the formulas $(\mathfrak{F} \vee \mathfrak{G})$, $(\mathfrak{F} \mathbin{\&} \mathfrak{G})$ and $(\mathfrak{F} \mathbin{\&} \neg\mathfrak{G})$.

perties of the corresponding operations of classical mathematics, on the other hand.

6.4.4. *The operations of addition and multiplication of duplexes is associative and commutative. In addition, for any duplexes x, y, and z,*

$$x \cdot (y + z) = x \cdot y + x \cdot z,$$

$$x + 0 = x, \quad x + (-x) = 0, \quad x - y = x + (-y),$$

$$x \cdot 1 = x, \quad x \neq 0 \supset x \cdot (1 : x) = 1, \quad y \neq 0 \supset x : y = x \cdot (1 : y).$$

The next proposition 6.4.5 combines somes simple logical consequences of proposition 6.4.4.

6.4.5. *For any duplexes x, y and z,*

$$x + (y - x) = y, \quad x - x = 0, \quad 0 - x = -x, \quad -(-x) = x,$$

$$x - (y + z) = (x - y) - z, \quad x \cdot (y - z) = x \cdot y - x \cdot z,$$

$$0 \cdot x = 0, \quad (-1) \cdot x = -x,$$

$$x \neq 0 \supset x \cdot (y : x) = y, \quad x \neq 0 \supset x : x = 1,$$

$$x \neq 0 \supset 1 : (1 : x) = x,$$

$$y \neq 0 \,\&\, z \neq 0 \supset x : (y \cdot z) = (x : y) : z.$$

It is not difficult to prove the following proposition.

6.4.6. *For any duplexes x and y,*

$$x \delta y \equiv (x - y) \delta 0$$

(here δ is any of the symbols $=, \geq, \leq, \neq, <, >$),

$$x > 0 \,\&\, y \geqslant 0 \supset x + y > 0,$$

$$x \geqslant 0 \,\&\, y \geqslant 0 \supset x + y \geqslant 0,$$

$$x + y \neq 0 \supset x \neq 0 \vee y \neq 0,$$

$$x \neq 0 \,\&\, y \neq 0 \equiv x \cdot y \neq 0,$$

$$x = 0 \vee y = 0 \supset x \cdot y = 0,$$

$$x \cdot y = 0 \supset \neg\neg(x = 0 \vee y = 0), \tag{3}$$

$$(x > 0 \,\&\, y > 0) \vee (x < 0 \,\&\, y < 0) \equiv x \cdot y > 0,$$

$$(x > 0 \,\&\, y < 0) \vee (x < 0 \,\&\, y > 0) \equiv x \cdot y < 0,$$

$$(x \geqslant 0 \,\&\, y \geqslant 0) \vee (x \leqslant 0 \,\&\, y \leqslant 0) \supset x \cdot y \geqslant 0,$$

$$x \cdot y \geqslant 0 \supset \neg\neg((x \geqslant 0 \,\&\, y \geqslant 0) \vee (x \leqslant 0 \,\&\, y \leqslant 0)), \tag{4}$$

$$(x \geqslant 0 \,\&\, y \leqslant 0) \vee (x \leqslant 0 \,\&\, y \geqslant 0) \supset x \cdot y \leqslant 0,$$

$$x \cdot y \leqslant 0 \supset \neg\neg((x \geqslant 0 \,\&\, y \leqslant 0) \vee (x \leqslant 0 \,\&\, y \geqslant 0)). \tag{5}$$

In connection with propositions (3) and (5), the question arises as to whether the assertions

$$\forall xy(x \cdot y = 0 \supset x = 0 \vee y = 0), \tag{6}$$

$$\forall xy(x \cdot y \geqslant 0 \supset (x \geqslant 0 \,\&\, y \geqslant 0) \vee (x \leqslant 0 \,\&\, y \leqslant 0)), \tag{7}$$

$$\forall xy(x \cdot y \leqslant 0 \supset (x \geqslant 0 \,\&\, y \leqslant 0) \vee (x \leqslant 0 \,\&\, y \geqslant 0)). \tag{8}$$

are true. The answer to this question is in the negative. G. S. Ceĭtin [17] has proved that

$$\neg \forall x(x \geqslant 0 \vee x \leqslant 0). \tag{9}$$

Basing ourselves on proposition (9), we can easily refute assertions (6), (7), and (8). Assertion (6) is disproved in the following way (cf. [17]). Let us suppose that the assertion (6) is true. From (6) and the obvious proposition

$$\forall x((M(x) - x) \cdot (M(x) + x) = 0)$$

we obtain

$$\forall x(M(x) - x = 0 \vee M(x) + x = 0).$$

Now we note that

$$\forall x(M(x) - x = 0 \equiv x \geqslant 0), \quad \forall x(M(x) + x = 0 \equiv x \leqslant 0).$$

Hence

$$\forall x(x \geqslant 0 \vee x \leqslant 0).$$

This contradicts (9). Therefore (6) is disproved.

Let us suppose that assertion (7) is true. Then

$$\forall x(x \cdot x \geqslant 0 \supset (x \geqslant 0 \,\&\, x \geqslant 0) \vee (x \leqslant 0 \,\&\, x \leqslant 0)).$$

Noting that $\forall x(x \cdot x \geq 0)$, we obtain

$$\forall x(x \geqslant 0 \vee x \leqslant 0).$$

This contradicts (9). Therefore (7) is disproved.

Let us suppose that statement (8) is true. Then

$$\forall x(x \cdot (-x) \leqslant 0 \supset (x \geqslant 0 \,\&\, -x \leqslant 0) \vee (x \leqslant 0 \,\&\, -x \geqslant 0)).$$

Noting that

$$\forall x(x \cdot (-x) \leqslant 0), \quad \forall x(-x \leqslant 0 \equiv x \geqslant 0), \quad \forall x(-x \geqslant 0 \equiv x \leqslant 0),$$

we obtain

$$\forall x(x \geqslant 0 \vee x \leqslant 0).$$

This contradicts (9). Therefore (8) is disproved.

What has just been said proves the following theorem.

6.4.7.

$$\neg\forall xy\,(x\cdot y=0\supset x=0\vee y=0),$$
$$\neg\forall xy\,(x\cdot y\geqslant 0\supset(x\geqslant 0\,\&\,y\geqslant 0)\vee(x\leqslant 0\,\&\,y\leqslant 0)),$$
$$\neg\forall xy\,(x\cdot y\leqslant 0\supset(x\geqslant 0\,\&\,y\leqslant 0)\vee(x\leqslant 0\,\&\,y\geqslant 0)).$$

Theorem 6.4.7 testifies to the existence of a significant divergence between the properties of the operation $\cdot_{\text{B}}$ and the properties of the corresponding operation of classical mathematics.

We proceed now to the operation M_{B}. It is not difficult to prove the following theorem.

6.4.8. *For any duplexes* x *and* y,

$$M(x)=\max(x\,\Box\,-x),$$
$$M(x)\geqslant 0,$$
$$M(x)=0\equiv x=0,$$
$$M(x+y)\leqslant M(x)+M(y),$$
$$M(x\cdot y)=M(x)\cdot M(y).$$

The following proposition 6.4.9 combines some simple logical consequences of the preceding theorem.

6.4.9. *For any duplexes* x *and* y,

$$M(-x)=M(x),$$
$$M(M(x)-M(y))\leqslant M(x-y),$$
$$y\neq 0\supset M(x:y)=M(x):M(y),$$
$$M(x)=x\equiv x\geqslant 0,$$
$$M(x)=-x\equiv x\leqslant 0,$$
$$M(x)>0\supset M(x)=x\vee M(x)=-x,$$
$$\neg\neg(M(x)=x\vee M(x)=-x), \quad (10$$
$$y>0\supset(M(x)=y\equiv x=-y\vee x=y),$$
$$y\geqslant 0\supset(x=-y\vee x=y\supset M(x)=y),$$
$$y\geqslant 0\supset(M(x)=y\supset\neg\neg(x=-y\vee x=y)), \quad (11)$$
$$y>0\supset(M(x)\geqslant y\equiv x\leqslant -y\vee x\geqslant y),$$
$$y\geqslant 0\supset(x\leqslant -y\vee x\geqslant y\supset M(x)\geqslant y),$$
$$y\geqslant 0\supset(M(x)\geqslant y\supset\neg\neg(x\leqslant -y\vee x\geqslant y)), \quad (12$$

$$y \geqslant 0 \supset (M(x) > y \equiv x < -y \vee x > y),$$
$$M(x) \leqslant y \equiv -y \leqslant x \leqslant y,$$
$$M(x) < y \equiv -y < x < y.$$

In connection with propositions (10)–(12), the question arises as to the truth of the assertions

$$\forall x\, (M(x) = x \vee M(x) = -x), \tag{13}$$
$$\forall xy\, (y \geqslant 0 \supset (M(x) = y \supset x = -y \vee x = y)), \tag{14}$$
$$\forall xy\, (y \geqslant 0 \supset (M(x) \geqslant y \supset x \leqslant -y \vee x \geqslant y)). \tag{15}$$

Assertion (13) is equivalent to the assertion

$$\forall x\, (x \geqslant 0 \vee x \leqslant 0).$$

Hence it is refutable. Let us suppose that assertion (14) is true. Then we have

$$\forall x\, (M(x) \geqslant 0 \supset (M(x) = M(x) \supset x = -M(x) \vee x = M(x))).$$

Therefore,

$$\forall x\, (x = -M(x) \vee x = M(x)).$$

This assertion is refutable. Hence (14) is also refutable.

Let us suppose that assertion (15) is true. Then we have

$$\forall x\, (0 \geqslant 0 \supset (M(x) \geqslant 0 \supset x \leqslant -0 \vee x \geqslant 0)).$$

Hence

$$\forall x\, (x \leqslant 0 \vee x \geqslant 0).$$

This statement is refutable. Therefore (15) is also refutable.

What has just been said proves the following theorem.

6.4.10.

$$\neg \forall x\, (M(x) = x \vee M(x) = -x),$$
$$\neg \forall xy\, (y \geqslant 0 \supset (M(x) = y \supset x = -y \vee x - y)),$$
$$\neg \forall xy\, (y \geqslant 0 \supset (M(x) \geqslant y \supset x \leqslant -y \vee x \geqslant y)).$$

Theorem 6.4.10 testifies to the existence of significant differences between the properties of the operation M_B and the properties of the corresponding operation of classical mathematics.

Now we shall mention some properties of the operations $\mathcal{A}_B$ and $\mathcal{A}^*_B$. It is not difficult to prove the following theorem.

6.4.11. *For any duplexes x and y, integers v and w, and rational numbers a and b*,

$$x \neq 0 \supset x \underset{B}{\Lambda} 0 = 1, \qquad x \neq 0 \supset x \underset{B}{\Lambda^*} 0 = 1,$$

$$x \underset{B}{\Lambda} 1 = x, \qquad x \underset{B}{\Lambda^*} 1 = M(x),$$

$$v > 1 \supset x \underset{B}{\Lambda} v = \underbrace{x \cdot \ldots \cdot x}_{v \text{ times}},$$

$$v > 1 \supset x \underset{B}{\Lambda^*} v = \underbrace{M(x) \cdot \ldots \cdot M(x)}_{v \text{ times}},$$

$$x \neq 0 \,\&\, v \neq 0 \supset x \underset{B}{\Lambda} - v = 1 : x \underset{B}{\Lambda} v,$$

$$x \neq 0 \,\&\, v \neq 0 \supset x \underset{B}{\Lambda^*} - v = 1 : x \underset{B}{\Lambda^*} v,$$

$$x \neq 0 \vee (v > 0 \,\&\, w > 0) \supset x \underset{B}{\Lambda} v \cdot x \underset{B}{\Lambda} w = x \underset{B}{\Lambda} (v + w),$$

$$x \neq 0 \vee (a > 0 \,\&\, b > 0) \supset x \underset{B}{\Lambda^*} a \cdot x \underset{B}{\Lambda^*} b = x \underset{B}{\Lambda^*} (a + b),$$

$$x \neq 0 \vee (v > 0 \,\&\, w > 0) \supset (x \underset{B}{\Lambda} v) \underset{B}{\Lambda} w = x \underset{B}{\Lambda} (v \cdot w),$$

$$x \neq 0 \vee (a > 0 \,\&\, b > 0) \supset (x \underset{B}{\Lambda^*} a) \underset{B}{\Lambda^*} b = x \underset{B}{\Lambda^*} (a \cdot b),$$

$$(x \neq 0 \,\&\, y \neq 0) \vee v > 0 \supset (x \cdot y) \underset{B}{\Lambda} v = x \underset{B}{\Lambda} v \cdot y \underset{B}{\Lambda} v,$$

$$(x \neq 0 \,\&\, y \neq 0) \vee a > 0 \supset (x \cdot y) \underset{B}{\Lambda^*} a = x \underset{B}{\Lambda^*} a \cdot y \underset{B}{\Lambda^*} a.$$

6.5. In the description of the operations M_B, $\max_B$, $\min_B$, $+_B$, $-_B$, $\cdot_B$, $:_B$, Λ_B, Λ^*_B in §§6.1 and 6.2, we formulated requirements imposed on the operation of the corresponding algorithms in those cases where the initially given objects are duplexes. With respect to those cases where the initially given objects are not duplexes, no requirements were imposed on the operation of the corresponding algorithms. This last fact allows us considerable freedom to vary the construction of the corresponding algorithms. We shall use this freedom in order to define all the indicated operations also in those cases where the initially given objects are *F*-numbers.

We introduce an algorithm $\mathfrak{S}$ in the alphabet Ч_3^{sa}, applicable to every word in the alphabet Ч_3^{s} and such that, for any words $c_{3,1}$ and $c_{3,2}$,

$$\mathfrak{S}(c_{3,1}) \doteq \Lambda \equiv c_{3,1} \in \underline{\text{one can}}_3,$$

$$\mathfrak{S}(c_{3,1} \square c_{3,2}) \doteq \Lambda \equiv c_{3,1} \in \underline{\text{one can}}_3 \,\&\, c_{3,2} \in \underline{\text{one can}}_3.$$

Now we shall make precise the requirements imposed on the algorithms M_B, $\max_{B,0}$, $\min_{B,0}$, $+_{B,0}$, $-_{B,0}$, $\cdot_{B,0}$, $:_B$, $\mathcal{A}_B$, $\mathcal{A}^*_B$, in the following manner.

1. In all conditions imposed on the algorithms $\mathfrak{A}_0, \mathfrak{A}_1, \cdots, \mathfrak{A}_7, \mathfrak{B}_0, \mathfrak{B}_*, \mathfrak{B}_5, \mathfrak{B}_6, \mathfrak{B}^*_6$, and $\mathfrak{B}_7$, we replace the variables x and y by the variables $c_{3,1}$ and $c_{3,2}$, respectively.

2. The conditions imposed on the algorithms M_B, $\max_{B,0}$, $\min_{B,0}$, $+_{B,0}$, $-_{B,0}$, $\cdot_{B,0}$, $:_B$, $\mathcal{A}_B$, $\mathcal{A}^*_B$ can be formulated as follows. For all admissible values of the variables,

$$\mathfrak{R}(c_{3,1}) \mathrel{\dot{=}} \Lambda \supset \underset{B}{M}(c_{3,1}) \simeq \underset{p}{M}(c_{3,1}),$$

$$\mathfrak{R}(c_{3,1}) \mathrel{\dot{\neq}} \Lambda \,\&\, \mathfrak{S}(c_{3,1}) \mathrel{\dot{=}} \Lambda \supset \underset{B}{M}(c_{3,1}) \simeq \mathfrak{A}_0(c_{3,1}) \diamondsuit,$$

$$\mathfrak{R}(c_{3,1}) \mathrel{\dot{\neq}} \Lambda \,\&\, \mathfrak{S}(c_{3,1}) \mathrel{\dot{\neq}} \Lambda \supset \underset{B}{M}(c_{3,1}) \simeq \mathfrak{A}_0(c_{3,1}) \diamondsuit \mathfrak{B}_0(c_{3,1}),$$

$$\mathfrak{R}(c_{3,1} \square c_{3,2}) \mathrel{\dot{=}} \Lambda \supset \underset{B}{\max}_0(c_{3,1} \square c_{3,2}) \simeq \underset{p}{\max}(c_{3,1} \square c_{3,2}),$$

$$\mathfrak{R}(c_{3,1} \square c_{3,2}) \mathrel{\dot{\neq}} \Lambda \,\&\, \mathfrak{S}(c_{3,1} \square c_{3,2}) \mathrel{\dot{=}} \Lambda \supset \underset{B}{\max}_0(c_{3,1} \square c_{3,2}) \simeq \mathfrak{A}_1(c_{3,1} \square c_{3,2}) \diamondsuit,$$

$$\mathfrak{R}(c_{3,1} \square c_{3,2}) \mathrel{\dot{\neq}} \Lambda \,\&\, \mathfrak{S}(c_{3,1} \square c_{3,2}) \mathrel{\dot{\neq}} \Lambda \supset \underset{B}{\max}_0(c_{3,1} \square c_{3,2})$$

$$\simeq \mathfrak{A}_1(c_{3,1} \square c_{3,2}) \diamondsuit \mathfrak{B}_*(c_{3,1} \square c_{3,2}),$$

. . . .

. . . .

(the dots indicate the conditions, composed according to the pattern presented here, on the operations $\min_{B,0}$, $+_{B,0}$, $-_{B,0}$, $\cdot_{B,0}$, $:_B$, $\mathcal{A}_B$, $\mathcal{A}^*_B$).

In order to demonstrate the possibility of constructing the normal algorithms satisfying these precise requirements, it suffices to refer to those theorems of the theory of normal algorithms to which we referred in §§6.1 and 6.2, replacing a reference to the theorem on the branching of algorithms by a reference to the generalized theorem on the branching of algorithms [1].

The operations $\max_B$, $\min_B$, $+_B$, $-_B$, $\cdot_B$ are constructed on the basis of the operations $\max_{B,0}$, $\min_{B,0}$, $+_{B,0}$, $-_{B,0}$, $\cdot_{B,0}$ by applying Theorem 6.1.1 and the theorem on the reduction of algorithms.

The following theorem is valid.

6.5.1.
a) $$\forall r\,(\underset{B}{M}(r) \overset{+}{\in} \underline{\text{real } F\text{-num}});$$

b) *for any natural number j not less than two,*

$$\tilde{\forall}(\delta(B_1 \square \ldots \square B_j) \stackrel{+}{\in} \underline{\text{real } F\text{-num}})$$

(*here* δ *is any of the algorithms* $\max_B$, $\min_B$, $+_B$, $-_B$, $\cdot_B$);

c) $$\forall rs(s \underset{B}{\neq} 0 \supset : (r \underset{B}{\square} s) \in \underline{\text{real } F\text{-num}});$$

d) $$\forall rv(r \underset{B}{\neq} 0 \vee v \underset{p}{>} 0 \supset \underset{B}{\Lambda}(r \square v) \stackrel{+}{\in} \underline{\text{real } F\text{-num}});$$

e) $$\forall rb(r \underset{B}{\neq} 0 \vee b \underset{p}{>} 0 \supset \underset{B}{\Lambda^*}(r \square b) \stackrel{+}{\in} \underline{\text{real } F\text{-num}}).$$

In accordance with the conventions accepted in §§3.5 and 1.14, the letters r and s denote variables of type B, the letter v is a variable of type Ц and the letter b a variable of type p.

Proof. The constructive problem which it is necessary to solve to justify proposition a) is exhibited above in §6.3 in the constructive reformulation of the condition "$\Phi_{3,1} \in (B \to B)_3$". The process of exhibiting the constructive problem leads to the formula

$$\exists \Phi_{3,3} \mathfrak{B}_1, \tag{1}$$

where

$$\mathfrak{B}_1 \leftrightharpoons \forall c_{3,1}\Phi_{0,1}(\mathfrak{M} \supset \underset{B}{M}(c_{3,1}) \stackrel{+}{\in} \underline{\text{one mean}}_3 \,\&\, \underset{B}{\underline{M(c_{3,1})}} \in (H \to p)_2$$

$$\& \,\Phi_{3,3}(c_{3,1} \square \{\Phi_{0,1}\}) \stackrel{+}{\in} c_0 \,\&\, \langle \Phi_{3,3}(c_{3,1} \square \{\Phi_{0,1}\})\rangle_0 \underline{\text{reg. con.}} \underset{B}{\underline{M(c_{3,1})}}),$$

$$\mathfrak{M} \leftrightharpoons c_{3,1} \in \underline{\text{one mean}}_3 \,\&\, \underline{c_{3,1}} \in (H \to p)_2 \,\&\, \Phi_{0,1}\, \underline{\text{reg. con.}} \underline{c_{3,1}}.$$

Formula (1) can be considered as a constructive reformulation of formula a). For a proof of the truth of this formula, we construct an algorithm $\mathfrak{C}_0$ in the alphabet $Ч_3^{sa}$ such that

$$\forall c_{3,1} c_{0,1}(\mathfrak{C}_0(c_{3,1} \square c_{0,1}) \simeq \mathfrak{B}_0(c_{3,1} c_{0,1})).$$

On the basis of the properties of the algorithm $\mathfrak{B}_0$ and the obvious assertion

$$\forall c_{3,1} c_{0,1}(c_{3,1} \in \underline{\text{one mean}}_3 \,\&\, \underline{c_{3,1}} \in (H \to p)_2 \,\&\, \langle c_{0,1}\rangle_0 \underline{\text{reg. con.}} \underline{c_{3,1}}$$

$$\supset c_{3,1} c_{0,1} \in \underline{\text{real dup}}),$$

it is not difficult to prove that

$$\mathbf{F}_{\mathfrak{C}_0}^{\Phi_{3,3}} \llcorner \mathfrak{B}_1 \lrcorner.$$

Hence proposition (1) is true, and a) follows from (1).

Propositions b), c), d) and e) are proved with the help of algorithms $\mathfrak{B}_*$, $\mathfrak{B}_5$, $\mathfrak{B}_6^*$ and $\mathfrak{B}_7$ by the same method as was used for proposition a).

It is not hard to establish that the operation M_{B} is a function of type (B → B) and that, for any natural number n, the operations $\max_{\text{B}}$, $\min_{\text{B}}$, $+_{\text{B}}$, $-_{\text{B}}$, $\cdot_{\text{B}}$ are functions of type ($\underbrace{\text{B}\cdots\text{B}}_{n \text{ times}} \to \text{B}$). One can also prove that, replacing the variables x, y, z in all theorems formulated in §6.4 by the variables q, r, s and replacing the word "duplex" by the expression "F-number", we obtain true propositions.

6.6. In this section we shall discuss constructive analogues of the function denoted in classical mathematics by sign. We shall use the expression sign as a designation for a concrete algorithm in the alphabet $Ч_3^{\text{sa}}$ such that, for any duplex x,

$$\text{sign}(x) \simeq -1 \underset{\text{p}}{\wedge} \mathfrak{C}(x \square 0),$$

where $\mathfrak{C}$ is the algorithm figuring in Theorem 4.4.3. From 4.4.3 it follows that, for any duplex x,

$$\text{sign}(x) \underset{\text{B}}{=} \begin{cases} -1, & \text{if} \quad x<0, \\ 1, & \text{if} \quad x>0. \end{cases}$$

The process of applying the algorithm sign to a duplex equal to zero does not terminate, and therefore sign is not a function of type (Д → Д). However, sign is a function of type (Д ⇢ Д).

From Markov's theorem on the impossibility of a constructive discontinuity of a constructive function at those points at which the value of the function is computable [8], it follows that there can be no function of type (Д → Д) the value of which for every duplex different from zero is equal to the value of the function sign.

We construct an algorithm sign_0 of type $(\text{Р} \to \text{Н})_2$ such that, for any rational number a,

$$\text{sign}_0(a) \underset{\text{P}}{=} \begin{cases} -1, & \text{if} \quad a<0, \\ 0, & \text{if} \quad a=0, \\ 1, & \text{if} \quad a>0. \end{cases}$$

Further, we construct an algorithm ψ of type $(\text{Д} \to \text{c}_0)_3$, such that, for any duplex x and any natural number n:

$$\langle\psi(x)\rangle_2(n) \simeq \begin{cases} \text{sign}_0(\underline{x}(n)), & \text{if} \quad G(x \square n) \mathrel{\dot{=}} \Lambda, \\ 0, & \text{if} \quad G(x \square n) \mathrel{\dot{\neq}} \Lambda. \end{cases}$$

Here G is an algorithm checking, for any x and n, the fulfillment of the condition "One can construct a natural number k not exceeding n and such that $\mathfrak{L}^*(x \square 0 \square k) > 2^{-k}$".

$\mathfrak{L}^*$ is the algorithm introduced in §4.4. We construct, finally, an algorithm sign_* in the alphabet $Ч_3^{sa}$ transforming any duplex x into the word $\psi(x)\Diamond$.

It is not difficult to prove the following proposition.

6.6.1. *For any duplex* x:

a) $$\text{sign}_*(x) \overset{+}{\in} \underline{\text{one can}}_3;$$

b) $$x < 0 \supset \text{sign}_*(x) \in \underline{\text{real } F\text{-num}} \;\&\; \text{sign}_*(x) \underset{\text{B}}{=} -1;$$

c) $$x = 0 \supset \text{sign}_*(x) \in \underline{\text{real } F\text{-num}} \;\&\; \text{sign}_*(x) \underset{\text{B}}{=} 0;$$

d) $$x > 0 \supset \text{sign}_*(x) \in \underline{\text{real } F\text{-num}} \;\&\; \text{sign}_*(x) \underset{\text{B}}{=} 1.$$

We note that, at the same time,

$$\neg\forall x(\text{sign}_*(x) \in \underline{\text{real } F\text{-num}}).$$

In fact, assuming that $\forall x(\text{sign}_*(x) \in \text{real } F\text{-}\underline{\text{num}})$, we are led to an assertion about the realizability of a function $\Phi_{3,1}$ of type $(Д \to Д)$ the value of which for every duplex different from zero is equal to the value of the function sign.

§7. ON SOME SUBSETS OF THE CONSTRUCTIVE CONTINUUM

7.1. Let A be any alphabet not containing the symbols $\square$, ι, and κ, and let α be any elementary symbol not belonging to A. Every word in the alphabet $A \cup \{\alpha\}$ will be called an *α-system of words in the alphabet* A.

If R is any α-system of words in the alphabet A, then the occurrences of the letter α in the word R divide R into parts which are words in the alphabet A. Every such part of the word R will be called an *α-term of the word* R. These parts of the word R will be numbered in order of succession from left to right and in this sense we shall speak about the first α-term of the word R, the second α-term of the word R, etc. If α does not occur in R, then R has a unique α-term, the word R itself.

We denote by L_α the algorithm in the alphabet $A \cup \{0, |, \alpha, \square, \iota, \kappa\}$ transforming every α-system of words R into the positive integer which is one greater than the number of occurrences of the letter α in R. It is obvious that $L_\alpha(R)$ is equal to the number of α-terms of the word R. By G_α we denote the algorithm in the alphabet $A \cup \{0, |, \alpha, \square, \iota, \kappa\}$ applicable to every word of the form $K \square R$, where K is a positive integer and R is a word in the alphabet $A \cup \{\alpha\}$, and transforming the word $K \square R$ into the Kth α-term of the word R, if $K \leq L_\alpha(R)$, and into the empty word if $K > L_\alpha(R)$.

In every concrete case of the application of the notation L_α and G_α, we shall assume that the algorithms denoted by these expressions are constructed with respect to the alphabet which, in the given case, plays the role of the alphabet A.

For brevity, we agree to denote the term $G_\alpha(K \square R)$ by $[R]^\alpha_K$.

If μ is any generic letter and every α-term of the word R is a word of type μ, then the word R will be called an *α-system of words of type μ*. In that sense, we shall use the terms "α-system of rational numbers", "α-system of duplexes", etc.

Two-termed α-systems of words of type μ will be called *α-pairs of words of type μ*, three-termed α-systems of words of type μ will be called *α-triples of words of type μ*, etc.

7.2. We introduce new elementary symbols

$$\underline{\nabla} \quad \nabla \quad \tau \quad \sigma$$

and we introduce the notation

$$Ч_4 \rightleftharpoons Ч_3 \cup \{\underline{\nabla}, \nabla, \tau, \sigma\}.$$

The alphabet $Ч_4$ is intended for the construction of $\underline{\nabla}$-, ∇-, τ-, and σ-systems of rational numbers and duplexes, and also for the construction of systems of words of more complicated types.

Let $c_{4,1}$ be a word in the alphabet $Ч_4$ representing a $\underline{\nabla}$-pair of duplexes. We shall say that $c_{4,1}$ is a *segment* if $[c_{4,1}]^{\underline{\nabla}}_1 \leq_B [c_{4,1}]^{\underline{\nabla}}_2$. A segment $c_{4,1}$ is said to be *degenerate* (*nondegenerate*) if $[c_{4,1}]^{\underline{\nabla}}_2 =_B [c_{4,1}]^{\underline{\nabla}}_1$ (respectively, $[c_{4,1}]^{\underline{\nabla}}_1 <_B [c_{4,1}]^{\underline{\nabla}}_2$). If $c_{4,1}$ is a segment, then the duplex $[c_{4,1}]^{\underline{\nabla}}_1$ is called the *left end* of the segment $c_{4,1}$ and the duplex $[c_{4,1}]^{\underline{\nabla}}_2$ is called the *right end* of the segment $c_{4,1}$.

Let $c_{4,2}$ be a word in the alphabet $Ч_4$ representing a ∇-pair of duplexes. We shall say that $c_{4,2}$ is an *interval* if $[c_{4,2}]^{\nabla}_1 <_B [c_{4,2}]^{\nabla}_2$. If $c_{4,2}$ is an interval, then the duplex $[c_{4,2}]^{\nabla}_1$ is called the *left end* of the interval $c_{4,2}$ and the duplex $[c_{4,2}]^{\nabla}_2$ is called the *right end* of the interval $c_{4,2}$.

To every segment $c_{4,1}$ we associate the set of duplexes given by the formula

$$([c_{4,1}]^{\underline{\nabla}}_1 \leqslant z \,\&\, z \leqslant [c_{4,1}]^{\underline{\nabla}}_2). \qquad (1)$$

We shall say that a duplex z belongs to the segment $c_{4,1}$, and we shall write $z \in c_{4,1}$ if z belongs to the set (1).

To every interval $c_{4,2}$ we associate a set of duplexes given by the formula

$$([c_{4,2}]_1^{\nabla} < z \,\&\, z < [c_{4,2}]_2^{\nabla}). \tag{2}$$

We shall say that a duplex z belongs to the interval $c_{4,2}$, and we shall write $z \in c_{4,2}$, if z belongs to the set (2).

The set of duplexes associated with the segment $c_{4,1}$ (the interval $c_{4,2}$) will be denoted by $\mathfrak{M}_{Д}(c_{4,1})$ [respectively, by $\mathfrak{M}_{Д}(c_{4,2})$] and will be called the set of $Д$-points of the segment $c_{4,1}$ (of the interval $c_{4,2}$).

In considering the simplest problems having to do with segments and intervals, we run into significant differences between constructive mathematics and classical mathematics. Let us consider as an example the following statement:

"The set $\mathfrak{M}_{Д}(0 \,\underline{\nabla}\, 1)$ is the union of the sets $\mathfrak{M}_{Д}(0 \,\underline{\nabla}\, 0)$, $\mathfrak{M}_{Д}(0 \,\nabla\, 1)$, and $\mathfrak{M}_{Д}(1 \,\underline{\nabla}\, 1)$,

It is easily seen that this statement is equivalent to the following statement:

$$\forall z\,(0 \leqslant z \leqslant 1 \equiv (0 = z \vee 0 < z < 1 \vee 1 = z)). \tag{3}$$

Let us assume that (3) is true. Then

$$\forall x\,(0 \leqslant \min(x \,\square\, 1) \supset (0 = \min(x \,\square\, 1) \vee 0 < \min(x \,\square\, 1))).$$

Hence

$$\forall x\,(0 \leqslant x \supset 0 = x \vee 0 < x). \tag{4}$$

In §4.5 it was noted that the negation of formula (4) is provable (cf. 4.5 (67)). Hence statement (3) is refutable.

It follows from what has been proved above that $\mathfrak{M}_{Д}(0 \,\underline{\nabla}\, 1)$ is not the union of the sets $\mathfrak{M}_{Д}(0 \,\underline{\nabla}\, 0)$, $\mathfrak{M}_{Д}(0 \,\nabla\, 1)$, and $\mathfrak{M}_{Д}(1 \,\underline{\nabla}\, 1)$. Thus we can state another point of essential divergence between constructive and classical mathematics.

The following two propositions can be easily proved.

$$\forall xy\,(x < y \supset \forall z\,(z = x \vee x < z < y \vee z = y \supset x \leqslant z \leqslant y)),$$
$$\forall xy\,(x < y \supset \forall z\,(x \leqslant z \leqslant y \equiv \neg\neg\,(z = x \vee x < z < y \vee z = y))).$$

From these propositions it follows that, for any duplexes x and y such that $x < y$, first, the set $\mathfrak{M}_{Д}(x \,\underline{\nabla}\, y)$ contains the union of the sets $\mathfrak{M}_{Д}(x \,\underline{\nabla}\, x)$, $\mathfrak{M}_{Д}(x \,\nabla\, y)$, and $\mathfrak{M}_{Д}(y \,\underline{\nabla}\, y)$, and second, the set $\mathfrak{M}_{Д}(x \,\underline{\nabla}\, y)$ is equal to the difference between the set of all duplexes and the union of the sets $\mathfrak{M}_{Д}(x \,\underline{\nabla}\, x)$, $\mathfrak{M}_{Д}(x \,\nabla\, y)$, and $\mathfrak{M}_{Д}(y \,\underline{\nabla}\, y)$.

7.3. Let $\mathfrak{F}$ be any set of duplexes, ϵ a positive rational number, and $c_{4,3}$ a

τ-system of duplexes. One says that $c_{4,3}$ is a *finite ϵ-net* in the set $\mathfrak{F}$ if, first, every τ-term of the τ-system $c_{4,3}$ belongs to the set $\mathfrak{F}$, i.e.

$$\forall k (k \leqslant L_\tau(c_{4,3}) \supset \mathbf{F}^\gamma_{[c_{4,3}]^\tau_k \llcorner} \mathfrak{F}\lrcorner),$$

(here γ is the parameter of the formula $\mathfrak{F}$), and second, for any duplex x belonging to the set $\mathfrak{F}$, one can find a τ-term of the τ-system $c_{4,3}$ differing from x by less than ϵ, i.e.

$$\forall x (\mathbf{F}^\gamma_{x\llcorner} \mathfrak{F}\lrcorner \supset \exists l (l \leqslant L_\tau(c_{4,3}) \,\&\, M(x - [c_{4,3}]^\tau_l) < \varepsilon)).$$

The set of duplexes $\mathfrak{F}$ is called *almost totally bounded* if, for any natural number k, one can construct a τ-system of duplexes which is a finite 2^{-k}-net in the set $\mathfrak{F}$.

7.3.1. *If* $c_{4,1}$ *is any segment, then* $\mathfrak{M}_Д(c_{4,1})$ *is an almost totally bounded set. If* $c_{4,2}$ *is any interval, then* $\mathfrak{M}_Д(c_{4,2})$ *is an almost totally bounded set.*

Let us prove the first part of the theorem. Let $c_{4,1}$ be any segment and k any natural number. We introduce the notation

$$X \rightleftharpoons [c_{4,1}]^\nabla_1, \quad Y \rightleftharpoons [c_{4,1}]^\nabla_2, \quad H \rightleftharpoons Y - X.$$

We have

$$0 \leqslant H \leqslant \underline{H}(\overline{H}(0)) + 1.$$

We introduce the notation

$$N \rightleftharpoons \mu_n(\underline{H}(\overline{H}(0)) + 1 \leqslant 2^n), \quad \nu \rightleftharpoons 2^{N+k+2},$$

$$U_l \rightleftharpoons X + (H : \nu) \cdot l \quad (l = 1, 2, 3, \ldots, \nu - 1),$$

$$S \rightleftharpoons U_1 \tau U_2 \tau \ldots \tau U_{\nu-1}.$$

The word S is a τ-system of duplexes, $L_\tau(S) = \nu - 1$, and, for every l satisfying the condition $1 \leq l \leq \nu - 1$, we have

$$[S]^\tau_l \doteq U_l, \quad X \leqslant [S]^\tau_l \leqslant Y, \quad 0 \leqslant U_{l+1} - U_l \leqslant 2^{-(k+2)}.$$

Moreover, if $X < Y$, then $X < [S]^\tau_l < Y$.

Let us prove that S is a 2^{-k}-net in the set $\mathfrak{M}_Д(c_{4,1})$. First, all τ-parts of the word S are elements of the set $\mathfrak{M}_Д(c_{4,1})$, and, in the case where $X < Y$, all τ-parts of the word S are also elements of the set $\mathfrak{M}_Д(X \nabla Y)$. Further, let z be any element of the set $\mathfrak{M}_Д(c_{4,1})$. We introduce the notation (cf. §5.3)

$$J \rightleftharpoons \mu_l(\underline{\gamma_\uparrow(z)}(k+3) \leqslant \underline{\gamma_\downarrow(U_l)}(k+3) + 2^{-(k+2)}) \tag{1}$$

and we shall prove that

$$M(z - [S]^\tau_J) < 2^{-k}. \tag{2}$$

First of all, we note that the condition standing after the symbol for the μ-operator in (1) is algorithmically verifiable for admissible values of the parameters (since, in this condition, to the left and right of the symbol $\leq$ stand terms taking rational values for admissible values of the parameters). Therefore J can be considered as a designation of a term. In addition,

$$\underline{\Upsilon_{\uparrow}(z)}\,(k+3) \leqslant \Upsilon_{\uparrow}(z) = z \leqslant Y \leqslant U_{\nu-1} + 2^{-(k+2)}$$
$$\leqslant \underline{\Upsilon_{\downarrow}(U_{\nu-1})}\,(k+3) + 2^{-(k+2)}.$$

Hence $1 \leq J \leq \nu - 1$. Therefore $[c_{4,1}]_J^{\uparrow}$ is a duplex. We introduce the notation

$$\lambda \leftrightharpoons z - \underline{\Upsilon_{\uparrow}(z)}\,(k+3), \quad \theta_l \leftrightharpoons \underline{\Upsilon_{\downarrow}(U_l)}\,(k+3) - U_l.$$

We have (on the basis of 5.3.3)

$$0 \leqslant \lambda \leqslant 2^{-(k+3)}, \quad 0 \leqslant \theta_l \leqslant 2^{-(k+3)},$$
$$\underline{\Upsilon_{\uparrow}(z)}\,(k+3) = z - \lambda, \quad \underline{\Upsilon_{\downarrow}(U_l)}\,(k+3) = U_l + \theta_l,$$
$$z - \lambda \leqslant U_J + \theta_J + 2^{-(k+2)},$$
$$z - U_J \leqslant \lambda + \theta_J + 2^{-(k+2)} \leqslant 2^{-(k+1)} < 2^{-k},$$
$$z - U_J < 2^{-k}. \tag{3}$$

Now we consider two cases.

A) $J = 1$. In this case

$$z \geqslant X \geqslant U_1 - 2^{-(k+2)},$$
$$z - U_1 \geqslant -2^{-(k+2)} > -2^{-k}. \tag{4}$$

(2) follows from (3) and (4).

B) $J > 1$. In this case

$$z - \lambda > U_{J-1} + \theta_{J-1} + 2^{-(k+2)}, \quad U_{J-1} \geqslant U_J - 2^{-(k+2)},$$
$$z - \lambda > U_J + \theta_{J-1}, \quad z - U_J > \lambda + \theta_{J-1} \geqslant 0,$$
$$z - U_J > -2^{-k}. \tag{5}$$

(2) follows from (3) and (5).

Noting that $(J = 1 \vee J > 1)$, we obtain (2). The first part of Theorem 7.3.1 has been proved. The second part is proved almost word for word like the first part.

Remark 1. The constructive reformulation of the first part of Theorem 7.3.1

is a statement about the realizability of algorithms $\Phi_{4,1}$ and $\Phi_{4,2}$ such that the algorithm $\Phi_{4,1}$ transforms every word of the form $c_{4,1} \square k$, where $c_{4,1}$ is a segment and k is a natural number, into some τ-system of duplexes, all τ-terms of which belong to the set $\mathfrak{M}_{Д}(c_{4,1})$, and the algorithm $\Phi_{4,2}$ transforms every word of the form $c_{4,1} \square k \square z$, where $c_{4,1}$ is a segment, k is a natural number, and z is a duplex belonging to the set $\mathfrak{M}_{Д}(c_{4,1})$, into a natural number $\Phi_{4,2}(c_{4,1} \square k \square z)$ such that

$$M(z - [\Phi_{4,1}(c_{4,1} \square k)]^{\tau}_{\Phi_{4,2}(c_{4,1} \square k \square z)}) < 2^{-k}.$$

The proof given above of Theorem 7.3.1 is a justification by the deductive methods of constructive logic of the realizability of such algorithms. From the proof of the theorem it is not difficult to extract a construction of the desired algorithms.

With respect to the second part of Theorem 7.3.1 a similar remark is valid (except that, in this case, intervals should occur in its formulation instead of segments).

Remark 2. The segments and intervals which we have been discussing in § §7.2 and 7.3 will also be called *Д-segments* and *Д-intervals*. If in all definitions formulated in 7.2 and 7.3 the words "segment" and "interval" are replaced, respectively, by "Д-segment" and "Д-interval", and if after this replacement we replace the word "duplex" by the expression "F-number" and the letter "Д" by the letter "B", then we obtain definitions of the concepts "B-segment", "B-interval", "almost totally bounded set of F-numbers", etc. If the same replacement of terms is carried out in Theorem 7.3.1, then we obtain a true proposition.[1] One can easily prove this by applying to Theorem 7.3.1 the natural generalization of Theorem 3.8.3 to those formulas in which, in addition to the individual variables of the types considered earlier, can also occur individual variables for which the admissible values are all τ-systems of duplexes and also individual variables for which the admissible values are all τ-systems of F-numbers.

7.4.[2] In §7.2 all segments and intervals (including segments and intervals having rational end points) were associated according to definition with sets of duplexes. It is also convenient to associate certain sets of rational numbers with all segments and intervals having rational end points.

---

1) However, Remark 1, changed in the same way, will not extend to this proposition.
2) The material presented in this section will not be used until §14.

To each segment $c_{4,1}$ having rational end points we associate the set of rational numbers given by the formula

$$([c_{4,1}]_1^{\underline{\nabla}} \leqslant a \,\&\, a \leqslant [c_{4,1}]_2^{\underline{\nabla}}). \tag{1}$$

This set will be denoted by $\mathfrak{M}_p(c_{4,1})$.

To each interval $c_{4,2}$ having rational end points we associate the set of rational numbers given by the formula

$$([c_{4,2}]_1^{\nabla} < a \,\&\, a < [c_{4,2}]_2^{\nabla}). \tag{2}$$

This set will be denoted by $\mathfrak{M}_p(c_{4,2})$.

Conditions (1) and (2) are algorithmically verifiable.

It is easily seen that the following proposition is valid.

7.4.1. *For any rational numbers* a *and* b *such that* $a < b$, *the set* $\mathfrak{M}_p(a \underline{\nabla} b)$ *is equal to the union of the sets* $\mathfrak{M}_p(a \underline{\nabla} a)$, $\mathfrak{M}_p(a \nabla b)$, *and* $\mathfrak{M}_p(b \underline{\nabla} b)$. *For any rational numbers* a, b, *and* d *such that* $a < d < b$, *the set* $\mathfrak{M}_p(a \nabla b)$ *is equal to the union of the sets* $\mathfrak{M}_p(a \nabla d)$, $\mathfrak{M}_p(d \underline{\nabla} d)$, *and* $\mathfrak{M}_p(d \nabla b)$.

A word $c_{4,3}$ in the alphabet $Ч_4$ will be called a *rational interval* if $c_{4,3}$ is an interval with rational end points or a degenerate segment with rational end points. The left end point and right end point of a rational interval $c_{4,3}$ will be denoted, respectively, by $[c_{4,3}]_\ell$ and $[c_{4,3}]_r$.

Let $c_{4,3}$ and $c_{4,4}$ be rational intervals. We shall say that $c_{4,3}$ *precedes* $c_{4,4}$, and also that $c_{4,4}$ *follows* $c_{4,3}$, if $[c_{4,3}]_r < [c_{4,4}]_\ell$ or at least one of the two rational intervals is an interval and $[c_{4,3}]_r \leq [c_{4,4}]_\ell$.

A word $c_{4,5}$ in the alphabet $Ч_4$ will be called a complex if $c_{4,5}$ is the empty word or for each l satisfying the condition $1 \leq l \leq L_\tau(c_{4,5})$ the word $[c_{4,5}]_l^\tau$ is a rational interval and $[c_{4,5}]_{l-1}^\tau$ precedes $[c_{4,5}]_l^\tau$ (for the additional condition $l > 1$).

We denote by $\overline{\text{end}}$ the algorithm in the alphabet $Ч_4^{sa}$ transforming any complex $c_{4,5}$ into the τ-system of rational numbers obtained in the following manner. To begin with, all occurrences in the word $c_{4,5}$ of the letters $\underline{\nabla}$ and ∇ are replaced by the letter τ (as a result a word is obtained which consists of all left and right end points of the rational intervals which are τ-terms of the word $c_{4,5}$), and then in the resulting τ-system of rational numbers we cancel every τ-term equal (as a rational number) to the preceding τ-term, and then we cancel all instances of the letter τ standing directly in front of canceled τ-terms. It is obvious that the word $\overline{\text{end}}(c_{4,5})$ is a τ-system of rational numbers such that the list of all τ-terms of this system can be obtained by successively writing down in increasing order and without repetition all left and right end points of the rational intervals which are τ-terms of the complex $c_{4,5}$.

Let $c_{4,2}$ be any interval having rational end points, and let $c_{4,5}$ be any complex. By the *refinement of the interval* $c_{4,2}$ *by the complex* $c_{4,5}$ we mean the complex obtained in the following way. First of all, we construct the word $\overline{\text{end}}\,(c_{4,5})$ and we write in increasing order all τ-terms of the word $\overline{\text{end}}\,(c_{4,5})$ belonging to the set $\mathfrak{M}_{\mathfrak{p}}(c_{4,2})$. If the empty list is obtained, then the one-termed complex $c_{4,2}$ will be called the refinement of $c_{4,2}$ by $c_{4,5}$. If we obtain the nonempty list of rational numbers

$$R_1,\ R_2,\ \ldots,\ R_j,$$

then the refinement of $c_{4,2}$ by $c_{4,5}$ will mean the complex

$$X \triangledown R_1 \tau R_1 \,\underline{\triangledown}\, R_1 \tau R_1 \triangledown R_2 \tau R_2 \,\underline{\triangledown}\, R_2 \tau \ldots \tau R_{j-1} \triangledown R_j \tau R_j \,\underline{\triangledown}\, R_j \tau R_j \triangledown Y,$$

where $X \leftrightharpoons [c_{4,2}]_{\ell}$ and $Y \leftrightharpoons [c_{4,2}]_{\pi}$.

Let $c_{4,1}$ be any degenerate segment having rational end points, and let $c_{4,5}$ be any complex. The refinement of the degenerate segment $c_{4,1}$ by the complex $c_{4,5}$ will mean the one-termed complex $c_{4,1}$.

Let $c_{4,5}$ and $c_{4,6}$ be any complexes. The refinement of the complex $c_{4,5}$ by the complex $c_{4,6}$ will mean the complex obtained by substituting in $c_{4,5}$ in place of every rational interval which is a τ-term of the complex $c_{4,5}$ its refinement by the complex $c_{4,6}$.

The algorithm for constructing the refinement of one complex by another complex can be given in the form of a normal algorithm in the alphabet $Ч_4^{sa}$. We construct some normal algorithm in the alphabet $Ч_4^{sa}$ realizing the construction of the refinement of one complex by another and we introduce the designation ref for this algorithm. The algorithm $\overline{\text{ref}}$ transforms every word of the form $c_{4,5} \,\square\, c_{4,6}$, where $c_{4,5}$ and $c_{4,6}$ are complexes, into the refinement of $c_{4,5}$ by $c_{4,6}$.

To each complex $c_{4,5}$ we associate a certain set of rational numbers equal to the union of the sets $\mathfrak{M}_{\mathfrak{p}}([c_{4,5}]_1^{\tau})$, $\mathfrak{M}_{\mathfrak{p}}([c_{4,5}]_2^{\tau})$, $\ldots$, $\mathfrak{M}_{\mathfrak{p}}([c_{4,5}]_{L_{\tau}(c_{4,5})}^{\tau})$. The union of all these sets will be denoted by $\mathfrak{M}_{\mathfrak{p}}(c_{4,5})$.

With the help of Proposition 7.4.1 the following proposition is easily proved.

7.4.2. *For any complexes* $c_{4,5}$ *and* $c_{4,6}$, *the set* $\mathfrak{M}_{\mathfrak{p}}(\overline{\text{ref}}\,(c_{4,5} \,\square\, c_{4,6}))$ *is equal to the set* $\mathfrak{M}_{\mathfrak{p}}(c_{4,5})$.

Now we shall define the following operations on complexes: the operations of union, intersection, difference, and symmetric difference.

The *union* of the complexes $c_{4,5}$ and $c_{4,6}$ is defined to be the complex obtained in the following way. We find all rational intervals which are τ-terms of at least one of the complexes $\overline{\mathrm{ref}}\ (c_{4,5} \square c_{4,6})$ and $\overline{\mathrm{ref}}\ (c_{4,6} \square c_{4,5})$, we form from them one word, ordering the rational intervals so that each rational interval follows (in the sense indicated above) all the rational intervals standing to the left of it, and we place between every two adjacent intervals the letter τ. The operation of constructing the union of complexes, given in the form of a normal algorithm in the alphabet $Ч_4^{sa}$ will be denoted by $\bigcup_K$.

The *intersection* of complexes $c_{4,5}$ and $c_{4,6}$ is defined to be the complex obtained by canceling from the complex $\overline{\mathrm{ref}}\ (c_{4,5} \square c_{4,6})$ all τ-terms which are not τ-terms of the complex $\overline{\mathrm{ref}}\ (c_{4,6} \square c_{4,5})$ and all instances of the letter τ standing immediately in front of canceled τ-terms. The operation of constructing the intersection of complexes, given in the form of a normal algorithm in the alphabet $Ч_4^{sa}$, will be denoted by $\bigcap_K$.

The *difference* of complexes $c_{4,5}$ and $c_{4,6}$ is defined to be the complex obtained by canceling from the complex $\overline{\mathrm{ref}}\ (c_{4,5} \square c_{4,6})$ all τ-terms which are τ-terms of the complex $\overline{\mathrm{ref}}\ (c_{4,6} \square c_{4,5})$ and all instances of the letter τ standing directly in front of canceled τ-terms. The operation of constructing the difference of complexes, given in the form of a normal algorithm in the alphabet $Ч_4^{sa}$ will be denoted by the symbol $\setminus_K$.

The *symmetric difference* of complexes $c_{4,5}$ and $c_{4,6}$ is defined to be the complex

$$\bigcup_K (\setminus_K (c_{4,5} \square c_{4,6}) \square \setminus_K (c_{4,6} \square c_{4,5})).$$

The operation of constructing the symmetric difference of complexes, given in the form of a normal algorithm in the alphabet $Ч_4^{sa}$, will be denoted by the symbol Δ_K.

The terms $\bigcup_K (\Theta_1 \square \Theta_2)$, $\bigcap_K (\Theta_1 \square \Theta_2)$, $\setminus_K (\Theta_1 \square \Theta_2)$, and $\Delta_K (\Theta_1 \square \Theta_2)$, where Θ_1 and Θ_2 are any terms, will be denoted, respectively, by the expressions

$$(\Theta_1 \underset{K}{\cup} \Theta_2),\quad (\Theta_1 \underset{K}{\cap} \Theta_2),\quad (\Theta_1 \underset{K}{\setminus} \Theta_2),\quad (\Theta_1 \underset{K}{\triangle} \Theta_2).$$

In using abbreviations of terms and formulas we shall assume that the symbols $\bigcup_K$, $\bigcap_K$, $\setminus_K$, Δ_K have rank 2 (cf. §1.14, V).

In the sequel we shall often use, instead of the notation $\bigcup_K$, $\bigcap_K$, $\setminus_K$, and Δ_K, the shorter notation $\cup$, $\cap$, $\setminus$, and Δ, if the use of these abbreviations does not lead to ambiguity.

We shall say that a complex $c_{4,5}$ is *included in* the complex $c_{4,6}$, and we shall write $(c_{4,5} \subseteq_K c_{4,6})$, if

$$(c_{4,5} \setminus c_{4,6}) \doteq \Lambda.$$

We shall say that a complex $c_{4,5}$ is *geometrically equal* to a complex $c_{4,6}$, and we shall write $(c_{4,5} =_K c_{4,6})$, if

$$(c_{4,5} \subseteq_K c_{4,6}) \,\&\, (c_{4,6} \subseteq_K c_{4,5}),$$

i.e., if

$$(c_{4,5} \triangle c_{4,6}) \doteq \Lambda.$$

We shall say that the complexes $c_{4,5}$ and $c_{4,6}$ are *disjoint*, and we shall write $(c_{4,5} \curlywedge_K c_{4,6})$, if

$$(c_{4,5} \cap c_{4,6}) \doteq \Lambda.$$

In abbreviating terms and formulas we shall assume that the symbols $\subseteq_K$, $=_K$, and $\curlywedge_K$ have rank 3.

In what follows we shall often use, instead of the symbols $\subseteq_K$, $=_K$, and $\curlywedge_K$, the symbols $\subseteq$, $=$, and $\curlywedge$, respectively, if the use of these simplified symbols does not lead to ambiguity.

It is easily seen that the following proposition holds.

7.4.3. *For any complexes* $c_{4,5}$ *and* $c_{4,6}$:

1) $c_{4,5} \subseteq_K c_{4,6}$ *if and only if the set* $\mathfrak{M}_p(c_{4,5})$ *is contained in the set* $\mathfrak{M}_p(c_{4,6})$;

2) $c_{4,5} =_K c_{4,6}$ *if and only if the set* $\mathfrak{M}_p(c_{4,5})$ *is equal to the set* $\mathfrak{M}_p(c_{4,6})$;

3) $c_{4,5} \curlywedge_K c_{4,6}$ *if and only if the intersection of the sets* $\mathfrak{M}_p(c_{4,5})$ *and* $\mathfrak{M}_p(c_{4,6})$ *is the empty set;*

4) *the sets* $\mathfrak{M}_K(c_{4,5} \cup c_{4,6})$, $\mathfrak{M}_K(c_{4,5} \cap c_{4,6})$, $\mathfrak{M}_K(c_{4,5} \setminus c_{4,6})$, *and* $\mathfrak{M}_K(c_{4,5} \Delta c_{4,6})$ *are equal, respectively, to the union, intersection, difference, and symmetric difference* [1] *of the sets* $\mathfrak{M}_p(c_{4,5})$ *and* $\mathfrak{M}_p(c_{4,6})$.

The carrying out of the operations of $\cup_K$, $\cap_K$, $\setminus_K$, and Δ_K on complexes $c_{4,5}$ and $c_{4,6}$ reduces essentially to carrying out on the finite set of all τ-terms of the complex $\overline{\text{ref}}\,(c_{4,5} \,\square\, c_{4,6})$ and the finite set of all τ-terms of the complex

1) The symmetric difference of the sets $\mathfrak{F}$ and $\mathfrak{G}$ is defined to be the union of the sets $\mathfrak{P}$ and $\mathfrak{Q}$, where $\mathfrak{P}$ is the difference of the sets $\mathfrak{F}$ and $\mathfrak{G}$, and $\mathfrak{Q}$ is the difference of the sets $\mathfrak{G}$ and $\mathfrak{F}$.

$\overline{\text{ref}}\,(c_{4,6} \,\square\, c_{4,5})$ of the corresponding operations of union, intersection, subtraction, and the construction of the symmetric difference. It follows from this remark that the basic properties of the operations $\cup_K$, $\cap_K$, $\setminus_K$, and Δ_K can be formulated by copying the properties of the corresponding operations on finite sets. Therefore we do not formulate here the properties of the indicated operations on complexes, except certain properties playing an important role in what follows.

Using the remark made just above, one can prove the following proposition.

7.4.4. *For any complexes* P_1, Q_1, P_2 *and* Q_2, *we have*

$$(P_1 \cup Q_1) \setminus (P_2 \cup Q_2) \underset{\kappa}{=} ((P_1 \setminus P_2) \setminus Q_2) \cup ((Q_1 \setminus Q_2) \setminus P_2),$$

$$(P_1 \cap Q_1) \setminus (P_2 \cap Q_2) \underset{\kappa}{=} ((P_1 \setminus P_2) \cap Q_1) \cup ((Q_1 \setminus Q_2) \cap P_1),$$

$$(P_1 \setminus Q_1) \setminus (P_2 \setminus Q_2) \underset{\kappa}{=} ((P_1 \setminus P_2) \setminus Q_1) \cup ((Q_2 \setminus Q_1) \cap P_1).$$

The following proposition is a consequence of 7.4.4.

7.4.5. *For any complexes* P_1, Q_1, P_2 *and* Q_2,

$$(P_1 \cup Q_1) \triangle (P_2 \cup Q_2) \subseteq (P_1 \triangle P_2) \cup (Q_1 \triangle Q_2),$$

$$(P_1 \cap Q_1) \triangle (P_2 \cap Q_2) \subseteq (P_1 \triangle P_2) \cup (Q_1 \triangle Q_2),$$

$$(P_1 \setminus Q_1) \triangle (P_2 \setminus Q_2) \subseteq (P_1 \triangle P_2) \cup (Q_1 \triangle Q_2).$$

The following proposition is also easily proved.

7.4.6. *For any complexes* P, Q *and* R,

$$P \triangle R \subseteq (P \triangle Q) \cup (Q \triangle R).$$

§8. SEQUENCES OF CONSTRUCTIVE REAL NUMBERS

8.1. We shall say that an algorithm $\Phi_{3,1}$ is a *sequence of FR-numbers* (second term: *sequence of duplexes*) if $\Phi_{3,1} \in (\text{Н} \to \text{Д})_3$. We shall say that an algorithm $\Phi_{3,2}$ is a *sequence of F-numbers* if $\Phi_{3,2} \in (\text{Н} \to \text{В})_3$.

The condition $\Phi_{3,1} \in (\text{Н} \to \text{Д})_3$ is given by a normal formula. Let us exhibit the constructive problem connected with the condition

$$\Phi_{3,2} \in (\text{Н} \to \text{В})_3. \tag{1}$$

Applying to (1) the algorithm for exhibiting constructive problems and simplifying the result by introducing natural variables, we arrive at the formula

$$\exists \varphi_{0,2} \forall n \, (\varphi_{3,2}(n) \overset{+}{\in} \underline{\text{one mean}}_3 \;\&\; \underline{\varphi_{3,2}(n)} \in (\text{н} \to \text{р})_2$$

$$\&\; \varphi_{0,2}(n) \overset{+}{\in} \text{c}_0 \;\&\; \langle \varphi_{0,2}(n) \rangle_0 \; \underline{\text{reg. con.}} \; \underline{\varphi_{3,2}(n)}). \tag{2}$$

The following theorem holds.

8.1.1

$$\forall \varphi_{3,2} (\varphi_{3,2} \in (\text{н} \to \text{в})_3 \equiv \exists \varphi_{3,1} (\varphi_{3,1} \in (\text{н} \to \text{д})_3 \;\&\; \mathfrak{R})),$$

where

$$\mathfrak{R} \leftrightharpoons \forall n \, (\overline{\text{prin}}_3 (\varphi_{3,1}(n)) \mathrel{\dot{=}} \varphi_{3,2}(n) \;\&\; \overline{\varphi_{3,1}(n)} \; \underline{\text{reg. con.}} \; \underline{\varphi_{3,2}(n)}) \, .$$

Proof. Let $\varphi_{3,2}$ be an algorithm such that

$$\varphi_{3,2} \in (\text{н} \to \text{в})_3.$$

Then on the basis of (2) we have

$$\exists \varphi_{0,2} \mathfrak{Q},$$

where

$$\mathfrak{Q} \leftrightharpoons \forall n \, (\varphi_{3,2}(n) \overset{+}{\in} \underline{\text{one mean}}_3 \;\&\; \underline{\varphi_{3,2}(n)} \in (\text{н} \to \text{р})_2$$

$$\&\; \varphi_{0,2}(n) \overset{+}{\in} \text{c}_0 \;\&\; \langle \varphi_{0,2}(n) \rangle_0 \; \underline{\text{reg. con.}} \; \underline{\varphi_{3,2}(n)}).$$

Let $\varphi_{0,2}$ be an algorithm such that

$$\mathfrak{Q}.$$

One can construct an algorithm $\varphi_{3,1}$ such that

$$\forall n \, (\varphi_{3,1}(n) \simeq \varphi_{3,2}(n) \, \varphi_{0,2}(n)).$$

We have

$$\forall n \, (\varphi_{3,1}(n) \overset{+}{\in} \underline{\text{real dup}} \;\&\; \overline{\text{prin}}_3 (\varphi_{3,1}(n)) \mathrel{\dot{=}} \varphi_{3,2}(n)$$

$$\&\; \overline{\varphi_{3,1}(n)} \mathrel{\dot{=}} \langle \varphi_{0,2}(n) \rangle_0).$$

Hence

$$\exists \varphi_{3,1} (\varphi_{3,1} \in (\text{н} \to \text{д})_3 \;\&\; \mathfrak{R}).$$

Therefore

$$\forall \varphi_{3,2} (\varphi_{3,2} \in (\text{н} \to \text{в})_3 \supset \exists \varphi_{3,1} (\varphi_{3,1} \in (\text{н} \to \text{д})_3 \;\&\; \mathfrak{R})). \tag{3}$$

Let $\varphi_{3,2}$ be an algorithm such that

$$\exists \varphi_{3,1} (\varphi_{3,1} \in (\text{н} \to \text{д})_3 \;\&\; \mathfrak{R})$$

Let us prove that $\varphi_{3,2} \in (\text{Н} \to \text{В})_3$. Assume $\varphi_{3,1}$ is an algorithm such that

$$\varphi_{3,1} \in (\text{н} \to \text{д})_3 \;\&\; \mathfrak{R}. \tag{4}$$

Then

$$\forall n\,(\phi_{3,2}(n) \rightleftharpoons \overline{\text{prin}_3(\phi_{3,1}(n))}\;\&\;\overline{\phi_{3,1}(n)}\;\underline{\text{reg. con.}\;\phi_{3,2}(n)}). \tag{5}$$

One can construct an algorithm $\dot{\phi}_{0,2}$ such that

$$\forall n\,(\phi_{0,2}(n) \simeq \overline{\{\phi_{3,1}(n)\}}).$$

By this assertion, (2) follows from (4) and (5). Hence

$$\phi_{3,2} \in (\text{н} \to \text{в})_3.$$

Therefore

$$\forall \phi_{3,2}(\exists \phi_{3,1}(\phi_{3,1} \in (\text{н} \to \text{д})_3 \,\&\, \mathfrak{R}) \supset \phi_{3,2} \in (\text{н} \to \text{в})_3). \tag{6}$$

The theorem to be proved follows immediately from (3) and (6).

Remark. Proposition (3), established in the course of the proof, gives no basis for the assertion that there is an algorithm transforming every sequence of F-numbers $\phi_{3,2}$ into a sequence of duplexes satisfying condition $\mathfrak{R}$. We have no basis for this assertion in view of the fact that formula (2), which was obtained by applying to the formula $\phi_{3,2} \in (\text{Н} \to \text{В})_3$ the algorithm for exhibiting constructive problems, begins with the symbol $\exists$.

In spite of this fact, Theorem 8.1.1, which established the logical equivalence of the condition $\phi_{3,2} \in (\text{Н} \to \text{В})_3$ and the condition $\exists \phi_{3,1}(\phi_{3,1} \in (\text{Н} \to \text{Д})_3 \,\&\, \mathfrak{R})$, in many cases presents the opportunity of easily obtaining theorems about sequences of F-numbers from corresponding theorems about sequences of duplexes. Hence, in the sequel, we shall formulate only theorems about sequences of duplexes.

8.1.2. *One can construct an algorithm* $\phi_{3,3}$ *such that, for any sequence of duplexes* $\phi_{3,1}$ *and any rational numbers* a *and* b *satisfying the condition* $a < b$, *the algorithm* $\phi_{3,3}$ *is applicable to the word* $\{\phi_{3,1}\} \square a \square b$ *and transforms this word into a duplex* $\phi_{3,3}(\{\phi_{3,1}\} \square a \square b)$ *such that*

1) $$a \leqslant \phi_{3,3}(\{\phi_{3,1}\} \square a \square b) \leqslant b,$$

2) $$\forall n\,(\phi_{3,1}(n) \underset{\text{в}}{\neq} \phi_{3,3}(\{\phi_{3,1}\} \square a \square b)).$$

Proof. On the basis of the theorem about branching of algorithms [1], we construct an algorithm Ψ in the alphabet Ч_3^{sa} such that, for any duplex x, rational number e and positive rational number d,

$$\Psi(x \square e \square d) \rightleftharpoons \begin{cases} e, & \text{if } \underline{x}(\bar{x}(D(d)+1)) > e+2\cdot d, \\ e+3\cdot d, & \text{if } \underline{x}(\bar{x}(D(d)+1)) \leqslant e+2\cdot d, \end{cases}$$

where $D(d) \simeq \mu_n(2^{-n} \leq d)$.

The construction of the algorithm Ψ is realized so that the result of applying this algorithm to any word in the alphabet $Ч_3^{sa}$ to which it is applicable is a word in the alphabet $Ч_2$.

The following two propositions are easily proved.

1) If $\underline{x}(\overline{x}(D(d)+1)) > e + 2 \cdot d$, then $x \geq e + 3/2 \cdot d$, and therefore x does not belong to the segment $e \,\underline{\nabla}\, e + d$.

2) If $\underline{x}(\overline{x}(D(d)+1)) \leq e + 2 \cdot d$, then $x \leq e + 5/2 \cdot d$, and therefore x does not belong to the segment $e + 3 \cdot d \,\underline{\nabla}\, e + 4 \cdot d$.

From what has been said it follows that the segment

$$\Psi(x \square e \square d) \,\underline{\nabla}\, \Psi(x \square e \square d) + d$$

is one fourth of the segment $e \,\underline{\nabla}\, e + 4 \cdot d$, namely that part which does not contain x.

Now we construct algorithms N and C in the alphabet $Ч_3^{sa}$ such that

$$\forall ab(N(a \square b) \simeq \mu_n((b - a) : 2^n \leqslant 4)),$$

$$\forall abi(C(a \square b \square i) \simeq (b - a) : 2^{N(a \square b)+2+2 \cdot i}).$$

We have

$$\forall abi(a < b \supset C(a \square b \square i) \leqslant 2^{-2 \cdot i}). \tag{7}$$

Now we construct an algorithm Γ in the alphabet $Ч_3^{sa}$ such that, for any sequence of duplexes $\phi_{3,1}$, any rational numbers a and b, and any natural number i,

$$\Gamma(\{\phi_{3,1}\} \square a \square b \square 0) \simeq \Psi(\phi_{3,1}(0) \square a \square C(a \square b \square 0)),$$

$$\Gamma(\{\phi_{3,1}\} \square a \square b \square i+1) \simeq \Psi(\phi_{3,1}(i+1) \square \Gamma(\{\phi_{3,1}\} \square a \square b \square i) \square C(a \square b \square i+1)).$$

We construct an algorithm Γ^* in the alphabet $Ч_2^{sa}$ transforming every word in the alphabet $Ч_2^s$ into a word in the alphabet $Ч_0$ and such that

$$\forall c_{0,1}abi(\Gamma(c_{0,1} \square a \square b \square i) \simeq \langle \Gamma^*(c_{0,1} \square a \square b) \rangle_2(i)).$$

We introduce the notation

$$H \leftrightharpoons \Gamma^*(\{\phi_{3,1}\} \square a \square b), \quad \widetilde{H} \leftrightharpoons \langle H \rangle_2.$$

It is easy to see that

$$\widetilde{H}(i) \leqslant \widetilde{H}(i+1) \leqslant \widetilde{H}(i) + 3/4 \cdot C(a \square b \square i). \tag{8}$$

Moreover, the duplex $\phi_{3,1}(i)$ does not belong to the segment

$$\widetilde{H}(i) \,\underline{\nabla}\, \widetilde{H}(i) + C(a \square b \square i). \tag{9}$$

At the same time, if $j \geq i$, then the rational number $\widetilde{H}(j)$ belongs to the segment (9).

A simple evaluation based on (8) and (7) shows that

$$\forall ikl(k,\ l \geqslant i \supset M(\widetilde{H}(k) - \widetilde{H}(l)) < 2^{-2\cdot i}).$$

Therefore the algorithm $\widetilde{H}$ is a fundamental sequence of rational numbers. As a regulator of convergence in itself of this sequence of rational numbers one can use, for example, the algorithm δ in the alphabet $Ч_0^{sa}$ such that

$$\forall i(\delta(i) \mathrel{\dot{=}} i).$$

Hence, for any sequence of duplexes $\Phi_{3,1}$ and any rational numbers a and b such that $a < b$, the word

$$H \diamond \{\delta\} \tag{10}$$

is a duplex. Moreover, for any natural numbers i and j such that $j \geq i$, the rational number $\underline{H \diamond \{\delta\}}(j)$ belongs to the segment (9). Hence for any natural number i the duplex (10) belongs to the segment (9). Therefore

$$\forall n(\Phi_{3,1}(n) \underset{\text{B}}{\neq} H \diamond \{\delta\}). \tag{11}$$

At the same time, the duplex (10) belongs to the segment

$$\widetilde{H}(0) \mathbin{\underline{\nabla}} \widetilde{H}(0) \dotplus C(a \square b \square i).$$

This segment is part of the segment $a \mathbin{\underline{\nabla}} b$. Hence

$$a \leqslant H \diamond \{\delta\} \leqslant b. \tag{12}$$

We denote by Φ an algorithm in the alphabet $Ч_3^{sa}$ such that

$$\forall c_{0,1}ab(\Phi(c_{0,1} \square a \square b) \simeq \Gamma^*(c_{0,1} \square a \square b) \diamond \{\delta\}).$$

From (12) and (11) it follows that the algorithm Φ is the required algorithm.

The next theorem is a direct corollary of Theorem 8.1.2.

8.1.3. *For any sequence of duplexes* $\Phi_{3,1}$ *and any rational numbers* a *and* b *such that* $a < b$, *a duplex* x *is potentially realizable such that*

1) $$a \leqslant x \leqslant b;$$

2) $$\forall n(\Phi_{3,1}(n) \underset{\text{B}}{\neq} x).$$

The following theorem is an important corollary of Theorem 8.1.3.

8.1.4. *There is no algorithm over the alphabet* $Ч_3$ *which distinguishes duplexes among all words in the alphabet* $Ч_3$, *i.e. there is no algorithm over the alphabet* $Ч_3$ *which is applicable to every word in the alphabet* $Ч_3$ *and transforms a word* $c_{3,1}$ *into the empty word if and only if* $c_{3,1}$ *is a duplex.*

Proof. Let us suppose that we can realize an algorithm over the alphabet $Ч_3$ which distinguishes duplexes among all words in the alphabet $Ч_3$. Then, on the basis of the theorem on the reduction of algorithms [1], we can realize an algorithm in the alphabet $Ч_3^{sa}$ with the same property. Let $\Phi_{3,1}$ be such an algorithm. We denote by γ an algorithm in the alphabet $Ч_3^{sa}$ which realizes a constructive one-one correspondence between the natural numbers and all words in the alphabet $Ч_3$, and, moreover, such that $\gamma(0) = 0$. We construct algorithms ψ and χ in the alphabet $Ч_3^{sa}$ such that

$$\psi(\Lambda) \dot{=} 1,$$

$$\forall c_{3,1} (c_{3,1} \dot{\neq} \Lambda \supset \psi(c_{3,1}) \dot{=} 0),$$

$$\forall n (\chi(n) \simeq \psi(\Phi_{3,1}(\gamma(n)))).$$

For any natural number n we have

$$\chi(n) \dot{=} \begin{cases} 1, & \text{if } \gamma(n) \text{ is a duplex,} \\ 0, & \text{if } \gamma(n) \text{ is not a duplex.} \end{cases}$$

Now we construct an algorithm θ in the alphabet $Ч_3^{sa}$ such that

$$\theta(0) \dot{=} 0,$$

$$\theta(k+1) \dot{=} (k+1) \cdot \chi(k+1) + \theta(k) \cdot (1 - \chi(k+1)).$$

For any natural number k we have

$$\theta(k+1) \dot{=} \begin{cases} k+1, & \text{if } \gamma(k+1) \text{ is a duplex,} \\ \theta(k), & \text{if } \gamma(k+1) \text{ is not a duplex.} \end{cases}$$

Noting that 0 is a duplex and $\gamma(0) = 0$, we arrive at the following conclusion: for any natural number n, the word $\gamma(\theta(n))$ is a duplex. On the other hand, if x is any duplex, then, applying to the word x the algorithm η inverse to the algorithm γ (see [30]), we obtain a natural number $\eta(x)$ such that $\gamma(\eta(x)) \dot{=} x$. We have $\theta(\eta(x)) \dot{=} x$. Hence $x \dot{=} \gamma(\theta(\eta(x)))$. Therefore

$$\forall x \exists n (x \dot{=} \gamma(\theta(n))).$$

We construct an algorithm δ in the alphabet $Ч_3^{sa}$ such that

$$\forall n (\delta(n) \simeq \gamma(\theta(n))).$$

From what has been said above it follows that δ is a sequence of duplexes possessing the property

$$\forall x \exists n (x \dot{=} \delta(n)). \tag{13}$$

However, it follows from 8.1.3 that

$$\exists x (0 < x \leqslant 1 \,\&\, \forall n (\delta(n) \underset{\text{B}}{\neq} x)).$$

Hence

$$\exists x \forall n (x \dot{\neq} \delta(n)). \tag{14}$$

It is easily seen that the negation of assertion (13) follows, according to the rules of constructive logic, from (14). The contradiction so obtained disproves the assumption made above about the possibility of an algorithm distinguishing duplexes among all words in the alphabet $Ч_3$.

Theorem 8.1.4. has been proved.

Remark. Theorems 8.1.3 and 8.1.4 have a fundamental significance in the theory of constructive real numbers. These theorems were established by A. M. Turing [13] with respect to the concept of constructive real number introduced in [13].

8.2. We note here the following theorem on the convergence of sequences of duplexes.

8.2.1. *For any sequences of duplexes* $\Phi_{3,1}$ *and* $\Phi_{3,2}$ *such that*

$$\forall n\,(\Phi_{3,1}(n) \leqslant \Phi_{3,2}(n)), \tag{1}$$

$$\forall n\,(\Phi_{3,1}(n) \leqslant \Phi_{3,1}(n+1)), \tag{2}$$

$$\forall n\,(\Phi_{3,2}(n+1) \leqslant \Phi_{3,2}(n)), \tag{3}$$

$$\forall i \exists j \forall n\,(n \geqslant j \supset \Phi_{3,2}(n) - \Phi_{3,1}(n) < 2^{-i}), \tag{4}$$

a duplex x *is potentially realizable such that*

$$\forall n\,(\Phi_{3,1}(n) \leqslant x \leqslant \Phi_{3,2}(n)). \tag{5}$$

Proof. Let $\Phi_{3,1}$ and $\Phi_{3,2}$ be sequences of duplexes such that conditions (1)–(4) are fulfilled. The constructive reformulation of condition (4) leads to the formula

$$\exists \Phi_{0,1}\,(\Phi_{0,1} \in (\text{н} \to \text{н})_0 \;\&\; \forall in\,(n \geqslant \Phi_{0,1}(i) \supset \Phi_{3,2}(n) - \Phi_{3,1}(n) < 2^{-i})).$$

Let $\Phi_{0,1}$ be an algorithm such that, first, $\Phi_{0,1} \in (\text{Н} \to \text{Н})_0$, and second,

$$\forall in\,(n \geqslant \Phi_{0,1}(i) \supset \Phi_{3,2}(n) - \Phi_{3,1}(n) < 2^{-i}). \tag{6}$$

We construct an algorithm $\Phi_{2,1}$ such that

$$\forall n\,(\Phi_{2,1}(n) \simeq \underline{\Phi_{3,1}(n)}\,(\overline{\Phi_{3,1}(n)}\,(n))).$$

It is obvious that $\Phi_{2,1} \in (\text{Н} \to \text{Д})_2$. Now we note that (on the basis of 4.9.3)

$$\forall xn\,(\underline{x}(\overline{x}(n)) - 2^{-n} \leqslant x \leqslant \underline{x}(\overline{x}(n)) + 2^{-n}).$$

Hence

$$\forall n\,(M(\Phi_{2,1}(n) - \Phi_{3,1}(n)) \leqslant 2^{-n}). \tag{7}$$

Further, it follows from (1), (2), (3), and (6) that

$$\forall ikl\,(k \geqslant l \geqslant \Phi_{0,1}(i+1) \supset \Phi_{3,1}(l) \leqslant \Phi_{3,1}(k) \leqslant \Phi_{3,2}(l) < \Phi_{3,1}(l) + 2^{-(i+1)}).$$

Hence

$$\forall ikl(k,\ l \geqslant \varphi_{0,1}(i+1) \supset M(\varphi_{3,1}(k) - \varphi_{3,1}(l)) < 2^{-(i+1)}). \qquad (8)$$

We construct an algorithm $\varphi_{0,2}$ such that

$$\forall i(\varphi_{0,2}(i) \simeq \max(\varphi_{0,1}(i+1) \square i+2)).$$

Let i, k, l be natural numbers such that $k,\ l \geq \varphi_{0,2}(i)$. Then it follows from (7) and (8) that

$$M(\varphi_{2,1}(k) - \varphi_{2,1}(l)) \leqslant M(\varphi_{2,1}(k) - \varphi_{3,1}(k)) + M(\varphi_{3,1}(k) - \varphi_{3,1}(l))$$
$$+ M(\varphi_{3,1}(l) - \varphi_{2,1}(l)) < 2^{-(i+2)} + 2^{-(i+1)} + 2^{-(i+2)} = 2^{-i}.$$

Hence $\varphi_{0,2}$ is a regulator of convergence in itself of the algorithm $\varphi_{2,1}$. Hence the word $\{\varphi_{2,1}\}\lozenge\{\varphi_{0,2}\}$ is a duplex.

We introduce the notation

$$D \leftrightharpoons \{\varphi_{2,1}\}\lozenge\{\varphi_{0,2}\}.$$

From (7) and (1) it follows that

$$\forall k(\varphi_{3,1}(k) - 2^{-k} \leqslant \underline{D}(k) \leqslant \varphi_{3,1}(k) + 2^{-k} \leqslant \varphi_{3,2}(k) + 2^{-k}). \qquad (9)$$

It follows from (9), (2) and (3) that, for any natural numbers i, k, and n,

$$k \geqslant \max(n \square i+1) \supset \varphi_{3,1}(n) - 2^{-i} < \underline{D}(k) < \varphi_{3,2}(n) + 2^{-i}. \qquad (10)$$

From (10) it is easy to deduce that

$$\forall n(\varphi_{3,1}(n) \leqslant D \leqslant \varphi_{3,2}(n)).$$

We have proved that a duplex x satisfying condition (5) is potentially realizable. Theorem 8.2.1 is proved.

Remark. G. S. Ceĭtin has proved [17] that we would obtain a refutable assertion if we should eliminate condition (4) from the formulation of Theorem 8.2.1. Comparing this fact with the corresponding theorems of classical mathematics, we can affirm here the existence of an essential difference between constructive and classical mathematics.

8.3. An important branch of constructive mathematical analysis consists of the theory of limits of sequences of duplexes. The basis of this theory is: a) a two-place relation "the duplex x is the limit of the sequence of duplexes $\varphi_{3,1}$", b) the concept of a fundamental sequence of duplexes, and c) the theorem that, for a sequence of duplexes $\varphi_{3,1}$, a duplex x which is a limit of the sequence $\varphi_{3,1}$ is potentially realizable if and only if $\varphi_{3,1}$ is a fundamental sequence.

The following chapter, devoted to constructive metric spaces, will deal with the theory of limits in arbitrary constructive metric spaces. The basic definitions and theorems of the theory of limits of sequences of duplexes can be obtained as special cases of the corresponding definitions and theorems of the theory of limits in arbitrary constructive metric spaces. Therefore we shall not be concerned at all in this chapter with the theory of limits of sequences of duplexes. Here we shall go into only one fundamental result of E. Specker, closely connected with the theory of limits, but not requiring for its exposition any definitions and theorems of the theory of limits. The result of Specker which we are talking about here plays a very important role in what follows, particularly in the construction of some examples revealing essential differences between constructive and classical mathematical analysis.

Specker's theorem can be formulated in the following way (see [15]).

8.3.1. *One can construct an algorithm* $\Phi_{2,1}$ *of type* $(\text{H} \rightarrow \text{Д})_2$ *such that*

a) $$\forall k\,(\Phi_{2,1}(k) \leqslant \Phi_{2,1}(k+1)), \tag{1}$$

b) $$\forall k\,(0 \leqslant \Phi_{2,1}(k) < 1), \tag{2}$$

c) *there is no algorithm which is a regulator of convergence in itself of the algorithm* $\Phi_{2,1}$.

We reproduce (up to technical details) Specker's proof.

Let α be any algorithm of type $(\text{HH} \rightarrow \text{H})_0$ possessing the following two properties:

$$\forall jk\,(0 \leqslant \alpha(j \square k) \leqslant 1), \tag{3}$$

$$\forall jk\,(\alpha(j \square k) \leqslant \alpha(j \square k+1)). \tag{4}$$

Let β be an algorithm in the alphabet Ч_2^{sa} such that, for any natural number k,

$$\beta(k) \doteqdot \sum_{j=0}^{k} \alpha(j \square k) \cdot 2^{-(j+1)}. \tag{5}$$

It follows from (3) and (4) that, for any k,

$$\beta(k) \leqslant \beta(k+1) \tag{6}$$

and

$$0 \leqslant \beta(k) \leqslant \sum_{j=0}^{k} 2^{-(j+1)} < 1. \tag{7}$$

Let us assume now that one can construct a regulator of convergence in itself of the algorithm β, and we shall derive from this assumption an important assertion concerning the algorithm α.

Let f_1 be an algorithm of type $(\text{H} \rightarrow \text{H})_0$ which is a regulator of convergence in itself of the algorithm β. We construct an algorithm f_2 in the alphabet Ч_0^{sa}

such that

$$\forall i (f_2(i) \simeq \max(i \square f_1(i))).$$

It is obvious that f_2 is also a regulator of convergence in itself of the algorithm β and

$$\forall i (f_2(i) \geqslant i). \tag{8}$$

For any natural numbers i and l we have

$$0 \leqslant \beta(f_2(i+1)+l) - \beta(f_2(i+1)) < 2^{-(i+1)}. \tag{9}$$

As an abbreviation we introduce the notation

$$\lambda \leftrightharpoons f_2(i+1).$$

On the basis of (9) we have

$$0 \leqslant \sum_{j=0}^{\lambda+l} \alpha(j \square \lambda+l) \cdot 2^{-(j+1)} - \sum_{j=0}^{\lambda} \alpha(j \square \lambda) \cdot 2^{-(j+1)} < 2^{-(i+1)}.$$

Hence

$$0 \leqslant \sum_{j=0}^{\lambda} (\alpha(j \square \lambda+l) - \alpha(j \square \lambda)) \cdot 2^{-(j+1)}$$

$$+ \sum_{j=\lambda+1}^{\lambda+l} \alpha(j \square \lambda+l) \cdot 2^{-(j+1)} < 2^{-(i+1)}.$$

Therefore

$$0 \leqslant \sum_{j=0}^{\lambda} (\alpha(j \square \lambda+l) - \alpha(j \square \lambda)) \cdot 2^{i-j}$$

$$+ \sum_{j=\lambda+1}^{\lambda+l} \alpha(j \square \lambda+l) \cdot 2^{i-j} < 1. \tag{10}$$

From (10), (3), (4), and the condition $\alpha \in (\mathrm{HH} \to \mathrm{H})_0$, it follows that

$$\forall j (j \leqslant \lambda \,\&\, j \leqslant i \supset \alpha(j \square \lambda+l) - \alpha(j \square \lambda) = 0). \tag{11}$$

From (8) it follows that

$$i < i+1 \leqslant \lambda. \tag{12}$$

On the basis of (12) and (11) we can conclude that

$$\alpha(i \square \lambda+l) - \alpha(i \square \lambda) = 0.$$

Hence

$$\forall il (\alpha(i \square f_2(i+1)+l) = \alpha(i \square f_2(i+1))). \tag{13}$$

From (13), (3), (4) and the condition $\alpha \in (\mathrm{HH} \to \mathrm{H})_2$ it follows that, for any natural number i,

$$\exists k (\alpha(i \square k) = 1) \equiv (\alpha(i \square f_2(i+1)) = 1).$$

We construct an algorithm γ in the alphabet $Ч_0^{sa}$ of type $(\mathrm{H} \to \mathrm{H})_0$ such that

$$\forall i\,(\gamma(i) \simeq 1 - \alpha(i \,\square\, f_2(i+1))).$$

For any natural number i we have

$$\exists k\,(\alpha(i \,\square\, k) = 1) \equiv (\gamma(i) = 0). \tag{14}$$

Thus we have proved the following statement.

(*) *If an algorithm* α *of type* $(\text{HH} \to \text{H})_0$ *is such that, first, conditions* (3) *and* (4) *are fulfilled, and second, for the algorithm* β *connected with the algorithm* α *by condition* (5), *a regulator of convergence in itself is potentially realizable, then one can construct an algorithm distinguishing among all natural numbers those natural numbers which satisfy the condition*

$$\exists k\,(\alpha(i \,\square\, k) = 1). \tag{15}$$

Now let us prove the following proposition.

(**) *For any algorithm* ξ *of type* $(\text{HH} \to \text{H})_0$, *an algorithm* α *of type* $(\text{HH} \to \text{H})_0$ *is potentially realizable such that* α *satisfies conditions* (3) *and* (4) *and, for any* i,

$$\exists k\,(\alpha(i \,\square\, k) = 1) \equiv \exists l\,(\xi(i \,\square\, l) = 0). \tag{16}$$

Let ξ be any algorithm of type $(\text{HH} \to \text{H})_0$. We denote by η any algorithm of type $(\text{H} \to \text{H})_0$ such that

$$\eta(0) = 1, \quad \forall k\,(\eta(k+1) = 0).$$

One can construct an algorithm α in the alphabet Ч_0^{sa} such that

$$\forall ik\,(\alpha(i \,\square\, k) \simeq \eta(\prod_{l=0}^{k} \xi(i \,\square\, l))). \tag{17}$$

The algorithm α satisfying condition (17) also satisfies conditions (3), (4), and (16). Proposition (**) is proved.

Now one can easily describe Specker's construction proving Theorem 8.3.1. As a starting point of the construction, the algorithm Ω of type $(\text{HH} \to \text{H})_0$ which was discussed in §2.3 will serve. The algorithm Ω is such that there is no algorithm distinguishing among all natural numbers those natural numbers which satisfy the condition

$$\exists l\,(\Omega(i \,\square\, l) = 0). \tag{18}$$

We construct, starting from Ω and using (**), an algorithm Θ of type $(\text{HH} \to \text{H})_0$ such that

$$\forall jk\,(0 \leqslant \Theta(j \,\square\, k) \leqslant 1),$$

$$\forall jk\,(\Theta(j \,\square\, k) \leqslant \Theta(j \,\square\, k+1)),$$

$$\forall i\,(\exists k\,(\Theta(i \,\square\, k) = 1) \equiv \exists l\,(\Omega(i \,\square\, l) = 0)). \tag{19}$$

Now we construct an algorithm S in the alphabet $Ч_2^{sa}$ such that, for any natural number k,

$$S(k) \doteq \sum_{j=0}^{k} \Theta(j \square k) \cdot 2^{-(j+1)}.$$

Assuming that a regulator of convergence in itself of the algorithm S is potentially realizable, we can conclude, on the basis of (*) and (19), that an algorithm is realizable which distinguishes among all natural numbers those natural numbers which satisfy condition (18). But there can be no algorithm possessing this property. Hence there is no regulator of convergence in itself of the algorithm S. Theorem 8.3.1 is proved.

From Theorem 8.3.1 it follows that

$$\neg \forall i \exists j \forall kl (k,\ l \geqslant j \supset M(S(k) - S(l)) < 2^{-i}), \tag{20}$$

where S is the sequence of rational numbers constructed in the proof of Theorem 8.3.1.

In connection with (20), we note the following theorem.

8.3.2. *For any sequence of rational numbers* $\Phi_{2,1}$ *such that*

$$\forall k (\Phi_{2,1}(k) \leqslant \Phi_{2,1}(k+1)) \tag{21}$$

and

$$\exists b \forall k (\Phi_{2,1}(k) \leqslant b), \tag{22}$$

the following assertion is true:

$$\forall i \neg\neg \exists j \forall kl (k,\ l \geqslant j \supset M(\Phi_{2,1}(k) - \Phi_{2,1}(l)) < 2^{-i}). \tag{23}$$

Proof. Let $\Phi_{2,1}$ be a sequence of rational numbers satisfying conditions (21) and (22). Let b be a rational number satisfying the condition

$$\forall k (\Phi_{2,1}(k) \leqslant b), \tag{24}$$

and let i be any natural number. Let us assume that

$$\neg \exists j \forall kl (k,\ l \geqslant j \supset M(\Phi_{2,1}(k) - \Phi_{2,1}(l)) < 2^{-i}). \tag{25}$$

Then

$$\forall j \neg \forall kl (k,\ l \geqslant j \supset M(\Phi_{2,1}(k) - \Phi_{2,1}(l)) < 2^{-i}). \tag{26}$$

Since $\Phi_{2,1}$ is a sequence of rational numbers, the condition

$$(k,\ l \geqslant j \supset M(\Phi_{2,1}(k) - \Phi_{2,1}(l)) < 2^{-i}),$$

having as its parameters the natural variables i, j, k, l, is an algorithmically verifiable condition. On the basis of this fact and §2.5 (2), we can conclude that

$$\forall j \exists kl \neg (k,\ l \geqslant j \supset M(\Phi_{2,1}(k) - \Phi_{2,1}(l)) < 2^{-i}).$$

The condition $(k,\ l \geq j)$ is algorithmically verifiable. Hence

$$\forall j \exists kl (k,\ l \geqslant j \,\&\, M(\Phi_{2,1}(k) - \Phi_{2,1}(l)) \geqslant 2^{-i}). \tag{27}$$

From (27) and (21) it is easy to deduce that

$$\forall j \exists mn (m > n \geqslant j \,\&\, \varphi_{2,1}(m) - \varphi_{2,1}(n) \geqslant 2^{-i}).$$

Hence

$$\exists \varphi_{0,1} \varphi_{0,2} \mathfrak{M},$$

where

$$\mathfrak{M} \leftrightharpoons \forall j (\varphi_{0,1}(j) \overset{+}{\in} \underline{\text{nat}} \,\&\, \varphi_{0,2}(j) \overset{+}{\in} \underline{\text{nat}} \,\&\, \varphi_{0,1}(j) > \varphi_{0,2}(j) \geqslant j$$
$$\&\, \varphi_{2,1}(\varphi_{0,1}(j)) - \varphi_{2,1}(\varphi_{0,2}(j)) \geqslant 2^{-i}).$$

Let $\varphi_{0,1}$ and $\varphi_{0,2}$ be algorithms satisfying condition $\mathfrak{M}$. One can construct algorithms $\varphi_{0,3}$ and $\varphi_{0,4}$ such that

$$\varphi_{0,3}(0) \doteq \varphi_{0,1}(0), \quad \varphi_{0,4}(0) \doteq \varphi_{0,2}(0),$$
$$\forall j (\varphi_{0,3}(j+1) \doteq \varphi_{0,1}(\varphi_{0,3}(j))),$$
$$\forall j (\varphi_{0,4}(j+1) \doteq \varphi_{0,2}(\varphi_{0,3}(j))).$$

For any natural number j we have

$$\varphi_{0,3}(j) \overset{+}{\in} \underline{\text{nat}}, \quad \varphi_{0,4}(j) \overset{+}{\in} \underline{\text{nat}},$$
$$\varphi_{0,3}(j) > \varphi_{0,4}(j), \quad \varphi_{0,4}(j+1) > \varphi_{0,3}(j),$$
$$\varphi_{2,1}(\varphi_{0,3}(j)) - \varphi_{2,1}(\varphi_{0,4}(j)) \geqslant 2^{-i}.$$

Hence

$$\varphi_{2,1}(\varphi_{0,3}(j+1)) - \varphi_{2,1}(\varphi_{0,4}(0)) = \sum_{l=0}^{j+1} (\varphi_{2,1}(\varphi_{0,3}(l)) - \varphi_{2,1}(\varphi_{0,4}(l)))$$
$$+ \sum_{l=0}^{j} (\varphi_{2,1}(\varphi_{0,4}(l+1)) - \varphi_{2,1}(\varphi_{0,3}(l))) \geqslant 2^{-i} \cdot (j+2).$$

Hence

$$\forall j (\varphi_{2,1}(\varphi_{0,3}(j+1)) \geqslant R + 2^{-i} \cdot (j+2)),$$

where $R \leftrightharpoons \varphi_{2,1}(\varphi_{0,4}(0))$.

It is obvious that

$$\exists n (R + 2^{-i} \cdot (n+2) > b).$$

Hence

$$\exists n (\varphi_{2,1}(\varphi_{0,3}(n+1)) > b).$$

We have obtained a contradiction with (24). Hence assumption (25) is refuted and we can conclude that

$$\neg\neg \exists j \forall kl (k, l \geqslant j \supset M(\varphi_{2,1}(k) - \varphi_{2,1}(l)) < 2^{-i}).$$

Theorem 8.3.2 has been proved.

Corollary.

$$\forall i \neg\neg \exists j \forall kl (k, l \geqslant j \supset M(S(k) - S(l)) < 2^{-i}), \tag{28}$$

where S is the sequence of rational numbers constructed in the proof of Theorem 8.3.1.

Remark. Introducing the notation

$$\mathfrak{A} \leftrightharpoons \forall kl\,(k,\ l \geqslant j \supset M(S(k) - S(l)) < 2^{-i}),$$

we can write proposition (28) in the form

$$\forall i \neg\neg \exists j \mathfrak{A}$$

and proposition (20) in the form

$$\neg \forall i \exists j \mathfrak{A}.$$

Therefore one can construct a formula $\mathfrak{F}$ having as its parameters the natural variables i, j and such that (under the constructive interpretation) both the propositions $\forall i \neg\neg \exists j \mathfrak{F}$ and $\neg \forall i \exists j \mathfrak{F}$ turn out to be true. At the same time, within classical logic these propositions are incompatible: the methods of the classical predicate calculus allow us to prove the equivalence of the first with the negation of the second.

8.4. We introduce now the following concept.

We say that a word $c_{3,1}$ is a *real pseudo-number* if $c_{3,1}$ is a one-sided meaningful word in the alphabet $Ч_3$ (cf. §3.4), the algorithm $\underline{c_{3,1}}$ is a sequence of rational numbers, and

$$\forall i \neg\neg \exists j \forall kl\,(k,\ l \geqslant j \supset M(\underline{c_{3,1}}(k) - \underline{c_{3,1}}(l)) < 2^{-i}).$$

It is obvious that every F-number is a real pseudo-number. On the other hand, it follows from Theorems 8.3.1 and 8.3.2 that one can construct a real pseudo-number which is not an F-number. Hence the concept of real pseudo-number is wider than the concept of real F-number.

Real pseudo-numbers (like real F-numbers) are constructive objects. Hence the question naturally arises as to the possible role of the concept of real pseudo-number in constructive mathematical analysis.

Theorem 8.3.2 might suggest that neither the concept of real FR-number nor the concept of real F-number, but rather the concept of real pseudo-number or an even wider concept would be more natural to consider as a constructive analogue of the concept of real number employed in classical mathematics.

The following fact speaks against this point of view. The real pseudo-number $\{S\} \Diamond$, where S is Specker's algorithm, is such that there is no algorithm which, for any natural number i, constructs a rational number whose distance from $\{S\} \Diamond$ is less than 2^{-i} (here one is assuming that the arithmetic operations on real pseudo-numbers and the order relations between them are defined in the natural way). This fact shows that the concept of real pseudo-number is to be found in the third group of the classification of the various concepts connected in the literature with the term "constructive real number", and which we discussed in §0.8. Therefore everything that was said in §0.8 about concepts lying in the third group is also applicable to the concept of real pseudo-number.

In addition, many theorems about real FR-numbers and real F-numbers which indicate an external similarity in many points of a fundamental nature between constructive mathematical analysis and classical mathematical analysis (for example, the theorem on the completeness of the set of all real FR-numbers and on the analogous property of the set of all real F-numbers, the theorem about the fact that the set of all real FR-numbers belonging to a given segment is almost totally bounded, and the analogous theorem about real F-numbers) do not carry over to real pseudo-numbers.

8.5. In the preceding sections no mention was ever made of the concept of constructive complex number. This concept will also not occur in the remainder of this book. Hence we shall limit ourselves here only to a few remarks on this theme.

It is natural to connect with the term "constructive complex number" two concepts: the concept of complex FR-number and the concept of complex F-number. It is natural to consider as the more fundamental of these two concepts (for reasons analogous to those which were expressed in the discussion about the concepts of real FR-number and real F-number) the concept of complex FR-number.

One of the variants of the concepts of complex FR-number and complex F-number consists in the following. We extend the alphabet Ч_3 by adding to it the symbol $\Diamond$. We say that a word C in the alphabet $\text{Ч}_3 \cup \{\Diamond\}$ is a complex FR-number (complex F-number) if C is a real FR-number (respectively, real F-number) or if C is a $\Diamond$-pair of words in the alphabet Ч_3 such that the words $[C]_1^{\Diamond}$ and $[C]_2^{\Diamond}$ (cf. §7.1) are real FR-numbers (real F-numbers).

A second variant of the concepts of complex FR-number and complex F-number consists in the following. We extend the alphabet Ч_3 by adding to it the symbols $\Diamond$ and ⟠. We say that a word C in the alphabet $\text{Ч}_3 \cup \{⟠\}$ is a complex FR-number if C is a real FR-number or if C is a ⟠-pair in the alphabet Ч_0 such that, first, the algorithm in the alphabet $\text{Ч}_2 \cup \{\Diamond, \square, \iota, \kappa\}$ whose transcription is the word $[C]_1^{⟠}$ (we denote this algorithm by Φ) transforms every natural number into a $\Diamond$-pair of rational numbers; second, the algorithm in the alphabet Ч_0^{sa} whose transcription is the word $[C]_2^{⟠}$ (we denote this algorithm by θ) is an algorithm of type $(\text{Н} \to \text{Н})_0$; and third,

$$\forall ikl(k,\ l \geqslant \theta(i) \supset \rho(\Phi(k) \square \Phi(l)) < 2^{-i}).$$

Here ρ denotes the algorithm in the alphabet $Ч_3 \cup \{\oplus, \square, \iota, \kappa\}$ transforming every word of the form $a \oplus b \square d \oplus e$, where a, b, d, e are rational numbers, into the square root of the rational number $(d-a)^2 + (e-b)^2$. We say that a word C in the alphabet $Ч_3 \cup \{\ominus\}$ is a complex F-number if C is a real F-number or if C is a $\ominus$-pair of words in the alphabet $Ч_0$ such that, first, the algorithm Φ, which was discussed above, transforms every natural number into a $\oplus$-pair of rational numbers; second, $[C]_2^{\ominus}$ is the empty word; and third, an algorithm f_1 of type $(\mathrm{H} \to \mathrm{H})_0$ is potentially realizable such that

$$\forall ikl(k,\ l \geqslant f_1(i) \supset \rho(\Phi(k) \square \Phi(l)) < 2^{-i}).$$

The theories of constructive complex numbers arising on the basis of the first and second variants of the concept are constructively similar, and therefore interchangeable. The details of the indicated theories will not be considered in this work.

CHAPTER II

CONSTRUCTIVE METRIC AND NORMED SPACES (AXIOMATIC PRESENTATION)

In this chapter we shall consider some problems having to do with the axiomatic theory of constructive metric and normed spaces. The discussion will be chiefly concerned with those problems which are closely connected with the construction of apparatus enabling us to define constructive analogues of a host of concrete metric and normed spaces playing an important role in modern functional analysis and its applications.

§9. THE CONCEPT OF CONSTRUCTIVE METRIC SPACE

9.1. We shall assume that some alphabets

$$A_0, A_1, \ldots, A_h \tag{1}$$

are given and that the list of these alphabets satisfies all the conditions imposed in [3], §3.4 on the list of basic alphabets taken as a basis for the construction of the logico-mathematical languages of the types described in [3], §§3 and 8. We shall assume, in addition, that the alphabet $Ч_3$ is one of the alphabets in the list (1). The logico-mathematical language of the type described in [3], §3, determined on the basis of the list of alphabets (1), will be denoted by the letter $Я$.

We further assume given a certain list Σ of basis one-parameter formulas of the language $Я$, and to each formula of the list Σ is associated a definite restricted generic letter. The logico-mathematical language of the type described in [3], §8, determined on the basis of the initially given elements just enumerated, will be denoted by $Я_\Sigma$.

Let $\mathfrak{m}$ be a natural number not exceeding h, and let $\mathfrak{n}$ be a natural number such that the alphabet $A_\mathfrak{n}$ is equal to the union of the alphabet $A_\mathfrak{m}$ and $Ч_3$. In addition, let $\mathfrak{P}$ be a one-parameter formula of the language $Я$, the parameter of which (denoted by the letter α) is a basis variable of type $t_{\mathfrak{m}}$ (see [3], §§3.4 and 8.2). We shall assume that the formula $\mathfrak{P}$ is one of the formulas of the list Σ. From this assumption it follows that in the language $Я_{\Sigma}$ there is associated with the formula $\mathfrak{P}$ a restricted generic individual letter intended for the construction of those restricted individual variables for which $\mathfrak{P}$ is the characterizing formula ([3], §8.2). We denote this generic letter by θ. For brevity we introduce the following notation for the first four variables of type θ:

$$X \leftrightharpoons (0), \quad Y \leftrightharpoons (00), \quad Z \leftrightharpoons (000), \quad U \leftrightharpoons (0000).$$

We shall say that an algorithm $\lambda_{\mathfrak{n},1}$ in the alphabet $\text{A}_{\mathfrak{n}}^{\text{sa}}$ is a *metric function* in the set $\mathfrak{P}$ if the following three conditions are fulfilled:

$$\forall XY(\lambda_{\mathfrak{n},1}(X \square Y) \overset{+}{\in} \underline{\text{real dup}}), \tag{1}$$

$$\forall X(\lambda_{\mathfrak{n},1}(X \square X) \underset{\text{B}}{=} 0), \tag{2}$$

$$\forall XYZ(\lambda_{\mathfrak{n},1}(Z \square X) \leqslant \lambda_{\mathfrak{n},1}(X \square Y) + \lambda_{\mathfrak{n},1}(Y \square Z)). \tag{3}$$

Remark. From the definition of the predicate $\underline{\text{real dup}}$ and Theorem 4.4.2, it follows that each of the formulas (1), (2), and (3) is equivalent to some normal formula. In what follows, when speaking about the constructive reformulations of formulas (1), (2), and (3), we shall have in mind not those formulas which are the direct results of applying the algorithm for exhibiting constructive problems, but rather the corresponding normal formulas obtained with the help of Theorem 4.4.2.

We shall say that an algorithm $\lambda_{\mathfrak{n},2}$ in the alphabet $\text{A}_{\mathfrak{n}}^{\text{sa}}$ is a *semimetric function* in the set $\mathfrak{P}$ if the following three conditions are fulfilled:

$$\forall XY(\lambda_{\mathfrak{n},2}(X \square Y) \overset{+}{\in} \underline{\text{real } F\text{-num}}), \tag{1*}$$

$$\forall X(\lambda_{\mathfrak{n},2}(X \square X) \underset{\text{B}}{=} 0), \tag{2*}$$

$$\forall XYZ(\lambda_{\mathfrak{n},2}(Z \square X) \leqslant \lambda_{\mathfrak{n},2}(X \square Y) + \lambda_{\mathfrak{n},2}(Y \square Z)). \tag{3*}$$

The following proposition is a direct consequence of the definitions of metric and semimetric functions.

9.1.1. *If $\lambda_{\mathfrak{n},3}$ is a metric function or a semimetric function in the set $\mathfrak{P}$, then, for any elements X, Y, Z, U in the set $\mathfrak{P}$,*

$$\lambda_{\mathfrak{n},3}(Y \square X) \underset{\text{B}}{=} \lambda_{\mathfrak{n},3}(X \square Y), \tag{4}$$

$$\lambda_{\mathfrak{n},3}(X \square Y) \geqslant 0, \tag{5}$$

$$\lambda_{\mathfrak{n},3}(X \square Z) \leqslant \lambda_{\mathfrak{n},}\ (X \square Y) + \lambda_{\mathfrak{n},3}(Y \square Z), \tag{6}$$

$$M(\lambda_{\mathfrak{n},3}(X \square Y) - \lambda_{\mathfrak{n},3}(Z \square U)) \leqslant \lambda_{\mathfrak{n},3}(X \square Z) + \lambda_{\mathfrak{n},3}(Y \square U). \tag{7}$$

Under the assumption that the language $\mathfrak{A}_\Sigma$ of the type characterized above is fixed, the concepts of constructive metric space and constructive semimetric space are introduced by the following definitions.

Definition. A three-termed list, consisting of an alphabet $A_\mathfrak{m}$, where $0 \le \mathfrak{m} \le h$, a one-parameter formula $\mathfrak{P}$ of the type characterized above, and an algorithm ρ in the alphabet $A_\mathfrak{n}^{sa}$, given in the form of a functor, where $\mathfrak{n}$ is a natural number such that the alphabet $A_\mathfrak{n}$ is equal to the alphabet $A_\mathfrak{m} \cup \text{Ч}_3$, is called a *constructive metric space* (*constructive semimetric space*) if ρ is a metric function (respectively, semimetric function) in the set $\mathfrak{P}$.

As a partition sign for writing in one line the three-termed lists of the kind just described above we shall use the comma.

If a list

$$A_\mathfrak{m}, \mathfrak{P}, \rho \tag{8}$$

is a constructive metric (semimetric) space, then $A_\mathfrak{m}$ will be called the *alphabet* of this space, the set $\mathfrak{P}$ will be called the *carrier*, and the algorithm ρ the *metric* (respectively, *semimetric*) *function* of this space. A word satisfying the condition $\mathfrak{P}$ will be called a point of the space (8).

Let X and Y be points of the constructive metric (semimetric) space (8). We shall say that the point X is *equal* to the point Y in this space, and we shall write

$$(X \underset{\rho}{=} Y),$$

if $\rho(X \square Y) =_B 0$. We shall say that the point X is *different* from the point Y in this space, and we shall write

$$(X \underset{\rho}{\neq} Y),$$

if $\rho(X \square Y) \neq_B 0$.

The following important property of a metric (semimetric) function ρ is an immediate consequence of proposition (7):

$$\forall XYZU((X \underset{\rho}{=} Z) \& (Y \underset{\rho}{=} U) \supset \rho(X \square Y) \underset{B}{=} \rho(Z \square U)). \tag{9}$$

We shall assume that the symbols $=_\rho$, $\neq_\rho$ have rank 3 (cf. §1.14, V).

To simplify the writing of formulas we agree to allow the replacement of the symbols $=_\rho$, $\neq_\rho$ by the symbols $=$, $\neq$ in those places in formulas and in the text where such a replacement cannot lead to ambiguity.

Remark 1. The language $\mathfrak{A}_\Sigma$ serves as the basis for the definition of the concepts of constructive metric and semimetric spaces. If, as a basis for the definitions, we choose a wider language than $\mathfrak{A}_\Sigma$ (for example, a language in which the objects of the statements are, first, the objects of the statements of the language $\mathfrak{A}_\Sigma$, and second, the sets given by means of the language $\mathfrak{A}_\Sigma$), then we obtain concepts of constructive metric and semimetric spaces more general than those introduced above. By going over to a still wider language we can proceed to still more general concepts, etc. However, for the introduction of constructive analogues of important concrete metric spaces actually occurring in modern functional analysis and its applications, we find completely sufficient that degree of generality of the indicated concepts which is achieved by the condition that the language $\mathfrak{A}_\Sigma$ serve as the basis of the definitions. This fact determined the choice of the fundamental definitions.

Remark 2. In the sequel the concept of constructive semimetric space will occur only in a few paragraphs. Our basic concern will be concentrated on the concept of constructive metric space and on some special cases of this concept.

We shall often omit the adjective "constructive" in the terms "constructive metric space" and "constructive semimetric space".

In certain cases we shall use the term "space" without any adjective. In all such cases it is meant that, instead of this term, one can substitute either one of the two terms: "constructive metric space" and "constructive semimetric space".

9.2. We shall assume given a space $A_{\mathfrak{m}}, \mathfrak{P}, \rho$ and a space $A_{\tilde{\mathfrak{m}}}, \tilde{\mathfrak{P}}, \tilde{\rho}$. The first we shall denote by $\mathfrak{M}$ and the second by $\tilde{\mathfrak{M}}$. Without loss of generality we can assume that $\mathfrak{M}$ and $\tilde{\mathfrak{M}}$ are constructed on the basis of one and the same language $\mathfrak{A}_\Sigma$ (if this is not so, then the languages on the basis of which $\mathfrak{M}$ and $\tilde{\mathfrak{M}}$ are constructed can be united in a natural way into one language).

We denote by η the index of that basic alphabet which is equal to the union of the alphabets $A_{\mathfrak{m}}$ and $A_{\tilde{\mathfrak{m}}}$. We denote by $\mathfrak{n}$ and $\tilde{\mathfrak{n}}$ the indices of the alphabets equal, respectively, to the alphabets $A_{\mathfrak{m}} \cup Ч_3$ and $A_{\tilde{\mathfrak{m}}} \cup Ч_3$. The restricted generic individual letters associated in the language $\mathfrak{A}_\Sigma$ with the basic sets $\mathfrak{P}$ and $\tilde{\mathfrak{P}}$ will be denoted by θ and $\tilde{\theta}$, respectively. For brevity we introduce the notation

$$X \leftrightharpoons (\theta), \quad Y \leftrightharpoons (\theta\theta), \quad Z \leftrightharpoons (\theta\theta\theta), \quad U \leftrightharpoons (\theta\theta\theta\theta),$$
$$\tilde{X} \leftrightharpoons (\tilde{\theta}), \quad \tilde{Y} \leftrightharpoons (\tilde{\theta}\tilde{\theta}), \quad \tilde{Z} \leftrightharpoons (\tilde{\theta}\tilde{\theta}\tilde{\theta}), \quad \tilde{U} \leftrightharpoons (\tilde{\theta}\tilde{\theta}\tilde{\theta}\tilde{\theta}).$$

On the basis of the given assumptions and conventions we shall formulate some definitions.

We shall say that an algorithm $\lambda_{\eta,1}$ in the alphabet A_{η}^{sa} is a *constructive operator* from $\mathfrak{M}$ into $\widetilde{\mathfrak{M}}$, or, more briefly, an operator of type $(\theta \dot{\to} \widetilde{\theta})$ if, first,

$$\lambda_{\eta,1} \in (\theta \dot{\to} \widetilde{\theta})_{\eta},$$

that is,

$$\forall X(!\lambda_{\eta,1}(X) \supset \lambda_{\eta,1}(X) \in \widetilde{\theta}),$$

and second,

$$\forall XY(!\lambda_{\eta,1}(X) \& X \underset{\rho}{=} Y \supset !\lambda_{\eta,1}(Y) \& \lambda_{\eta,1}(Y) \underset{\widetilde{\rho}}{=} \lambda_{\eta,1}(X)).$$

This definition is a natural extension to the theory of constructive metric spaces of the definition of constructive function of a real variable formulated by Markov (see §6.3; in the present paper, instead of the term "constructive function of a real variable", we use the term "function of type $(Д \dot{\to} Д)$").

If the set of all duplexes plays the role of $\widetilde{\mathfrak{P}}$ and the algorithm computing the absolute value of the difference of any two duplexes plays the role of $\widetilde{\rho}$, then any constructive operator from $\mathfrak{M}$ into $\widetilde{\mathfrak{M}}$ shall also be called a function of type $(\theta \dot{\to} Д)$.

Let k be a positive integer and let $\lambda_{\eta,1}$ be an algorithm in the alphabet A_{η}^{sa}. We shall say that $\lambda_{\eta,1}$ is a *constructive k-ary operator* from $\mathfrak{M}$ into $\widetilde{\mathfrak{M}}$, or, more briefly, an operator of type $(\underbrace{\theta \cdots \theta}_{k \text{ times}} \dot{\to} \widetilde{\theta})$, if, first,

$$\lambda_{\eta,1} \in (\underbrace{\theta \ldots \theta}_{k \text{ times}} \dot{\to} \widetilde{\theta})_{\eta}$$

and second,

$$\widetilde{\forall}(!\lambda_{\eta,1}(\theta_1 \square \ldots \square \theta_k) \& \theta_1 \underset{\rho}{=} \theta_{k+1} \& \ldots \& \theta_k \underset{\rho}{=} \theta_{k+k}$$
$$\supset !\lambda_{\eta,1}(\theta_{k+1} \square \ldots \square \theta_{k+k}) \& \lambda_{\eta,1}(\theta_{k+1} \square \ldots \square \theta_{k+k}) \underset{\widetilde{\rho}}{=} \lambda_{\eta,1}(\theta_1 \square \ldots \square \theta_k)).$$

We shall say that $\lambda_{\eta,1}$ is an *everywhere-defined k-ary operator* from $\mathfrak{M}$ into $\widetilde{\mathfrak{M}}$, and also that $\lambda_{\eta,1}$ is an operator of type $(\underbrace{\theta \cdots \theta}_{k \text{ times}} \to \widetilde{\theta})$, if $\lambda_{\eta,1}$ is an operator of type $(\theta \cdots \theta \dot{\to} \widetilde{\theta})$ and

$$\forall \theta_1 \ldots \theta_k !\lambda_{\eta,1}(\theta_1 \square \ldots \square \theta_k).$$

Every operator of type $(\theta \to \widetilde{\theta})$ is called a *mapping* of the space $\mathfrak{M}$ into the space $\widetilde{\mathfrak{M}}$.

We say that an operator $\lambda_{\eta,1}$ of type $(\theta \dot{\to} \widetilde{\theta})$ is a *mapping* of the space $\mathfrak{M}$ *onto* the space $\widetilde{\mathfrak{M}}$ if $\lambda_{\eta,1}$ is a mapping of $\mathfrak{M}$ into $\widetilde{\mathfrak{M}}$ and

$$\forall \tilde{X} \exists X(!\lambda_{\eta,1}(X) \& \lambda_{\eta,1}(X) \underset{\tilde{\rho}}{=} \tilde{X}). \tag{1}$$

If $\tilde{\mathfrak{P}}$ is a normal formula, then, on the basis of 2.4.3, formula (1) is equivalent to the formula

$$\exists \lambda_{\eta,2} \forall \tilde{X}(\lambda_{\eta,2}(\tilde{X}) \overset{+}{\in} \theta \& !\lambda_{\eta,1}(\lambda_{\eta,2}(\tilde{X})) \& \lambda_{\eta,1}(\lambda_{\eta,2}(\tilde{X})) \underset{\tilde{\rho}}{=} \tilde{X}). \tag{2}$$

If the set of all duplexes plays the role of $\tilde{\mathfrak{P}}$ and the algorithm computing the absolute value of the difference of any two duplexes plays the role of $\tilde{\rho}$, then every operator of type $(\underbrace{\theta \cdots \theta}_{k \text{ times}} \dashrightarrow Д)$ [operator of type $(\underbrace{\theta \cdots \theta}_{k \text{ times}} \to Д)$] is also called a function of type $(\underbrace{\theta \cdots \theta}_{k \text{ times}} \dashrightarrow Д)$ [respectively, a function of type $(\underbrace{\theta \cdots \theta}_{k \text{ times}} \to Д)$].

An operator $\lambda_{\eta,1}$ of type $(\theta \dashrightarrow \theta)$ will be called a *separating operator* if

$$\forall XY(!\lambda_{\eta,1}(X) \& !\lambda_{\eta,1}(Y) \& X \underset{\rho}{\neq} Y \supset \lambda_{\eta,1}(X) \underset{\tilde{\rho}}{\neq} \lambda_{\eta,1}(Y)).$$

An important special case of the concept of separating operator is the concept of isometric operator. An operator $\lambda_{\eta,1}$ of type $(\theta \dashrightarrow \tilde{\theta})$ is called an *isometric operator* from $\mathfrak{M}$ into $\tilde{\mathfrak{M}}$ if

$$\forall XY(!\lambda_{\eta,1}(X) \& !\lambda_{\eta,1}(Y) \supset \tilde{\rho}(\lambda_{\eta,1}(X) \square \lambda_{\eta,1}(Y)) = \rho(X \square Y)).$$

Let $\lambda_{\eta,1}$ be an operator of type $(\theta \dashrightarrow \tilde{\theta})$. We shall say that an algorithm $\lambda_{\eta,2}$ in the alphabet A_η^{sa} is an *operator inverse to* the operator $\lambda_{\eta,1}$, and we shall write $(\lambda_{\eta,2} \,\underline{\text{inv}}\, \lambda_{\eta,1})$, if $\lambda_{\eta,2}$ is an operator of type $(\tilde{\theta} \dashrightarrow \theta)$ and

$$\forall \tilde{X}(\exists X(!\lambda_{\eta,1}(X) \& \lambda_{\eta,1}(X) \underset{\tilde{\rho}}{=} \tilde{X}) \supset !\lambda_{\eta,1}(\lambda_{\eta,2}(\tilde{X})) \& \lambda_{\eta,1}(\lambda_{\eta,2}(\tilde{X})) \underset{\tilde{\rho}}{=} \tilde{X}). \tag{3}$$

It is easily seen that the last condition can be replaced by the condition

$$\forall X(!\lambda_{\eta,1}(X) \supset !\lambda_{\eta,1}(\lambda_{\eta,2}(\lambda_{\eta,1}(X))) \& \lambda_{\eta,1}(\lambda_{\eta,2}(\lambda_{\eta,1}(X))) \underset{\tilde{\rho}}{=} \lambda_{\eta,1}(X)). \tag{4}$$

The next theorem 9.2.1, which is easily proved on the basis of (2) and (3), gives a condition which suffices for the potential realizability of an operator inverse to a given operator.

9.2.1. *If $\lambda_{\eta,1}$ is a separating mapping of $\mathfrak{M}$ onto $\tilde{\mathfrak{M}}$ and $\tilde{\mathfrak{P}}$ is a normal formula, then a mapping $\lambda_{\eta,2}$ of the space $\tilde{\mathfrak{M}}$ into the space $\mathfrak{M}$ is potentially realizable such that $\lambda_{\eta,2}$ is an operator inverse to the operator $\lambda_{\eta,1}$.*

Remark. As a result of the constructive reformulation of the condition "$\lambda_{\eta,1}$ is a mapping of $\mathfrak{M}$ onto $\tilde{\mathfrak{M}}$", one obtains a formula beginning with the quantifier of potential realizability. Hence one cannot apply Theorem 2.4.3 to the formulation of Theorem 9.2.1, and therefore Theorem 9.2.1 does not justify the assertion that there is an algorithm transforming the transcription of any mapping of the space $\mathfrak{M}$ onto the space $\tilde{\mathfrak{M}}$ into the transcription of some operator inverse to the given mapping. Here the situation is analogous to that discussed in the remark after 3.7.3.

The following theorem is easily proved.

9.2.2. *If* $\lambda_{\eta,1}$ *is a separating (isometric) mapping of* $\mathfrak{M}$ *onto* $\tilde{\mathfrak{M}}$ *and* $\lambda_{\eta,2}$ *is an operator inverse to the operator* $\lambda_{\eta,1}$, *then* $\lambda_{\eta,2}$ *is a separating (respectively, isometric) mapping of* $\tilde{\mathfrak{M}}$ *onto* $\mathfrak{M}$.

We shall say that the space $\tilde{\mathfrak{M}}$ is *weakly isometric with* the space $\mathfrak{M}$ if one can construct an isometric mapping of $\mathfrak{M}$ onto $\tilde{\mathfrak{M}}$.

Example. The constructive semimetric space of all real F-numbers is weakly isometric with the constructive metric space of all real duplexes (cf. 3.7.3).

We shall say that the space $\tilde{\mathfrak{M}}$ is *isometric with* the space $\mathfrak{M}$ if one can construct an isometric mapping of $\mathfrak{M}$ onto $\tilde{\mathfrak{M}}$ and an operator inverse to this mapping.

It is easy to see that the following theorem holds.

9.2.3. *In order for a space* $\tilde{\mathfrak{M}}$ *to be isometric with a space* $\mathfrak{M}$, *it is necessary and sufficient that isometric mappings* $\lambda_{\eta,1}$ *of the space* $\mathfrak{M}$ *into the space* $\tilde{\mathfrak{M}}$ *and* $\lambda_{\eta,2}$ *of the space* $\tilde{\mathfrak{M}}$ *into the space* $\mathfrak{M}$ *be potentially realizable such that*

$$\forall X(\lambda_{\eta,2}(\lambda_{\eta,1}(X)) \underset{\rho}{=} X), \quad \forall \tilde{X}(\lambda_{\eta,1}(\lambda_{\eta,2}(\tilde{X})) \underset{\tilde{\rho}}{=} \tilde{X}).$$

The symmetry of the relation "isometric" follows from 9.2.2.

The next theorem is an immediate consequence of 9.2.1 and 9.2.2.

9.2.4. *If* $\mathfrak{P}$ *is a normal formula, then the space* $\tilde{\mathfrak{M}}$ *is isometric with the space* $\mathfrak{M}$ *if and only if an isometric mapping of* $\mathfrak{M}$ *onto* $\tilde{\mathfrak{M}}$ *is potentially realizable.*

9.3. In this section we keep all the assumptions, notation, and conventions introduced in the preceding section.

Let k be a positive integer, $\lambda_{\eta,1}$ a constructive k-ary operator from the space $\mathfrak{M}$ into the space $\tilde{\mathfrak{M}}$, and $\theta_1, \cdots, \theta_k$ points of the space $\mathfrak{M}$. One says that the operator $\lambda_{\eta,1}$ is *continuous* at the k-tuple of points $\theta_1, \cdots, \theta_k$ if, first, $!\lambda_{\eta,1}(\theta_1 \square \cdots \square \theta_k)$, and second,

$$\forall l \exists m \forall \theta_{k+1} \ldots \theta_{k+k} (!\lambda_{\eta,1}(\theta_{k+1} \square \ldots \square \theta_{k+k}) \,\&\, \rho(\theta_{k+1} \square \theta_1) < 2^{-m}$$
$$\& \ldots \& \, \rho(\theta_{k+k} \square \theta_k) < 2^{-m} \supset \tilde{\rho}(\lambda_{\eta,1}(\theta_{k+1} \square \ldots \square \theta_{k+k}) \square \lambda_{\eta,1}(\theta_1 \square \ldots \square \theta_k)) < 2^{-l}).$$

One says that $\lambda_{\eta,1}$ is a *continuous k-ary operator* from the space $\mathfrak{M}$ into the space $\widetilde{\mathfrak{M}}$ if $\lambda_{\eta,1}$ is continuous at every k-tuple of points $\theta_1, \cdots, \theta_k$ for which $!\,\lambda_{\eta,1}(\theta_1 \square \cdots \square \theta_k)$.

One can easily prove (with the help of Theorems 2.4.3, 2.1.1, and 2.1.3) that, in the case where $\mathfrak{P}$ is a normal formula, the condition

"$\lambda_{\eta,1}$ is a continuous k-ary operator from the space $\mathfrak{M}$ into the space $\widetilde{\mathfrak{M}}$" imposed on a constructive k-ary operator $\lambda_{\eta,1}$ is equivalent to the condition

$$\exists \lambda_{\mathrm{n},2} \mathfrak{T},$$

where

$$\mathfrak{T} \rightleftharpoons \forall \theta_1 \ldots \theta_k l\,(!\,\lambda_{\eta,1}(\theta_1 \square \ldots \square \theta_k) \supset \Gamma \overset{+}{\in} \underline{\text{nat}}$$

$$\& \forall \theta_{k+1} \ldots \theta_{k+k}(!\,\lambda_{\eta,1}(\theta_{k+1} \square \ldots \square \theta_{k+k}) \,\&\, \rho(\theta_{k+1} \square \theta_1) < 2^{-\Gamma}$$

$$\& \ldots \& \rho(\theta_{k+k} \square \theta_k) < 2^{-\Gamma} \supset \tilde{\rho}(\lambda_{\eta,1}(\theta_{k+1} \square \ldots \square \theta_{k+k}) \square \lambda_{\eta,1}(\theta_1 \square \ldots \square \theta_k)) < 2^{-l})).$$

Here $\Gamma \rightleftharpoons \lambda_{\mathrm{n},2}(\theta_1 \square \ldots \square \theta_k \square l)$.

For the case where $\mathfrak{P}$ is a normal formula, we introduce the following definition. We shall say that an algorithm $\lambda_{\mathrm{n},2}$ in the alphabet $A_{\mathrm{n}}^{\mathrm{sa}}$ is a *regulator of continuity* of a constructive k-ary operator $\lambda_{\eta,1}$, and we shall write

$$(\lambda_{\mathrm{n},2}\ \underline{\text{reg. cont}}_k\ \lambda_{\eta,1}),$$

if the algorithm $\lambda_{\mathrm{n},2}$ satisfied condition $\mathfrak{T}$.

From what has been said it follows that *in the case where $\mathfrak{P}$ is a normal formula a constructive k-ary operator $\lambda_{\eta,1}$ is a continuous k-ary operator from $\mathfrak{M}$ into $\widetilde{\mathfrak{M}}$ if and only if*

$$\exists \lambda_{\mathrm{n},2}(\lambda_{\mathrm{n},2}\ \underline{\text{reg. cont}}_k\ \lambda_{\eta,1}).$$

One says that $\lambda_{\eta,1}$ is a *uniformly continuous k-ary operator* from $\mathfrak{M}$ into $\widetilde{\mathfrak{M}}$ if

$$\forall l \exists m \forall \theta_1 \ldots \theta_k \theta_{k+1} \ldots \theta_{k+k}(!\,\lambda_{\eta,1}(\theta_1 \square \ldots \square \theta_k) \,\&\, !\,\lambda_{\eta,1}(\theta_{k+1} \square \ldots \square \theta_{k+k})$$

$$\& \rho(\theta_{k+1} \square \theta_1) < 2^{-m} \& \ldots \& \rho(\theta_{k+k} \square \theta_k) < 2^{-m}$$

$$\supset \tilde{\rho}(\lambda_{\eta,1}(\theta_{k+1} \square \ldots \square \theta_{k+k}) \square \lambda_{\eta,1}(\theta_1 \square \ldots \square \theta_k)) < 2^{-l}). \tag{5}$$

Applying Theorem 2.4.3 to (5), we arrive at the formula

$$\exists \lambda_{0,2} \mathfrak{R}, \tag{6}$$

where

$$\mathfrak{R} \rightleftharpoons \forall l\,(\lambda_{0,2}(l) \overset{+}{\in} \underline{\text{nat}} \,\&\, \forall \theta_1 \ldots \theta_k \theta_{k+1} \ldots \theta_{k+k}(!\,\lambda_{\eta,1}(\theta_1 \square \ldots \square \theta_k)$$

$$\& !\,\lambda_{\eta,1}(\theta_{k+1} \square \ldots \square \theta_{k+k}) \,\&\, \rho(\theta_{k+1} \square \theta_1) < 2^{-\lambda_{0,2}(l)} \& \ldots \& \rho(\theta_{k+k} \square \theta_k) < 2^{-\lambda_{0,2}(l)}$$

$$\supset \tilde{\rho}(\lambda_{\eta,1}(\theta_{k+1} \square \ldots \square \theta_{k+k}) \square \lambda_{\eta,1}(\theta_1 \square \ldots \square \theta_k)) < 2^{-l})).$$

We shall say that an algorithm $\lambda_{0,2}$ in the alphabet A_0^{sa} is a *regulator of uniform continuity* of a constructive k-ary operator $\lambda_{\eta,1}$, and we shall write

$$(\lambda_{0,2} \underline{\text{reg. unif. cont}_k} \lambda_{\eta,1}),$$

if condition $\mathfrak{R}$ is fulfilled.

From what has been said it follows that a constructive k-ary operator $\lambda_{\eta,1}$ is a uniformly continuous k-ary operator from $\mathfrak{M}$ into $\widetilde{\mathfrak{M}}$ if and only if

$$\exists \lambda_{0,2} (\lambda_{0,2} \underline{\text{reg. unif. cont}_k} \lambda_{\eta,1}).$$

Assuming that k denotes a given natural number, we introduce a new elementary symbol $\boxed{K}$ and a new alphabet $A_0 \cup \{\boxed{K}\}$. Adding to the language $\mathfrak{A}$ this new alphabet and its union with every alphabet of the language $\mathfrak{A}$, we obtain a new language, denoted below by $\mathfrak{A}'$. The language $\mathfrak{A}'_\Sigma$ is determined on the basis of $\mathfrak{A}'$. In the general indexing of the alphabets of the language $\mathfrak{A}'$, the alphabet $A_0 \cup \{\boxed{K}\}$ receives a certain index. Let us denote this index by the letter π. In accordance with this, the alphabet $A_0 \cup \{\boxed{K}\}$ receives the designation A_π.

We shall say that a word $t_{\pi,1}$ in the alphabet A_π is a *canonical word* in the alphabet A_π if $t_{\pi,1}$ contains one and only one occurrence of the symbol $\boxed{K}$. We construct and fix concrete algorithms $\overline{\text{lef}}_\pi$ and $\overline{\text{rig}}_\pi$ in the alphabet A_π^{sa} such that, for any word $t_{\pi,1}$, the following conditions are fulfilled.

1. If $t_{\pi,1}$ is a canonical word in the alphabet A_π, then the algorithm $\overline{\text{lef}}_\pi$ (algorithm $\overline{\text{rig}}_\pi$) transforms the word $t_{\pi,1}$ into the word which is the left (respectively, right) wing of the occurrence of the symbol $\boxed{K}$ in the word $t_{\pi,1}$; in other words, for any words $t_{0,1}$ and $t_{0,2}$ in the alphabet A_0, we have

$$\overline{\text{lef}}_\pi (t_{0,1} \boxed{K} t_{0,2}) \mathrel{\dot{=}} t_{0,1}, \quad \overline{\text{rig}}_\pi (t_{0,1} \boxed{K} t_{0,2}) \mathrel{\dot{=}} t_{0,2};$$

2. If $t_{\pi,1}$ is not a canonical word in the alphabet A_π, then the algorithms $\overline{\text{lef}}_\pi$ and $\overline{\text{rig}}_\pi$ transform $t_{\pi,1}$ into the transcription of the normal algorithm defined by the schema

$$\{ \rightarrow .$$

We shall say that a word $t_{\pi,1}$ is a *one-sided canonical word* in the alphabet A_π if $t_{\pi,1}$ is a canonical word in the alphabet A_π and $\overline{\text{rig}}_\pi (t_{\pi,1}) \mathrel{\dot{=}} \Lambda$.

Let Θ be any term. We introduce the notation

$$\underline{\Theta}_\pi \rightleftharpoons \langle \overline{\text{lef}}_\pi (\Theta) \rangle_\eta, \quad \overline{\Theta}^\pi \rightleftharpoons \langle \overline{\text{rig}}_\pi (\Theta) \rangle_0.$$

To every canonical word in the alphabet A_π we associate a one-sided canonical word in the alphabet A_π which we shall call the *principal part* of the given canonical word. We construct and fix an algorithm $\overline{\text{prin}}_\pi$ in the alphabet

$\mathrm{A}_{\pi}^{\mathrm{sa}}$ such that, for any word $t_{\pi,1}$ in the alphabet A_{π},

$$\overline{\mathrm{prin}_{\pi}}\,(t_{\pi,1}) \simeq \overline{\mathrm{lef}_{\pi}}\,(t_{\pi,1})\ \boxed{K}.$$

Now we introduce the following definition. We shall say that a word $t_{\pi,1}$ is a *one-sided cipher* for an everywhere-defined uniformly continuous k-ary operator from $\mathfrak{M}$ into $\tilde{\mathfrak{M}}$, and we shall write

$$(t_{\pi,1} \in \underline{\text{one ciph}_k}),$$

if, first, $t_{\pi,1}$ is a one-sided canonical word in the alphabet A_{π}, second,

$$\underline{t_{\pi,1}}_{\pi} \in (\underbrace{\theta \ldots \theta}_{k \text{ times}} \to \tilde{\theta})_{\eta}$$

and third,

$$\exists \lambda_{0,2} (\lambda_{0,2}\ \underline{\text{reg. unif. cont}_k\, \underline{t_{\pi,1}}_{\pi}}).$$

We shall say that a word $t_{\pi,2}$ is a *complete cipher* for an everywhere-defined uniformly continuous k-ary operator from $\mathfrak{M}$ into $\tilde{\mathfrak{M}}$, and we shall write

$$(t_{\pi,2} \in \underline{\text{comp. ciph}_k}),$$

if, first, $t_{\pi,2}$ is a canonical word in the alphabet A_{π}, second,

$$\underline{t_{\pi,1}}_{\pi} \in (\underbrace{\theta \ldots \theta}_{k \text{ times}} \to \tilde{\theta})_{\eta}$$

and third,

$$\overline{t_{\pi,1}}^{\pi}\ \underline{\text{reg. unif. cont}_k\, \underline{t_{\pi,1}}_{\pi}}.$$

The following proposition is obvious.

9.3.1. $\forall t_{\pi,2} (t_{\pi,2} \in \underline{\text{comp. ciph}_k} \supset \overline{\mathrm{prin}_{\pi}}(t_{\pi,2}) \in \underline{\text{one ciph}_k})$.

Remark 1. In many respects the connection between the concepts $\underline{\text{comp. ciph}_k}$ and $\underline{\text{one ciph}_k}$ are analogous to the connection between the concepts $\underline{\text{real } FR\text{-num}}$ and $\underline{\text{real } F\text{-num}}$.

Remark 2. Complete and one-sided ciphers for everywhere-defined uniformly continuous k-ary operators from $\mathfrak{M}$ into $\tilde{\mathfrak{M}}$ are words in the alphabet A_{π}, and therefore can serve as initially given objects for normal algorithms over the alphabet A_{π}. Hence in many cases it turns out to be convenient to consider not the operators themselves, but rather their complete or one-sided ciphers.

Let $t_{\pi,1}$ and $t_{\pi,2}$ be one-sided or complete ciphers for everywhere-defined uniformly continuous k-ary operators from $\mathfrak{M}$ into $\tilde{\mathfrak{M}}$. We shall say that the cipher $t_{\pi,1}$ is *equivalent in dimension* k to the cipher $t_{\pi,2}$ if

$$\forall \theta_1 \ldots \theta_k (\underline{t_{\pi,1}}_{\pi} (\theta_1 \square \ldots \square \theta_k) \underset{\tilde{\rho}}{=} \underline{t_{\pi,2}}_{\pi} (\theta_1 \square \ldots \square \theta_k)).$$

It is obvious that the binary relation introduced by this definition is reflexive symmetric, and transitive.

9.4. Keeping all the assumptions and notation introduced at the beginning of §9.2, we now formulate the following definition.

We shall say that a space $\widetilde{\mathfrak{M}}$ is a *subspace* of a space $\mathfrak{M}$ if the set $\widetilde{\mathfrak{P}}$ is contained in the set $\mathfrak{P}$ (cf. [3], §7.2) and

$$\forall \tilde{X}\tilde{Y}(\tilde{\rho}(\tilde{X}\,\square\,\tilde{Y}) \underset{\text{B}}{=} \rho(\tilde{X}\,\square\,\tilde{Y})).$$

We note that in the case where different alphabets are associated with parameters of the formulas $\mathfrak{P}$ and $\widetilde{\mathfrak{P}}$ the condition "the set $\widetilde{\mathfrak{P}}$ is contained in the set $\mathfrak{P}$" is made clear by changing from the sets $\mathfrak{P}$ and $\widetilde{\mathfrak{P}}$ to the equivalent sets in the alphabet A_η (see [3]).

Let $\mathfrak{Q}$ be any basis set contained in the set $\mathfrak{P}$. Let us denote by ι the index of that basic alphabet which is associated with the parameter of the formula $\mathfrak{Q}$, and by ζ the index of the basic alphabet which is equal to the union of the alphabets $\mathrm{A}_\mathfrak{m}$ and A_ι. Let us denote by δ_0 the natural extension of the algorithm ρ to the alphabet A_ζ^{sa} (see [1]) and by δ the translation of the algorithm δ_0 into the alphabet A_ι^{sa} (see [1]).

It is evident that the list

$$\mathrm{A}_\iota,\ \mathfrak{Q},\ \delta$$

is a subspace of the space $\mathfrak{M}$. This subspace will be called the *subspace induced by the space* $\mathfrak{M}$ *in the set* $\mathfrak{Q}$.

We shall say that the set $\mathfrak{Q}$ is *almost dense* in the space $\mathfrak{M}$ if $\mathfrak{Q}$ is contained in $\mathfrak{P}$ and

$$\forall Xk\exists Y(\mathbf{F}^\beta_{Y\llcorner}\mathfrak{Q}_\lrcorner\ \&\ \rho(X\,\square\,Y) < 2^{-k}), \tag{1}$$

where β is the parameter of the formula $\mathfrak{Q}$.

We shall say that an algorithm $\mathfrak{A}$ over the alphabet $\mathrm{A}_\mathfrak{m}$ *approximates* the space $\mathfrak{M}$ by means of the set $\mathfrak{Q}$ if

$$\forall Xk(\mathfrak{A}(X\,\square\,k) \overset{+}{\in} \theta\ \&\ \mathbf{F}^\beta_{\mathfrak{A}(X\square k)\llcorner}\mathfrak{Q}_\lrcorner\ \&\ \rho(X\,\square\,\mathfrak{A}(X\,\square\,k)) < 2^{-k}).$$

We shall say that a set $\mathfrak{Q}$ is *dense* in the space $\mathfrak{M}$ if $\mathfrak{Q}$ is contained in $\mathfrak{P}$ and an algorithm which approximates $\mathfrak{M}$ by means of $\mathfrak{Q}$ is potentially realizable.

If a set $\mathfrak{Q}$ is dense in $\mathfrak{M}$, then obviously $\mathfrak{Q}$ is almost dense in $\mathfrak{M}$. If $\mathfrak{Q}$ is almost dense in $\mathfrak{M}$ and $\mathfrak{P}$ is a normal formula, then, as is easily seen by applying Theorem 2.4.3 to formula (1), $\mathfrak{Q}$ is dense in $\mathfrak{M}$. If $\mathfrak{P}$ is not a normal formula, then it can happen that $\mathfrak{Q}$ is almost dense in $\mathfrak{M}$ and at the same time there is no algorithm approximating $\mathfrak{M}$ by means of $\mathfrak{Q}$. For example, the set of all rational numbers is almost dense in the semimetric space of all real F-numbers. At the same time, there is no algorithm approximating this space by means of the set of all rational numbers. (If such an algorithm were possible, then without difficulty we could construct an algorithm transforming any real F-number q into the duplex which is the limit of the sequence of rational numbers $\underset{\to}{q}$. Recently G. E. Minc has proved that the latter algorithm is impossible.)[1)]

The following theorem will be used in the sequel.

9.4.1. *Let k be a positive integer, $\lambda_{\eta,1}$ and $\lambda_{\eta,2}$ constructive continuous k-ary operators of type $(\underbrace{\theta\cdots\theta}_{k\text{ times}}\to\tilde{\theta})$. In addition, let $\mathfrak{Q}$ be a subset of the space $\mathfrak{M}$ which is almost dense in $\mathfrak{M}$. If for any words $\theta_1,\cdots\theta_k$ belonging to the set $\mathfrak{Q}$ the condition*

$$\lambda_{\eta,1}(\theta_1\square\ldots\square\theta_k)\underset{\tilde{\rho}}{=}\lambda_{\eta,2}(\theta_1\square\ldots\square\theta_k), \tag{2}$$

is fulfilled, then the condition (2) *is also fulfilled when $\theta_1,\cdots,\theta_k$ are arbitrary points of the space $\mathfrak{M}$. In other words, if*

$$\forall\theta_1\ldots\theta_k(\mathbf{F}^{\beta}_{\theta_1\llcorner}\mathfrak{Q}_\lrcorner\,\&\ldots\&\,\mathbf{F}^{\beta}_{\theta_k\llcorner}\mathfrak{Q}_\lrcorner\supset\lambda_{\eta,1}(\theta_1\square\ldots\square\theta_k)\underset{\tilde{\rho}}{=}\lambda_{\eta,2}(\theta_1\square\ldots\square\theta_k)), \tag{3}$$

then

$$\forall\theta_1\ldots\theta_k(\lambda_{\eta,1}(\theta_1\square\ldots\square\theta_k)\underset{\tilde{\rho}}{=}\lambda_{\eta,2}(\theta_1\square\ldots\square\theta_k)). \tag{4}$$

If $\tilde{\mathfrak{M}}$ is the space of all real duplexes or all real F-numbers, then, replacing in (2), (3), *and* (4) *the symbol $=_{\tilde{\rho}}$ by the symbol $\leq_{B}$, we also obtain a true proposition.*

Proof. Assume that a positive integer k, operators $\lambda_{\eta,1}$ and $\lambda_{\eta,2}$ and a set $\mathfrak{Q}$ are such that all the conditions of the theorem, including condition (3), are fulfilled. In addition, let $\theta_1,\cdots,\theta_k$ be any points of the space $\mathfrak{M}$ and let l be any natural number. Then, by virtue of the continuity of the operators $\lambda_{\eta,1}$ and $\lambda_{\eta,2}$ at the k-tuple of points $\theta_1,\cdots,\theta_k$, we have

$$\exists m\mathfrak{A},\quad \exists n\mathfrak{B},$$

where

1) *Translator's note.* Published in G. E. Minc, *On predicate and operator variants of the formation of the theories of constructive mathematics*, Trudy Mat. Inst. Steklov. 72 (1964), 383–436. (Russian) MR 33 #2543.

$$\mathfrak{U} \rightleftharpoons \forall \theta_{k+1} \ldots \theta_{k+k} (\rho(\theta_{k+1} \square \theta_1) < 2^{-m} \& \ldots \& \rho(\theta_{k+k} \square \theta_k) < 2^{-m}$$
$$\supset \tilde{\rho}(\lambda_{\eta,1}(\theta_{k+1} \square \ldots \square \theta_{k+k}) \square \lambda_{\eta,1}(\theta_1 \square \ldots \square \theta_k)) < 2^{-(l+1)}),$$
$$\mathfrak{B} \rightleftharpoons \forall \theta_{k+1} \ldots \theta_{k+k} (\rho(\theta_{k+1} \square \theta_1) < 2^{-n} \& \ldots \& \rho(\theta_{k+k} \square \theta_k) < 2^{-n}$$
$$\supset \tilde{\rho}(\lambda_{\eta,2}(\theta_{k+1} \square \ldots \square \theta_{k+k}) \square \lambda_{\eta,2}(\theta_1 \square \ldots \square \theta_k)) < 2^{-(l+1)}).$$

Let the natural numbers m and n be such that conditions $\mathfrak{U}$ and $\mathfrak{B}$ are fulfilled. We introduce the notation

$$\Gamma \rightleftharpoons \max(m \square n).$$

Since the set $\mathfrak{Q}$ is almost dense in $\mathfrak{M}$, for every $j (j = 1, \cdots, k)$ we have

$$\exists \theta_{k+j} (\mathbf{F}^{\beta}_{\theta_{k+j}\llcorner} \mathfrak{Q}_{\lrcorner} \& \rho(\theta_{k+j} \square \theta_j) < 2^{-\Gamma}).$$

Let $\theta_{k+1}, \cdots, \theta_{k+k}$ be points in the space $\mathfrak{M}$ such that, for every $j (j = 1, \cdots, k)$,

$$\mathbf{F}^{\beta}_{\theta_{k+j}\llcorner} \mathfrak{Q}_{\lrcorner} \& \rho(\theta_{k+j} \square \theta_j) < 2^{-\Gamma}.$$

Then, first,

$$\lambda_{\eta,1}(\theta_{k+1} \square \ldots \square \theta_{k+k}) \underset{\tilde{\rho}}{=} \lambda_{\eta,2}(\theta_{k+1} \square \ldots \square \theta_{k+k})$$

and second,

$$\tilde{\rho}(\lambda_{\eta,1}(\theta_1 \square \ldots \square \theta_k) \square \lambda_{\eta,2}(\theta_1 \square \ldots \square \theta_k))$$
$$\leqslant \tilde{\rho}(\lambda_{\eta,1}(\theta_1 \square \ldots \square \hat{\theta}_k) \square \lambda_{\eta,1}(\theta_{k+1} \square \ldots \square \theta_{k+k}))$$
$$+ \tilde{\rho}(\lambda_{\eta,2}(\theta_{k+1} \square \ldots \square \theta_{k+k}) \square \lambda_{\eta,2}(\theta_1 \square \ldots \square \theta_k)) < 2^{-(l+1)} + 2^{-(l+1)} = 2^{-l}.$$

Hence

$$\forall l (\tilde{\rho}(\lambda_{\eta,1}(\theta_1 \square \ldots \square \theta_k) \square \lambda_{\eta,2}(\theta_1 \square \ldots \square \theta_k)) < 2^{-l}).$$

Therefore proposition (4) is true.

The second part of the theorem easily reduces to the first part of the theorem with the help of the propositions

$$\forall xy (x \leqslant y \equiv M(y - x) = y - x),$$
$$\forall rs (r \leqslant s \equiv M(s - r) = s - r).$$

Theorem 9.4.1 is proved.

Remark. Theorem 9.4.1 was proved by the method of "natural deduction", which in the given case was applied to formulas containing restricted variables. The algorithm for eliminating restricted variables and the algorithm for exhibiting constructive problems (see [3], §§4 and 8) permit us to justify the admissibility in constructive mathematics of the method of logical inference used above.

In concluding this section we formulate some more definitions to be used in the sequel.

A space $\mathfrak{M}$ is called a *separable* space if an algorithmically enumerable subset of the set $\mathfrak{P}$, dense in the space $\mathfrak{M}$, is potentially realizable.

A space $\mathfrak{M}$ is called a *completely separable* space if an algorithmically solvable subset of the set $\mathfrak{P}$, dense in the space $\mathfrak{M}$, is potentially realizable.

If $\mathfrak{Q}$ is a subset of the set $\mathfrak{P}$, then by the *closure* of $\mathfrak{Q}$ in the space $\mathfrak{M}$ we mean the set given by the one-parameter condition

$$\forall l \exists Y (\mathbf{F}^{\beta}_{\ulcorner Y \llcorner} \mathfrak{Q}_{\lrcorner} \,\&\, \rho(X \square Y) < 2^{-l}). \tag{5}$$

The restricted variable X is the parameter of the formula (5). In accordance with the convention accepted in [3], §8.8, the set (5) is identified, under that interpretation, with the basis set obtained by applying to (5) the algorithm $\mathfrak{c}$ described in [3], §8.7.

A set $\mathfrak{Q}$ is called a *closed subset* of the space $\mathfrak{M}$ if $\mathfrak{Q}$ is contained in $\mathfrak{P}$ and the closure of the set $\mathfrak{Q}$ in the space $\mathfrak{M}$ is contained in the set $\mathfrak{Q}$ (cf. [3], §§8.8 and 7.2).

A set $\mathfrak{Q}$ is called a *faithful subset* of the space $\mathfrak{M}$ if $\mathfrak{Q}$ is a subset of the set $\mathfrak{P}$ and

$$\forall XY (X \underset{\rho}{=} Y \supset (\mathbf{F}^{\beta}_{X \llcorner} \mathfrak{Q}_{\lrcorner} \supset \mathbf{F}^{\beta}_{Y \llcorner} \mathfrak{Q}_{\lrcorner})).$$

The following proposition is obvious.

9.4.2. *Every closed subset of the space $\mathfrak{M}$ is a faithful subset of this space.*

§10. COMPLETION OF CONSTRUCTIVE METRIC SPACES

In this section we shall keep the assumptions and notation introduced at the beginning of §9.2.

10.1. One says that an algorithm $\lambda_{\mathfrak{n},1}$ in the alphabet $\mathrm{A}_{\mathfrak{n}}$ is a *sequence of points of a space* $\mathfrak{M}$ if $\lambda_{\mathfrak{n},1} \in (\mathrm{H} \to \theta)_{\mathfrak{n}}$.

We shall say that a point X of a space $\mathfrak{M}$ is a *limit* in $\mathfrak{M}$ of the sequence of points $\lambda_{\mathfrak{n},1}$, and we shall write

$$(X \underline{\ \lim\ }_{\mathfrak{M}} \lambda_{\mathfrak{n},1}),$$

if

$$\forall k \exists l \forall m (m \geqslant l \supset \rho(X \square \lambda_{\mathfrak{n},1}(m)) < 2^{-k}). \tag{1}$$

On the basis of 2.4.3, formula (1) is equivalent to the formula

$$\exists \lambda_{0,2} \mathfrak{F}, \tag{2}$$

where

$$\mathfrak{F} \rightleftharpoons \forall k (\lambda_{0,2}(k) \overset{+}{\in} \underline{\text{nat}} \;\&\; \forall m (m \geqslant \lambda_{0,2}(k) \supset \rho(X \square \lambda_{n,1}(m)) < 2^{-k})).$$

Remark. If $\mathfrak{M}$ is a metric space, then ρ is a function of type $(\theta\theta \to Д)$, and therefore $\mathfrak{F}$ is equivalent to a normal formula obtained from $\mathfrak{F}$ by replacing the subformula denoted by the expression "$\rho(X \square \lambda_{n,1}(m)) < 2^{-k}$" by the normal formula in accordance with Theorem 4.4.2.

One says that a sequence $\lambda_{n,1}$ of points of a space $\mathfrak{M}$ is a *convergent* sequence in $\mathfrak{M}$ if $\exists X (X \underline{\lim}_{\mathfrak{M}} \lambda_{n,1})$.

It is easy to prove the following proposition.

10.1.1. *For any sequence of points* $\lambda_{n,1}$ *of the space* $\mathfrak{M}$ *and any points* X *and* Y,

$$X \underline{\lim}_{\mathfrak{M}} \lambda_{n,1} \;\&\; Y \underline{\lim}_{\mathfrak{M}} \lambda_{n,1} \supset X = Y.$$

Let $\lambda_{n,1}$ be any sequence of points of a space $\mathfrak{M}$. We say that an algorithm $\lambda_{n,2}$ is a *subsequence* of the sequence $\lambda_{n,1}$ if an algorithm $\lambda_{0,1}$ of type $(\mathrm{H} \to \mathrm{H})_0$ is potentially realizable such that, for every m,

$$\lambda_{0,1}(m) < \lambda_{0,1}(m+1)$$

and

$$\lambda_{n,2}(m) \simeq \lambda_{n,1}(\lambda_{0,1}(m)).$$

The next proposition is obvious.

10.1.2. *For any point* X *of a space* $\mathfrak{M}$, *any sequence* $\lambda_{n,1}$ *of points of the space* $\mathfrak{M}$, *and any subsequence* $\lambda_{n,2}$ *of the sequence* $\lambda_{n,1}$,

$$X \underline{\lim}_{\mathfrak{M}} \lambda_{n,1} \supset X \underline{\lim}_{\mathfrak{M}} \lambda_{n,2}.$$

We note (without proof) the following theorem, which, in analogy with the corresponding theorem of classical mathematics, it is natural to call the theorem on the realizability of the "diagonal" sequence.

10.1.3. *For any point* X *of a space* $\mathfrak{M}$, *any algorithm* $\lambda_{n,1}$ *of type* $(\mathrm{H} \to \theta)_n$ *and any algorithm* $\lambda_{0,1}$ *of type* $(\mathrm{H} \to t_0)_0$ *such that, for every* m,

$$\langle \lambda_{0,1}(m) \rangle_n \in (\mathrm{H} \to \theta)_n,$$

the following assertion is true:

$$(X \underline{\lim}_{\mathfrak{M}} \lambda_{n,1}) \;\&\; \forall m (\lambda_{n,1}(m) \underline{\lim}_{\mathfrak{M}} \langle \lambda_{0,1}(m) \rangle_n)$$
$$\supset \dot{\exists} \lambda_{0,2} (\lambda_{0,2} \in (\mathrm{H} \to \mathrm{H})_0 \;\&\; X \underline{\lim}_{\mathfrak{M}} \langle \Gamma(\{\lambda_{0,1}\} \square \{\lambda_{0,2}\}) \rangle_n),$$

where Γ *denotes the algorithm in the alphabet* A_0^{sa} *constructed in such a way that*

$$\forall \lambda_{0,1} \lambda_{0,2} m (\langle \Gamma(\{\lambda_{0,1}\} \square \{\lambda_{0,2}\}) \rangle_n (m) \simeq \langle \lambda_{0,1}(m) \rangle_n (\lambda_{0,2}(m))).$$

Applying to proposition 10.1.3 the algorithm for exhibiting constructive problems, we find a formulation of a construction problem corresponding to the given proposition. The solution of this constructive problem can be found without difficulty.

Basing oneself on the definitions at the beginning of §9.3 and on the definition of the relation $\underline{\lim}_{\mathfrak{M}}$, one can easily establish the following theorem.

10.1.4. *Let k be any integer, $\theta_1, \cdots, \theta_k$ points of a space $\mathfrak{M}$, $\lambda_{\eta,1}$ a constructive k-ary operator from the space $\mathfrak{M}$ into the space $\widetilde{\mathfrak{M}}$ which is continuous at the k-tuple of points $\theta_1, \cdots, \theta_k$. In addition, let $\lambda_{\mathfrak{n},1}, \cdots, \lambda_{\mathfrak{n},k}$ be sequences of points of the space $\mathfrak{M}$ such that, first, for every m,*

$$!\lambda_{\eta,1}(\lambda_{\mathfrak{n},1}(m)\square\ldots\square\lambda_{\mathfrak{n},k}(m))$$

and second

$$\theta_1 \ \underline{\lim}_{\mathfrak{M}} \lambda_{\mathfrak{n},1}, \ \ldots, \ \theta_k \ \underline{\lim}_{\mathfrak{M}} \lambda_{\mathfrak{n},k}.$$

Let $\lambda_{\tilde{\mathfrak{n}},k+1}$ be an algorithm in the alphabet $\text{A}^{\text{sa}}_{\tilde{\mathfrak{n}}}$ such that, for every m,

$$\lambda_{\tilde{\mathfrak{n}},k+1}(m) \simeq \lambda_{\eta,1}(\lambda_{\mathfrak{n},1}(m)\square\ldots\square\lambda_{\mathfrak{n},k}(m)).$$

Then, first, $\lambda_{\tilde{\mathfrak{n}},k+1}$ is a sequence of points of the space $\widetilde{\mathfrak{M}}$, and second,

$$\lambda_{\eta,1}(\theta_1\square\ldots\square\theta_k) \ \underline{\lim}_{\widetilde{\mathfrak{M}}} \lambda_{\tilde{\mathfrak{n}},k+1}.$$

The algorithm $\lambda_{\mathfrak{n},1}$ will be called a *fundamental sequence* of points of the space $\mathfrak{M}$, and also a *convergent-in-itself sequence* of points of the space $\mathfrak{M}$, and we shall write

$$(\lambda_{\mathfrak{n},1} \in \underline{\text{fund. seq}}_{\mathfrak{M}}),$$

if $\lambda_{\mathfrak{n},1}$ is a sequence of points of the space $\mathfrak{M}$ and

$$\forall k \exists l \forall mn (m, \ n \geqslant l \supset \rho(\lambda_{\mathfrak{n},1}(m)\square\lambda_{\mathfrak{n},1}(n)) < 2^{-k}). \tag{3}$$

On the basis of 2.4.3, formula (3) is equivalent to the formula

$$\exists \lambda_{0,3}\mathfrak{G}, \tag{4}$$

where

$$\mathfrak{G} \rightleftharpoons \forall k(\lambda_{0,3}(k) \dot{\in} \underline{\text{nat}} \ \& \ \forall mn(m, \ n \geqslant \lambda_{0,3}(k) \supset \rho(\lambda_{\mathfrak{n},1}(m)\square\lambda_{\mathfrak{n},1}(n)) < 2^{-k})).$$

Remark. If $\mathfrak{M}$ is a metric space, then the formula $\mathfrak{G}$ is equivalent to the normal formula obtained from $\mathfrak{G}$ by replacing the subformula denoted by the expression "$\rho(\lambda_{\mathfrak{n},1}(m)\square\lambda_{\mathfrak{n},1}(n)) < 2^{-k}$" by the normal formula formed in accordance with Theorem 4.4.2.

Let $\lambda_{\mathfrak{n},1}$ be a sequence of points of the space $\mathfrak{M}$ and let $\lambda_{0,3}$ be an algorithm in the alphabet A^{sa}_0. We shall say that $\lambda_{0,3}$ is a *regulator of convergence in itself* of the sequence of points $\lambda_{n,1}$, and we shall write [1)]

$$(\lambda_{0,3}\,\underline{\text{reg. conv}_{\mathfrak{M}}}\,\lambda_{n,1}),$$

if the condition $\mathfrak{G}$ is fulfilled.

It is obvious that a sequence of points of the space $\mathfrak{M}$ is a fundamental sequence if and only if a regulator of convergence in itself of this sequence is potentially realizable.

10.1.5. *If* $\lambda_{n,1}$ *is a sequence of points of the space* $\mathfrak{M}$, *then*

$$\exists X(X\,\underline{\lim_{\mathfrak{M}}}\,\lambda_{n,1}) \supset \lambda_{n,1} \in \underline{\text{fund. seq}_{\mathfrak{M}}}.$$

Proof. Let $\lambda_{n,1}$ be a sequence of points of the space $\mathfrak{M}$. Let us assume that

$$\exists X(X\,\underline{\lim_{\mathfrak{M}}}\,\lambda_{n,1}).$$

Let X be a point of the space $\mathfrak{M}$ such that $X\,\underline{\lim_{\mathfrak{M}}}\,\lambda_{n,1}$. Then

$$\exists\lambda_{0,2}\mathfrak{F}.$$

Let the algorithm $\lambda_{0,2}$ be such that condition $\mathfrak{F}$ is fulfilled. It is obvious that

$$\exists\lambda_{0,3}\forall k(\lambda_{0,3}(k) \simeq \lambda_{0,2}(k+1)).$$

Let the algorithm $\lambda_{0,3}$ be such that

$$\forall k(\lambda_{0,3}(k) \simeq \lambda_{0,2}(k+1)).$$

It is easily seen that $\lambda_{0,3}$ satisfies condition $\mathfrak{G}$. Hence $\exists\lambda_{0,3}\mathfrak{G}$. The theorem is proved.

A space $\mathfrak{M}$ is called almost complete if

$$\forall\lambda_{n,1}(\lambda_{n,1} \in \underline{\text{fund. seq}_{\mathfrak{M}}} \supset \exists X(X\,\underline{\lim_{\mathfrak{M}}}\,\lambda_{n,1})). \tag{5}$$

We note that the condition

$$\lambda_{n,1} \in \underline{\text{fund. seq}_{\mathfrak{M}}} \tag{6}$$

is equivalent to the condition

$$\lambda_{n,1} \in (\text{H} \to 0)_n \,\&\, \exists\lambda_{0,3}\mathfrak{G}. \tag{7}$$

Let us construct the constructive reformulation of formula (5) in the case where $\mathfrak{M}$ is a metric space and $\mathfrak{P}$ is a normal formula. In this case the formula

---

1) We shall permit the use, instead of the term "regulator of convergence in itself of the sequence of points $\lambda_{n,1}$", of the shorter term "regulator of convergence of the sequence of points $\lambda_{n,1}$". This abbreviation could lead to ambiguity if, along with regulators of convergence in itself, we also considered regulators of convergence to a given point of the space, defined in the natural way in the theory of limits. However, regulators of the second kind will not be considered in this book.

$$\lambda_{n,1} \in (H \to \theta)_n$$

is a normal formula. The condition (6) is equivalent to the condition

$$\exists \lambda_{0,3} \mathfrak{H}, \tag{8}$$

where

$$\mathfrak{H} \rightleftharpoons (\lambda_{n,1} \in (H \to \theta)_n \,\&\, \mathfrak{G}$$

Moreover, the formula $\mathfrak{H}$ is equivalent (on the basis of 4.4.2) to a normal formula. In addition, the formula

$$\exists X (X \underline{\lim}_{\mathfrak{M}} \lambda_{n,1}) \tag{9}$$

is equivalent to the formula

$$\exists t_{m,1} \lambda_{0,2} \mathfrak{R}, \tag{10}$$

where

$$\mathfrak{R} \rightleftharpoons ((t_{m,1} \in \theta) \,\&\, \mathbf{F}^X_{t_{m,1}} \llcorner \mathfrak{F} \lrcorner).$$

Moreover, the formula $\mathfrak{R}$ is equivalent (on the basis of 4.4.2) to a normal formula.

From what has been said it follows that in the case where $\mathfrak{M}$ is a metric space and $\mathfrak{P}$ is a normal formula, the construction of the constructive reformulation of the formula (5) is reduced to the construction of the constructive reformulation of the formula

$$\forall \lambda_{n,1} (\exists \lambda_{0,3} \mathfrak{H}^* \supset \exists t_{m,1} \lambda_{0,2} \mathfrak{R}^*), \tag{11}$$

where $\mathfrak{H}^*$ and $\mathfrak{R}^*$ are normal formulas equivalent (on the basis of 4.4.2) to the formulas $\mathfrak{H}$ and $\mathfrak{R}$ respectively.

Carrying out the constructive reformulation of formula (11) and making certain obvious transfomations on the basis of Theorems 2.1.1 and 2.1.3, we arrive at the formula

$$\exists \lambda_{n,2} \lambda_{0,4} \forall \lambda_{n,1} \lambda_{0,3} \left(\mathfrak{H}^* \supset H_1 \mathrel{\dot{\in}} t_m \,\&\, H_2 \mathrel{\dot{\in}} t_0 \,\&\, \mathbf{F}^{t_m,1,\lambda_{0,2}}_{H_1, \langle H_2 \rangle_0} \llcorner \mathfrak{R}^* \lrcorner \right), \tag{12}$$

where

$$H_1 \rightleftharpoons \lambda_{n,2} (\{\lambda_{n,1}\} \square \{\lambda_{0,3}\}), \quad H_2 \rightleftharpoons \lambda_{0,4} (\{\lambda_{n,1}\} \square \{\lambda_{0,3}\}).$$

If $\mathfrak{P}$ is not a normal formula, then the constructive problem exhibited in the constructive reformulation of condition (5) turns out to be more complicated than in the case considered above. The complexity has its source in the fact that the formulas obtained as a result of the constructive reformulation of the formulas $(\lambda_{n,1} \in (H \to \tilde{\theta})_n)$ and $(t_{m,1} \in \theta)$ are not normal formulas.

Now we return to the case where $\mathfrak{M}$ is a metric space and $\mathfrak{P}$ is a normal formula. Formula (12) is in this case the constructive reformulation of formula (5). From (12) it is evident that if $\mathfrak{M}$ is an almost complete metric space, then there is potentially realizable an algorithm $\lambda_{n,2}$ which constructs, for every fundamental sequence of points of the space and every regulator of convergence in itself of the given sequence, a point which is a limit of the given sequence. However, from the possibility of construction of such an algorithm it does not follow that an algorithm is realizable which, for any fundamental sequence, constructs (without using as a second initially given object a regulator of convergence in itself of the given fundamental sequence) a point which is a limit of the given sequence.

From what has been said above it follows that it is advisable to consider independently, first, fundamental sequences of points of the space $\mathfrak{M}$, and, second, pairs of objects in which the first term is a sequence of points of the space $\mathfrak{M}$ and the second term is a regulator of convergence in itself of the first term of the pair. Moreover, it is advisable to reduce the consideration of all such objects, by means of a definite method of coding, to the consideration of words in some alphabet. In the following section we shall introduce concepts and algorithms by means of which such a reduction can be carried out.

10.2. With the space $\mathfrak{M}$ given in the form of the list

$$\mathrm{A}_{\mathrm{m}},\ \mathfrak{P},\ \rho,$$

we associate a new elementary symbol, and we introduce a new alphabet obtained by adding this new elementary symbol to the alphabet A_n. Let us denote the new elementary symbol by $\odot$. The new alphabet $A_n \cup \{\odot\}$ is called the *alphabet of constructs in the space* $\mathfrak{M}$. Adding this alphabet to the given language and forming its union with every alphabet of the given language, we obtain a new language. In the general enumeration of the alphabets of this new language the alphabet $A_n \cup \{\odot\}$ has some index. We denote this index by the letter ψ. In accordance with this, the alphabet $A_n \cup \{\odot\}$ obtains the designation A_ψ.

We say that a word $t_{\psi,1}$ in the alphabet A_ψ is a *canonical word* in the alphabet A_ψ, and we shall write

$$(t_{\psi,1} \in \underline{\mathrm{can}}_\psi),$$

if $t_{\psi,1}$ is a word in the alphabet $\{0, |, \odot\}$ and contains one and only one ocurrence of the symbol $\odot$. We shall say that a word $t_{\psi,1}$ is a *meaningful word* in the alphabet A_ψ, and we shall write

$$(t_{\psi,1} \in \underline{\mathrm{mean}}_\psi),$$

if $t_{\psi,1}$ is a word in the alphabet A_n or a canonical word in the alphabet A_ψ.

Now we associate with every point of the space $\mathfrak{M}$ a definite canonical word in the alphabet A_ψ. First of all, we construct and fix an algorithm χ in the alphabet A_n^{sa} transforming any word Q in the alphabet A_n into the transcription of the normal algorithm in the alphabet A_n^{sa} defined by the schema

$$\begin{cases} \xi \to & (\xi \in A_n) \\ \to \cdot\, Q & \end{cases}$$

For any words $t_{n,1}$ and $t_{n,2}$ in the alphabet A_n, we have

$$\langle \chi(t_{n,1})\rangle_n (t_{n,2}) \doteq t_{n,1}.$$

In particular,

$$\forall X k (\langle \chi(X)\rangle_n (k) \doteq X),$$

and thus for any X the algorithm $\langle \chi(X)\rangle_n$ is an algorithm of type $(H \to \theta)_n$. We introduce another algorithm in the alphabet A_0^{sa} defined by the schema

$$\begin{cases} \xi \to & (\xi \in A_0) \\ \to \cdot\, 0 & . \end{cases}$$

We denote the transcription of this algorithm by Ъ. The algorithm $\langle Ъ\rangle_0$ transforms any natural number into 0, and therefore it is an algorithm of type $(H \to H)_0$.

Let us denote by χ_* the algorithm in the alphabet A_ψ^{sa} such that, for any word $t_{n,1}$ in the alphabet A_n,

$$\chi_*(t_{n,1}) \doteq \chi(t_{n,1}) \odot Ъ.$$

If X is a point of the space $\mathfrak{M}$, then the word $\chi_*(X)$ will be called the duplex image of the point X and will be denoted by $\hat{X}$.

We construct and fix concrete algorithms $\overline{\text{lef}}_\psi$ and $\overline{\text{rig}}_\psi$ in the alphabet A_ψ^{sa} such that, for any word $t_{\psi,1}$, the following conditions are fulfilled.

1) If $t_{\psi,1}$ is a canonical word in the alphabet A_ψ, then the algorithm $\overline{\text{lef}}_\psi$ (algorithm $\overline{\text{rig}}_\psi$) transforms $t_{\psi,2}$ into the word which is the left (respectively, right) wing of the unique occurrence of the symbol $\odot$ in the word $t_{\psi,1}$; in other words, for any words $t_{0,1}$ and $t_{0,2}$ in the alphabet A_0, we have:

$$\overline{\text{lef}}_\psi (t_{0,1} \odot t_{0,2}) \doteq t_{0,1}, \qquad \overline{\text{rig}}_\psi (t_{0,1} \odot t_{0,2}) \doteq t_{0,2};$$

2) If $t_{\psi,1}$ is a word in the alphabet A_n, then the algorithm $\overline{\text{lef}}_\psi$ (algorithm $\overline{\text{rig}}_\psi$) transforms the word $t_{\psi,1}$ into the same word into which $\overline{\text{lef}}_\psi$ (respectively, $\overline{\text{rig}}_\psi$) transforms the canonical word $\chi_*(t_{\psi,1})$, i.e.

$$\overline{\text{lef}}_\psi (t_{\psi,1}) \doteq \overline{\text{lef}}_\psi (\chi_*(t_{\psi,1})), \qquad \overline{\text{rig}}_\psi (t_{\psi,1}) \doteq \overline{\text{rig}}_\psi (\chi_*(t_{\psi,1}));$$

3) If $t_{\psi,1}$ is not a canonical word in the alphabet A_ψ, but contains the letter $\odot$, then the algorithms $\overline{\text{lef}}_\psi$ and $\overline{\text{rig}}_\psi$ transform $t_{\psi,1}$ into the transcription of the normal algorithm defined by the schema

$$\{ \to \cdot$$

Let H be any word in the alphabet A_ψ. We introduce the notation

$$\underline{H}_\psi \leftrightharpoons \langle \overline{\mathrm{lef}}_\psi (H) \rangle_n, \quad \overline{H}^\psi \leftrightharpoons \langle \overline{\mathrm{rig}}_\psi (H) \rangle_0.$$

The expression $\underline{H}_\psi$ denotes an algorithm in the alphabet A_n^{sa} and $\overline{H}^\psi$ denotes an algorithm in the alphabet A_0^{sa}. Moreover, if H is a word in the alphabet A_n, then $\underline{H}_\psi$ is an algorithm of type $(\mathrm{H} \to \theta)_n$ if and only if H is a point of the space $\mathfrak{M}$. If H is a point of the space $\mathfrak{M}$, then

$$\forall n (\underline{H}_\psi (n) \doteq H), \quad \forall n (\overline{H}^\psi (n) \doteq 0).$$

Let Θ be any individual term. We introduce the notation

$$\underline{\Theta}_\psi \leftrightharpoons \langle \overline{\mathrm{lef}}_\psi (\Theta) \rangle_n, \quad \overline{\Theta}^\psi \leftrightharpoons \langle \overline{\mathrm{rig}}_\psi (\Theta) \rangle_0.$$

This notation will be systematically employed in what follows.

We shall say that a word $t_{\psi,1}$ is a *one-sided canonical word* in the alphabet A_ψ, and we shall write

$$(t_{\psi,1} \in \underline{\text{one can}}_\psi),$$

if

$$t_{\psi,1} \in \underline{\mathrm{can}}_\psi \;\&\; \overline{\mathrm{rig}}_\psi (t_{\psi,1}) \doteq \Lambda.$$

We shall say that a word $t_{\psi,1}$ is a *one-sided meaningful word* in the alphabet A_ψ, and we shall write

$$(t_{\psi,1} \in \underline{\text{one mean}}_\psi),$$

if $t_{\psi,1}$ is a word in the alphabet A_n or a one-sided canonical word in the alphabet A_ψ.

With every meaningful word in the alphabet A_ψ we associate a definite one-sided meaningful word which we shall call the *principal part* of the given meaningful word. We construct and fix an algorithm $\overline{\mathrm{prin}}_\psi$ in the alphabet A_ψ^{sa} (the algorithm for isolating the principal part) such that, for any word $t_{\psi,1}$, the following conditions are satisfied:

1) if $t_{\psi,1}$ is a canonical word in the alphabet A_ψ, then

$$\overline{\mathrm{prin}}_\psi (t_{\psi,1}) \doteq \overline{\mathrm{lef}}_\psi (t_{\psi,1}) \odot;$$

2) if $t_{\psi,1}$ is a word in the alphabet A_n, then

$$\overline{\mathrm{prin}}_\psi (t_{\psi,1}) \doteq t_{\psi,1};$$

3) if $t_{\psi,1}$ is not a canonical word in the alphabet A_ψ, but contains the letter $\odot$, then the algorithm $\overline{\mathrm{prin}}_\psi$ is not applicable to $t_{\psi,1}$.

It is obvious that

$$\forall t_{\psi,1} (t_{\psi,1} \in \underline{\mathrm{mean}}_\psi \supset \overline{\mathrm{lef}}_\psi (\overline{\mathrm{prin}}_\psi (t_{\psi,1})) \doteq \overline{\mathrm{lef}}_\psi (t_{\psi,1})).$$

We shall say that a word $t_{\psi,1}$ is an *F-construct* in the space $\mathfrak{M}$, and we shall write

$$(t_{\psi,1} \in \underline{F\text{-const}_{\mathfrak{M}}}),$$

if $t_{\psi,1}$ is a one-sided meaningful word in the alphabet A_ψ and the algorithm $\underline{t_{\psi,1}}_\psi$ is a fundamental sequence of points of the space $\mathfrak{M}$.

The condition $(t_{\psi,1} \in \underline{F\text{-const}_{\mathfrak{M}}})$ can be expressed by the formula

$$t_{\psi,1} \in \underline{\text{one mean}}_\psi \; \& \; \underline{t_{\psi,1}}_\psi \in (\text{H} \to \theta)_n \; \& \; \exists \lambda_{0,1} (\lambda_{0,1} \, \underline{\text{reg. conv}_{\mathfrak{M}}} \, \underline{t_{\psi,1}}_\psi). \qquad (1)$$

Formula (1) is equivalent to the formula

$$\exists \lambda_{0,1} (\lambda_{0,1} \, \underline{\text{reg. conv}^{+}_{\mathfrak{M}}} \, \underline{t_{\psi,1}}_\psi),$$

where

$$(\lambda_{0,1} \, \underline{\text{reg. conv}^{+}_{\mathfrak{M}}} \, \underline{t_{\psi,1}}_\psi) \rightleftharpoons (t_{\psi,1} \in \underline{\text{one mean}}_\psi$$

$$\& \; \underline{t_{\psi,1}}_\psi \in (\text{H} \to \theta)_n \; \& \; \lambda_{0,1} \, \underline{\text{reg. conv}_{\mathfrak{M}}} \, \underline{t_{\psi,1}}_\psi).$$

We shall say that a word $t_{\psi,2}$ is an *FR-construct* in the space $\mathfrak{M}$, and we shall write[1)]

$$(t_{\psi,2} \in \underline{FR\text{-const}_{\mathfrak{M}}}),$$

if $t_{\psi,2}$ is a meaningful word in the alphabet A_ψ, the algorithm $\underline{t_{\psi,2}}_\psi$ is a sequence of points of the space $\mathfrak{M}$, and the algorithm $\overline{t_{\psi,2}}^\psi$ is a regulator of convergence in itself of the algorithm $\underline{t_{\psi,2}}_\psi$.

We remark that every point of the space $\mathfrak{M}$ is both an *F*-construct and an *FR*-construct in the space $\mathfrak{M}$. *FR*-constructs in the space $\mathfrak{M}$ will also be called duplexes in $\mathfrak{M}$ and we shall use the expression

$$(t_{\psi,2} \in \underline{\text{dup}_{\mathfrak{M}}})$$

as an expression equivalent to $(t_{\psi,2} \in \underline{FR\text{-const}_{\mathfrak{M}}})$.

The condition $(t_{\psi,2} \in \underline{\text{dup}_{\mathfrak{M}}})$ is expressed by the formula

$$t_{\psi,2} \in \underline{\text{mean}}_\psi \; \& \; \underline{t_{\psi,2}}_\psi \in (\text{H} \to \theta)_n \; \& \; \overline{t_{\psi,2}}^\psi \, \underline{\text{reg. conv}_{\mathfrak{M}}} \, \underline{t_{\psi,2}}_\psi. \qquad (2)$$

Now we note the following. The conditions

$$t_{\psi,1} \in \underline{\text{one mean}}_\psi, \quad t_{\psi,2} \in \underline{\text{mean}}_\psi$$

are algorithmically verifiable, and therefore they can be given by means of normal

1) We note another (less clumsy) variant of the terminology: instead of the terms "*F*-construct" and "*FR*-construct", the terms "construct" and "biconstruct" are suggested.

formulas. In addition, if $\mathfrak{P}$ is a normal formula, then the condition

$$\underline{t_{\psi,2_\psi}} \in (\text{H} \to \theta)_{\text{n}}$$

is also expressible by means of a normal formula.[1] Hence, if $\mathfrak{M}$ is a metric space and $\mathfrak{P}$ is a normal formula, then the formula (2) and the formula

$$\lambda_{0,1}\, \underline{\text{reg. con}^{+}_{\mathfrak{M}}}\, \underline{t_{\psi,1}}_{\psi}$$

are equivalent normal formulas.

10.3. We introduce now any two new restricted generic letters different from all previously introduced letters. We denote these new generic letters by $\mathfrak{v}$ and $\mathfrak{w}$. The formula

$$(t_{\psi,1} \in \underline{F\text{-const}}_{\mathfrak{M}}) \tag{1}$$

will be taken as the characterizing formula of the generic letter $\mathfrak{v}$ and F-constructs in the space $\mathfrak{M}$ will also be called *words of type* $\mathfrak{v}$. The formula

$$(t_{\psi,2} \in \underline{FR\text{-const}}_{\mathfrak{M}})$$

will be taken as the characterizing formula of the letter $\mathfrak{w}$ and FR-constructs (duplexes) in the space $\mathfrak{M}$ will also be called *words of type* $\mathfrak{w}$.

In accordance with the general convention accepted earlier, the individual variables

$$(\mathfrak{v}),\ (\mathfrak{v}\mathfrak{v}),\ (\mathfrak{v}\mathfrak{v}\mathfrak{v}),\ \ldots,$$

$$(\mathfrak{w}),\ (\mathfrak{w}\mathfrak{w}),\ (\mathfrak{w}\mathfrak{w}\mathfrak{w}),\ \ldots$$

will be denoted, respectively, by

$$\mathfrak{v}_1,\ \mathfrak{v}_2,\ \mathfrak{v}_3,\ \ldots,$$

$$\mathfrak{w}_1,\ \mathfrak{w}_2,\ \mathfrak{w}_3,\ \ldots.$$

For the sake of brevity, we also introduce the following notation:

$$\mathfrak{Q}_1 \rightleftharpoons (t_{\psi,1} \in \underline{F\text{-const}}_{\mathfrak{M}}), \qquad \mathfrak{Q}_2 \rightleftharpoons (t_{\psi,2} \in \underline{FR\text{-const}}_{\mathfrak{M}}).$$

Now we shall introduce two definitions which will play an important role in what follows.

We shall say that an algorithm $\lambda_{\psi,1}$ in the alphabet A_ψ^{sa} is an *algorithm of passage to the limit* in the space $\mathfrak{M}$ if, for any FR-construct $\mathfrak{w}_1$ in the space $\mathfrak{M}$,

$$\lambda_{\psi,1}(\mathfrak{w}_1) \overset{+}{\in} \theta \ \&\ \lambda_{\psi,1}(\mathfrak{w}_1)\ \underline{\text{lim}}_{\mathfrak{M}}\, \underline{\mathfrak{w}_1}_{\psi}.$$

---

1) This condition can be expressed by means of a normal formula, also in the case where $\mathfrak{P}$ is not a normal formula but is equivalent to a normal formula. (We note that the formula $\mathfrak{P}$ is equivalent to a normal formula if and only if $\tilde{\forall}(\neg\neg\mathfrak{P} \equiv \mathfrak{P})$.)

The space $\mathfrak{M}$ is called *complete* if an algorithm of passage to the limit in the space $\mathfrak{M}$ is potentially realizable.

It is easily seen that

10.3.1. *Every complete space is an almost complete space.*

From what was said at the end of §10.1, the following proposition is easily derivable.

10.3.2. *If $\mathfrak{M}$ is an almost complete metric space and $\mathfrak{P}$ is a normal formula, then $\mathfrak{M}$ is a complete space.*

If $\mathfrak{M}$ is a complete metric space and if, among all the algorithms in the alphabet A_ψ^{sa} which are algorithms of passage to the limit, we select and fix any one such algorithm (denoted by Lim), and if we consider the pair of objects consisting of the metric space $\mathfrak{M}$ and the algorithm Lim, then, for an object composed in this way, which it is natural to call a *constructive metric space with a fixed algorithm of passage to the limit*, one can construct two variants of the theory of limits: a predicate variant (as for any constructive metric space) the basis of which is the binary relation "$\underline{\text{lim}}_{\mathfrak{M}}$", and an algorithmic variant the basis of which is the algorithm Lim for constructing limits, considered on the set $\mathfrak{Q}_2$ (and not on the set $\mathfrak{Q}_1$!).

10.4. In this section we shall assume that $\mathfrak{M}$ is a metric space (i.e. that ρ is a function of type $(\theta\theta \to \text{Д})$). Basing ourselves on this assumption, we introduce in the set $\mathfrak{Q}_1$ a semimetric function ρ_1 and in the set $\mathfrak{Q}_2$ a metric function ρ_2, defining the algorithms ρ_1 and ρ_2 in the following way.

First of all, we construct algorithms α, β, and β_* in the alphabet A_ψ^{sa} such that, for any words $t_{\psi,1}$ and $t_{\psi,2}$ in the alphabet A_ψ, any natural number k, and any algorithms $\lambda_{0,1}$ and $\lambda_{0,2}$ in the alphabet A_0^{sa},

$$\alpha(t_{\psi,1}\square t_{\psi,2}\square k)\simeq\rho(\underbrace{t_{\psi,1}}_{\psi}(k)\square\underbrace{t_{\psi,2}}_{\psi}(k)),$$

$$\beta(\{\lambda_{0,1}\}\square\{\lambda_{0,2}\}\square k)\simeq\max(\lambda_{0,1}(k+2)\square\lambda_{0,2}(k+2)\square k+2),$$

$$\beta_*(t_{\psi,1}\square t_{\psi,2}\square k)\simeq\max(\overline{t_{\psi,1}}^{\psi}(k+2)\square\overline{t_{\psi,2}}^{\psi}(k+2)\square k+2).$$

It is obvious that

$$\beta_*(t_{\psi,1}\square t_{\psi,2}\square k)\simeq\beta(\{\overline{t_{\psi,1}}^{\psi}\}\square\{\overline{t_{\psi,2}}^{\psi}\}\square k).$$

Now we construct algorithms γ, δ, and δ_* in the alphabet A_ψ^{sa} such that, for any $t_{\psi,1}$, $t_{\psi,2}$, $\lambda_{0,1}$, $\lambda_{0,2}$, and k,

$$\gamma(t_{\psi,1}\Box t_{\psi,2})\overset{+}{\in} t_0,\qquad \delta(\{\lambda_{0,1}\}\Box\{\lambda_{0,2}\})\overset{+}{\in} t_0,\qquad \delta_*(t_{\psi,1}\Box t_{\psi,2})\overset{+}{\in} t_0,$$

$$\langle\gamma(t_{\psi,1}\Box t_{\psi,2})\rangle_2(k)\simeq \underline{\alpha(t_{\psi,1}\Box t_{\psi,2}\Box k)}\,(\overline{\alpha(t_{\psi,1}\Box t_{\psi,2}\Box k)}(k)),$$

$$\langle\delta(\{\lambda_{0,1}\}\Box\{\lambda_{0,2}\})\rangle_0(k)\simeq\beta(\{\lambda_{0,1}\}\Box\{\lambda_{0,2}\}\Box k),$$

$$\langle\delta_*(t_{\psi,1}\Box t_{\psi,2})\rangle_0(k)\simeq\beta_*(t_{\psi,1}\Box t_{\psi,2}\Box k).$$

We construct, finally, algorithms ρ_1 and ρ_2 in the alphabet A_ψ^{sa} such that, for any $t_{\psi,1}$ and $t_{\psi,2}$,

$$\rho_1(t_{\psi,1}\Box t_{\psi,2})\simeq\gamma(t_{\psi,1}\Box t_{\psi,2})\diamondsuit,$$

$$\rho_2(t_{\psi,1}\Box t_{\psi,2})\simeq\gamma(t_{\psi,1}\Box t_{\psi,2})\diamondsuit\,\delta_*(t_{\psi,1}\Box t_{\psi,2}).$$

We shall prove that

$$\forall\mathfrak{v}_1\mathfrak{v}_2(\rho_1(\mathfrak{v}_1\Box\mathfrak{v}_2)\overset{+}{\in}\underline{\text{real }F\text{-num}}),\qquad \forall\mathfrak{w}_1\mathfrak{w}_2(\rho_2(\mathfrak{w}_1\Box\mathfrak{w}_2)\overset{+}{\in}\underline{\text{real dup}}).$$

Eliminating the restricted variables in these formulas, we find that it suffices to prove the following assertions:

$$\forall t_{\psi,1}t_{\psi,2}(t_{\psi,1}\in\underline{F\text{-const}}_{\mathfrak{M}}\,\&\,t_{\psi,2}\in\underline{F\text{-const}}_{\mathfrak{M}}$$
$$\supset\rho_1(t_{\psi,1}\Box t_{\psi,2})\overset{+}{\in}\underline{\text{real }F\text{-num}}),\tag{3}$$

$$\forall t_{\psi,1}t_{\psi,2}(t_{\psi,1}\in\underline{\text{dup}}_{\mathfrak{M}}\,\&\,t_{\psi,2}\in\underline{\text{dup}}_{\mathfrak{M}}\supset\rho_2(t_{\psi,1}\Box t_{\psi,2})\overset{+}{\in}\underline{\text{real dup}}).\tag{4}$$

Assume the words $t_{\psi,1}$ and $t_{\psi,2}$ are such that $t_{\psi,1}\in\underline{F\text{-const}}_{\mathfrak{M}}$ and $t_{\psi,2}\in\underline{F\text{-const}}_{\mathfrak{M}}$. Then

$$\exists\lambda_{0,1}(\lambda_{0,1}\ \underline{\text{reg. conv}}\overset{+}{_{\mathfrak{M}}}\ \underline{t_{\psi,1}}_{\psi}),\qquad \exists\lambda_{0,2}(\lambda_{0,2}\ \underline{\text{reg. conv}}\overset{+}{_{\mathfrak{M}}}\ \underline{t_{\psi,2}}_{\psi}).$$

Assume the algorithms $\lambda_{0,1}$ and $\lambda_{0,2}$ are such that

$$\lambda_{0,1}\ \underline{\text{reg. conv}}\overset{+}{_{\mathfrak{M}}}\ \underline{t_{\psi,1}}_{\psi},\qquad \lambda_{0,2}\ \underline{\text{reg. conv}}\overset{+}{_{\mathfrak{M}}}\ \underline{t_{\psi,2}}_{\psi}.\tag{5}$$

We have

$$\gamma(t_{\psi,1}\Box t_{\psi,2})\overset{+}{\in} t_0$$

Hence $\rho_1(t_{\psi,1}\Box t_{\psi,2})\overset{+}{\in}\underline{\text{one can}}_3$. In addition, let k, m, and n be such that

$$m,\ n\geqslant\beta(\{\lambda_{0,1}\}\Box\{\lambda_{0,2}\}\Box k).\tag{6}$$

We introduce the notation

$$P_m\leftrightharpoons\alpha(t_{\psi,1}\Box t_{\psi,2}\Box m),\qquad P_n\leftrightharpoons\alpha(t_{\psi,1}\Box t_{\psi,2}\Box n).$$

We note that

$$P_m \simeq \rho(\underline{t_{\psi,1}}_{\psi}(m) \,\square\, \underline{t_{\psi,2}}_{\psi}(m)),$$

$$\underline{\rho_1(t_{\psi,1} \square t_{\psi,2})}(m) \simeq \underline{P_m}(\overline{P_m}(m)).$$

On the basis of 9.1.1, (5) and (6), we have

$$M(P_m - P_n) \leqslant \rho(\underline{t_{\psi,1}}_{\psi}(m) \square \underline{t_{\psi,1}}_{\psi}(n)) + \rho(\underline{t_{\psi,2}}_{\psi}(m) \square \underline{t_{\psi,2}}_{\psi}(n))$$
$$< 2^{-(k+2)} + 2^{-(k+2)} = 2^{-(k+1)}. \qquad (7)$$

In addition, noting that $m, n \geq k+2$, we obtain

$$M(P_m - \underline{P_m}(\overline{P_m}(m))) \leqslant 2^{-m} \leqslant 2^{-(k+2)}, \qquad (8)$$

$$M(P_n - \underline{P_n}(\overline{P_n}(n))) \leqslant 2^{-n} \leqslant 2^{-(k+2)}. \qquad (9)$$

Hence

$$M(\underline{\rho_1(t_{\psi,1} \square t_{\psi,2})}(m) - \underline{\rho_1(t_{\psi,1} \square t_{\psi,2})}(n)) < 2^{-k}.$$

Therefore the algorithm $\langle \delta(\{\lambda_{0,1}\} \square \{\lambda_{0,2}\}) \rangle_0$ is a regulator of convergence in itself of the sequence of rational numbers $\underline{\rho_1(t_{\psi,1} \square t_{\psi,2})}$. Hence

$$\exists \lambda_{0,3}(\lambda_{0,3} \ \underline{\text{reg. conv}} \ \underline{\rho_1(t_{\psi,1} \square t_{\psi,2})}).$$

Therefore $\rho_1(t_{\psi,1} \square t_{\psi,2}) \in \underline{\text{real } F\text{-num}}$. Proposition (3) is proved.

We note that the following proposition follows from the argument just given.

For any $\mathfrak{v}_1, \mathfrak{v}_2, \lambda_{0,1}, \lambda_{0,2}, k, m, n,$

$$\mathfrak{T} \,\&\, (m, n \geqslant R_k \supset M(\underline{\rho_1(\mathfrak{v}_1 \square \mathfrak{v}_2)}(m) - \underline{\rho_1(\mathfrak{v}_1 \square \mathfrak{v}_2)}(n)) < 2^{-k}, \qquad (10)$$

where
$$\mathfrak{T} \leftrightharpoons \lambda_{0,1} \ \underline{\text{reg. conv}_{\mathfrak{M}}} \ \underline{\mathfrak{v}_1}_{\psi} \ \& \ \lambda_{0,2} \ \underline{\text{reg. conv}_{\mathfrak{M}}} \ \underline{\mathfrak{v}_2}_{\psi},$$
$$R_k \leftrightharpoons \beta(\{\lambda_{0,1}\} \square \{\lambda_{0,2}\} \square k).$$

We proceed to the proof of proposition (4). Let words $t_{\psi,1}$ and $t_{\psi,2}$ be such that $t_{\psi,1} \in \underline{\text{dup}}_{\mathfrak{M}}$ and $t_{\psi,2} \in \underline{\text{dup}}_{\mathfrak{M}}$. Then $\rho_2(t_{\psi,1} \square t_{\psi,2}) \in \underline{\text{can}}_3$. In addition, let k, m, and n be such that

$$m, n \geqslant \beta_*(t_{\psi,1} \square t_{\psi,2} \square k). \qquad (11)$$

Then, preserving the meaning of the designations P_m and P_n, we can repeat (7) [on the basis of 9.1.1 and (11)], and then (8) and (9). We obtain as a result that

$$M(\underline{\rho_2(t_{\psi,1} \square t_{\psi,2})}(m) - \underline{\rho_2(t_{\psi,1} \square t_{\psi,2})}(n)) < 2^{-k}.$$

Hence the algorithm $\langle \delta_*(t_{\psi,1} \square t_{\psi,2}) \rangle_0$ is a regulator of convergence in itself of the sequence of rational numbers $\underline{\rho_2(t_{\psi,1} \square t_{\psi,2})}$. Hence

$\rho_2(t_{\psi,1} \square t_{\psi,2}) \overset{+}{\in} \underline{\text{real dup}}$. Proposition (4) is proved.

We note that from the given argument we can obtain the following proposition. *For any* $\mathfrak{w}_1, \mathfrak{w}_2, k, m, n$,

$$m, n \geqslant R_k^* \supset M(\underline{\rho_2(\mathfrak{w}_1 \square \mathfrak{w}_2)}(m) - \underline{\rho_2(\mathfrak{w}_1 \square \mathfrak{w}_2)}(n)) < 2^{-k}, \tag{12}$$

where

$$R_k^* \leftrightharpoons \beta_*(\mathfrak{w}_1 \square \mathfrak{w}_2 \square k).$$

We denote by ρ_0 the composition of the algorithms ρ and $\overline{\text{prin}}_3$, constructed in the form of a normal algorithm in the alphabet $A_{\mathfrak{n}}^{sa}$. We shall prove the following proposition.

10.4.1. *For any* $\mathfrak{v}_1, \mathfrak{v}_2, \lambda_{0,1}, \lambda_{0,2}, \mathfrak{w}_1, \mathfrak{w}_2, k$ *and* m,

$$\mathfrak{T} \,\&\, m \geqslant R_{k+1} \supset M(\rho_1(\mathfrak{v}_1 \square \mathfrak{v}_2) - \rho_0(\underline{\mathfrak{v}_1}_{\psi}(m) \square \underline{\mathfrak{v}_2}_{\psi}(m))) < 2^{-k}, \tag{13}$$

$$m \geqslant R_{k+1}^* \supset M(\rho_2(\mathfrak{w}_1 \square \mathfrak{w}_2) - \rho(\underline{\mathfrak{w}_1}_{\psi}(m) \square \underline{\mathfrak{w}_2}_{\psi}(m))) < 2^{-k}. \tag{14}$$

In fact, introducing the notation

$$A \leftrightharpoons \rho_1(\mathfrak{v}_1 \square \mathfrak{v}_2), \qquad B_m \leftrightharpoons \rho_0(\underline{\mathfrak{v}_1}_{\psi}(m) \square \underline{\mathfrak{v}_2}_{\psi}(m)),$$

we can write

$$M(A - B_m) \leqslant M(A - \underline{A}(m)) + M(\underline{A}(m) - B_m).$$

It follows from (10) that, for any $\mathfrak{v}_1, \mathfrak{v}_2, \lambda_{0,1}, \lambda_{0,2}, k$ and m,

$$\mathfrak{T} \,\&\, m \geqslant R_{k+1} \supset M(A - \underline{A}(m)) \leqslant 2^{-(k+1)}.$$

Further, noting that $B_m \doteq \overline{\text{prin}}_3(\alpha(\mathfrak{v}_1 \square \mathfrak{v}_2 \square m))$, we obtain, on the basis of (8),

$$M(\underline{A}(m) - B_m) \leqslant 2^{-m}.$$

Hence if $(\mathfrak{T} \,\&\, m \geq R_{k+1})$, then

$$M(A - B_m) \leqslant 2^{-(k+1)} + 2^{-(k+3)} < 2^{-k}.$$

Proposition (13) has been proved. In a similar way, using (12) and (8) one proves (14).

We construct algorithms $\mathfrak{U}_1$ and $\mathfrak{U}_2$ in the alphabet A_{ψ}^{sa} such that, for any $t_{\psi,1}, t_{\psi,2}$ and m,

$$\mathfrak{U}_1(t_{\psi,1} \square t_{\psi,2}) \overset{+}{\in} t_0, \qquad \langle \mathfrak{U}_1(t_{\psi,1} \square t_{\psi,2}) \rangle_3(m) \simeq \rho_0(\underline{t_{\psi,1}}_{\psi}(m) \square \underline{t_{\psi,2}}_{\psi}(m)),$$

$$\mathfrak{U}_2(t_{\psi,1} \square t_{\psi,2}) \overset{+}{\in} t_0, \qquad \langle \mathfrak{U}_2(t_{\psi,1} \square t_{\psi,2}) \rangle_3(m) \simeq \rho(\underline{t_{\psi,1}}_{\psi}(m) \square \underline{t_{\psi,2}}_{\psi}(m)).$$

It is obvious that

$$\forall \mathfrak{v}_1\mathfrak{v}_2 (\langle \mathfrak{U}_1(\mathfrak{v}_1 \square \mathfrak{v}_2)\rangle_3 \in (\text{н} \to \text{в})_3),$$
$$\forall \mathfrak{w}_1\mathfrak{w}_2 (\langle \mathfrak{U}_2(\mathfrak{w}_1 \square \mathfrak{w}_2)\rangle_3 \in (\text{н} \to \text{д})_3).$$

The following proposition is derived from (13) and (14) in obvious fashion.

10.4.2. *For any* $\mathfrak{v}_1$, $\mathfrak{v}_2$, $\mathfrak{w}_1$ *and* $\mathfrak{w}_2$,

$$\rho_1(\mathfrak{v}_1 \square \mathfrak{v}_2) \ \underline{\lim}_{\text{в}} \ \langle \mathfrak{U}_1(\mathfrak{v}_1 \square \mathfrak{v}_2)\rangle_3,$$
$$\rho_2(\mathfrak{w}_1 \square \mathfrak{w}_2) \ \underline{\lim}_{\text{д}} \ \langle \mathfrak{U}_2(\mathfrak{w}_1 \square \mathfrak{w}_2)\rangle_3.$$

Here the letter "В" plays the role of a designation of the semimetric space of all real F-numbers, and the letter "Д" plays the role of a designation of the metric space of all real FR-numbers.

The estimates given above allow us to prove without difficulty the next two propositions.

10.4.3. *The algorithm* ρ_1 *is a semimetric function in the set* $\mathfrak{Q}_1$. *The list*

$$\text{A}_\psi, \ \mathfrak{Q}_1, \ \rho_1 \tag{15}$$

is a semimetric space, and the semimetric space

$$\text{A}_m, \ \mathfrak{P}, \ \rho_0$$

is a subspace of the space (15). *The set* $\mathfrak{P}$ *is almost dense in the space* (15).

10.4.4. *The algorithm* ρ_2 *is a metric function in the set* $\mathfrak{Q}_2$. *The list*

$$\text{A}_\psi, \ \mathfrak{Q}_2, \ \rho_2 \tag{16}$$

is a metric space, and the metric space

$$\text{A}_m, \ \mathfrak{P}, \ \rho$$

(denoted above by the letter $\mathfrak{M}$*) is a subspace of the metric space* (16). *The set* $\mathfrak{P}$ *is dense in the space* (16), *and as an algorithm approximating the space* (16) *by means of the set* $\mathfrak{P}$ *(cf.* §9.4), *one can take the algorithm transforming any word of the form* $\mathfrak{w}_1 \square k$, *where* $\mathfrak{w}_1$ *is a point of the space* (16) *and* k *is a natural number, into the word*

$$\underset{\llcorner\!\lrcorner_\psi}{\mathfrak{w}_1}(\overline{\mathfrak{w}_1}^{\psi}(k+1)).$$

We denote the semimetric space (15) by $\mathfrak{M}_1$, and the metric space (16) by $\mathfrak{M}_2$. Now let us prove the following theorem.

10.4.5. *The semimetric space* $\mathfrak{M}_1$ *is an almost complete space.*

Proof. Let $\lambda_{\psi,1}$ be a fundamental sequence of points of the space $\mathfrak{M}_1$. Then, first,

$$\forall k\,(\lambda_{\psi,1}(k) \overset{+}{\in} \underline{F\text{-}\mathrm{const}}_{\mathfrak{M}}) \tag{17}$$

and second,

$$\exists \lambda_{0,1}\,(\lambda_{0,1}\,\underline{\mathrm{reg.\ conv}}_{\mathfrak{M}_1}\,\lambda_{\psi,1}). \tag{18}$$

From (17) it follows that

$$\forall k \exists \lambda_{0,4}\,(\lambda_{0,4}\,\underline{\mathrm{reg.\ conv}}_{\mathfrak{M}}\,\underbrace{\lambda_{\psi,1}(k)}_{\psi})$$

and therefore, on the basis of 2.4.3,

$$\exists \lambda_{0,3} \forall k\,(\lambda_{0,3}(k) \overset{+}{\in} t_0 \,\&\, \langle \lambda_{0,3}(k)\rangle_0\,\underline{\mathrm{reg.\ conv}}_{\mathfrak{M}}\,\underbrace{\lambda_{\psi,1}(k)}_{\psi}).$$

Let $\lambda_{0,1}$ be a regulator of convergence in itself of the sequence $\lambda_{\psi,1}$, and let $\lambda_{0,3}$ be an algorithm satisfying the condition

$$\forall k\,(\lambda_{0,3}(k) \overset{+}{\in} t_0 \,\&\, \langle \lambda_{0,3}(k)\rangle_0\,\underline{\mathrm{reg.\ conv}}_{\mathfrak{M}}\,\underbrace{\lambda_{\psi,1}(k)}_{\psi}). \tag{19}$$

Then

$$\forall kmn\,(m,\, n \geqslant \lambda_{0,1}(k) \supset \rho_1(\lambda_{\psi,1}(m) \square \lambda_{\psi,1}(n)) < 2^{-k}). \tag{20}$$

We construct an algorithm $\lambda_{\mathrm{n},2}$ such that, for any k,

$$\lambda_{\mathrm{n},2}(k) \simeq \underbrace{\lambda_{\psi,1}(k)}_{\psi}\,(\langle \lambda_{0,3}(k)\rangle_0(k)).$$

Let us introduce the notation

$$H \leftrightharpoons \max\,(\beta(\lambda_{0,3}(m) \square \lambda_{0,3}(n) \square k+3) \square \langle \lambda_{0,3}(m)\rangle_0(m) \square \langle \lambda_{0,3}(n)\rangle_0(n)).$$

From (13) it follows that for any k, m and n,

$$\rho_0(\lambda_{\mathrm{n},2}(m) \square \lambda_{\mathrm{n},2}(n)) \leqslant \rho_0(\lambda_{\mathrm{n},2}(m) \square \underbrace{\lambda_{\psi,1}(m)}_{\psi}\,(H))$$

$$+\rho_0(\underbrace{\lambda_{\psi,1}(m)}_{\psi}\,(H) \square \underbrace{\lambda_{\psi,1}(n)}_{\psi}\,(H)) + \rho_0(\underbrace{\lambda_{\psi,1}(n)}_{\psi}\,(H) \square \lambda_{\mathrm{n},2}(n))$$

$$< 2^{-m} + \rho_1(\lambda_{\psi,1}(m) \square \lambda_{\psi,1}(n)) + 2^{-(k+2)} + 2^{-n}.$$

Hence, if $m,\, n \geq \max\,(\lambda_{0,1}(k+2) \square k+2)$, then

$$\rho_0(\lambda_{\mathrm{n},2}(m) \square \lambda_{\mathrm{n},2}(n)) < 2^{-(k+2)} + 2^{-(k+2)} + 2^{-(k+2)} + 2^{-(k+2)} = 2^{-k}.$$

In addition,

$$\rho_0(\lambda_{\mathrm{n},2}(m) \square \lambda_{\mathrm{n},2}(n)) = \overline{\mathrm{prin}_3}\,(\rho(\lambda_{\mathrm{n},2}(m) \square \lambda_{\mathrm{n},2}(n))).$$

Hence

$$m,\, n \geqslant \lambda_{0,2}(k) \supset \rho(\lambda_{\mathrm{n},2}(m) \square \lambda_{\mathrm{n},2}(n)) < 2^{-k}, \tag{21}$$

where $\lambda_{0,2}$ is an algorithm in the alphabet A_0^{sa} such that

$$\forall k(\lambda_{0,2}(k) \simeq \max(\lambda_{0,1}(k+2)\square k+2)).$$

From (21) it follows that the word

$$\{\lambda_{n,2}\}\odot \tag{22}$$

is a point of the space $\mathfrak{M}_1$. We denote this point by the letter G and we shall prove that

$$G \ \underline{\lim}_{\mathfrak{M}_1} \lambda_{\psi,1}.$$

More precisely, we shall prove that, for any k and n,

$$n \geqslant \lambda_{0,2}(k+2) \supset \rho_1(G\square\lambda_{\psi,1}(n)) < 2^{-k}. \tag{23}$$

In fact, assume $n \geq \lambda_{0,2}(k+2)$. We introduce the notation

$$Q \leftrightharpoons \max(\beta(\{\lambda_{0,2}\}\square\lambda_{0,3}(n)\ \square k+2)\square\lambda_{0,2}(k+2)\square\langle\lambda_{0,3}(n)\rangle_0(n)).$$

We have

$$Q \geqslant \beta(\{\lambda_{0,2}\}\square\lambda_{0,3}(n)\square k+2), \quad Q \geqslant \lambda_{0,2}(k+2),$$
$$Q \geqslant \langle\lambda_{0,3}(n)\rangle_0(n), \quad n \geqslant k+4.$$

Hence, using (13), we obtain

$$\rho_1(G\square\lambda_{\psi,1}(n)) < \rho_0(\underline{G}_{\psi}(Q)\square\underline{\lambda_{\psi,1}(n)}_{\psi}(Q)) + 2^{-(k+1)}$$

$$\leqslant \rho_0(\lambda_{n,2}(Q)\square\lambda_{n,2}(n)) + \rho_0(\lambda_{n,2}(n)\square\underline{\lambda_{\psi,1}(n)}_{\psi}(Q)) + 2^{-(k+1)}$$

$$< 2^{-(k+2)} + \rho_0(\underline{\lambda_{\psi,1}(n)}_{\psi}(\langle\lambda_{0,3}(n)\rangle_0(n))\square\underline{\lambda_{\psi,1}(n)}_{\psi}(Q)) + 2^{-(k+1)}$$

$$< 2^{-(k+2)} + 2^{-n} + 2^{-(k+1)} < 2^{-k}.$$

Proposition (23) has been proved. Hence

$$\exists\mathfrak{v}_1(\mathfrak{v}_1 \ \underline{\lim}_{\mathfrak{M}_1} \lambda_{\psi,1}).$$

Theorem 10.4.5 is proved.

Remark. For any point $\mathfrak{v}_1$ of the space $\mathfrak{M}_1$, the algorithm $\underline{\mathfrak{v}_1}_{\psi}$ is a fundamental sequence of points of the space $\mathfrak{M}$, and therefore a fundamental sequence of points of the space $\mathfrak{M}_1$. It is not difficult to prove that

$$\forall\mathfrak{v}_1(\mathfrak{v}_1 \ \underline{\lim}_{\mathfrak{M}_1} \underline{\mathfrak{v}_1}_{\psi}).$$

Let us denote by $\mathfrak{H}$ the algorithm in the alphabet A_{ψ}^{sa} transforming every word $c_{0,1}$ in the alphabet A_0 into the word $c_{0,1}\odot$. From what has been said above the next proposition follows.

For any algorithm $\lambda_{\psi,1}$ which is a fundamental sequence of points of the space $\mathfrak{M}_1$ and is such that for every k the word $\lambda_{\psi,1}(k)$ is a point of the space $\mathfrak{M}$, the algorithm $\mathfrak{H}$ transforms the transcription of the algorithm $\lambda_{\psi,1}$ into the point of the space $\mathfrak{M}_1$ which is the limit of the sequence $\lambda_{\psi,1}$ in the space $\mathfrak{M}_1$.

We note that we could use (in implicit form) the algorithm $\mathfrak{H}$ to extend the arithmetic operations on rational numbers to real F-numbers, taking the space of all rational numbers to be $\mathfrak{M}$.

We emphasize that $\mathfrak{H}$ plays the role of an algorithm for constructing limits only for those fundamental sequences of points of the space $\mathfrak{M}_1$ which are at the same time sequences of points of the space $\mathfrak{M}$.

We proceed now to the consideration of the metric space $\mathfrak{M}_2$. For the construction of FR-constructs in $\mathfrak{M}_2$, we introduce a new alphabet $A_\psi \cup \{\circledcirc\}$. We denote the ordinal number of this alphabet by the letter γ. We construct algorithms $\mathfrak{C}$ and $\mathfrak{E}$ in the alphabet A_γ^{sa} such that, for any word $t_{\gamma,1}$ in the alphabet A_γ and any natural number k,

$$\mathfrak{C}(t_{\gamma,1}) \overset{+}{\in} t_0, \qquad \mathfrak{E}(t_{\gamma,1}) \overset{+}{\in} t_0,$$

$$\langle \mathfrak{C}(t_{\gamma,1}) \rangle_{\text{п}}(k) \simeq \underbrace{B(k)}_{\psi} (\overline{B(k)}^{\psi}(k)),$$

$$\langle \mathfrak{E}(t_{\gamma,1}) \rangle_0(k) \simeq \max(D(k+2) \square k+2),$$

where

$$B \leftrightharpoons \underbrace{t_{\gamma,1}}_{\gamma}, \qquad D \leftrightharpoons \overline{t_{\gamma,1}}^{\gamma}.$$

In addition, we construct an algorithm $\mathrm{Lim}_{\mathfrak{M}_2}$ in the alphabet A_γ^{sa} such that, for any word $t_{\gamma,1}$ in the alphabet A_γ,

$$\mathrm{Lim}_{\mathfrak{M}_2}(t_{\gamma,1}) \simeq \mathfrak{C}(t_{\gamma,1}) \odot \mathfrak{E}(t_{\gamma,1}).$$

The role of the algorithm $\mathrm{Lim}_{\mathfrak{M}_2}$ is made clear by the following theorem.

10.4.6. *The metric space $\mathfrak{M}_2$ is a complete space. Moreover, the algorithm $\mathrm{Lim}_{\mathfrak{M}_2}$ constructed above is an algorithm of passage to the limit in $\mathfrak{M}_2$.*

Proof. Let $t_{\gamma,1}$ be any FR-construct in $\mathfrak{M}_2$. Then B is a fundamental sequence of points of the space $\mathfrak{M}_2$ and D is a regulator of convergence in itself of this sequence. Hence

$$\forall kmn\,(m,\ n \geqslant D(k) \supset \rho_2(B(m) \square B(n)) < 2^{-k}).$$

We introduce the notation

$$S \rightleftharpoons \max(\beta_*(B(m) \square B(n) \square k+3) \square \overline{B(m)}^{\psi}(m) \square \overline{B(n)}^{\psi}(n)),$$

$$C \rightleftharpoons \langle \mathfrak{C}(t_{\gamma,1}) \rangle_n, \qquad E \rightleftharpoons \langle \mathfrak{C}(t_{\gamma,1}) \rangle_0.$$

On the basis of (14) we have, for any k, m and n,

$$\rho(C(m) \square C(n)) \leqslant \rho(C(m) \square \underline{B(m)}_{\psi}(S))$$

$$+\rho(\underline{B(m)}_{\psi}(S) \square \underline{B(n)}_{\psi}(S)) + \rho(\underline{B(n)}_{\psi}(S) \square C(n))$$

$$< 2^{-m} + \rho_2(B(m) \square B(n)) + 2^{-(k+2)} + 2^{-n}.$$

Hence, if $m, n \geq \max(D(k+2) \square k+2)$, then

$$\rho(C(m) \square C(n)) < 2^{-(k+2)} + 2^{-(k+2)} + 2^{-(k+2)} + 2^{-(k+2)} = 2^{-k}.$$

The word

$$\{C\} \odot \{E\}$$

is a point of the space $\mathfrak{M}_2$. We denote this point by the letter T and we shall prove that

$$T \underline{\lim}_{\mathfrak{M}_2} B.$$

More precisely, we shall prove that, for any k and n,

$$n \geqslant E(k+2) \supset \rho_2(T \square B(n)) < 2^{-k}. \tag{24}$$

In fact, assume that $n \geq E(k+2)$. We introduce the notation

$$Q^* \rightleftharpoons \max(\beta_*(T \square B(n) \square k+2) \square E(k+2) \square \overline{B(n)}^{\psi}(n)).$$

We have

$$Q^* \geqslant \beta_*(T \square B(n) \square k+2), \qquad Q^* \geqslant E(k+2),$$

$$Q^* \geqslant \overline{B(n)}^{\psi}(n), \qquad n \geqslant k+4.$$

Hence, using (14), we obtain

$$\rho_2(T \square B(n)) < \rho(\underline{T}_{\psi}(Q^*) \square \underline{B(n)}_{\psi}(Q^*)) + 2^{-(k+1)}$$

$$\leqslant \rho(C(Q^*) \square C(n)) + \rho(C(n) \square \underline{B(n)}_{\psi}(Q^*)) + 2^{-(k+1)}$$

$$< 2^{-(k+2)} + \rho(\underline{B(n)}_{\psi}(\overline{B(n)}^{\psi}(n)) \square \underline{B(n)}_{\psi}(Q^*)) + 2^{-(k+1)}$$

$$< 2^{-(k+2)} + 2^{-n} + 2^{-(k+1)} < 2^{-k}.$$

Proposition (24) is proved. Hence Theorem 10.4.6 is also proved.

We agree to call the algorithm $\mathrm{Lim}_{\mathfrak{M}_2}$ *the standard algorithm of passage to the limit* in the space $\mathfrak{M}_2$.

Remark 1. For any point $\mathfrak{w}_1$ of the space $\mathfrak{M}_2$, the algorithm $\underline{\mathfrak{w}_1}_{\psi}$ is a sequence of points of the space $\mathfrak{M}$, and therefore a sequence of points of the space $\mathfrak{M}_2$, and the algorithm $\overline{\mathfrak{w}_1}^{\psi}$ is a regulator of convergence in itself of this sequence in the space $\mathfrak{M}$ and therefore in the space $\mathfrak{M}_2$. From this it follows that the word

$$\{\underline{\mathfrak{w}_1}_{\psi}\} \circledcirc \{\overline{\mathfrak{w}_1}^{\psi}\}$$

is an *FR*-construct in the space $\mathfrak{M}_2$. It is not difficult to prove that

$$\forall \mathfrak{w}_1 (\mathfrak{w}_1 \underset{\rho_2}{=} \mathrm{Lim}_{\mathfrak{M}_2} (\{\underline{\mathfrak{w}_1}_{\psi}\} \circledcirc \{\overline{\mathfrak{w}_1}^{\psi}\})).$$

Remark 2. The proof of Theorem 10.4.6 gives an algorithm which, for every fundamental sequence of points of the space $\mathfrak{M}_2$ and every regulator of convergence in itself of the given sequence, constructs the point of the space $\mathfrak{M}_2$ which is the limit of the given sequence. From the proof of 10.4.6 it is also clear how one can construct an algorithm which, for every fundamental sequence of points of the space $\mathfrak{M}_2$, constructs a point of the space $\mathfrak{M}_1$ which is the limit in the space $\mathfrak{M}_1$ of that sequence of points of the space $\mathfrak{M}_1$ which is the composition of two algorithms: the algorithm providing the given fundamental sequence of points of the space $\mathfrak{M}_2$, and the algorithm $\overline{\mathrm{prin}}_{\psi}$. As the algorithm constructing, for every fundamental sequence of points of the space $\mathfrak{M}_2$, the required point of the space $\mathfrak{M}_1$, one can take the algorithm Ψ transforming the transcription of any algorithm $\lambda_{\psi,1}$ into the word

$$P(\{\lambda_{\psi,1}\}) \bigcirc,$$

where P is an algorithm of type $(t_0 \to t_0)_0$ such that

$$\forall \lambda_{\psi,1} k (\langle P(\{\lambda_{\psi,1}\}) \rangle_n (k) \simeq \underline{\lambda_{\psi,1}(k)}_{\psi} (\overline{\lambda_{\psi,1}(k)}^{\psi} (k))).$$

However, we do not have at our disposal any algorithm which would construct, for any fundamental sequence of points of the space $\mathfrak{M}_2$ (without using as a second initially given object a regulator of convergence in itself of the fundamental sequence), a point of the space $\mathfrak{M}_2$ which would be the limit in $\mathfrak{M}_2$ of the given fundamental sequence.[1)]

---

1) Recently G. E. Minc has proved that there can be no such algorithm, if $\mathfrak{M}$ has at least two different points. *Translator's note.* Published in G. E. Minc, *On predicate and operator variants of the formation of the theories of constructive mathematics*, Trudy Mat. Inst. Steklov. 72 (1964), 383–436. (Russian) MR 33 #2543.

The proof of Theorem 10.4.5 has a different character. It does not give us an algorithm which constructs, for any fundamental sequence of points of the space $\mathfrak{M}_1$ and any regulator of convergence in itself of the given sequence, a point in the space $\mathfrak{M}_1$ which is a limit in $\mathfrak{M}_1$ of the given sequence. For the construction of the desired point, one draws upon, instead of a regulator of convergence in itself of the given sequence $\lambda_{\psi,1}$, a different initially given object, namely the algorithm $\lambda_{0,3}$ transforming every natural number k into the transcription of a regulator of convergence in itself of the algorithm $\underline{\lambda_{\psi,1}(k)}_{\psi}$.

Let us introduce some definitions.

We shall say that a semimetric space $\mathfrak{B}$ is an *F-completion* of the metric space $\mathfrak{M}$ if the following conditions are fulfilled: 1) the semimetric space $\mathrm{A}_{\mathfrak{m}}$, $\mathfrak{P}$, ρ_0 is a subspace of the space $\mathfrak{B}$; 2) the set $\mathfrak{P}$ is almost dense in $\mathfrak{B}$; and 3) $\mathfrak{B}$ is an almost complete space. The semimetric space $\mathfrak{M}_1$ will be called *the standard F-completion* of the space $\mathfrak{M}$.

We shall say that a metric space $\mathfrak{D}$ is an *FR-completion* of the metric space $\mathfrak{M}$ if the following conditions are fulfilled: 1) the metric space $\mathfrak{M}$ is a subspace of the space $\mathfrak{D}$; 2) the set $\mathfrak{P}$ is dense in $\mathfrak{D}$; and 3) $\mathfrak{D}$ is a complete space. The metric space $\mathfrak{M}_2$ will be called *the standard FR-completion* of the space $\mathfrak{M}$.

The next theorem follows immediately from 10.4.3–10.4.6.

10.4.7. *For any metric space, F-completions and FR-completions are potentially realizable.*

We note also (without proof) the following theorem.

10.4.8. *For any FR-completion $\mathfrak{D}$ of the metric space $\mathfrak{M}$, there are potentially realizable an isometric mapping $\mathfrak{F}$ of the space $\mathfrak{D}$ onto $\mathfrak{M}_2$, transforming any point of the set into an equal (with respect to the metric ρ_2) point of the space $\mathfrak{M}_2$, and a mapping of the space $\mathfrak{M}_2$ onto $\mathfrak{D}$ inverse to the mapping $\mathfrak{F}$.*

As a result of the construction of an F-completion of a metric space we obtain a semimetric space, and therefore we go outside the theory of constructive metric spaces. In the rest of this book we shall not consider F-constructs in metric spaces and F-completions of metric spaces. The principal objects of study will be FR-constructs and FR-completions of metric spaces.

However, we note that many theorems about F-constructs and F-completions of metric spaces are automatically obtained from corresponding theorems about FR-constructs and FR-completions with the help of the algorithm for eliminating restricted variables and the algorithm for exhibiting constructive problems. The results of applying these algorithms to propositions about F-constructs are in many cases easily translated into equivalent propositions about FR-constructs. The transformations considered in the first chapter of certain propositions about real F-numbers into equivalent propositions about real FR-numbers are examples of such translations.

In the following theorems 10.4.9 and 10.4.10, as in the preceding theorems of this section, we start from the assumptions introduced at the beginning of §9.2 and the beginning of §10.4, and we use the notation introduced in §9.2 and in succeeding sections. In addition, assuming that k denotes a given positive integer, we introduce a new elementary symbol $\boxed{K}$ and a new alphabet $A_0 \cup \{\boxed{K}\}$, and, with respect to this new symbol and new alphabet, we repeat everything that was said in §9.3 with respect to the symbol $\boxed{K}$ and the alphabet $A_0 \cup \{\boxed{K}\}$, with the following changes: the index of the alphabet $A_0 \cup \{\boxed{K}\}$ will be denoted by π'; the index of the alphabet equal to the union of the alphabets A_ψ and $A_{\widetilde{\mathfrak{m}}}$ will be denoted by η'; we replace the letters $\mathfrak{m}$, π, η, $\mathfrak{M}$, θ and the symbol $\boxed{K}$ by the expressions ψ, π', η', $\mathfrak{M}_2$, $\mathfrak{w}$, and $\boxed{K}$; and replace the terms

$$\underline{\text{one ciph}}_k,\ \underline{\text{comp. ciph}}_k,\ \underline{\text{reg. unif. cont}}_k$$

by the terms

$$\underline{\text{one ciph}}'_k,\ \underline{\text{comp. ciph}}'_k,\ \underline{\text{reg. unif. cont}}'_k.$$

We shall base ourselves also on the following definitions.

Let $\lambda_{\eta,1}$ be an everywhere-defined k-ary operator from $\mathfrak{M}$ into $\widetilde{\mathfrak{M}}$, and let $\lambda_{\eta',1}$ be an everywhere-defined k-ary operator from $\mathfrak{M}_2$ into $\widetilde{\mathfrak{M}}$. We shall say that $\lambda_{\eta',1}$ is a *k-ary extension* of the operator $\lambda_{\eta,1}$ on the space $\mathfrak{M}_2$, and we shall write

$$(\lambda_{\eta',1}\ \underline{\text{ext. op}}_{k,\,\mathfrak{M}_2}\ \lambda_{\eta,1}),$$

if

$$\forall \theta_1 \ldots \theta_k (\lambda_{\eta',1}(\theta_1 \square \ldots \square \theta_k) \underset{\tilde{\rho}}{=} \lambda_{\eta,1}(\theta_1 \square \ldots \square \theta_k)).$$

Let $t_{\pi,1}$ be a complete cipher (one-sided cipher) of an everywhere-defined uniformly continuous k-ary operator from $\mathfrak{M}$ into $\widetilde{\mathfrak{M}}$. We shall say that the word $t_{\pi',1}$ is a *k-ary extension* of the cipher $t_{\pi,1}$ on the space $\mathfrak{M}_2$, and we shall write

$$(t_{\pi',1}\ \underline{\text{ext. ciph}}_{k,\,\mathfrak{M}_2}\ t_{\pi,1}),$$

if $t_{\pi',1}$ is a complete cipher (respectively, one-sided cipher) of an everywhere-defined uniformly continuous k-ary operator from $\mathfrak{M}_2$ into $\tilde{\mathfrak{M}}$ and the operator $\underline{t_{\pi',1}}_{\pi'}$ is a k-ary extension on $\mathfrak{M}_2$ of the k-ary operator $\underline{t_{\pi,1}}_{\pi}$.

We agree to denote the ordinal number of the alphabet $A_0 \cup \{\boxed{K}, \boxed{K}\}$ by π''

10.4.9. *If* $\tilde{\mathfrak{M}}$ *is a complete metric space, then one can construct an algorithm* $\lambda_{\pi'',1}$ *in the alphabet* $A^{sa}_{\pi''}$ *such that, for any word* $t_{\pi,1}$ *in the alphabet* A_{π},

$$t_{\pi,1} \in \underline{\text{comp. ciph}}_k \supset \lambda_{\pi'',1}(t_{\pi,1}) \ \underline{\text{ext. 1 ciph}}_{k,\mathfrak{M}_2} t_{\pi,1}.$$

Proof. Assume that $\tilde{\mathfrak{M}}$ is a complete metric space. Then an algorithm of passage to the limit in $\tilde{\mathfrak{M}}$ is potentially realizable. Let Lim be an algorithm of passage to the limit in $\tilde{\mathfrak{M}}$. On the basis of the algorithm Lim we shall construct the desired algorithm.

First of all, we construct algorithms $\mathfrak{S}$ and $\mathfrak{T}$ in the alphabet $A^{sa}_{\psi} \cup \{\boxed{K}\}$ such that, for any words $t_{\pi,1}, t_{\psi,1}, \cdots, t_{\psi,k}$ and any natural numbers m and l,

$$\mathfrak{S}(t_{\pi,1} \square t_{\psi,1} \square \ldots \square t_{\psi,k}) \overset{+}{\in} t_0, \qquad \mathfrak{T}(t_{\pi,1} \square t_{\psi,1} \square \ldots \square t_{\psi,k}) \overset{+}{\in} t_0,$$

$$\langle \mathfrak{S}(t_{\pi,1} \square t_{\psi,1} \square \ldots \square t_{\psi,k}) \rangle_{\tilde{\pi}}(m) \simeq \underline{t_{\pi,1}}_{\pi}(\underline{t_{\psi,1}}_{\psi}(m) \square \ldots \square \underline{t_{\psi,k}}_{\psi}(m)),$$

$$\langle \mathfrak{T}(t_{\pi,1} \square t_{\psi,1} \square \ldots \square t_{\psi,k}) \rangle_0(l) \simeq \max(\overline{t_{\psi,1}}^{\psi}(\overline{t_{\pi,1}}^{\pi}(l)) \square \ldots \square \overline{t_{\psi,k}}^{\psi}(\overline{t_{\pi,1}}^{\pi}(l))).$$

Let us introduce the notation

$$P \rightleftharpoons \mathfrak{S}(t_{\pi,1} \square t_{\psi,1} \square \ldots \square t_{\psi,k}), \quad Q \rightleftharpoons \mathfrak{T}(t_{\pi,1} \square t_{\psi,1} \square \ldots \square t_{\psi,k}).$$

If

$$t_{\pi,1} \in \underline{\text{comp. ciph}}_k, \quad t_{\psi,1} \in \underline{FR\text{-const}}_{\mathfrak{M}}, \ldots, t_{\psi,k} \in \underline{FR\text{-const}}_{\mathfrak{M}}, \tag{25}$$

then the algorithm $\langle P \rangle_{\tilde{\pi}}$ is a sequence of points of the space $\tilde{\mathfrak{M}}$ and the algorithm $\langle Q \rangle_0$ is a regulator of convergence in itself of the algorithm $\langle P \rangle_{\tilde{\pi}}$. In fact, let l, m and n be such that $m, n \geq \langle Q \rangle_0(l)$. Then

$$m, n \geqslant \overline{t_{\psi,1}}^{\psi}(\overline{t_{\pi,1}}^{\pi}(l)), \ldots, m, n \geqslant \overline{t_{\psi,k}}^{\psi}(\overline{t_{\pi,1}}^{\pi}(l)).$$

Hence

$$\rho(\underline{t_{\psi,1}}_{\psi}(m) \square \underline{t_{\psi,1}}_{\psi}(n)) < 2^{-R},$$

$$\cdots\cdots\cdots\cdots$$

$$\cdots\cdots\cdots\cdots$$

$$\rho(\underline{t_{\psi,k}}_{\psi}(m) \square \underline{t_{\psi,k}}_{\psi}(n)) < 2^{-R},$$

where $R \rightleftharpoons \overline{t_{\pi,1}}^{\pi}(l)$. Noting that

$$\overline{t_{\pi,1}}^{\pi} \ \underline{\text{reg. unif. cont}}_k \ \underline{t_{\pi,1}}_{\pi},$$

we obtain

$$\tilde{\rho}(\langle P\rangle_{\tilde{n}}(m)\,\Box\,\langle P\rangle_{\tilde{n}}(n)) < 2^{-l}.$$

From what has been proved it follows that, by the fulfillment of condition (25), the word $P \odot Q$ is an FR-construct in the space $\widetilde{\mathfrak{M}}$, and therefore $\mathrm{Lim}\,(P \odot Q)$ is a point of the space $\widetilde{\mathfrak{M}}$.

Now we construct an algorithm $\mathfrak{N}_k$ in the alphabet A_π^{sa} such that, for any words $t_{\pi,1}, t_{\psi,1}, \cdots, t_{\psi,k}$,

$$\langle \mathfrak{N}_k(t_{\pi,1})\rangle_{\eta'}(t_{\psi,1}\,\Box \ldots \Box\, t_{\psi,k}) \simeq \mathrm{Lim}\,(P \odot Q),$$

where η' denotes the ordinal number of the alphabet $A_\psi \cup A_{\widetilde{\mathfrak{m}}}$.

Finally, we construct an algorithm $\mathfrak{Z}_k$ in the alphabet $A_{\pi''}^{sa}$ such that, for any word $t_{\pi,1}$,

$$\mathfrak{Z}_k(t_{\pi,1}) \simeq \mathfrak{N}_k(t_{\pi,1}) \boxed{K} \mathfrak{R}(t_{\pi,1}),$$

where $\mathfrak{R}$ is an algorithm in the alphabet A_π^{sa} constructed in such a way that, for any word $t_{\pi,1}$ in the alphabet A_π and for any natural number l, the condition

$$\langle \mathfrak{R}(t_{\pi,1})\rangle_0(l) \simeq \overline{t_{\pi,1}}^{\pi}(l+1).$$

is fulfilled.

It is evident that for any word $\underset{\sim}{t}_{\pi,1}$, if $t_{\pi,1} \in \underline{\text{comp. ciph}}_k$, then $\langle \mathfrak{N}_k(t_{\pi,1})\rangle_{\eta'}$ is an operator of type $(\underbrace{\mathfrak{m} \cdots \mathfrak{m}}_{k \text{ times}} \rightarrow \mathcal{O})$.

Let the word $t_{\pi,1}$ be such that $t_{\pi,1} \in \underline{\text{comp. ciph}}_k$, let l be any natural number, and let $\mathfrak{w}_1, \cdots, \mathfrak{w}_k, \mathfrak{w}_{k+1}, \cdots, \mathfrak{w}_{k+k}$ be any points of the space $\mathfrak{M}_2$ such that

$$\rho_2(\mathfrak{w}_1\,\Box\,\mathfrak{w}_{k+1}) < 2^{-S}, \ldots, \quad \rho_2(\mathfrak{w}_k\,\Box\,\mathfrak{w}_{k+k}) < 2^{-S}, \tag{26}$$

where $S \leftrightharpoons \langle \mathfrak{R}(t_{\pi,1})\rangle_0(l)$. From 10.4.2 it follows that there is a potentially realizable n such that for every $m \geq n$ the propositions

$$\rho(\underline{\mathfrak{w}_1}_\psi(m)\,\Box\,\underline{\mathfrak{w}_{k+1}}_\psi(m)) < 2^{-S}, \ldots, \rho(\underline{\mathfrak{w}_k}_\psi(m)\,\Box\,\underline{\mathfrak{w}_{k+k}}_\psi(m)) < 2^{-S} \tag{27}$$

are true, and the proposition arising from (27),

$$\tilde{\rho}(\underline{t_{\pi,1}}_\pi(\underline{\mathfrak{w}_1}_\psi(m)\,\Box \ldots \Box\,\underline{\mathfrak{w}_k}_\psi(m))\,\Box\,\underline{t_{\pi,1}}_\pi(\underline{\mathfrak{w}_{k+1}}_\psi(m)\,\Box\, \ldots \,\Box\,\underline{\mathfrak{w}_{k+k}}_\psi(m))) < 2^{-(l+1)}. \tag{28}$$

is also true.

We introduce the notation

$$P' \leftrightharpoons \mathfrak{S}(t_{\pi,1} \square \mathfrak{w}_1 \square \ldots \square \mathfrak{w}_k), \quad P'' \leftrightharpoons \mathfrak{S}(t_{\pi,1} \square \mathfrak{w}_{k+1} \square \ldots \square \mathfrak{w}_{k+k}),$$
$$Q' \leftrightharpoons \mathfrak{T}(t_{\pi,1} \square \mathfrak{w}_1 \square \ldots \square \mathfrak{w}_k), \quad Q'' \leftrightharpoons \mathfrak{T}(t_{\pi,1} \square \mathfrak{w}_{k+1} \square \ldots \square \mathfrak{w}_{k+k}).$$

On the basis of (28) we have

$$\exists n \forall m (m \geqslant n \supset \tilde{\rho}(\langle P' \rangle_{\tilde{\mathfrak{n}}}(m) \square \langle P'' \rangle_{\tilde{\mathfrak{n}}}(m)) < 2^{-(l+1)}). \tag{29}$$

We introduce the additional notation

$$\Pi' \leftrightharpoons \mathrm{Lim}(P' \odot Q'), \quad \Pi'' \leftrightharpoons \mathrm{Lim}(P'' \odot Q'').$$

We have

$$\Pi' \simeq \langle \mathfrak{N}_k(t_{\pi,1}) \rangle_{\eta'} (\mathfrak{w}_1 \square \ldots \square \mathfrak{w}_k), \quad \Pi'' \simeq \langle \mathfrak{N}_k(t_{\pi,1}) \rangle_{\eta'} (\mathfrak{w}_{k+1} \square \ldots \square \mathfrak{w}_{k+k}).$$

On the other hand,

$$\forall m (m \geqslant \langle Q' \rangle_0 (l+2) \supset \tilde{\rho}(\Pi' \square \langle P' \rangle_{\tilde{\mathfrak{n}}}(m)) \leqslant 2^{-(l+2)}), \tag{30}$$

$$\forall m (m \geqslant \langle Q'' \rangle_0 (l+2) \supset \tilde{\rho}(\Pi'' \square \langle P'' \rangle_{\tilde{\mathfrak{n}}}(m)) \leqslant 2^{-(l+2)}). \tag{31}$$

Proposition (30) can be proved in the following manner. From the proposition

$$\langle Q' \rangle_0 \underset{\mathfrak{M}}{\underline{\text{reg. conv}}} \langle P' \rangle_{\tilde{\mathfrak{n}}}$$

it follows that for any m and n, if $m, n \geq \langle Q' \rangle_0 (l+2)$, then

$$\tilde{\rho}(\Pi' \square \langle P' \rangle_{\tilde{\mathfrak{n}}}(m)) \leqslant \tilde{\rho}(\Pi' \square \langle P' \rangle_{\tilde{\mathfrak{n}}}(n))$$
$$+ \tilde{\rho}(\langle P' \rangle_{\tilde{\mathfrak{n}}}(n) \square \langle P' \rangle_{\tilde{\mathfrak{n}}}(m)) < \tilde{\rho}(\Pi' \square \langle P' \rangle_{\tilde{\mathfrak{n}}}(n)) + 2^{-(l+2)}. \tag{32}$$

Now we note that $\tilde{\rho}(\Pi' \square \langle P' \rangle_{\tilde{\mathfrak{n}}}(n))$ becomes smaller than any positive rational number for sufficiently large values of the variable n. From this remark and from (32), (30) follows. (31) is proved analogously.

Now we shall start from (29). Let n be such that

$$\forall m (m \geqslant n \supset \tilde{\rho}(\langle P' \rangle_{\tilde{\mathfrak{n}}}(m) \square \langle P'' \rangle_{\tilde{\mathfrak{n}}}(m)) < 2^{-(l+1)}). \tag{33}$$

We introduce the notation

$$E \leftrightharpoons \max(n \square \langle Q' \rangle_0 (l+2) \square \langle Q'' \rangle_0 (l+2)).$$

On the basis of (30), (31) and (33) we have

$$\tilde{\rho}(\Pi' \square \langle P' \rangle_{\tilde{\mathfrak{n}}}(E)) \leqslant 2^{-(l+2)}, \quad \tilde{\rho}(\Pi'' \square \langle P'' \rangle_{\tilde{\mathfrak{n}}}(E)) \leqslant 2^{-(l+2)},$$

$$\tilde{\rho}(\langle P' \rangle_{\tilde{\mathfrak{n}}}(E) \square \langle P'' \rangle_{\tilde{\mathfrak{n}}}(E)) < 2^{-(l+1)}.$$

Hence $\tilde{\rho}(\Pi' \square \Pi'') < 2^{-l}$. Therefore

$$\langle \mathfrak{R}(t_{\pi,1}) \rangle_0 \underset{k}{\underline{\text{reg. unif. cont}}} \langle \mathfrak{N}_k(t_{\pi,1}) \rangle_{\eta'}.$$

Hence

$$\forall t_{\pi,1}(t_{\pi,1} \in \underline{\text{comp. ciph}}_k \supset \mathfrak{Z}_k(t_{\pi,1}) \in \underline{\text{comp. ciph}'}_k).$$

It is easily seen that, for any word $t_{\pi,1}$, if $t_{\pi,1} \in \underline{\text{comp. ciph}}_k$, then

$$\forall \theta_1 \ldots \theta_k (\underline{\mathfrak{Z}_k(t_{\pi,1})}_{\pi'} (\theta_1 \square \ldots \square \theta_k) \underset{\tilde{\rho}}{=} \underline{t_{\pi,1}}_{\pi} (\theta_1 \square \ldots \square \theta_k)).$$

Hence

$$\forall t_{\pi,1}(t_{\pi,1} \in \underline{\text{comp. ciph}}_k \supset \mathfrak{Z}_k(t_{\pi,1}) \, \underline{\text{ext. ciph}}_{k,\mathfrak{M}_2} \, t_{\pi,1}).$$

Theorem 10.4.9 has been proved.

The algorithm $\mathfrak{Z}_k$, constructed in the proof of Theorem 10.4.9, will be called (for a fixed algorithm of passage to the limit in the space $\widetilde{\mathfrak{M}}$) *the standard algorithm for extending complete ciphers of uniformly continuous k-ary operators.*

In what follows Theorem 10.4.9 will often be applied to operators of one special type, called Lipschitz operators (by analogy with the Lipschitz functions considered in classical mathematical analysis).

Let $\lambda_{\eta,1}$ be an algorithm in the alphabet A_η^{sa} and let G be a real duplex. We shall say that G is a *Lipschitz coefficient in dimension* k for the algorithm $\lambda_{\eta,1}$ if, for any points $\theta_1, \cdots, \theta_k, \theta_{k+1}, \cdots, \theta_{k+k}$ of the space $\mathfrak{M}$,

$$\tilde{\rho}(\lambda_{\eta,1}(\theta_1 \square \ldots \square \theta_k) \square \lambda_{\eta,1}(\theta_{k+1} \square \ldots \square \theta_{k+k})) \leqslant G \cdot (\rho(\theta_1 \square \theta_{k+1}) + \ldots + \rho(\theta_k \square \theta_{k+k})). \quad (34)$$

We shall say that an algorithm $\lambda_{\eta,1}$ in the alphabet A_η^{sa} is a *k-ary Lipschitz operator* from the metric space $\mathfrak{M}$ into the metric space $\widetilde{\mathfrak{M}}$ if $\lambda_{\eta,1}$ is an algorithm of type $(\underbrace{\theta \cdots \theta}_{k \text{ times}} \to \widetilde{\theta})_\eta$ and a real duplex C which is a Lipschitz coefficient in dimension k for the algorithm $\lambda_{\eta,1}$ is potentially realizable.

The metric function in any metric space is a binary Lipschitz operator from the given space into the metric space of real duplexes. In fact, for any points X, Y, Z, and U of the metric space $\mathfrak{M}$ we have (on the basis of 9.1.1)

$$M(\rho(X \square Y) - \rho(Z \square U)) \leqslant \rho(X \square Z) + \rho(Y \square U). \quad (35)$$

It is obvious that every k-ary Lipschitz operator is an operator of type $(\underbrace{\theta \cdots \theta}_{k \text{ times}} \to \widetilde{\theta})$ and, moreover, a uniformly continuous operator. If any Lipschitz coefficient in dimension k for the operator $\lambda_{\eta,1}$ is found, then we can construct a regulator of uniform continuity of the operator $\lambda_{\eta,1}$. As an algorithm carrying out such a construction, one can, for example, make use of the algorithm ξ in the alphabet $\mathrm{A}_0^{\mathrm{sa}}$ such that, for every l,

$$\xi(l) \rightleftharpoons l + \mu_m (G \cdot k \leqslant 2^m),$$

where G is the given Lipschitz coefficient in dimension k for $\lambda_{\eta,1}$. Applying to the word $\{\lambda_{\eta,1}\} \boxed{K} \{\xi\}$ the standard algorithm $\mathfrak{Z}_k$ for extending complete ciphers, we obtain a word H in the alphabet $\mathrm{A}_{\pi'}$ which is a k-ary extension of the complete cipher $\{\lambda_{\eta,1}\} \boxed{K} \{\xi\}$ on the space $\mathfrak{M}_2$. Moreover, one can prove (using (35) and Theorem 9.4.1) that, for any points $\mathfrak{w}_1, \cdots, \mathfrak{w}_k, \mathfrak{w}_{k+1}, \cdots, \mathfrak{w}_{k+k}$ of the space $\mathfrak{M}_2$,

$$\begin{aligned} \tilde{\rho}\,(\underline{H}_{\pi'}(\mathfrak{w}_1 \square \ldots \square \mathfrak{w}_k) \square \underline{H}_{\pi'}(\mathfrak{w}_{k+1} \square \ldots \square \mathfrak{w}_{k+k})) \\ \leqslant G \cdot (\rho_2(\mathfrak{w}_1 \square \mathfrak{w}_{k+1}) + \ldots + \rho_2(\mathfrak{w}_k \square \mathfrak{w}_{k+k})). \end{aligned} \tag{36}$$

From what has been said it is immediately obvious how to construct an algorithm which, for any k-ary Lipschitz operator and any Lipschitz coefficient in dimension k for this operator, constructs a k-ary extension of the given operator on the space $\mathfrak{M}_2$. We fix an algorithm carrying out this construction, agreeing to denote it by $\mathfrak{Z}_k^*$, and we shall call it *the standard algorithm for extending k-ary Lipschitz operators.*

From Theorem 10.4.9 and everything said above about Lipschitz operators, the next theorem follows.

10.4.10. *If $\widetilde{\mathfrak{M}}$ is a complete metric space, then:*

1) *for any everywhere-defined uniformly continuous k-ary operator $\lambda_{\eta,1}$ from $\mathfrak{M}$ into $\widetilde{\mathfrak{M}}$, there is a potentially realizable operator $\lambda_{\eta',1}$ which is a k-ary extension of the operator $\lambda_{\eta,1}$ on $\mathfrak{M}_2$ and is an everywhere-defined uniformly continuous k-ary operator from $\mathfrak{M}_2$ into $\widetilde{\mathfrak{M}}$;*

2) *for any k-ary Lipschitz operator $\lambda_{\eta,1}$ from $\mathfrak{M}$ into $\widetilde{\mathfrak{M}}$, there is a potentially realizable operator $\lambda_{\eta',1}$ which is a k-ary extension of the operator $\lambda_{\eta,1}$ on $\mathfrak{M}_2$, which is also a k-ary Lipschitz operator from $\mathfrak{M}_2$ into $\widetilde{\mathfrak{M}}$, and is such that every real duplex which is a Lipschitz coefficient in dimension k for the operator $\lambda_{\eta,1}$ is at the same time a Lipschitz coefficient in dimension k for the operator $\lambda_{\eta',1}$.*

10.5. Let us consider the case where the metric space of all rational numbers plays the role of $\mathfrak{M}$. In this case Ч_2 plays the role of $\mathrm{A}_{\mathfrak{m}}$, the role of $\mathfrak{P}$ is played by the formula $(\mathrm{c}_{2,1} \in \underline{\mathrm{rat}})$ and the role of the metric function ρ by the composition of two algorithms: the subtraction algorithm "$-_{\mathrm{p}}$" and the algorithm for constructing the absolute value M_{p}. In addition, it is assumed that the composition of these algorithms is constructed in the form of a normal algorithm in the alphabet $Ч_2^{sa}$. In the case now being considered the FR-completion of the space $\mathfrak{M}$ is the metric space of all real FR-numbers (real duplexes). Moreover, the metric function ρ_2, constructed according to the general rule for constructing the metric function in the FR-completion of a metric space, is such that

$$\forall xy\,(\rho_2(x \mathop{\square}_{\text{B}} y) = \mathop{M}_{\text{B}}(x \mathop{-}_{\text{B}} y)). \tag{1}$$

For the proof of proposition (1) we note the following. For any rational numbers a and b,

$$\rho_2(a \mathop{\square}_{\text{B}} b) = \mathop{M}_{\text{B}}(a \mathop{-}_{\text{B}} b).$$

This follows from the definition of the metric function in the space of rational numbers and from the fact that $\mathfrak{M}$ is a subspace of the space $\mathfrak{M}_2$. Further, the functions given by the terms $\rho_2(x \square y)$ and $M_{\text{B}}(x -_{\text{B}} y)$ are uniformly continuous in the space of real FR-numbers (and what is more, they are binary Lipschitz operators from the space of real FR-numbers into the same space). From these remarks and Theorem 9.4.1, proposition (1) follows.

The metric space of all real duplexes is denoted by the letter E.

The next theorem follows from Theorem 10.4.6.

10.5.1. *The metric space E is a complete space.*

Let x and y be any real duplexes such that $x \leq y$. The set of real duplexes belonging to the segment $x \mathbin{\underline{\nabla}} y$ (cf. §7) is denoted (in accordance with the convention accepted in §7.2) by $\mathfrak{M}_{Д}(x \mathbin{\underline{\nabla}} y)$. The subspace of the metric space E, induced by E in the set $\mathfrak{M}_{Д}(x \mathbin{\underline{\nabla}} y)$, will be denoted by $E[x \mathbin{\underline{\nabla}} y]$.

The following proposition is easily proved.

For any duplexes x and y such that $x \leq y$ and for any sequence of duplexes $\Phi_{3,1}$ and any duplex z, if

$$\forall n\,(x \leqslant \Phi_{3,1}(n) \leqslant y)\,\&\,(z \mathop{\underline{\lim}}_E \Phi_{3,1}),$$

then $x \leq z \leq y$.

The following theorem is a consequence of this proposition and Theorem 10.5.1.

10.5.2. *For any duplexes x and y such that $x \leq y$, the space $E[x \mathbin{\underline{\nabla}} y]$ is a complete metric space. Moreover, as an algorithm of passage to the limit in the space $E[x \mathbin{\underline{\nabla}} y]$, one can take the algorithm of passage to the limit in the space E.*

We proceed now to the F-completion of the metric space of all rational numbers.

The F-completion of the space of all rational numbers is the semimetric space of all real F-numbers. Moreover, the semimetric function ρ_1, constructed according to the general rule for constructing the semimetric function in the F-completion of a metric space, is such that

$$\forall rs (\rho_1 (r \underset{B}{\square} s) \underset{B}{=} M (r \underset{B}{-} s)). \tag{2}$$

The proof of proposition (2) is analogous to the proof of proposition (1).

We shall denote the semimetric space of all real F-numbers by E_0.

The next theorem follows from Theorem 10.4.5.

10.5.3. *The semimetric space E_0 is an almost complete space.*

Let r and s be any real F-numbers such that $r \leq s$. The set of real F-numbers belonging to the B-segment $r \underline{\nabla} s$ (cf. §7.3) will be denoted by $\mathfrak{M}_B (r \underline{\nabla} s)$. The subspace of the semimetric spaće E_0 in the set $\mathfrak{M}_B (r \underline{\nabla} s)$, will be denoted by $E_0 [r \underline{\nabla} s]$.

10.5.4. *For any real F-numbers r and s such that $r \leq s$, the space $E_0[r \underline{\nabla} s]$ is an almost complete semimetric space.*

The proof of Theorem 10.5.4 is analogous to the proof of Theorem 10.5.2.

10.6. We shall formulate here some theorems about limits of sequences of points in the metric space of all real duplexes.

The expression Lim_E will denote the standard algorithm of passage to the limit in this space. For the construction of FR-constructs in this space we introduce the alphabet $\text{Ч}_3 \cup \{◎\}$. Assuming that in the enumeration of alphabets this alphabet receives a certain index, we agree to denote this index by the letter γ.

If $\Phi_{3,1}$ and $\Phi_{3,2}$ are two sequences of real duplexes, then the expression

$$(\Phi_{3,1} \underset{\text{seq}}{-} \Phi_{3,2})$$

will denote the difference of these sequences, i.e. the algorithm in the alphabet Ч_3^{sa} such that

$$\forall m ((\Phi_{3,1} \underset{\text{seq}}{-} \Phi_{3,2}) (m) \simeq \Phi_{3,1} (m) \underset{B}{-} \Phi_{3,2} (m)).$$

If $\mathfrak{w}_1$ and $\mathfrak{w}_2$ are two FR-constructs in the space E, then the expression

$$(\mathfrak{w}_1 \underset{\text{con}}{-} \mathfrak{w}_2)$$

will denote the difference of these two FR-constants, i.e. the FR-construct in the space E such that

$$\forall m (\underbrace{(\mathfrak{w}_1 \underset{\text{con}}{-} \mathfrak{w}_2)}_{\gamma} (m) \simeq \underbrace{\mathfrak{w}_1}_{\gamma} (m) \underset{B}{-} \underbrace{\mathfrak{w}_2}_{\gamma} (m))$$

and

$$\forall m\,((\mathfrak{w}_1 \underset{\text{con}}{-} \mathfrak{w}_2)^{\urcorner\gamma}(m) \simeq \max(\overline{\mathfrak{w}}^{\gamma}_1(m+1)\,\square\,\overline{\mathfrak{w}}^{\gamma}_2(m+1))).$$

10.6.1. *For any duplexes x, y and z and any sequences of duplexes* $\Phi_{3,1}$ *and* $\Phi_{3,2}$,

$$\exists m \forall n\,(n \geqslant m \supset x \leqslant \Phi_{3,1}(n))\,\&\,z\ \underline{\lim}_E \Phi_{3,1} \supset x \leqslant z, \tag{1}$$

$$\exists m \forall n\,(n \geqslant m \supset \Phi_{3,1}(n) \leqslant y)\,\&\,z\ \underline{\lim}_E \Phi_{3,1} \supset z \leqslant y, \tag{2}$$

$$\exists m \forall n\,(n \geqslant m \supset \Phi_{3,1}(n) \leqslant \Phi_{3,2}(n))\,\&\,x\ \underline{\lim}_E \Phi_{3,1}\,\&\,y\ \underline{\lim}\ \Phi_{3,2} \supset x \leqslant y, \tag{3}$$

$$\forall n\,(\Phi_{3,1}(n) \leqslant \Phi_{3,1}(n+1) \leqslant \Phi_{3,2}(n+1) \leqslant \Phi_{3,2}(n))$$
$$\&\,0\ \underline{\lim}_E(\Phi_{3,2} \underset{\text{seq}}{-} \Phi_{3,1}) \supset \exists z\,(z\ \underline{\lim}_E \Phi_{3,1}\,\&\,z\ \underline{\lim}_E \Phi_{3,2}). \tag{4}$$

Propositions (1)–(3) are proved without difficulty, and proposition (4) is provable with the aid of Theorem 8.2.1.

10.6.2. *For any duplexes x, y and FR-constructs* $\mathfrak{w}_1$ *and* $\mathfrak{w}_2$ *in the space E,*

$$\exists m \forall n\,(n \geqslant m \supset x \leqslant \underline{\mathfrak{w}_1}_{\gamma}(n)) \supset x \leqslant \mathrm{Lim}_E(\mathfrak{w}_1), \tag{5}$$

$$\exists m \forall n\,(n \geqslant m \supset \underline{\mathfrak{w}_1}_{\gamma}(n) \leqslant y) \supset \mathrm{Lim}_E(\mathfrak{w}_1) \leqslant y, \tag{6}$$

$$\exists m \forall n\,(n \geqslant m \supset \underline{\mathfrak{w}_1}_{\gamma}(n) \leqslant \underline{\mathfrak{w}_2}_{\gamma}(n)) \supset \mathrm{Lim}_E(\mathfrak{w}_1) \leqslant \mathrm{Lim}_E(\mathfrak{w}_2). \tag{7}$$

In classical mathematical analysis there is a theorem asserting that every monotonically nondecreasing and bounded above sequence of real numbers has a limit. This point is an essential difference between constructive and classical mathematical analysis.

In the proof of Theorem 8.3.1 we reproduced a fundamental result of E. Specker, consisting of the construction of a concrete algorithm S of type $(\mathrm{H} \to \mathrm{D})_2$ possessing the following properties:

1) $\forall k\,(S(k) \leqslant S(k+1))$;

2) $\forall k\,(0 \leqslant S(k) < 1)$;

3) there is no algorithm which is a regulator of convergence in itself of the algorithm S.

The algorithm S is a sequence of duplexes. Assuming that $\exists z\,(z\ \underline{\lim}_E\ S)$, we can conclude on the basis of 10.1.5 that a regulator of convergence in itself of the algorithm S is potentially realizable. But this contradicts the third property cited above of the algorithm S. Hence we have

10.6.3. *There is no duplex which is a limit in E of the sequence of duplexes*

S (Specker's sequence). In other words, S is not a convergent-in-E sequence of duplexes.

It is easily seen that if $\Phi_{3,1}$ is any nondecreasing sequence of duplexes and $\Phi_{3,1}$ does not converge in E, then any subsequence of the sequence $\Phi_{3,1}$ also does not converge in E. The next theorem follows from this proposition and 10.6.3.

10.6.4. *There is no subsequence of the sequence S which converges in E.*

Hence we get

10.6.5. *One can construct a monotonically nondecreasing sequence of duplexes*[1] *such that all of its terms belong to the seqment* $0 \mathbin{\underline{\nabla}} 1$, *and, at the same time, there is no subsequence of this sequence which converges in the space* $E[0 \mathbin{\underline{\nabla}} 1]$.

10.7. In [8] A. A. Markov has proved that a constructive function of type (Д $\dot{\to}$ Д) cannot have a constructive discontinuity at any of the points at which it is defined. In [16] G. S. Ceĭtin carried this result to its logical conclusion: Ceĭtin's basic result is fomulated and proved for a very general case, namely for constructive operators from any complete separable metric space into any metric space. This result, formulated here with respect to k-ary operators (k is any positive integer), consists of the following.

10.7.1. *If* $\mathfrak{M}$ *is a complete separable metric space,* $\widetilde{\mathfrak{M}}$ *is any metric space, and* $\lambda_{\eta,1}$ *is any operator of type* $(\underbrace{\theta \cdots \theta}_{k\ times} \dot{\to} \widetilde{\theta})$, *then the operator* $\lambda_{\eta,1}$ *is continuous at any k-tuple of points* $\theta_1, \cdots, \theta_k$ *for which* $!\,\lambda_{\eta,1}(\theta_1 \square \cdots \square \theta_k)$.

The space E is a complete separable metric space. From Theorem 10.7.1 it follows that the operator M_{B} is continuous at every point of the space E, that, for every k ($k \geq 2$), the operators $\max_{\text{B}}$, $\min_{\text{B}}$, $+_{\text{B}}$, $-_{\text{B}}$, $\cdot_{\text{B}}$ are continuous at every k-tuple of points of the space E, and that the operator $:_{\text{B}}$ is continuous at every pair of points x, y of the space E such that $y \neq_{\text{B}} 0$. These assertions about the indicated arithmetic operations can be proved, of course, without reference to Ceĭtin's theorem, which has a complicated proof (both from a theoretical and a technical standpoint). It suffices to carry out elementary and perfectly

---

1) One says that a sequence of duplexes $\Phi_{3,1}$ is a monotonically nondecreasing sequence if

$$\forall k\, (\Phi_{3,1}(k) \leqslant \Phi_{3,1}(k+1)).$$

obvious estimates of the increase of the given functions for given increases of the arguments.

One can define in a natural way the usual arithmetic operations on sequences of real duplexes and on FR-constructs in the space E. We shall not formulate here the appropriate definitions. We only remark that these operations (with the exception of division of one sequence by another and division of one FR-construct by another) are defined in such a way that, for every n, the computation of the nth term of the sequence resulting from the application of the given operation to the initial sequences consists of carrying out the arithmetic operation of the same name on the nth terms of the initial sequences. (The operation of division, in view of certain obvious facts, has a more complicated nature.) The construction of regulators of convergence in itself of the sequences of real duplexes in the definition of the arithmetic operations on FR-constructs in the space E, is analogous to the construction of regulators of convergence in itself of sequences of rational numbers in the definition of the operations with the same names on real FR-numbers.

The arithmetic operations on sequences of real duplexes are, by definition, normal algorithms in the alphabet $Ч_0^{sa}$ transforming every system of words in the alphabet $Ч_0$, composed of the transcriptions of the initially given sequences of real duplexes which are admissible for the given operations, into some word in the alphabet $Ч_0$. The sequence of real duplexes, the transcription of which is the resulting word, is considered to be the result of the application of the given operation to the initially given sequences. We denote by

$$\underset{\text{seq}}{M}, \quad \underset{\text{seq}}{\max}, \quad \underset{\text{seq}}{\min}, \quad \underset{\text{seq}}{+}, \quad \underset{\text{seq}}{-}, \quad \underset{\text{seq}}{\cdot}, \quad \underset{\text{seq}}{:}$$

the normal algorithms in the alphabet $Ч_0^{sa}$ defining, respectively, in the sense just indicated, the operations of constructing the absolute value of a sequence of real duplexes, and the maximum, minimum, sum, difference, product, and quotient of sequences. We denote by

$$\underset{\text{con}}{M}, \quad \underset{\text{con}}{\max}, \quad \underset{\text{con}}{\min}, \quad \underset{\text{con}}{+}, \quad \underset{\text{con}}{-}, \quad \underset{\text{con}}{\cdot}, \quad \underset{\text{con}}{:}$$

the normal algorithms in the alphabet $Ч_\gamma^{sa}$ which are the operations on FR-constructs in the space E having the same name as the corresponding operations on sequences of real duplexes in the list of operations just enumerated.

As direct corollaries of Theorem 10.1.4 we obtain the following two theorems.

10.7.2. a) *For any positive integer* k, *any real duplexes* $Д_1, \cdots, Д_k$, *and any sequences of real duplexes* $\Phi_{3,1}, \cdots, \Phi_{3,k}$, *if*

$$Д_1 \ \underline{\lim}_E \Phi_{3,1} \& \ldots \& Д_k \ \underline{\lim}_E \Phi_{3,k},$$

then

$$\underset{\text{В}}{\delta}(Д_1 \square \ldots \square Д_k) \ \underline{\lim}_E \langle \underset{\text{seq}}{\delta} (\{\Phi_{3,1}\} \square \ldots \square \{\Phi_{3,k}\})\rangle_3,$$

where any of the expressions

$$\max, \min, +, \cdot$$

can serve as δ.

b) *For any duplexes* x *and* y *and any sequences of duplexes* $\Phi_{3,1}$ *and* $\Phi_{3,2}$

$$x \ \underline{\lim}_E \Phi_{3,1} \supset \underset{\text{В}}{M}(x) \ \underline{\lim}_E \langle \underset{\text{seq}}{M}(\{\Phi_{3,1}\})\rangle_3,$$

$$x \ \underline{\lim}_E \Phi_{3,1} \& y \ \underline{\lim}_E \Phi_{3,2} \supset \underset{\text{В}}{-}(x \square y) \ \underline{\lim}_E \langle \underset{\text{seq}}{-} (\{\Phi_{3,1}\} \square \{\Phi_{3,2}\})\rangle_3,$$

$$x \ \underline{\lim}_E \Phi_{3,1} \& y \ \underline{\lim}_E \Phi_{3,2} \& y \underset{\text{В}}{\neq} 0$$

$$\supset \underset{\text{В}}{:}(x \square y) \ \underline{\lim}_E \langle \underset{\text{seq}}{:} (\{\Phi_{3,1}\} \square \{\Phi_{3,2}\})\rangle_3.$$

10.7.3. a) *For any positive integer* k *and any FR-constructs* $\mathfrak{w}_1, \cdots, \mathfrak{w}_k$ *in the space* E,

$$\mathrm{Lim}_E(\underset{\text{con}}{\delta}(\mathfrak{w}_1 \square \ldots \square \mathfrak{w}_k)) \underset{\text{В}}{=} \underset{\text{В}}{\delta}(\mathrm{Lim}_E(\mathfrak{w}_1) \square \ldots \square \mathrm{Lim}_E(\mathfrak{w}_k)),$$

where any of the expressions

$$\max, \min, +, \cdot.$$

can figure as δ.

b) *For any FR-constructs* $\mathfrak{w}_1$ *and* $\mathfrak{w}_2$ *in the space* E,

$$\mathrm{Lim}_E(\underset{\text{con}}{M}(\mathfrak{w}_1)) \underset{\text{В}}{=} \underset{\text{В}}{M}(\mathrm{Lim}_E(\mathfrak{w}_1)),$$

$$\mathrm{Lim}_E(\underset{\text{con}}{-}(\mathfrak{w}_1 \square \mathfrak{w}_2)) \underset{\text{В}}{=} \underset{\text{В}}{-}(\mathrm{Lim}_E(\mathfrak{w}_1) \square \mathrm{Lim}_E(\mathfrak{w}_2)),$$

$$\mathrm{Lim}_E(\mathfrak{w}_2) \underset{\text{В}}{\neq} 0 \supset \mathrm{Lim}_E(\underset{\text{con}}{:}(\mathfrak{w}_1 \square \mathfrak{w}_2)) \underset{\text{В}}{=} \underset{\text{В}}{:}(\mathrm{Lim}_E(\mathfrak{w}_1) \square \mathrm{Lim}_E(\mathfrak{w}_2)).$$

Everything said here about arithmetic operations on sequences of real duplexes and FR-constructs in the space E can be extended in a suitable way to operations corresponding to the operations Λ_{B} and Λ^*_{B}.

§11. TOTALLY BOUNDED AND COMPACT CONSTRUCTIVE METRIC SPACES

In this section we shall keep the assumptions and notation introduced at the beginning of §9.2.

11.1. We shall assume that the letter τ does not belong to the alphabet $A_{\mathfrak{m}}$. We introduce a new alphabet $A_{\mathfrak{m}} \cup \{\tau\}$ and we assume that this alphabet is included among the basic alphabets of the given language. The ordinal number of the alphabet $A_{\mathfrak{m}} \cup \{\tau\}$ in the general enumeration of all the basic alphabets of the given language will be denoted by the letter $\mathfrak{g}$. We shall denote the ordinal number of the alphabet $A_{\mathfrak{g}} \cup A_0$ by the letter $\mathfrak{b}$.

Let $t_{\mathfrak{g},1}$ be a τ-system of words in the alphabet $A_{\mathfrak{m}}$ (i.e. a word in the alphabet $A_{\mathfrak{g}}$; cf. §7.1), and let ϵ be a positive rational number. We shall say that $t_{\mathfrak{g},1}$ is a *finite ϵ-net* in the space $\mathfrak{M}$ if, first, every τ-term of the τ-system $t_{\mathfrak{g},1}$ is a point of the space $\mathfrak{M}$, and second, for any point X of the space $\mathfrak{M}$, one can construct a τ-term of the τ-system $t_{\mathfrak{g},1}$ which is at a distance less than ϵ away from X in the space $\mathfrak{M}$, i.e.

$$\forall X \exists l (l \leqslant L_\tau(t_{\mathfrak{g},1}) \,\&\, \rho(X \square [t_{\mathfrak{g},1}]_l^\tau) < \varepsilon).$$

The notation occurring in this formula was explained in §7.1.

We shall say that $t_{\mathfrak{g},1}$ is a *perfect finite ϵ-net* in the space $\mathfrak{M}$ if, first, every τ-term of the τ-system $t_{\mathfrak{g},1}$ is a point of the space $\mathfrak{M}$, and second, there is potentially realizable an algorithm $\lambda_{\mathfrak{b},1}$ in the alphabet $A_{\mathfrak{b}}^{sa}$ such that

$$\forall X (\lambda_{\mathfrak{b},1}(X) \mathrel{\dot{\in}} \underline{\text{nat}} \,\&\, \lambda_{\mathfrak{b},1}(X) \leqslant L_\tau(t_{\mathfrak{g},1}) \,\&\, \rho(X \square [t_{\mathfrak{g},1}]^\tau_{\lambda_{\mathfrak{b},1}(X)}) < \varepsilon).$$

It is obvious that, for any positive rational number ϵ, every perfect finite ϵ-net in $\mathfrak{M}$ is a finite ϵ-net in $\mathfrak{M}$.

The following proposition is a direct consequence of Theorem 2.4.3.

11.1.1. *If $\mathfrak{P}$ is a normal formula then, for any positive rational number ϵ, every finite ϵ-net in the space $\mathfrak{M}$ is a perfect finite ϵ-net in the space $\mathfrak{M}$.*

We shall say that a space $\mathfrak{M}$ is *almost totally bounded* if, for every positive rational number ϵ, a finite ϵ-net is potentially realizable. We shall say that a space $\mathfrak{M}$ is *totally bounded* if, for every positive rational number ϵ, a perfect finite ϵ-net is potentially realizable.

Let $\mathfrak{Q}$ be a subset of the set $\mathfrak{P}$. We shall say that $\mathfrak{Q}$ is an *almost totally bounded subset* of the space $\mathfrak{M}$ (totally bounded subset of the space $\mathfrak{M}$) if the subspace of the space $\mathfrak{M}$ induced by the space $\mathfrak{M}$ in the set $\mathfrak{Q}$ is an almost totally bounded (respectively, totally bounded) space.

The following proposition is obvious.

11.1.2. *Every totally bounded space is an almost totally bounded space.*

The next proposition is a direct consequence of 11.1.1.

11.1.3. *If the space $\mathfrak{M}$ is almost totally bounded and $\mathfrak{P}$ is a normal formula, then $\mathfrak{M}$ is totally bounded.*

Let $\mathfrak{M}$ be an almost totally bounded space (totally bounded space). Let $\mathfrak{S}$ be an algorithm in the alphabet $A_{\mathfrak{b}}^{sa}$ transforming every natural number m into a finite 2^{-m}-net (respectively, into a perfect finite 2^{-m}-net) in the space $\mathfrak{M}$. We shall call any such algorithm an algorithm *constructing nets* (*perfect nets*) in the space $\mathfrak{M}$. The condition

$$\exists ml\,(l \leqslant L_{\tau}(\mathfrak{E}(m))\,\&\,X \rightleftharpoons [\mathfrak{E}(m)]_l^{\tau}), \tag{1}$$

having the variable X as its parameter, gives the union of the sets consisting of the elements of a finite 2^{-0}-net (perfect finite 2^{-0}-net), the elements of a finite 2^{-1}-net (perfect finite 2^{-1}-net), etc. It is easily seen that, first, the set (1) is algorithmically enumerable, and second, it is almost dense (respectively, dense) in $\mathfrak{M}$. Hence we have

11.1.4. *If $\mathfrak{M}$ is an almost totally bounded (totally bounded) space, then there is potentially realizable an algorithmically enumerable subset of the set $\mathfrak{P}$, almost dense (respectively, dense) in the space $\mathfrak{M}$.*

Above in §7.3 it was proved that the set of Д-points of any Д-segment and the set of Д-points of any Д-interval are almost totally bounded subsets of the metric space of all real duplexes (Theorem 7.3.1). From 11.1.3 it follows that they are also totally bounded sets. One can also prove that the set of all B-points of any B-segment and the set of all B-points of any B-interval are almost totally bounded subsets of the semimetric space of all real F-numbers.[1] The latter assertion can be proved by reducing it to Theorem 7.3.1 with the help of the algorithm for eliminating restricted variables and the algorithm for exhibiting constructive problems.

---

1) However, these subsets are not totally bounded (cf. 11.1.4 and §9.4).

11.2. Let $\lambda_{\mathfrak{n},1}$ be a function of type $(\theta \to Д)$ and let x be a real duplex. One says that x is a *least upper bound* of the function $\lambda_{\mathfrak{n},1}$ in the space $\mathfrak{M}$ if, first, $\forall X(\lambda_{\mathfrak{n},1}(X) \leq x)$, and second, $\forall n \exists Y(x - 2^{-n} < \lambda_{\mathfrak{n},1}(Y))$.

One says that a duplex x is a *greatest lower bound* of the function $\lambda_{\mathfrak{n},1}$ in the space $\mathfrak{M}$ if, first, $\forall X(x \leq \lambda_{\mathfrak{n},1}(X))$ and second $\forall n \exists Y(\lambda_{\mathfrak{n},1}(Y) < x + 2^{-n})$.

The expressions

$$(x \,\underline{\text{lub}}_{\mathfrak{M}} \lambda_{\mathfrak{n},1}), \qquad (x \,\underline{\text{glb}}_{\mathfrak{M}} \lambda_{\mathfrak{n},1})$$

will be read as follows: "x is a least upper bound of the function $\lambda_{\mathfrak{n},1}$ in the space $\mathfrak{M}$", "x is a greatest lower bound of the function $\lambda_{\mathfrak{n},1}$ in the space $\mathfrak{M}$".

In the following Theorem 11.2.1 we shall be talking about complete ciphers of uniformly continuous functions of type $(\theta \to Д)$. A uniformly continuous function of type $(\theta \to Д)$ is an everywhere-defined uniformly continuous 1-ary operator from the space $\mathfrak{M}$ into the metric space of all real duplexes E. The definitions and notation connected with complete ciphers of everywhere-defined uniformly continuous operators, introduced in §9.3, will be used in 11.2.1 with respect to the case where the space E plays the role of $\tilde{\mathfrak{M}}$, the number 1 plays the role of k, and the number $\mathfrak{n}$ plays the role of η.

We denote by $\mathfrak{p}$ the ordinal number of the alphabet $A_\pi \cup Ч_3$.

11.2.1. *If $\mathfrak{M}$ is an almost totally bounded space, then one can construct an algorithm $\lambda_{\mathfrak{p},1}$ in the alphabet $A_{\mathfrak{p}}^{sa}$ such that, for any word $t_{\pi,1}$ in the alphabet A_π which is a complete cipher of a uniformly continuous function of type $(\theta \to Д)$,*

$$\lambda_{\mathfrak{p},1}(t_{\pi,1}) \in \underline{\text{real dup}} \;\&\; \lambda_{\mathfrak{p},1}(t_{\pi,1}) \,\underline{\text{lub}}_{\mathfrak{M}}\, \underline{t_{\pi,1}}_{\pi}. \tag{1}$$

Proof. Let $\mathfrak{M}$ be an almost totally bounded space and let $\mathfrak{S}$ be an algorithm in the alphabet $A_{\mathfrak{p}}^{sa}$ transforming any natural number m into a finite 2^{-m}-net in the space $\mathfrak{M}$. One can assume that the algorithm $\mathfrak{S}$ is such that, for every m, the word $\mathfrak{S}(m+1)$ begins with the word $\mathfrak{S}(m)$. We shall assume that the algorithm $\mathfrak{S}$ possesses this property, and, therefore, every τ-term of the τ-system $\mathfrak{S}(m)$ is a τ-term of the τ-system $\mathfrak{S}(m+1)$.

We introduce the following notation:

$$Q_m \leftrightharpoons \overline{t_{\pi,1}}^{\pi}(m+2), \qquad R_m \leftrightharpoons L_\tau(\mathfrak{S}(Q_m)),$$

$$\left.\begin{aligned} U_{m,i} &\leftrightharpoons [\mathfrak{S}(Q_m)]_i^\tau, \\ V_{m,i} &\leftrightharpoons \underline{t_{\pi,1}}_{\pi}(U_{m,i}), \\ W_{m,i} &\leftrightharpoons \underline{V_{m,i}}(\overline{V_{m,i}}(m+3)) \end{aligned}\right\} i = 1, 2, \ldots, R_m.$$

If $t_{\pi,1}$ is a complete cipher of a uniformly continuous function of type $(\theta \to Д)$ and m, i are natural numbers, then

$$Q_m \overset{+}{\in} \underline{\text{nat}}, \quad R_m \overset{+}{\in} \underline{\text{nat}}, \quad U_{m,i} \overset{+}{\in} \theta, \quad V_{m,i} \overset{+}{\in} \underline{\text{real dup}}, \quad W_{m,i} \overset{+}{\in} \underline{\text{rat}}.$$

Let us construct algorithms $\mathfrak{T}$ and ϕ in the alphabet A_π^{sa} such that, for any $t_{\pi,1}$ and m, first,

$$\mathfrak{T}(t_{\pi,1}) \overset{+}{\in} t_0, \qquad \varphi(t_{\pi,1}) \overset{+}{\in} t_0$$

and second,

$$\langle \mathfrak{T}(t_{\pi,1}) \rangle_2 (m) \simeq \underset{\text{p}}{\max}(W_{m,1} \square \ldots \square W_{m,R_m}), \tag{2}$$

$$\langle \varphi(t_{\pi,1}) \rangle_0 (m) \simeq \mu_n (W_{m,n} \underset{\text{p}}{=} \max(W_{m,1} \square \ldots \square W_{m,R_m})). \tag{3}$$

Let $t_{\pi,1}$ be a complete cipher of a uniformly continuous function of type $(\theta \to Д)$. Then $\langle \mathfrak{T}(t_{\pi,1}) \rangle_2 (m) \overset{+}{\in} \underline{\text{rat}}$. In addition, the condition

$$W_{m,n} \underset{\text{p}}{=} \max(W_{m,1} \square \ldots \square W_{m,R_m})$$

is algorithmically verifiable for admissible values of the parameters, and we have

$$\forall m(\langle \varphi(t_{\pi,1}) \rangle_0 (m) \overset{+}{\in} \underline{\text{nat}}).$$

We introduce the notation

$$H \leftrightharpoons \langle \mathfrak{T}(t_{\pi,1}) \rangle_2, \quad \alpha \leftrightharpoons \langle \varphi(t_{\pi,1}) \rangle_0.$$

We have, for every m,

$$H(m) \doteq \langle \mathfrak{T}(t_{\pi,1}) \rangle_2 (m) \underset{\text{p}}{=} W_{m,\alpha(m)}.$$

Let m be any natural number. We shall bound $M(H(m+1) - H(m))$ above.

Since $\mathfrak{S}(Q_m)$ is a finite 2^{-Q_m}-net in the space $\mathfrak{M}$ and $U_{m+1,\alpha(m+1)} \overset{+}{\in} \theta$, we have

$$\exists j \mathfrak{A},$$

where

$$\mathfrak{A} \leftrightharpoons (j \leqslant R_m \,\&\, \rho(U_{m+1,\alpha(m+1)} \square U_{m,j}) < 2^{-Q_m}).$$

Let j be a natural number satisfying condition $\mathfrak{A}$. Then

$$M(V_{m+1,\alpha(m+1)} - V_{m,j}) < 2^{-(m+2)}. \tag{4}$$

Further, since $V_{m+1,\alpha(m+1)} \overset{+}{\in} \underline{\text{real dup}}$ & $V_{m,j} \overset{+}{\in} \underline{\text{real dup}}$, we have

$$M(V_{m+1,\alpha(m+1)} - W_{m+1,\alpha(m+1)}) \leqslant 2^{-(m+4)}, \tag{5}$$

$$M(V_{m,j} - W_{m,j}) \leqslant 2^{-(m+3)}. \tag{6}$$

On the basis of (3) we have

$$W_{m,j} \leqslant W_{m,\alpha(m)}. \tag{7}$$

From (4)–(7) it follows that

$$W_{m+1,\,\alpha(m+1)} \leqslant V_{m+1,\,\alpha(m+1)} + 2^{-(m+4)} < V_{m,\,j} + 2^{-(m+2)}$$
$$+ 2^{-(m+4)} \leqslant W_{m,\,j} + 2^{-(m+3)} + 2^{-(m+2)} + 2^{-(m+4)} < W_{m,\,\alpha(m)} + 2^{-(m+1)}.$$

Hence

$$W_{m+1,\,\alpha(m+1)} - W_{m,\,\alpha(m)} < 2^{-(m+1)}. \quad (8)$$

In addition, from the special property of the algorithm $\mathfrak{C}$ mentioned above, it follows that

$$\forall i\,(i \leqslant R_m \supset U_{m+1,\,i} \doteq U_{m,\,i}).$$

Hence

$$V_{m+1,\,\alpha(m)} \doteq V_{m,\,\alpha(m)}. \quad (9)$$

In addition,

$$M(V_{m+1,\,\alpha(m)} - W_{m+1,\,\alpha(m)}) \leqslant 2^{-(m+4)}, \quad (10)$$

$$M(V_{m,\,\alpha(m)} - W_{m,\,\alpha(m)}) \leqslant 2^{-(m+3)}. \quad (11)$$

From (9)–(11) it follows that

$$M(W_{m,\,\alpha(m)} - W_{m+1,\,\alpha(m)}) \leqslant 2^{-(m+4)} + 2^{-(m+3)} < 2^{-(m+2)}. \quad (12)$$

Further, it follows from (3) that

$$W_{m+1,\,\alpha(m)} \leqslant W_{m+1,\,\alpha(m+1)}. \quad (13)$$

From (12) and (13) we obtain

$$W_{m,\,\alpha(m)} < W_{m+1,\,\alpha(m)} + 2^{-(m+2)} \leqslant W_{m+1,\,\alpha(m+1)} + 2^{-(m+2)}.$$

Hence

$$W_{m,\,\alpha(m)} - W_{m+1,\,\alpha(m+1)} < 2^{-(m+2)}. \quad (14)$$

(8) and (14) imply the inequality

$$M(W_{m+1,\,\alpha(m+1)} - W_{m,\,\alpha(m)}) < 2^{-(m+1)}. \quad (15)$$

From (15), (3), and (2) it follows that

$$M(H(m+1) - H(m)) < 2^{-(m+1)}. \quad (16)$$

This implies that

$$\forall kmn\,(m,\ n \geqslant k \supset M(H(m) - H(n)) < 2^{-k}).$$

Therefore H is a fundamental sequence of rational numbers and the algorithm in the alphabet $\mathrm{A}_0^{\mathrm{sa}}$ transforming any natural number k into k is a regulator of convergence in itself of this fundamental sequence. We denote by $\mathfrak{C}$ the algorithm in the alphabet $\mathrm{A}_\pi^{\mathrm{sa}}$ transforming any word in the alphabet A_π into the transcription of the normal algorithm in the alphabet A_0^{sa} defined by the schema

$$\{\rightarrow\cdot$$

We have

$$\forall t_{\pi,1} m (\langle \mathfrak{C}(t_{\pi,1})\rangle_0 (m) \doteq m).$$

From what has been said above it follows that the word

$$\mathfrak{T}(t_{\pi,1}) \Diamond \mathfrak{C}(t_{\pi,1})$$

is a real duplex.

Let us denote by $\mathfrak{A}$ the algorithm in the alphabet $A_\text{Д}^{sa}$ such that

$$\forall t_{\pi,1} (\mathfrak{A}(t_{\pi,1}) \simeq \mathfrak{T}(t_{\pi,1}) \Diamond \mathfrak{C}(t_{\pi,1})).$$

The algorithm $\mathfrak{A}$ is the one required: it satisfies condition (1).

In fact, let $t_{\pi,1}$ be a complete cipher of a uniformly continuous function of type $(\theta \rightarrow Д)$, let X be an arbitrary point of the space $\mathfrak{M}$, and let m be any natural number. We introduce the notation

$$T \leftrightharpoons \underbrace{t_{\pi,1}}_{\pi}(X).$$

We have

$$\exists j \mathfrak{B},$$

where

$$\mathfrak{B} \leftrightharpoons (j \leqslant R_m \& \rho(X \square U_{m,j}) < 2^{-\varrho m}).$$

Let j be a natural number satisfying condition $\mathfrak{B}$. We have

$$M(T - V_{m,j}) < 2^{-(m+2)}.$$

In addition,

$$M(V_{m,j} - W_{m,j}) \leqslant 2^{-(m+3)},$$

$$W_{m,j} \leqslant W_{m,\alpha(m)} = \underbrace{\mathfrak{A}(t_{\pi,1})}(m) \leqslant \mathfrak{A}(t_{\pi,1}) + 2^{-m}.$$

Hence

$$T < V_{m,j} + 2^{-(m+2)} \leqslant W_{m,j} + 2^{-(m+3)} + 2^{-(m+2)} < \mathfrak{A}(t_{\pi,1}) + 2 \cdot 2^{-m}.$$

Therefore

$$\forall m (T - \mathfrak{A}(t_{\pi,1}) < 2 \cdot 2^{-m}). \tag{17}$$

From (17) it follows that

$$T \leqslant \mathfrak{A}(t_{\pi,1}). \tag{18}$$

On the other hand, let n be any natural number. We have

$$\forall m (m \geqslant n+1 \supset M(H(m) - H(n+1)) < 2^{-(n+1)}).$$

Hence

$$M(\mathfrak{A}(t_{\pi,1}) - H(n+1)) \leqslant 2^{-(n+1)},$$

$$\mathfrak{A}(t_{\pi,1}) - 2^{-(n+1)} \leqslant H(n+1). \tag{19}$$

Now we note that

$$H(n+1) = W_{n+1,\,\alpha(n+1)} \leqslant V_{n+1,\,\alpha(n+1)} + 2^{-(n+4)}$$
$$= \underline{t_{\pi,1}}_{\pi}(U_{n+1,\,\alpha(n+1)}) + 2^{-(n+4)}.$$

We also have

$$M(\mathfrak{A}(t_{\pi,1}) - H(n+1)) \leqslant 2^{-(n+1)}.$$

Hence $\mathfrak{A}(t_{\pi,1}) - (2^{-(n+1)} + 2^{-(n+4)}) \leqslant \underline{t_{\pi,1}}_{\pi}(U_{n+1,\,\alpha(n+1)})$,

$$\mathfrak{A}(t_{\pi,1}) - 2^{-n} < \underline{t_{\pi,1}}_{\pi}(U_{n+1,\,\alpha(n+1)}). \tag{20}$$

From (20) it follows that $\forall n \exists Y(\mathfrak{A}(t_{\pi,1}) - 2^{-n} < \underline{t_{\pi,1}}_{\pi}(Y))$. Hence

$$\mathfrak{A}(t_{\pi,1})\ \underline{\text{lub}}_{\mathfrak{M}}\ \underline{t_{\pi,1}}_{\pi}.$$

Theorem 11.2.1 is proved.

11.2.2. *If* $\mathfrak{M}$ *is an almost totally bounded space, then, for any algorithm* $\lambda_{\mathrm{n},1}$ *in the alphabet* $\mathrm{A}_{\mathrm{n}}^{\mathrm{sa}}$ *which is a uniformly continuous function of type* $(\theta \to Д)$, *a duplex* x *such that* $x\ \underline{\text{lub}}_{\mathfrak{M}}\ \lambda_{\mathrm{n},1}$ *is potentially realizable.*

Theorem 11.2.2 is easily proved on the basis of 11.2.1 by the method of "natural" logical deduction (i.e. by logical deduction from assumed premises).

If in the formulations of Theorems 11.2.1 and 11.2.2 we substitute the expression "$\underline{\text{glb}}_{\mathfrak{M}}$" for the expression "$\underline{\text{lub}}_{\mathfrak{M}}$", we obtain true propositions. For the proof it suffices to note that, for any duplex x and any functions $\lambda_{\mathrm{n},1}$ and $\lambda_{\mathrm{n},2}$ of type $(\theta \to Д)$ such that $\lambda_{\mathrm{n},2}$ is obtained from $\lambda_{\mathrm{n},1}$ by multiplication by -1,

$$x\ \underline{\text{glb}}_{\mathfrak{M}}\ \lambda_{\mathrm{n},1} \equiv -x\ \underline{\text{lub}}_{\mathfrak{M}}\ \lambda_{\mathrm{n},2}. \tag{21}$$

The initially given object for the construction of the algorithm $\mathfrak{A}$ figuring in the proof of Theorem 11.2.2 is the algorithm $\mathfrak{S}$. In the theory of almost totally bounded (totally bounded) spaces the natural objects of study are pairs consisting of a space and a fixed algorithm for constructing nets (perfect nets) in this space. Such a pair we shall call a *space with fixed algorithm for constructing nets* (respectively, *perfect nets*).

Having in mind some space $\mathfrak{M}$ with fixed algorithm for constructing nets (perfect nets) $\mathfrak{S}$, we shall call the algorithm $\mathfrak{A}$ mentioned above *the standard algorithm for constructing least upper bounds* and we shall denote it by $\mathrm{Sup}_{\mathfrak{M},\mathfrak{S}}$. The algorithm for constructing greatest lower bounds of complete ciphers of uniformly continuous functions of type $(\theta \to Д)$, obtained from $\mathfrak{A}$ with the help of

(21), will be called *the standard algorithm for constructing greatest lower bounds* and will be denoted by $\mathrm{Inf}_{\mathfrak{M},\mathfrak{S}}$. In those cases where it is clear from the context which algorithm for constructing nets (perfect nets) is meant, we shall use the designations $\mathrm{Sup}_{\mathfrak{M}}$ and $\mathrm{Inf}_{\mathfrak{M}}$ instead of $\mathrm{Sup}_{\mathfrak{M},\mathfrak{S}}$ and $\mathrm{Inf}_{\mathfrak{M},\mathfrak{S}}$, respectively.

In §7.3 we proved (Theorem 7.3.1) that the set of Δ-points of any Δ-segment and the set of Δ-points of any Δ-interval are almost totally bounded sets. Hence in Theorems 11.2.1 and 11.2.2 we can use as $\mathfrak{M}$ the metric spaces induced by the metric space of all real duplexes E in these sets.

11.3. The set $(t_{\pi,1} \in \underline{\text{comp. ciph}_1})$, constructed for the case where the role of $\widetilde{\mathfrak{M}}$ is played by the metric space of all real duplexes E, is denoted by $\amalg_{\mathfrak{M}}$. For the elements of this set one defines in a natural way the operations of constructing the absolute value of an element, the maximum, minimum and sum of any finite sequence of elements, the difference of any two elements, and the product of an element and a real duplex. These operations will be denoted, respectively, as follows:

$$\underset{\text{c.c}}{M},\ \underset{\text{c.c}}{\max},\ \underset{\text{c.c}}{\min},\ \underset{\text{c.c}}{+},\ \underset{\text{c.c}}{-},\ \underset{\text{c.c}}{\cdot}\,.$$

We shall not describe here the algorithms giving each of these operations. We shall only mention that the operations $M_{\text{c.c}}$, $+_{\text{c.c}}$, and $-_{\text{c.c}}$ are defined in such a way that, for any elements $t_{\pi,1}$ and $t_{\pi,2}$ of the set $\amalg_{\mathfrak{M}}$,

$$\forall X(\underline{\underset{\text{c.c}}{M}(t_{\pi,1})}_{\pi}(X) = \underset{\text{B}}{M}(\underline{t_{\pi,1}}_{\pi}(X))),$$

$$\forall m\ (\overline{\underset{\text{c.c}}{M}(t_{\pi,1})}^{\pi}(m) = \overline{t_{\pi,1}}^{\pi}(m)),$$

$$\forall X(\underline{(t_{\pi,1} \underset{\text{c.c}}{\delta} t_{\pi,2})}_{\pi}(X) = \underline{t_{\pi,1}}_{\pi}(X) \underset{\text{B}}{\delta} \underline{t_{\pi,2}}_{\pi}(X)),$$

$$\forall m\ (\overline{(t_{\pi,1} \underset{\text{c.c}}{\delta} t_{\pi,2})}^{\pi}(m) = \max(\overline{t_{\pi,1}}^{\pi}(m+1) \,\square\, \overline{t_{\pi,2}}^{\pi}(m+1))),$$

where δ is either of the symbols $+$, $-$.

For elements of the set $\amalg_{\mathfrak{M}}$ one introduces also a binary relation $\leq_{\text{c.c}}$. We shall assume that $(t_{\pi,1} \leq_{\text{c.c}} t_{\pi,2})$ if

$$\forall X(\underline{t_{\pi,1}}_{\pi}(X) \underset{\text{B}}{\leqslant} \underline{t_{\pi,2}}_{\pi}(X)).$$

By simple arguments one can prove that, for any elements $t_{\pi,1}$ and $t_{\pi,2}$ of the set $\amalg_{\mathfrak{M}}$,

$$t_{\pi,1} \underset{c.c}{\leqslant} t_{\pi,2} \supset \mathrm{Sup}_{\mathfrak{M}}(t_{\pi,1}) \leqslant \mathrm{Sup}_{\mathfrak{M}}(t_{\pi,2}), \tag{22}$$

$$\mathrm{Sup}_{\mathfrak{M}}(t_{\pi,1} \underset{c.c}{+} t_{\pi,2}) \leqslant \mathrm{Sup}_{\mathfrak{M}}(t_{\pi,1}) + \mathrm{Sup}_{\mathfrak{M}}(t_{\pi,2}), \tag{23}$$

$$\underset{c.c}{M}(t_{\pi,1} \underset{c.c}{+} t_{\pi,2}) \underset{c.c}{\leqslant} \underset{c.c}{M}(t_{\pi,1}) \underset{c.c}{+} \underset{c.c}{M}(t_{\pi,2}). \tag{24}$$

In (22) and (23) it is assumed that $\mathfrak{M}$ is an almost totally bounded space with fixed algorithm for constructing nets.

With the help of (22)–(24) the following theorem is easily proved.

11.3.1. *If* $\mathfrak{M}$ *is an almost totally bounded space with fixed algorithm for constructing nets, then the algorithm* ρ^* *in the alphabet* $\mathrm{A}_{\mathfrak{p}}^{sa}$ *such that, for any words* $t_{\pi,1}$ *and* $t_{\pi,2}$ *in the alphabet* A_{π},

$$\rho^*(t_{\pi,1} \square t_{\pi,2}) \simeq \mathrm{Sup}_{\mathfrak{M}}(\underset{c.c}{M}(t_{\pi,2} \underset{c.c}{-} t_{\pi,1})),$$

is a metric function in the space $\text{Ш}_{\mathfrak{M}}$. *Moreover, for any elements* $t_{\pi,1}$ *and* $t_{\pi,2}$ *of the set* $\text{Ш}_{\mathfrak{M}}$,

$$\rho^*(t_{\pi,1} \square t_{\pi,2}) = 0 \equiv (t_{\pi,1} \underset{c.c}{\leqslant} t_{\pi,2}) \,\&\, (t_{\pi,2} \underset{c.c}{\leqslant} t_{\pi,1}).$$

The metric space

$$\mathrm{A}_{\pi},\ \text{Ш}_{\mathfrak{M}},\ \rho^*$$

will be denoted by $C_{\mathfrak{M}}$. This notation will be used only in the case where $\mathfrak{M}$ is an almost totally bounded space with fixed algorithm for constructing nets.

11.4. In this section we shall use the notation $\mathrm{A}_{\mathfrak{m}}$, $\mathrm{A}_{\mathfrak{n}}$, $\mathrm{A}_{\mathfrak{p}}$, θ, and the symbolism connected with it, with respect to the concrete case where the role of $\mathfrak{M}$ is played by the metric space $E\lfloor \mathfrak{x} \mathbin{\underline{\nabla}} \mathfrak{y}\rfloor$ (cf. §10.5), where $\mathfrak{x}$ and $\mathfrak{y}$ are fixed duplexes such that $\mathfrak{x} < \mathfrak{y}$. In the case considered here the alphabet $\mathrm{A}_{\mathfrak{n}}$ coincides with the alphabet $\mathrm{A}_{\mathfrak{m}}$. We shall also consider the alphabet Ч_4 (cf. 7.2).

We shall say that a word $c_{4,1}$ in the alphabet Ч_4 is the *standard description of a canonical polygonal function*, and also that it is a Π-*word*, if the following conditions are fulfilled:

1) $c_{4,1}$ is a σ-pair such that the σ-terms $[c_{4,1}]_1^{\sigma}$ and $[c_{4,1}]_2^{\sigma}$ of this pair are τ-systems of rational numbers;

2) $L_{\tau}([c_{4,1}]_1^{\sigma}) = L_{\tau}([c_{4,1}]_2^{\sigma})$;

3) if i is such that $1 \leq i < L_{\tau}([c_{4,1}]_1^{\sigma})$, then

$$[[c_{4,1}]_1^{\sigma}]_i^{\tau} < [[c_{4,1}]_1^{\sigma}]_{i+1}^{\tau}.$$

Briefly speaking, the word $c_{4,1}$ is called a Π-word if it has the form

$$R_1 \tau R_2 \tau \ldots \tau R_{\mathfrak{k}} \sigma R_{\mathfrak{k}+1} \dot{\tau} R_{\mathfrak{k}+2} \tau \ldots \tau R_{\mathfrak{k}+\mathfrak{k}}, \tag{1}$$

where $\mathfrak{k}$ is some natural number, $R_i \in \underline{\text{rat}}$ $(i = 1,2, \cdots, \mathfrak{k}+\mathfrak{k})$ and $R_1 < R_2 < \ldots \ldots < R_{\mathfrak{k}}$.

We associate with the П-word (1) a certain function of type (Д→ Д) in the following way. To begin with, we construct an algorithm $\mathfrak{L}$ in the alphabet $Ч_2^{sa}$ such that, for any rational number a,

if $a \leqslant R_1$, then $\mathfrak{L}(a) \doteqdot R_{\mathfrak{k}+1}$;

if $R_i < a \leqslant R_{i+1}$, then $\mathfrak{L}(a) \doteqdot R_{\mathfrak{k}+1} \dot{+} U_i \dot{\cdot} (a - R_i)$, where

$$U_i \leftrightharpoons (R_{\mathfrak{k}+i+1} - R_{\mathfrak{k}+i}) : (R_{i+1} - R_i) \quad (i = 1, \ldots, \mathfrak{k}-1);$$

if $R_{\mathfrak{k}} < a$, then $\mathfrak{L}(a) \doteqdot R_{\mathfrak{k}+\mathfrak{k}}$.

For rational numbers, each of the conditions standing immediately after the word "if" is algorithmically verifiable. Therefore the possibility of constructing an algorithm possessing the indicated properties follows from the theorem on the branching of algorithms, and from a proof of that theorem we obtain a construction of the desired algorithm.

The algorithm $\mathfrak{L}$ is a function of type (р→ р). It is easy to construct, starting from (1), its least Lipschitz coefficient in dimension 1. It is equal to

$$\max(M(U_1) \square \ldots \square M(U_{\mathfrak{k}-1})). \tag{2}$$

We denote it by Ξ. Applying to $\mathfrak{L}$ and Ξ the standard algorithm $\mathfrak{Z}_1^*$ for extending Lipschitz operators (cf. §10.4), we obtain a function of type (Д→ Д). We associate this function with the П-word (1).

From the given description it is clear that one can construct a normal algorithm in the alphabet $Ч_4^{sa}$ transforming any П-word into the transcription of the function of type (Д→ Д) corresponding to the given П-word. We shall denote this algorithm by the letter Γ and call it the *algorithm for polygonal interpretation of П-words*.

Speaking intuitive geometric language, one can say that the Γ-image of the word (1) is the transcription of the function of type (Д → Д) whose graph is the polygonal line having vertices at the points $(R_1, R_{\mathfrak{k}+1})$, $(R_2, R_{\mathfrak{k}+2})$, $\cdots$, $(R_{\mathfrak{k}} R_{\mathfrak{k}+\mathfrak{k}})$ and proceeding to the left of the point $(R_1, R_{\mathfrak{k}+1})$ and to the right of the point $(R_{\mathfrak{k}}, R_{\mathfrak{k}+\mathfrak{k}})$ on the halflines parallel to the x-axis.

We shall denote by Θ the algorithm in the alphabet $Ч_4^{sa}$ transforming any П-word $c_{4,1}$ into the transcription of a regulator of uniform continuity of the function $\langle\Gamma(c_{4,1})\rangle_3$ obtained in the following manner. First, we construct the least Lipschitz coefficient in dimension 1 of the function $\langle\Gamma(c_{4,1})\rangle_3$ (if $c_{4,1}$ has the form (1), then this coefficient is equal to (2)), and then, by the method described in §10.4, we construct, starting from this coefficient, the desired regulator of uniform continuity.

The algorithm in the alphabet $Ч_4^{sa} \cup \{\boxed{1}\}$, transforming any П-word $c_{4,1}$ into the word $\Gamma(c_{4,1})\boxed{1}\Theta(c_{4,1})$ will be denoted by $\mathfrak{V}$.

We shall say that the π-word (1) is *imbedded* in the segment $\mathfrak{x}\nabla\mathfrak{y}$ if $\mathfrak{x} \le R_1 < R_{\mathfrak{k}} \le \mathfrak{y}$.

For our immediate purposes it suffices to consider only those П-words which are imbedded in the segment $\mathfrak{x}\nabla\mathfrak{y}$.

Assuming that the role of $\mathfrak{M}$ is played by $E[\mathfrak{x}\nabla\mathfrak{y}]$, we can, on the basis of what has been said above, assert that if $c_{4,1}$ is a П-word imbedded in $\mathfrak{x}\nabla\mathfrak{y}$, then $\mathfrak{V}(c_{4,1})$ is an element of the set $Ш_{\mathfrak{M}}$. Under the same assumption about $\mathfrak{M}$, the following theorem about uniform approximation of complete ciphers of functions uniformly continuous on the segment by complete ciphers of polygonal functions is true.

11.4.1. *One can construct an algorithm Φ in the alphabet $A_\pi^{sa} \cup Ч_4$ transforming any word of the form $t_{\pi,1} \square k$, where $t_{\pi,1}$ is an element of the set $Ш_{\mathfrak{M}}$ and k is a natural number, into the* П*-word $\Phi(t_{\pi,1} \square k)$ imbedded in the segment $\mathfrak{x}\nabla\mathfrak{y}$ and such that*

$$\rho^*(t_{\pi,1}\square\mathfrak{V}(\Phi(t_{\pi,1}\square k))) < 2^{-k}, \tag{3}$$

where ρ^* is the metric function in the space $C_{\mathfrak{M}}$.[1] *(The letter Φ denotes some function variable corresponding to the alphabet $A_\pi \cup Ч_4$).*

Proof. From the inequality $\mathfrak{x} < \mathfrak{y}$ it follows that

$$\exists n(\underline{\gamma_\downarrow(\mathfrak{x})}(n) < \underline{\gamma_\uparrow(\mathfrak{y})}(n))$$

[cf. 5.2.1 and §5.3 (1)–(2)]. In addition, it follows from 5.3.3 that, for every n,

$$0 \leqslant \underline{\gamma_\downarrow(\mathfrak{x})}(n) - \mathfrak{x} \leqslant 2^{-n}, \qquad 0 \leqslant \mathfrak{y} - \underline{\gamma_\uparrow(\mathfrak{y})}(n) \leqslant 2^{-n}.$$

---

1) Here it is assumed that in the space $E[\mathfrak{x}\nabla\mathfrak{y}]$ an algorithm for constructing nets is fixed (for example, the one which is obtained on the basis of Remark 1 after 7.3.1).

We introduce the notation

$$Q_k \rightleftharpoons \overline{t_{\pi,1}}^{\pi}(k+1),$$

$$D \rightleftharpoons \mu_n(\underline{\gamma_\downarrow(\mathfrak{x})}(n) < \underline{\gamma_\uparrow(\mathfrak{y})}(n)).$$

We construct an algorithm $\mathfrak{R}$ in the alphabet A_π^{sa} such that, for any $t_{\pi,1}$ and k,

$$\mathfrak{R}(t_{\pi,1}\square k) \simeq \max(D \square Q_k + 1).$$

We introduce the notation

$$F_k \rightleftharpoons \underline{\gamma_\downarrow(\mathfrak{x})}(\mathfrak{R}(t_{\pi,1}\square k)), \quad G_k \rightleftharpoons \underline{\gamma_\uparrow(\mathfrak{y})}(\mathfrak{R}(t_{\pi,1}\square k)).$$

It follows from 5.3.3 that, for any element $t_{\pi,1}$ of the set $\text{Ш}_{\mathfrak{M}}$ and any natural number k,

$$\mathfrak{x} \leqslant F_k < G_k \leqslant \mathfrak{y},$$

$$F_k - \mathfrak{x} \leqslant 2^{-(Q_k+1)}, \qquad \mathfrak{y} - G_k \leqslant 2^{-(Q_k+1)}. \tag{4}$$

We also introduce the following notation:

$$T_k \rightleftharpoons \mu_n(G_k - F_k \leqslant 2^n),$$

$$\xi_k \rightleftharpoons 2^{T_k+Q_k+1}, \qquad \zeta_k \rightleftharpoons (G_k - F_k) : \xi_k,$$

$$\left.\begin{array}{l} N_{k,l} \rightleftharpoons F_k + \zeta_k \cdot (l-1), \\ P_{k,l} \rightleftharpoons \underline{t_{\pi,1}}_{\pi}(N_{k,l}), \\ H_{k,l} \rightleftharpoons \underline{P_{k,l}}(\overline{P_{k,l}}(k+1)) \end{array}\right\} l = 1, 2, \ldots, \xi_k + 1.$$

If $t_{\pi,1}$ is an element of the set $\text{Ш}_{\mathfrak{M}}$ and k is a natural number, then

$$0 < \zeta_k \leqslant 2^{-(Q_k+1)} < 2^{-Q_k}, \tag{5}$$

$$N_{k,0} = F_k, \qquad N_{k,\xi_k+1} = G_k.$$

We construct an algorithm $\mathfrak{F}$ in the alphabet $A_\pi^{sa} \cup \text{Ч}_4$ such that, for any $t_{\pi,1}$ and k,

$$\mathfrak{F}(t_{\pi,1}\square k) \simeq N_{k,1}\tau N_{k,2}\tau\ldots\tau N_{k,\xi_k+1}\sigma H_{k,1}\tau H_{k,2}\tau\ldots\tau H_{k,\xi_k+1}.$$

Let us prove that, for any word $t_{\pi,1}$ which is an element of the set $\text{Ш}_{\mathfrak{M}}$ and any natural number k,

a) $\mathfrak{F}(t_{\pi,1}\square k)$ is a Π-word imbedded in the segment $\mathfrak{x} \underline{\nabla} \mathfrak{y}$, and

b) the algorithm $\mathfrak{F}$ satisfies condition (3) (in this condition the function variable Φ serves as parameter).

Let $t_{\pi,1}$ be an arbitrary element of the set $\amalg_{\mathfrak{M}}$ and let k be any natural number. Then

$$N_{k,l} \dot{\in} \underline{\text{rat}} \,\&\, \mathfrak{x} \leqslant N_{k,l} \leqslant \mathfrak{y} \quad (l=1,\ldots,\ \xi_k+1),$$
$$N_{k,l} < N_{k,l+1} \quad (l=1,\ldots,\ \xi_k),$$
$$H_{k,l} \dot{\in} \underline{\text{rat}} \quad (l=1,\ldots,\ \xi_k+1).$$

From these statements, a) follows.

We introduce the notation

$$U \leftrightharpoons \underline{t_{\pi,1}}_{\pi}, \quad V_k \leftrightharpoons \underline{\mathfrak{B}(\mathfrak{F}(t_{\pi,1} \square k))}_{|\pi}.$$

Let z be any point of the segment $\mathfrak{x} \nabla \mathfrak{y}$. We estimate an upper bound on $M(U(z)-V_k(z))$.

Let us suppose that $z \leq N_{k,1}$. Then, on the basis of (4), we have

$$M(z - N_{k,1}) \leqslant 2^{-(Q_k+1)} < 2^{-Q_k}.$$

Hence

$$M(U(z) - U(N_{k+1})) < 2^{-(k+1)}.$$

Further,

$$V_k(z) = V_k(N_{k,1}) = H_{k,1},$$
$$M(H_{k,1} - U(N_{k,1})) \leqslant 2^{-(k+1)}.$$

Hence

$$M(U(z) - V_k(z)) < 2^{-k}. \tag{6}$$

If $N_{k,\xi_k+1} \leq z$, then in similar fashion we obtain (6).

Thus

$$(z \leqslant N_{k,1} \vee N_{k,\xi_k+1} \leqslant z) \supset M(U(z) - V_k(z)) < 2^{-k}. \tag{7}$$

Let us assume that $N_{k,l} \leq z \leq N_{k,l+1}$, where l is one of the numbers 1, 2, $\cdots$ $\cdots$, ξ_k. Then on the basis of (5) we have

$$M(z - N_{k,l}) < 2^{-Q_k}, \quad M(z - N_{k,l+1}) < 2^{-Q_k}.$$

Hence

$$P_{k,l} - 2^{-(k+1)} < U(z) < P_{k,l} + 2^{-(k+1)}, \tag{8}$$
$$P_{k,l+1} - 2^{-(k+1)} < U(z) < P_{k,l+1} + 2^{-(k+1)}. \tag{9}$$

If $H_{k,l} \leq H_{k,l+1}$, then

$$P_{k,l} - 2^{-(k+1)} \leqslant H_{k,l} \leqslant V_k(z) \leqslant H_{k,l+1} \leqslant P_{k,l+1} + 2^{-(k+1)},$$
$$P_{k,l} \leqslant V_k(z) + 2^{-(k+1)}, \quad V_k(z) - 2^{-(k+1)} \leqslant P_{k,l+1}. \tag{10}$$

From (8)–(10) it follows that

$$V_k(z) - 2^{-k} < U(z) < V_k(z) + 2^{-k},$$
$$M(U(z) - V_k(z)) < 2^{-k}.$$

If $H_{k,l+1} < H_{k,l}$, then

$$P_{k,l+1} - 2^{-(k+1)} \leqslant H_{k,l+1} \leqslant V_k(z) \leqslant H_{k,l} \leqslant P_{k,l} + 2^{-(k+1)},$$
$$P_{k,l+1} \leqslant V_k(z) + 2^{-(k+1)}, \quad V_k(z) - 2^{-(k+1)} \leqslant P_{k,l}.$$

Hence we obtain the inequality (6) also in the case where $H_{k,l+1} < H_{k,l}$.

$H_{k,l}$ and $H_{k,l+1}$ are rational numbers. Hence

$$(H_{k,l} \leqslant H_{k,l+1}) \vee (H_{k,l+1} < H_{k,l}).$$

Therefore

$$N_{k,l} \leqslant z \leqslant N_{k,l+1} \supset M(U(z) - V_k(z)) < 2^{-k}. \tag{11}$$

Let us introduce the notation

$$\mathfrak{P} \leftrightharpoons (z \leqslant N_{k,1} \vee N_{k,1} \leqslant z \leqslant N_{k,2} \vee \ldots \vee N_{k,\xi_k} \leqslant z \leqslant N_{k,\xi_k+1} \vee N_{k,\xi_k+1} \leqslant z)$$

$$\mathfrak{Q} \leftrightharpoons (z \leqslant N_{k,1} \vee N_{k,1} \leqslant z) \,\&\, (z \leqslant N_{k,2} \vee N_{k,2} \leqslant z)$$
$$\ldots \&(z \leqslant N_{k,\xi_k+1} \vee N_{k,\xi_k+1} \leqslant z).$$

It is not difficult to prove that

$$\mathfrak{P} \equiv \mathfrak{Q}.$$

In addition, it follows from §2.6 (7) and §4.5 (42) that

$$\neg\neg\mathfrak{Q}.$$

Hence

$$\neg\neg\mathfrak{P}.$$

Further, on the basis of (7) and (11) we have

$$\mathfrak{P} \supset M(U(z) - V_k(z)) < 2^{-k}.$$

Hence

$$\neg\neg(M(U(z) - V_k(z)) < 2^{-k}).$$

Finally, on the basis of §4.5 (20) we obtain

$$M(U(z) - V_k(z)) < 2^{-k}.$$

From this it follows that

$$\rho^*(t_{\pi,1}\square\mathfrak{B}(\mathfrak{F}(t_{\pi,1}\square k)))<2^{-k}.$$

Theorem 11.4.1 is proved.

11.4.2. *For any uniformly continuous function* $\lambda_{3,1}$ *of type* $(\theta \to Д)$ *and any natural number* k, *there is a potentially realizable* Π*-word* $c_{4,1}$ *imbedded in the segment* $\mathfrak{x}\,\underline{\nabla}\,\mathfrak{y}$ *and such that*

$$\forall x\,(M(\lambda_{3,1}(x)-\langle\Gamma(c_{4,1})\rangle_3(x))<2^{-k}).$$

This theorem is easily proved on the basis of 11.4.1 by the method of "natural" deduction.

11.5. We shall say that a space $\mathfrak{M}$ is *almost compact* if $\mathfrak{M}$ is almost complete and almost totally bounded. We shall say that a space $\mathfrak{M}$ is *compact* if it is complete and totally bounded.

The next theorem follows from 10.3.1 and 11.1.2.

11.5.1. *Every compact space is almost compact.*

The following theorem is a consequence of 10.3.2 and 11.1.3.

11.5.2. *If* $\mathfrak{M}$ *is an almost compact space and* $\mathfrak{P}$ *is a normal formula, then* $\mathfrak{M}$ *is a compact space.*

Let x and y be real duplexes such that $x \leq y$, and let r and s be real F-numbers such that $r \leq s$. As in the preceding sections, we shall denote by $E[x\,\underline{\nabla}\,y]$ the metric space induced by the metric space of all real duplexes E in the set of all $Д$-points of the $Д$-segment $x\,\underline{\nabla}\,y$; we denote by $E_0[r\,\underline{\nabla}\,s]$ the semimetric space induced by the semimetric space of all real F-numbers in the set of all B-points of the B-segment $r\,\underline{\nabla}\,s$. The next theorem follows from theorems about $Д$-segments and B-segments proved in preceding sections.

11.5.3. $E[x\,\underline{\nabla}\,y]$ *is a compact metric space.* $E_0[r\,\underline{\nabla}\,s]$ *is an almost compact semimetric space.*

In the classical theory of metric spaces one proves (by classical logic and classical set theory) the pairwise equivalence of the following properties of metric spaces.

a) From every covering of the space by open sets one can extract a finite covering.

b) From every sequence of points one can extract a subsequence converging in the space.

c) The space is complete and totally bounded.

In statements a)–c) we have in mind those definitions of the concepts occurring in them which are given in classical mathematics. Each of the properties a)–c) is considered in classical mathematics as a characteristic property of the concept "compact space".

Going over to the concepts of constructive mathematics with the same names and to the constructive interpretation of propositions, one can state the following.

The space $E[x \underline{\nabla} y]$ possesses property c), but does not possess property b) (cf. 10.6.5) and does not possess property a) (cf. Zaslavskiĭ [18]).

We note (without proof) the following theorem.

11.5.4. *The standard FR-completion of any totally bounded metric space is a compact metric space. The standard F-completion of any almost totally bounded metric space is an almost compact semimetric space.*

§12. CONSTRUCTIVE NORMED AND CONSTRUCTIVE HILBERT SPACES

In this section we keep all the assumptions and notation introduced at the beginning of §§9.1 and 9.2.

12.1. Having in mind some metric or semimetric space

$$A_{\mathfrak{m}}, \mathfrak{P}, \rho,$$

we assume that the following constructive objects are also given:

a) a normal algorithm $+_{\theta}$ in the alphabet $A^{sa}_{\mathfrak{m}}$ of type $(\mathfrak{p}\theta \to \theta)_{\mathfrak{m}}$, called the *addition algorithm*;

b) a normal algorithm $\cdot_{\theta}$ in the alphabet $A^{sa}_{\mathfrak{n}}$ of type $(\mathfrak{p}\theta \to \theta)_{\mathfrak{n}}$, called the *algorithm for multiplying by rational numbers*;

c) an element $\mathfrak{O}$ of the set $\mathfrak{P}$, called *the standard null element* of the set $\mathfrak{P}$.

Basing ourselves on the initially given objects just enumerated, we construct two more algorithms: first, an algorithm $-_{\theta}$ in the alphabet $A^{sa}_{\mathfrak{m}}$ such that

$$\forall Y(\underset{\theta}{-}(Y) \simeq \underset{\theta}{\cdot}(-1 \square Y)),$$

$$\forall XY(\underset{\theta}{-}(X \square Y) \simeq \underset{\theta}{+}(X \square \underset{\theta}{\cdot}(-1 \square Y))),$$

and second, an algorithm N_{θ} in the alphabet $A^{sa}_{\mathfrak{m}}$ such that

$$\forall X(N_{\theta}(X) \simeq \rho(\mathfrak{O} \square X)).$$

We make some conventions about abbreviation of certain terms. Let Θ_1, Θ_2, and Θ_3 be any individual terms. In accordance with established mathematical practice, we agree to denote the terms

$$\underset{\theta}{+}(\Theta_1 \square \Theta_2), \quad \underset{\theta}{-}(\Theta_1 \square \Theta_2), \quad \underset{\theta}{\cdot}(\Theta_3 \square \Theta_1)$$

by the expressions

$$(\Theta_1 \underset{\theta}{+} \Theta_2), \quad (\Theta_1 \underset{\theta}{-} \Theta_2), \quad (\Theta_3 \underset{\theta}{\cdot} \Theta_1).$$

respectively. In using abbreviations of terms and formulas, we shall assume that the symbol $\cdot_\theta$ has rank 1 and the symbols $+_\theta$ and $-_\theta$ have rank 2 (cf. §1.14, V).

Instead of the notation $+_\theta$, $-_\theta$, $\cdot_\theta$ and N_θ, we shall use the shorter notation $+$, $-$, $\cdot$, N, if the use of these abbreviations does not lead to ambiguity.

The sextuple

$$\mathrm{A}_{\mathfrak{m}},\ \mathfrak{P},\ \rho,\ \underset{\theta}{+},\ \underset{\theta}{\cdot},\ \mathfrak{O}$$

will be called a *constructive normed space* (*constructive seminormed space*) if the list

$$\mathrm{A}_{\mathfrak{m}},\ \mathfrak{P},\ \rho$$

is a constructive metric (respectively, semimetric) space and, for any elements X, Y, Z of the set $\mathfrak{P}$ and any rational numbers a and b, the following conditions are fulfilled:

$$X + Y \underset{\rho}{=} Y + X, \tag{1}$$

$$X + (Y + Z) \underset{\rho}{=} (X + Y) + Z, \tag{2}$$

$$X + \mathfrak{O} \underset{\rho}{=} X, \tag{3}$$

$$+(X \square -(X)) \underset{\rho}{=} \mathfrak{O}, \tag{4}$$

$$a \underset{\theta}{\cdot} (b \underset{\theta}{\cdot} X) \underset{\rho}{=} (a \underset{\mathrm{P}}{\cdot} b) \underset{\theta}{\cdot} X, \tag{5}$$

$$1 \cdot X \underset{\rho}{=} X, \tag{6}$$

$$a \cdot (X + Y) \underset{\rho}{=} a \cdot X + a \cdot Y, \tag{7}$$

$$(a \underset{\mathrm{P}}{+} b) \cdot X \underset{\rho}{=} a \cdot X \underset{\theta}{+} b \cdot X, \tag{8}$$

$$\rho(X \square Y) \underset{\mathrm{B}}{=} \rho(\mathfrak{O} \square Y - X), \tag{9}$$

$$N_\theta(a \underset{\theta}{\cdot} X) \underset{\mathrm{B}}{=} M(a) \underset{\mathrm{B}}{\cdot} N_\theta(X). \tag{10}$$

We shall often omit the adjective "constructive" in the terms "constructive normed space" and "constructive seminormed space". In some cases we shall use the term "space" without any modifiers. We did this earlier in §§9–11 on the basis of the convention introduced in §9.1. However, now we shall introduce a new convention which nullifies for §12 the earlier convention and consists of the following. In every case where the term "space" is used without modifiers, one intends that, instead of this term, one can substitute either of the two terms "constructive normed space" and "constructive seminormed space".

If the list $A_{\mathfrak{m}}$, $\mathfrak{P}$, ρ, $+_\theta$, $\cdot_\theta$, $\mathfrak{O}$ is a normed space (seminormed space), then the algorithm N_θ is called the *algorithm computing the norm* (respectively, *the seminorm*) in this space. Formula (10) gives one of the properties of the norm (seminorm). The following states some other simple properties of the norm (seminorm).

12.1.1. *If the list* $A_{\mathfrak{m}}$, $\mathfrak{P}$, ρ, $+_\theta$, $\cdot_\theta$, $\mathfrak{O}$ *is a normed (seminormed) space and if* X, Y *and* Z *are arbitrary elements of the set* $\mathfrak{P}$, *then*

$$N(X-X)=0. \tag{11}$$

$$N(X-\mathfrak{O})=N(X), \tag{12}$$

$$N(X-Z)\leqslant N(Y-X)+N(Z-Y). \tag{13}$$

It is possible to present constructive normed (seminormed) spaces in such a way that, to start with, one gives the algorithm computing the norm (seminorm), but not the metric (semimetric) function. Let us assume that there is given an alphabet $A_{\mathfrak{m}}$, a set $\mathfrak{P}$ of the type characterized above, an algorithm $+_\theta$ in the alphabet $A_{\mathfrak{m}}^{sa}$ of type $(\theta\theta\to\theta)_{\mathfrak{m}}$, an algorithm $\cdot_\theta$ in the alphabet $A_{\mathfrak{n}}^{sa}$ of type $(\mathfrak{p}\theta\to\theta)_{\mathfrak{n}}$ and some element $\mathfrak{O}$ of the set $\mathfrak{P}$. Let us also assume that there is given an algorithm N^* in the alphabet $A_{\mathfrak{n}}^{sa}$ of type $(\theta\to Д)_{\mathfrak{n}}$ [of type $(\theta\to В)_{\mathfrak{n}}$], such that, for any elements X, Y, and Z of the set $\mathfrak{P}$ and any rational number a,

$$\left.\begin{array}{l} N^*(X-X)=0, \\ N^*(X-\mathfrak{O})=N^*(X), \\ N^*(X-Z)\leqslant N^*(Y-X)+N^*(Z-Y), \\ N^*(a \underset{\theta}{\cdot} X)=M(a)\underset{В}{\cdot} N^*(X). \end{array}\right\} \tag{*}$$

We construct an algorithm ρ in the alphabet $A_{\mathfrak{n}}^{sa}$ such that

$$\forall XY(\rho(X\square Y)\simeq N^*(Y-X)).$$

It is not difficult to prove that ρ is a metric function in the set $\mathfrak{P}$ such that, first,

$$\forall X (N_\theta(X) \simeq N^*(X))$$

and second, for any X, Y, and a, conditions (9) and (10) are fulfilled, Moreover, if for any X, Y, Z, a and b conditions (1)–(8) are fulfilled, then the list $\mathrm{A}_{\mathfrak{m}}$, $\mathfrak{P}$, ρ, $+_\theta$, $\cdot_\theta$, $\mathfrak{O}$ is a normed (seminormed) space.[1)]

Let us assume now that there is given a normed space (seminormed space)

$$\mathrm{A}_{\mathfrak{m}},\ \mathfrak{P},\ \rho,\ \underset{\theta}{+},\ \underset{\theta}{\cdot},\ \mathfrak{O}.$$

Let us denote this space by the letter $\mathfrak{N}$.

The following theorem 12.1.2, easily proved on the basis of the properties of the metric (respectively, semimetric) function and propositions (1)–(13), states some additional properties of the algorithms ρ, N_θ, $+_\theta$, $-_\theta$, and $\cdot_\theta$.

12.1.2. *For any elements* X, Y, Z *and* U *of the set* $\mathfrak{P}$ *and any rational numbers* a *and* b,

$$\rho(X+Z \square Y+Z) = \rho(X \square Y); \tag{14}$$

$$\rho(X \square Y) = N(Y - X) = N(X - Y); \tag{15}$$

$$N(X) \geqslant 0, \quad N(\mathfrak{O}) = 0; \tag{16}$$

$$N(X) = 0 \supset X \underset{\rho}{=} \mathfrak{O}; \tag{17}$$

$$N(X+Y) \leqslant N(X) + N(Y); \tag{18}$$

$$M(N(X) - N(Y)) \leqslant N(X - Y) = \rho(X \square Y), \tag{19}$$

and therefore N *is a* 1-*ary Lipschitz operator from the space* $\mathfrak{N}$ *into the space of all real duplexes (respectively, into the space of all real F-numbers)*;

$$X \underset{\rho}{=} Y \supset N(X) \underset{\text{B}}{=} N(Y); \tag{20}$$

$$\rho(X+Y \square Z+U) \leqslant \rho(X \square Z) + \rho(Y \square U), \tag{21}$$

and therefore the algorithm $+_\theta$ *is a binary Lipschitz operator from* $\mathfrak{N}$ *into* $\mathfrak{N}$;

$$X \underset{\rho}{=} Z \,\&\, Y \underset{\rho}{=} U \supset X+Y \underset{\rho}{=} Z+U; \tag{22}$$

$$\rho(X - Y \square Z - U) \leqslant \rho(X \square Z) + \rho(Y \square U), \tag{23}$$

and therefore the algorithm $-_\theta$ *is a binary Lipschitz operator from* $\mathfrak{N}$ *into* $\mathfrak{N}$;

---

1)The condition (*) differs from the axiom imposed on the norm in classical functional analysis. If, instead of condition (*), we imposed the condition borrowed from classical functional analysis, we would face the necessity of proving the proposition (20) formulated below. It is not known to the author whether such a proof is possible.

$$X \underset{\rho}{=} Z \,\&\, Y \underset{\rho}{=} U \supset X - Y \underset{\rho}{=} Z - U; \tag{24}$$

$$0 \cdot X \underset{\rho}{=} \mathfrak{O}, \qquad a \cdot \mathfrak{O} \underset{\rho}{=} \mathfrak{O}; \tag{25}$$

$$a \cdot X \underset{\rho}{=} \mathfrak{O} \supset a \underset{p}{=} 0 \vee X \underset{\rho}{=} \mathfrak{O}; \tag{26}$$

$$\rho(a \underset{\theta}{\cdot} X \square b \underset{\theta}{\cdot} Y) \leqslant M(a) \underset{\text{B}}{\cdot} \rho(X \square Y) + M(b - a) \underset{\text{B}}{\cdot} N(Y); \tag{27}$$

$$X \underset{\rho}{=} Y \,\&\, a \underset{p}{=} b \supset a \cdot X \underset{\rho}{=} b \cdot Y; \tag{28}$$

$$\rho(a \underset{\theta}{\cdot} X \square a \underset{\theta}{\cdot} Y) = M(a) \underset{\text{B}}{\cdot} \rho(X \square Y), \tag{29}$$

and thus, for any rational number a, the operation of multiplying the points of the space $\mathfrak{N}$ by a is a 1-ary Lipschitz operator of type $(\theta \to \theta)$, and one of the Lipschitz coefficients of this operator is $M(a)$;

$$\rho(a \underset{\theta}{\cdot} X \square b \underset{\theta}{\cdot} X) = N(X) \underset{\text{B}}{\cdot} M(b - a), \tag{30}$$

and thus for any point X of the space $\mathfrak{N}$, the operation of multiplying this point by rational numbers is a 1-ary Lipschitz operator of type $(\mathfrak{p} \to \theta)$, where one of the Lipschitz coefficients of this operator is $N(X)$.

Propositions (21) and (29) give us the opportunity of constructing normed *FR*-completions of normed spaces. The notation introduced in §10.4 will be used below.

Let $\mathfrak{N}$ be a normed space. We denote by $\mathfrak{M}$ the metric space $\text{A}_{\mathfrak{m}}$, $\mathfrak{P}$, ρ and we construct the complete metric space $\mathfrak{M}_2$ which is the standard *FR*-completion of the space $\mathfrak{M}$ (see §10.4). Basing ourselves on (21) and applying to the algorithm $+_\theta$ and the real duplex 1 the standard algorithm $\mathfrak{Z}_2^*$ for extending binary Lipschitz operators (§10.4), we construct an extension of the algorithm $+_\theta$ to the space $\mathfrak{M}_2$. The resulting algorithm in the alphabet $\text{A}_\psi^{\text{sa}}$ will be denoted by $\mathfrak{C}$. In addition, we construct an algorithm $\mathfrak{R}$ of type $(\mathfrak{p} \to t_0)_2$ such that

$$\forall Xa (\langle \mathfrak{R}(a) \rangle_{\mathfrak{m}} (X) \simeq a \underset{\theta}{\cdot} X).$$

Using (29) and applying to $\langle \mathfrak{R}(a) \rangle_{\mathfrak{m}}$ and the real duplex $M(a)$ the standard algorithm $\mathfrak{Z}_1^*$ for extending 1-ary Lipschitz operators, we construct an algorithm $\mathfrak{S}$ of type $(\mathfrak{p} \to t_0)_2$ such that, for every a, the algorithm $\langle \mathfrak{S}(a) \rangle_\psi$ is an extension of the operator $\langle \mathfrak{R}(a) \rangle_{\mathfrak{m}}$ to the space $\mathfrak{M}_2$. Finally, we construct an operator $\mathfrak{D}$ in the alphabet $\text{A}_\psi^{\text{sa}} \cup \text{Ч}_2$ such that

$$\forall t_{\psi,1} a (\mathfrak{D}(a \square t_{\psi,1}) \simeq \langle \mathfrak{S}(a) \rangle_\psi (t_{\psi,1})).$$

The algorithm $\mathfrak{D}$ will be called the *standard extension* of the algorithm $\cdot_\theta$ to the space $\mathfrak{M}_2$.

It is not difficult to prove the following theorem.

12.1.3. *The list*

$$A_\psi,\ \mathfrak{Q}_2,\ \rho_2,\ \mathfrak{C},\ \mathfrak{D},\ \mathfrak{O} \tag{31}$$

is a complete normed space. Moreover, the initial space $\mathfrak{N}$ *is a subspace of this space, the set* $\mathfrak{P}$ *is dense in this space, and the norm in this space is an extension of the function* N_θ *to this space.*

The space (31) will be called the *standard normed FR-completion* of the space $\mathfrak{N}$.

Remark. We shall not consider the standard seminormed *F*-completions of normed spaces, since they present considerably less interest than the standard normed *FR*-completions. We note only that the algorithm $\mathfrak{H}$, introduced in the remark after Theorem 10.4.5, provides us with the opportunity of extending from a normed space $\mathfrak{N}$ to its standard semimetric *F*-completion the operation of addition and the operation of multiplication by rational numbers.

In complete normed spaces with a fixed algorithm for passage to the limit one can define in a natural way an operation of multiplication of points of the space by real duplexes.

Let $\mathfrak{N}$ be a complete normed space and let Lim be an algorithm of passage to the limit in this space. We construct an algorithm $\mathfrak{U}$ of type $(\theta \to t_0)_\mathfrak{n}$ such that

$$\forall Xa\,(\langle \mathfrak{U}(X)\rangle_\mathfrak{n}(a) \simeq a \underset{\theta}{\cdot} X).$$

Using (30) and applying to $\langle \mathfrak{U}(X)\rangle_\mathfrak{n}$ and to $N(X)$ the algorithm $\mathfrak{Z}_1^*$ for extending 1-ary Lipschitz operators, we construct an algorithm $\mathfrak{B}$ of type $(\theta \to t_0)_\mathfrak{n}$ such that for every X the algorithm $\langle \mathfrak{B}(X)\rangle_\mathfrak{n}$ is an extension of the operator $\langle \mathfrak{U}(X)\rangle_\mathfrak{n}$ to the metric space of all real duplexes. Finally, we construct an algorithm $\mathfrak{W}$ in the alphabet $A_\mathfrak{n}^{sa}$ such that

$$\forall Xx\,(\mathfrak{W}(x \square X) \simeq \langle \mathfrak{B}(X)\rangle_\mathfrak{n}(x)).$$

The algorithm $\mathfrak{W}$ will be called *the algorithm for multiplying points of the space* $\mathfrak{N}$ *by real duplexes*, and we shall denote it, like the initial algorithm, by the symbol $\cdot_\theta$.

It is not hard to prove that after replacing in formulas (5), (7), (8), and (10) the variables a and b by the variables x and y, respectively, and the letter

"$\mathfrak{p}$" under the symbols "+" and "." by the letter "B", we obtain true propositions.

We say that a normed (seminormed) space $\mathfrak{N}$ is a *space with multiplication by real duplexes* (respectively, *space with multiplication by real F-numbers*) if, first, $\cdot_\theta$ is not only an algorithm of type $(\mathfrak{p}\theta \to \theta)_\mathfrak{n}$ but also an algorithm of type $(Д\theta \to \theta)_\mathfrak{n}$ (respectively, an algorithm of type $(\mathrm{B}\,\theta \to \theta)_\mathfrak{n}$), and second, after replacing in the formulas (5), (7), (8), and (10) the variables a and b by the variables x and y (by the variables r and s) and replacing the letter "$\mathfrak{p}$" under the symbols "+" and "." by the letter "B", we obtain true assertions.

We note that in normed (seminormed) spaces with multiplication by real duplexes (by real F-numbers) the propositions obtained from formulas (25) and (27)–(30) as a result of the indicated replacements and replacement of the letter "$\mathfrak{p}$" under the symbol = by the letter "B" are also true. This remark does not extend to the formula (26) (see 6.4.7).

From what has been said above it follows that every complete normed space with fixed algorithm for passage to the limit can be considered to be a space with multiplication by real duplexes. However one can also exhibit noncomplete normed spaces of the same kind.

12.1.4. *Let $\mathfrak{N}$ be a normed (seminormed) space with multiplication by real duplexes (respectively, multiplication by real F-numbers), let X be a point of the space $\mathfrak{N}$ and let α be a real duplex (respectively, real F-number). Denote by $\mathfrak{G}$ the algorithm in the alphabet $\mathrm{A}_\mathfrak{n}^{\mathrm{sa}}$ such that, for every n,*

$$\mathfrak{G}(n) \simeq \underline{\alpha}(n) \cdot X.$$

Then $\alpha \cdot X \,\underline{\lim}_{\mathfrak{N}} \mathfrak{G}$.

For the proof it suffices to note that

$$\rho(\alpha \cdot X \,\square\, \underline{\alpha}(n) \cdot X) = M(\alpha - \underline{\alpha}(n)) \cdot N(X),$$

and then to refer to the remarks after Theorems 10.4.5 and 10.4.6.

12.2. Let us assume that $\mathfrak{N}$ is a normed (seminormed) space with multiplication by real duplexes (by real F-numbers). We shall say that elements $\theta_1, \cdots, \theta_n$ of the space $\mathfrak{N}$ are *linearly dependent* in the space $\mathfrak{N}$, and we shall write

$$(\theta_1 \square \ldots \square \theta_n \in \underline{\text{lin. dep}_{\mathfrak{N}}}),$$

if real duplexes (respectively, real F-numbers) $\alpha_1, \cdots, \alpha_n$ are potentially realizable such that

$$(\alpha_1 \neq 0 \vee \ldots \vee \alpha_n \neq 0) \,\&\, (\alpha_1 \cdot \theta_1 + \ldots + \alpha_n \cdot \theta_n \underset{\rho}{=} \mathfrak{O}).$$

Here and in the rest of this section $\alpha_1, \cdots, \alpha_n$ denote some pairwise distinct variables of type Д (respectively, type B).

We shall say that elements $\theta_1, \cdots, \theta_n$ of the space $\mathfrak{N}$ are *linearly independent* in the space $\mathfrak{N}$, and we shall write

$$(\theta_1 \square \ldots \square \theta_n \in \underline{\text{lin. ind}}_{\mathfrak{N}}),$$

if

$$\neg(\theta_1 \square \ldots \square \theta_n \in \underline{\text{lin. dep}}_{\mathfrak{N}}). \tag{1}$$

Within the frame of constructive logic one can prove (using §2.6 (3), (5), (6) and §4.5 (16), (25)) that condition (1) is equivalent to each of the following two conditions:

$$\forall \alpha_1 \ldots \alpha_n (\alpha_1 \cdot \theta_1 + \ldots + \alpha_n \cdot \theta_n \underset{\rho}{=} \mathfrak{O} \supset \alpha_1 = 0 \,\&\, \ldots \,\&\, \alpha_n = 0),$$

$$\forall \alpha_1 \ldots \alpha_n (\alpha_1 \neq 0 \vee \ldots \vee \alpha_n \neq 0 \supset \alpha_1 \cdot \theta_1 + \ldots + \alpha_n \cdot \theta_n \underset{\rho}{\neq} \mathfrak{O}).$$

12.3. Let us assume that there are given two normed spaces: the space $A_{\mathfrak{m}}$, $\mathfrak{P}$, ρ, $+_\theta$, $\cdot_\theta$, $\mathfrak{O}$ and the space $A_{\tilde{\mathfrak{m}}}$, $\tilde{\mathfrak{P}}$, $\tilde{\rho}$, $+_{\tilde{\theta}}$, $\cdot_{\tilde{\theta}}$, $\tilde{\mathfrak{O}}$. The first of these shall be denoted by $\mathfrak{N}$, and the second by $\tilde{\mathfrak{N}}$. The notation

$$\eta,\ \mathfrak{n},\ \tilde{\mathfrak{n}},\ \theta,\ \tilde{\theta},\ X,\ Y,\ Z,\ U,\ \tilde{X},\ \tilde{Y},\ \tilde{Z},\ \tilde{U}$$

will be used in the same sense as in §9.2.

Let $\lambda_{\eta,1}$ be a 1-ary operator from $\mathfrak{N}$ into $\tilde{\mathfrak{N}}$. We shall say that $\lambda_{\eta,1}$ is a *linear operator* from $\mathfrak{N}$ into $\tilde{\mathfrak{N}}$ if, for any points X and Y of the space $\mathfrak{N}$ and any rational number a, first,

$$!\lambda_{\eta,1}(X) \,\&\, !\lambda_{\eta,1}(Y) \supset !\lambda_{\eta,1}(X \underset{\theta}{+} Y) \,\&\, \lambda_{\eta,1}(X \underset{\theta}{+} Y) \underset{\tilde{\rho}}{=} \lambda_{\eta,1}(X) \underset{\tilde{\theta}}{+} \lambda_{\eta,1}(Y)$$

and second,

$$!\lambda_{\eta,1}(X) \supset !\lambda_{\eta,1}(a \underset{\theta}{\cdot} X) \,\&\, \lambda_{\eta,1}(a \underset{\theta}{\cdot} X) \underset{\tilde{\rho}}{=} a \underset{\tilde{\theta}}{\cdot} \lambda_{\eta,1}(X).$$

Every linear operator of type $(\theta \to \tilde{\theta})$ will be called a *linear mapping* of the space $\mathfrak{N}$ into the space $\tilde{\mathfrak{N}}$.

We shall say that $\lambda_{\eta,1}$ is a *locally bounded linear operator* if $\lambda_{\eta,1}$ is a linear operator of type $(\theta \to \tilde{\theta})$ and a real duplex y is potentially realizable such that

$$\forall X (N_{\tilde{\theta}}(\lambda_{\eta,1}(X)) \leqslant y \cdot N_\theta(X)). \tag{1}$$

12.3.1. *If* $\lambda_{\eta,1}$ *is a locally bounded operator, then* $\lambda_{\eta,1}$ *is a* 1-*ary Lipschitz operator and every real duplex* y *satisfying condition* (1) *is a Lipschitz coefficient in dimension* 1 *for this operator. On the other hand, if* $\lambda_{\eta,1}$ *is a linear operator which is a* 1-*ary Lipschitz operator, then* $\lambda_{\eta,1}$ *is a locally bounded operator and every real duplex* y *which is a Lipschitz coefficient in dimension* 1 *satisfies condition* (1).

The proof of this theorem is obvious.

Basing ourselves on 12.3.1, we shall call every real duplex satisfying condition (1) a *Lipschitz coefficient of the operator* $\lambda_{\eta,1}$.

We shall say that a real duplex z is the *norm* of the linear operator $\lambda_{\eta,1}$, and we shall write

$$(z \underline{\text{ norm }} \lambda_{\eta,1}),$$

if z is the least upper bound of the set of real duplexes given by the formula

$$\exists X (X \underset{\rho}{\neq} \mathfrak{O} \,\&\, y \underset{B}{=} N_{\tilde{\theta}}(\lambda_{\eta,1}(X)) : N_{\theta}(X)).$$

The latter means that, first, z majorizes every real duplex belonging to this set, and second, for any k, there is potentially realizable a real duplex belonging to this set and greater than $(z - 2^{-k})$.

We shall say that $\lambda_{\eta,1}$ is a *normed operator* if $\lambda_{\eta,1}$ is a linear operator of type $(\theta \to \tilde{\theta})$ and there is potentially realizable a real duplex which is a norm of the operator $\lambda_{\eta,1}$.

It is obvious that every normed operator is also a locally bounded linear operator. However, the converse is false. In the next chapter we shall construct an example of a locally bounded linear mapping of one concrete infinite-dimensional complete normed space into the space of all real duplexes which is not a normed operator. Hence this point is an essential difference between the theory of constructive normed spaces and the theory of normed spaces in classical mathematics.

12.3.2. *If* $\lambda_{\eta,1}$ *is a locally bounded linear operator and* $\mathfrak{N}$ *and* $\tilde{\mathfrak{N}}$ *are normed spaces with multiplication by real duplexes, then*

$$\forall x X (\lambda_{\eta,1}(x \underset{\theta}{\cdot} X) \underset{\tilde{\rho}}{=} x \underset{\tilde{\theta}}{\cdot} \lambda_{\eta,1}(X)).$$

Proof. Let $\lambda_{\eta,1}$ be a locally bounded linear operator, x a real duplex, and X a point of the space $\mathfrak{N}$. Then one can construct a real duplex y such that

$$\forall Y (N_{\tilde{\theta}}(\lambda_{\eta,1}(Y)) \leqslant y \cdot N_{\theta}(Y)). \tag{2}$$

Let y be a real duplex satisfying condition (2). Further, let k be any natural number. On the basis of Remark 1 after Theorem 10.4.6, we construct a natural number G such that, first,

$$M(\underline{x}(G)-x)\cdot y\cdot N_{\theta}(X)<2^{-(k+1)}$$

and second,

$$M(\underline{x}(G)-x)\cdot N_{\tilde{\theta}}(\lambda_{\eta,1}(X))<2^{-(k+1)}.$$

We have

$$\begin{aligned}\tilde{\rho}(\lambda_{\eta,1}(x\cdot X)\square x\cdot\lambda_{\eta,1}(X))&\leqslant\tilde{\rho}(\lambda_{\eta,1}(x\cdot X)\square\lambda_{\eta,1}(\underline{x}(G)\cdot X))\\&+\tilde{\rho}(\lambda_{\eta,1}(\underline{x}(G)\cdot X)\square x\cdot\lambda_{\eta,1}(X))=N_{\tilde{\theta}}(\lambda_{\eta,1}((\underline{x}(G)-x)\cdot X))\\&+N_{\tilde{\theta}}((x-\underline{x}(G))\cdot\lambda_{\eta,1}(X))\leqslant y\cdot M(\underline{x}(G)-x)\cdot N_{\theta}(X)\\&+M(\underline{x}(G)-x)\cdot N_{\tilde{\theta}}(\lambda_{\eta,1}(X))<2^{-(k+1)}+2^{-(k+1)}=2^{-k}.\end{aligned}$$

Thus $\forall k(\tilde{\rho}(\lambda_{\eta,1}(x\cdot X)\square x\cdot\lambda_{\eta,1}(X))<2^{-k})$. Hence

$$\lambda_{\eta,1}(x\cdot X)\underset{\tilde{\rho}}{=}x\cdot\lambda_{\eta,1}(X).$$

The theorem is proved.

12.3.3. *If $\tilde{\mathfrak{N}}$ is a complete normed space with fixed algorithm of passage to the limit, $\lambda_{\eta,1}$ is a locally bounded linear operator, and y is a Lipschitz coefficient of this operator, then the result of applying to $\lambda_{\eta,1}$ and y the standard algorithm $\mathfrak{Z}_1^*$ for extending 1-ary Lipschitz operators (see §10.4) is a locally bounded linear operator mapping the standard normed FR-completion of the space $\mathfrak{N}$ into the space $\tilde{\mathfrak{N}}$, and y is a Lipschitz coefficient of this operator. Moreover, if $\lambda_{\eta,1}$ is a normed operator and y is the norm of $\lambda_{\eta,1}$, then the result of applying $\mathfrak{Z}_1^*$ to $\lambda_{\eta,1}$ and y is also a normed operator and y is the norm of this operator.*

This theorem is proved by referring to part 2) of Theorem 10.4.10 and to Theorem 9.4.1 (the second of these theorems is used for the proof of additivity and homogeneity of the operator obtained by applying $\mathfrak{Z}_1^*$ to $\lambda_{\eta,1}$ and y).

The next theorem is derived easily from the definition of an operator inverse to a given one and from Theorem 9.2.2.

12.3.4. *If $\lambda_{\eta,1}$ is a linear separating (linear isometric) mapping from $\mathfrak{N}$ onto $\tilde{\mathfrak{N}}$, and $\lambda_{\eta,2}$ is an operator inverse to the operator $\lambda_{\eta,1}$, then $\lambda_{\eta,2}$ is a linear separating (respectively, linear isometric) mapping of $\tilde{\mathfrak{N}}$ onto $\mathfrak{N}$.*

We note that every linear isometric mapping of the space $\mathfrak{N}$ into $\tilde{\mathfrak{N}}$ is a normed operator and the number 1 is the norm of every such mapping.

We shall say that the space $\tilde{\mathfrak{N}}$ is *weakly linearly isometric* to the space $\mathfrak{N}$ if one can construct a linear isometric mapping of $\mathfrak{N}$ onto $\tilde{\mathfrak{N}}$. We shall say that the space $\tilde{\mathfrak{N}}$ is *linearly isometric* to the space $\mathfrak{N}$ if one can construct a linear isometric mapping of $\mathfrak{N}$ onto $\tilde{\mathfrak{N}}$ and an operator inverse to this mapping.

From 12.3.4 the symmetry of the relation "linearly isometric" follows.

The next theorem follows from 9.2.1 and 12.3.4.

12.3.5. *If* $\tilde{\mathfrak{P}}$ *is a normal formula, then the space* $\tilde{\mathfrak{N}}$ *is linearly isometric to the space* $\mathfrak{N}$ *if and only if a linear isometric mapping of* $\mathfrak{N}$ *onto* $\tilde{\mathfrak{N}}$ *is potentially realizable.*

An important special case of the concept of linear operator is the concept of *linear FR-functional.* If the linear normed space of all real duplexes plays the role of $\tilde{\mathfrak{N}}$ and $\lambda_{\eta,1}$ is an everywhere-defined linear operator (locally bounded linear operator, normed operator) from $\mathfrak{N}$ into $\tilde{\mathfrak{N}}$, then we shall say that $\lambda_{\eta,1}$ is a *linear FR-functional* in the space $\mathfrak{N}$ (respectively, *locally bounded linear FR-functional* in $\mathfrak{N}$, *normed FR-functional* in $\mathfrak{N}$). The terms occurring in this definition will usually be shortened by replacing the expression "*FR*-functional" by the word "functional". This abbreviation could lead to ambiguity if in this exposition, along with *FR*-functionals, we also dealt with *F*-functionals, defined by analogy with *FR*-functionals under the assumption that the space of all real *F*-numbers plays the role of $\tilde{\mathfrak{N}}$. However, we shall not consider *F*-functionals in this book, and therefore the indicated abbreviation of terms will not give rise to ambiguity.

In the sequel we shall make use of the following theorems 12.3.6–12.3.8.

12.3.6. *If* $\mathfrak{N}$ *is a normed space with multiplication by real duplexes and* $\lambda_{\eta,1}$ *is a locally bounded linear functional in the space* $\mathfrak{N}$, *then the set given by the formula*

$$\lambda_{\eta,1}(X)=0,$$

is a linear closed, and therefore faithful (*see* 9.4.2), *subset of the space* $\mathfrak{N}$.

The term "linear subset of the space $\mathfrak{N}$" is applied here in the following sense. One says that a set $\mathfrak{Q}$ is a *linear subset* of the normed space $\mathfrak{N}$, if, first, $\mathfrak{Q}$ is a subset of the set $\mathfrak{P}$, and second, for any elements X and Y of the set $\mathfrak{P}$ and any real duplex z, the elements $X+Y$ and $z \cdot X$ of the space $\mathfrak{N}$ are elements of the set $\mathfrak{Q}$.

Theorem 12.3.6 is easily derived from 10.1.4.

12.3.7. *Let* $\mathfrak{N}$ *be a normed space with multiplication by real duplexes, and let* $\lambda_{\eta,1}$ *be a locally bounded linear functional such that*

$$\exists X(\lambda_{\eta,1}(X)\neq 0).$$

Denote by $\mathfrak{R}$ *the set of points of the space* $\mathfrak{N}$ *given by the formula*

$$\lambda_{\eta,1}(Y)=1$$

and by $\mathfrak{S}$ *the set of real duplexes given by the formula*

$$\exists Y(\lambda_{\eta,1}(Y)=1 \,\&\, y=N(Y)).$$

Under these conditions, the following assertions are true for any real duplexes z *and* u.

1) *If* (z $\underline{\text{norm}}$ $\lambda_{\eta,1}$), *then* $z > 0$ *and the real duplex* $(1 : z)$ *is a greatest lower bound of the set* $\mathfrak{S}$ *(any real duplex which is a greatest lower bound of the set* $\mathfrak{S}$ *is naturally called the distance from the point* $\mathfrak{D}$ *to the set* $\mathfrak{R}$*). Hence if the functional* $\dot{\lambda}_{\eta,1}$ *is normed, there is a potentially realizable real duplex which is the distance from the point* $\mathfrak{D}$ *to the set* $\mathfrak{R}$.

2) *If* u *is a greatest lower bound of the set* $\mathfrak{S}$, *then* $u > 0$ *and* $((1 : u)$ $\underline{\text{norm}}$ $\lambda_{\eta,1})$. *Hence if there is a potentially realizable real duplex which is the distance from the point* $\mathfrak{D}$ *to the set* $\mathfrak{R}$, *then the functional* $\lambda_{\eta,1}$ *is normed.*

Proof. Let z be a real duplex satisfying the condition (z $\underline{\text{norm}}$ $\lambda_{\eta,1}$) and let X be a point of the space $\mathfrak{N}$ such that $\lambda_{\eta,1}(X) \neq 0$. We have $N(X) \neq 0$ and

$$M(\lambda_{\eta,1}(X)) \leqslant z \cdot N(X).$$

Hence $z > 0$. In addition, let y be any element of the set $\mathfrak{S}$ and let Y be any point of the space $\mathfrak{N}$ such that

$$\lambda_{\eta,1}(Y)=1 \,\&\, y=N(Y).$$

Then $1 = M(\lambda_{\eta,1}(Y)) \leq z \cdot N(Y) = z \cdot y$. Hence $1 : z \leq y$. Therefore the real duplex $1 : z$ is a greatest lower bound of the set $\mathfrak{S}$.

On the other hand, let k be any natural number. One can construct a natural number l such that

$$z-2^{-l}>0 \,\&\, 1:(z-2^{-l}) \leqslant (1:z)+2^{-k}. \qquad (3)$$

Let l be a natural number satisfying (3). Since (z $\underline{\text{norm}}$ $\lambda_{\eta,1}$), it follows that $\exists U \mathfrak{H}$, where

$$\mathfrak{H} \rightleftharpoons (U \underset{\rho}{\neq} \mathfrak{D} \,\&\, M(\lambda_{\eta,1}(U)) : N(U) > z-2^{-l}).$$

Let U be a point of the space $\mathfrak{N}$ satisfying condition $\mathfrak{H}$. Then $\lambda_{\eta,1}(U) \neq 0$. We introduce the notation

$$P \rightleftharpoons \lambda_{\eta,1}(U), \quad Q \rightleftharpoons (1:P) \cdot U.$$

We have

$$U=P \cdot Q, \quad \lambda_{\eta,1}(Q)=1, \quad 1:N(Q)>z-2^{-l}.$$

Hence the real duplex $N(Q)$ belongs to the set $\mathfrak{S}$ and

$$N(Q) < 1 : (z - 2^{-l}) \leqslant (1 : z) + 2^{-k}.$$

Therefore $(1 : z)$ is a greatest lower bound of the set $\mathfrak{S}$, and proposition 1) has been proved.

We shall not use proposition 2) in the sequel and therefore we shall not carry out its proof.

12.3.8. *Let* $\mathfrak{N}$ *be a normed space,* $\lambda_{\eta,1}$ *a normed functional in* $\mathfrak{N}$, *and* z *a norm of this functional. Then*

$$z \neq 0 \equiv \exists X(\lambda_{\eta,1}(X) \neq 0),$$

$$z = 0 \equiv \forall X(\lambda_{\eta,1}(X) = 0).$$

This theorem is obvious.

12.4. We shall say that a normed space $\mathfrak{N}$ is a *Hilbert space* if, for any points X and Y of the space $\mathfrak{N}$,

$$N_\theta^2(X + Y) + N_\theta^2(X - Y) = 2 \cdot (N_\theta^2(X) + N_\theta^2(Y)). \quad (1)$$

Here and below N_θ^2 denotes the algorithm in the alphabet A_n^{sa} such that

$$\forall X(N_\theta^2(X) \simeq N_\theta(X) \underset{B}{\wedge} 2).$$

In this section and in §§12.5 and 12.6 we shall assume that $\mathfrak{N}$ is a Hilbert space.

We construct an algorithm C_θ in the alphabet A_n^{sa} such that, for any points X and Y of the space $\mathfrak{N}$,

$$C_\theta(X \square Y) \simeq (N_\theta^2(X + Y) - N_\theta^2(X) - N_\theta^2(Y)) : 2. \quad (2)$$

The algorithm C_θ is called *the algorithm for computing the scalar product* in the space $\mathfrak{N}$.

We shall denote the algorithm C_θ by the single letter C in those cases where this simplified notation does not lead to ambiguity.

The next proposition follows from §12.1 (22), §12.1 (20), and (2).

12.4.1. *For any* X, Y, Z *and* U,

$$X \underset{\rho}{=} Z \,\&\, Y \underset{\rho}{=} U \supset C(X \square Y) \doteq C(Z \square U).$$

The following theorem summarizes the fundamental properties of the algorithm C.

12.4.2. *For any points* X, Y, Z *and* U *of the space* $\mathfrak{N}$ *and any rational number* a,

$$C(X\square Y+Z)=C(X\square Y)+C(X\square Z), \tag{3}$$
$$C(X\square a\cdot Y)=a\cdot C(X\square Y), \tag{4}$$
$$C(X\square Y)=C(Y\square X), \tag{5}$$
$$C(X\square X)=N^2(X), \tag{6}$$
$$M(C(X\square Y))\leqslant N(X)\cdot N(Y). \tag{7}$$

Proof. Let X, Y and Z be points of the space $\mathfrak{N}$ and let a be a rational number. We introduce the notation

$$Q\leftrightharpoons(1/2\cdot Y).$$

From (1) the following equations are easily derived:

$$N^2(X+Y+Z)=2\cdot N^2(X+Q)+2\cdot N^2(Q+Z)-N^2(X-Z),$$
$$N^2(X+Y)=2\cdot N^2(X+Q)+2\cdot N^2(Q)-N^2(X),$$
$$N^2(Y+Z)=2\cdot N^2(Q)+2\cdot N^2(Q+Z)-N^2(Z),$$
$$N^2(X+Z)+N^2(X-Z)=2\cdot N^2(X)+2\cdot N^2(Z).$$

These equations and (2) imply immediately the truth of equation (3).

Let us proceed to equation (4). First, by simple arguments based on (1)–(3), we can prove equation (4) in the following special cases: A) $a=-1$; B) $a=0$; C) a is a positive integer; D) $a=1/n$, where n is a positive integer. The following cases are easily reducible to the special cases above: E) $a=-m$; F) $a=m/n$; G) $a=-m/n$ (here m and n are positive integers). Every rational number a falls under at least one of the cases A)–G).

Propositions (5) and (6) are obvious. Proposition (7) is easily derived with the aid of (2) from §12.1 (18), (19), (10). The theorem is proved.

We construct an algorithm D in the alphabet $\mathrm{A}_{\mathfrak{n}}^{\mathrm{sa}}$ of type $(\theta\rightarrow t_0)_{\mathfrak{n}}$ such that

$$\forall XY(\langle D(X)\rangle_{\mathfrak{n}}(Y)\simeq C(X\square Y)).$$

The next theorem follows immediately from (3)–(7).

12.4.3. *For any point X of the space $\mathfrak{N}$ the algorithm $\langle D(X)\rangle_{\mathfrak{n}}$ is a linear normed functional in $\mathfrak{N}$ and $N(X)$ is the norm of this functional.*

The following theorem is an immediate consequence of 12.4.3 and 12.3.2.

12.4.4. *If $\mathfrak{N}$ is a Hilbert space with multiplication by real duplexes, then, for any points X and Y of the space $\mathfrak{N}$ and any real duplex z,*

$$C(X\square z\cdot Y)=z\cdot C(X\square Y).$$

The next theorem about FR-completions of Hilbert spaces follows from 12.1.3 and 9.4.1.

12.4.5. *The standard normed FR-completion of any Hilbert space is a Hilbert space, and the scalar product in this FR-completion is a binary extension to this FR-completion of the scalar product in the space* $\mathfrak{N}$.

12.5. In classical functional analysis a great role is played by the well-known theorem of F. Riesz about the general form of linear locally bounded functionals in a complete Hilbert space. Replacing in the formulation of this theorem the concepts of classical mathematics by the corresponding concepts of constructive mathematics and replacing the word "exists" by the expression "is potentially realizable", we obtain the following assertion.

If $\mathfrak{N}$ *is a complete Hilbert space, and* $\lambda_{\eta,1}$ *is a locally bounded linear operator in* $\mathfrak{N}$, *then an element* X *of the space* $\mathfrak{N}$ *is potentially realizable such that*

$$\forall Y(\lambda_{\eta,1}(Y) = C(X \square Y)).$$

In the next chapter this assertion will be refuted by the construction in a concrete complete Hilbert space of a locally bounded linear functional which is not a normed functional. Hence Riesz's theorem does not carry over in unchanged form to constructive mathematics. However, certain analogues of Riesz's theorem can nevertheless be found in constructive mathematics. These analogues will be formulated and proved in the next subsection.

Let us formulate some definitions of an auxiliary character.

Let X and Y be elements of the space $\mathfrak{N}$. One says that the element X is *orthogonal to the element* Y, and one writes $X \perp Y$, if $C(X \square Y) = 0$.

Let $\mathfrak{Q}$ be a subset of the set $\mathfrak{P}$ and let X be an element of the space $\mathfrak{N}$. One says that X is *orthogonal to the set* $\mathfrak{Q}$, and one writes $X \perp \mathfrak{Q}$, if X is orthogonal to every element of the set $\mathfrak{Q}$.

We shall say that a set $\mathfrak{Q}$ is a *full subset* of the space $\mathfrak{N}$ if $\mathfrak{Q}$ is a linear closed subset of the space $\mathfrak{N}$ and an element X of the space $\mathfrak{N}$ is potentially realizable such that $X \neq_\rho \mathfrak{Q}$ and $X \perp \mathfrak{Q}$.

Remark. In the next chapter we shall construct for a concrete complete Hilbert space a linear closed subset not coinciding with the whole space which is at the same time not a full subset.

12.6. We shall assume that $\mathfrak{N}$ is a complete Hilbert space and $\lambda_{\eta,1}$ is a locally bounded linear functional in $\mathfrak{N}$. These assumptions will be considered a component part of each of the following theorems 12.6.1–12.6.5.

We introduce the notation

$$\mathfrak{Q} \leftrightharpoons (\lambda_{\eta,1}(X)=0).$$

From our hypotheses and 12.3.6 it follows that $\mathfrak{Q}$ is a linear closed subset of the space $\mathfrak{N}$.

12.6.1. *If an element X of the space $\mathfrak{N}$ is potentially realizable such that $X \neq_\rho \mathfrak{Q}$ and*

$$\forall Y(\lambda_{\eta,1}(Y)=C(X \square Y)), \tag{1}$$

then $\mathfrak{Q}$ is a full subset of the space $\mathfrak{N}$.

This theorem is obvious.

12.6.2. *If $\mathfrak{Q}$ is a full subset of the space $\mathfrak{N}$, then an element X of the space $\mathfrak{N}$ is potentially realizable such that $X \neq_\rho \mathfrak{Q}$ and condition (1) is fulfilled.*

Proof. Let us assume that $\mathfrak{Q}$ is a full subset of the space $\mathfrak{N}$. Then an element Z of the space $\mathfrak{N}$ is potentially realizable such that

$$Z \neq_\rho \mathfrak{Q} \,\&\, Z \perp \mathfrak{Q}. \tag{2}$$

Let Z be an element of the space $\mathfrak{N}$ satisfying condition (2), and let Y be any point of the space $\mathfrak{N}$. It is obvious that $\lambda_{\eta,1}(Z) \neq 0$. We introduce the notation

$$\varepsilon \leftrightharpoons \lambda_{\eta,1}(Y):\lambda_{\eta,1}(Z).$$

A computation shows that $\lambda_{\eta,1}(Y - \epsilon \cdot Z) = 0$. Hence $C(Y - \epsilon \cdot Z \square Z) = 0$, and thus

$$C(Y \square Z) - \varepsilon \cdot N^2(Z)=0,$$

$$\lambda_{\eta,1}(Y)=C(H \square Y),$$

where

$$H \leftrightharpoons (\lambda_{\eta,1}(Z):N^2(Z)) \cdot Z.$$

The theorem is proved.

From 12.6.2 and 12.4.3 we immediately obtain

12.6.3. *If $\mathfrak{Q}$ is a full subset of the space $\mathfrak{N}$, then the functional $\lambda_{\eta,1}$ is normed.*

12.6.4. *If the functional $\lambda_{\eta,1}$ is normed and a point U is potentially realiz-*

able such that $\lambda_{\eta,1}(U) \neq 0$, *then* $\mathfrak{Q}$ *is a full subset of the space* $\mathfrak{N}$.

Proof. Let us assume that $\lambda_{\eta,1}$ is a normed functional. Let z be the norm of this functional. Then on the basis of 12.3.7 the real duplex $1:z$ is the distance from the point $\mathfrak{O}$ to the set $\mathfrak{R}$, i.e. a greatest lower bound of the set $\mathfrak{S}$. Here $\mathfrak{R}$ and $\mathfrak{S}$ are the designations introduced in 12.3.7. Hence an algorithm $\lambda_{\mathrm{n},2}$ in the alphabet A_{n}^{sa} is potentially realizable such that, first,

$$\forall k(\lambda_{\eta,1}(\lambda_{\mathrm{n},2}(k))=1) \tag{3}$$

and second,

$$\forall k(M(1:z-N(\lambda_{\mathrm{n},2}(k)))<2^{-k}). \tag{4}$$

Let $\lambda_{\mathrm{n},2}$ be an algorithm satisfying conditions (3) and (4). We introduce the notation

$$\varphi \rightleftharpoons 1:z, \quad H_\alpha \rightleftharpoons \lambda_{\mathrm{n},2}(\alpha), \quad G_\alpha \rightleftharpoons N(H_\alpha)-1:z.$$

Any natural variable can serve as α.

For any m and n we have

$$M(G_m)<2^{-m}, \quad M(G_n)<2^{-n},$$
$$N(H_m)=\varphi+G_m, \quad N(H_n)=\varphi+G_n,$$
$$\lambda_{\eta,1}(2^{-1}\cdot(H_m+H_n))=1.$$

Hence

$$\varphi \leqslant N(2^{-1}\cdot(H_m+H_n)) \leqslant \varphi+2^{-1}\cdot(G_m+G_n)<\varphi+2^{-\min(m\square n)}.$$

We introduce the notation

$$R_{m,n} \rightleftharpoons N(2^{-1}\cdot(H_m+H_n))-\varphi.$$

We have

$$M(R_{m,n})<2^{-\min(m\square n)}, \qquad N(2^{-1}\cdot(H_m+H_n))=\varphi+R_{m,n},$$
$$N^2(H_m-H_n)=2\cdot N^2(H_m)+2\cdot N^2(H_n)-4\cdot N^2(2^{-1}\cdot(H_m+H_n))$$
$$=2\cdot(\varphi+G_m)^2+2\cdot(\varphi+G_n)^2-4\cdot(\varphi+R_{m,n})^2$$
$$=4\cdot\varphi\cdot(G_m+G_n-2\cdot R_{m,n})+2\cdot(G_m^2+G_n^2-2\cdot R_{m,n}^2).$$

If $m, n \geq l$, then

$$N^2(H_m-H_n) \leqslant 4\cdot\varphi\cdot(2^{-l}+2^{-l}+2^{-l+1})$$
$$+2\cdot(2^{-2\cdot l}+2^{-2\cdot l}+2^{-2\cdot l+1})=\varphi\cdot 2^{-l+4}+2^{-2\cdot l+3}.$$

From the latter estimate it is clear that an algorithm $\lambda_{0,3}$ of type $(\mathrm{H}\rightarrow\mathrm{H})_0$ is potentially realizable such that

$$\lambda_{0,3}\,\underline{\text{reg. conv}_{\mathfrak{N}}}\,\lambda_{\mathrm{n},2}. \tag{5}$$

Let $\lambda_{0,3}$ be an algorithm satisfying condition (5). Then the word $\{\lambda_{n,2}\} \odot \{\lambda_{0,3}\}$ is an FR-construct in the space $\mathfrak{N}$. In this space we can potentially realize an algorithm of passage to the limit. Let Lim be such an algorithm. We introduce the notation

$$\mathfrak{q} \leftrightharpoons \mathrm{Lim}\,(\{\lambda_{n,2}\} \odot \{\lambda_{0,3}\}).$$

It can be easily verified that

$$\lambda_{\eta,1}(\mathfrak{q}) = 1, \quad N(\mathfrak{q}) = 1 : z.$$

Hence $\mathfrak{q} \neq_\rho \mathfrak{O}$. Now let us prove that

$$\forall Y(\lambda_{\eta,1}(Y) = 0 \supset C(\mathfrak{q} \,\Box\, Y) = 0). \tag{6}$$

Let us assume that a point Y is potentially realizable such that

$$\lambda_{\eta,1}(Y) = 0 \,\&\, C(\mathfrak{q} \,\Box\, Y) \neq 0. \tag{7}$$

Let Y be a point satisfying condition (7). Then $Y \neq_\rho \mathfrak{O}$ and therefore $N(Y) \neq 0$. We introduce the notation

$$B \leftrightharpoons C(\mathfrak{q} \,\Box\, Y), \quad \mathfrak{r} \leftrightharpoons \mathfrak{q} - (B : N^2(Y)) \cdot Y.$$

We have

$$\lambda_{\eta,1}(\mathfrak{r}) = \lambda_{\eta,1}(\mathfrak{q}) - (B : N^2(Y)) \cdot \lambda_{\eta,1}(Y) = 1 - 0 = 1.$$

Hence $\mathfrak{r}$ belongs to the set $\mathfrak{R}$. In addition,

$$N^2(\mathfrak{r}) = N^2(\mathfrak{q}) - 2 \cdot (B : N^2(Y)) \cdot C(\mathfrak{q} \,\Box\, Y) + (B : N^2(Y))^2 \cdot N^2(Y)$$
$$= N^2(\mathfrak{q}) - 2 \cdot (B : N(Y))^2 + (B : N(Y))^2 = N^2(\mathfrak{q}) - (B : N(Y))^2,$$
$$N^2(\mathfrak{r}) < N^2(\mathfrak{q}) = (1 : z)^2.$$

On the other hand, since $1 : z$ is the distance from $\mathfrak{O}$ to the set $\mathfrak{R}$, we have

$$N(\mathfrak{r}) \geqslant 1 : z.$$

The resulting contradiction proves that

$$\neg \exists Y(\lambda_{\eta,1}(Y) = 0 \,\&\, C(\mathfrak{q} \,\Box\, Y) \neq 0). \tag{8}$$

(6) follows from (8) and 4.5 (16) by the rules of constructive logic [see §2.6 (3) and §2.6 (5)].

Theorem 12.6.4 is proved.

The next theorem follows immediately from 12.6.4 and 12.6.2.

12.6.5. *If the functional* $\lambda_{\eta,1}$ *is normed and*

$$\exists U(\lambda_{\eta,1}(U) \neq 0),$$

then

$$\exists X \forall Y(\lambda_{\eta,1}(Y) = C(X \,\Box\, Y)).$$

The propositions proved above yield the following theorem.

12.6.6. *If $\mathfrak{N}$ is a complete Hilbert space, then, for any normed linear functional $\lambda_{\eta,1}$ in the space $\mathfrak{N}$,*

a) *if*

$$\exists U(\lambda_{\eta,1}(U)\neq 0)\vee\forall U(\lambda_{\eta,1}(U)=0),$$

then

$$\exists X\forall Y(\lambda_{\eta,1}(Y)=C(X\square Y));$$

b) *if*

$$\exists z\,(z\neq 0\,\&\,z\ \underline{\text{norm}}\ \lambda_{\eta,1})\vee(0\ \underline{\text{norm}}\ \lambda_{\eta,1}),$$

then

$$\exists X\forall Y(\lambda_{\eta,1}(Y)=C(X\square Y));$$

c)

$$\neg\neg\exists X\forall Y(\lambda_{\eta,1}(Y)=C(X\square Y)).$$

It is natural to consider each of the parts a)–c) as a constructive analogue of the theorem of F. Riesz mentioned above.

Proposition a) follows from 12.6.5 and the following remark: if the functional $\lambda_{\eta,1}$ is such that

$$\forall U(\lambda_{\eta,1}(U)=0),$$

then

$$\forall Y(\lambda_{\eta,1}(Y)=C(\mathfrak{D}\square Y)).$$

Proposition b) follows from a) and 12.3.8. Proposition c) is easily obtained from a) by the rules of logical inference of constructive logic.

Remark. From part c) of Theorem 12.6.6 it follows that in a complete Hilbert space there is no normed linear functional $\lambda_{\eta,1}$ such that there is no point X satisfying the condition

$$\forall Y(\lambda_{\eta,1}(Y)=C(X\square Y)). \tag{9}$$

However it remains an open problem as to whether the following assertion is true: for any normed linear functional $\lambda_{\eta,1}$ in a complete Hilbert space $\mathfrak{N}$, a point X is potentially realizable such that condition (9) is fulfilled.

The differences between Riesz's theorem and the constructive analogues of this theorem proved above are the sources of a series of essential differences between the theory of Hilbert spaces constructed in classical mathematics and the theory of constructive Hilbert spaces formed in constructive mathematics.

CHAPTER III

SOME CONCRETE CONSTRUCTIVE SPACES

§13. CONSTRUCTIVE ANALOGUES OF EUCLIDEAN SPACE OF A GIVEN DIMENSION AND THE SPACE OF REAL SEQUENCES SUMMABLE TO A GIVEN POWER

13.1. In §7.2 we introduced the alphabet $Ч_4$:

$$Ч_4 \rightleftharpoons Ч_3 \cup \{\underline{\nabla}, \nabla, \tau, \sigma\}.$$

τ-systems of rational numbers are words in the alphabet $Ч_2 \cup \{\tau\}$ and, therefore, they are words in the alphabet $Ч_4$.

τ-systems of rational numbers will also be called *words of type* T. If $\mathfrak{k}$ is a given positive integer, then the $\mathfrak{k}$th terms of τ-systems of rational numbers will be called *words of type* ${}_{\mathfrak{k}}\mathrm{T}$ (the expression ${}_{\mathfrak{k}}\mathrm{T}$ will be considered a single symbol).

We introduce two algorithms in the alphabet $Ч_4^{sa}$: an algorithm for adding words of type T (denoted by $+_{\mathrm{T}}$) and an algorithm for multiplying words of type T by rational numbers (denoted by $\cdot_{\mathrm{T}}$). The algorithm $+_{\mathrm{T}}$ is constructed so that, for any words T_1 and T_2 of type T, the word $+_{\mathrm{T}}(\mathrm{T}_1 \square \mathrm{T}_2)$ is a word of type T satisfying the condition $L_\tau(+_{\mathrm{T}}(\mathrm{T}_1 \square \mathrm{T}_2)) = \max(L_\tau(\mathrm{T}_1) \square L_\tau(\mathrm{T}_2))$, and, for any T_1, T_2 and any positive integer i not exceeding $\max(L_\tau(\mathrm{T}_1) \square L_\tau(\mathrm{T}_2))$, the condition

$$[\underset{\mathrm{T}}{+}(\mathrm{T}_1 \square \mathrm{T}_2)]_i^\tau \simeq \begin{cases} [\mathrm{T}_1]_i^\tau \underset{\mathrm{P}}{+} [\mathrm{T}_2]_i^\tau, & \text{if } i \leqslant L_\tau(\mathrm{T}_1) \,\&\, i \leqslant L_\tau(\mathrm{T}_2), \\ [\mathrm{T}_1]_i^\tau, & \text{if } L_\tau(\mathrm{T}_2) < i \leqslant L_\tau(\mathrm{T}_1), \\ [\mathrm{T}_2]_i^\tau, & \text{if } L_\tau(\mathrm{T}_1) < i \leqslant L_\tau(\mathrm{T}_2). \end{cases}$$

is fulfilled. Here and below the notation introduced in §7 will be used.

Intuitively speaking, the addition of τ-systems of rational numbers is carried out component-wise, where, if the given τ-systems have different numbers of terms, then, as a preliminary, to the τ-system with the smaller number of terms we write on the right as new τ-terms the required number of zeros, separating them by the letter τ.

The algorithm $\cdot_{\mathrm{T}}$ is constructed so that, for any word T_1 of type T and any rational number a, the word $\cdot_{\mathrm{T}}(a \,\square\, \mathrm{T}_1)$ is a word of type T satisfying the condition $L_\tau(\cdot_{\mathrm{T}}(a \,\square\, \mathrm{T}_1)) = L_\tau(\mathrm{T}_1)$, and, for any T_1, any a and any positive integer i not exceeding $L_\tau(\mathrm{T}_1)$, the condition

$$[\underset{\mathrm{T}}{\cdot}(a \,\square\, \mathrm{T}_1)]_i^\tau \simeq a \underset{\mathrm{P}}{\cdot} [\mathrm{T}_1]_i^\tau.$$

is fulfilled. Intuitively speaking, multiplication of τ-systems of rational numbers by rational numbers is carried out component-wise.

By $-_{\mathrm{T}}$ we denote the algorithm for subtraction, defined in terms of $+_{\mathrm{T}}$ and $\cdot_{\mathrm{T}}$ in the way described in §12.1. By ${}_{\mathfrak{k}}0$ we denote the word $0\tau0\tau\ldots0\tau0$ (the symbol 0 occurs $\mathfrak{k}$ times).

It is obvious that

$$\forall \mathrm{T}_1\mathrm{T}_2(\mathrm{T}_1 \in {}_{\mathfrak{k}}\mathrm{T} \,\&\, \mathrm{T}_2 \in {}_{\mathfrak{k}}\mathrm{T} \supset \underset{\mathrm{T}}{+}(\mathrm{T}_1 \,\square\, \mathrm{T}_2) \in {}_{\mathfrak{k}}\mathrm{T} \,\&\, \underset{\mathrm{T}}{-}(\mathrm{T}_1 \,\square\, \mathrm{T}_2) \in {}_{\mathfrak{k}}\mathrm{T}),$$

$$\forall \mathrm{T}_1 a\,(\mathrm{T}_1 \in {}_{\mathfrak{k}}\mathrm{T} \supset \underset{\mathrm{T}}{\cdot}(a \,\square\, \mathrm{T}_1) \in {}_{\mathfrak{k}}\mathrm{T}).$$

Let $\mathfrak{a}$ be a fixed rational number such that $\mathfrak{a} \geq 1$. We construct an algorithm ${}_{\mathfrak{a}}N^*$ in the alphabet Ч_4^{sa} such that, for any T_1,

$${}_{\mathfrak{a}}N^*(\mathrm{T}_1) \simeq \left(\sum_{i=1}^{L_\tau(\mathrm{T}_1)} M([\mathrm{T}_1]_i^\tau)^{\mathfrak{a}}\right)^{1:\mathfrak{a}}.$$

It is easily seen that the algorithm ${}_{\mathfrak{a}}N^*$ satisfies the conditions 12.1 (*) both in the case where one takes the word 0 as $\mathfrak{O}$ and in the case where one takes the word ${}_{\mathfrak{k}}0$ (for given $\mathfrak{k}$) as $\mathfrak{O}$.

We construct an algorithm ${}_{\mathfrak{a}}\rho$ in the alphabet Ч_4^{sa} such that

$$\forall \mathrm{T}_1\mathrm{T}_2({}_{\mathfrak{a}}\rho(\mathrm{T}_2 \,\square\, \mathrm{T}_2) \simeq {}_{\mathfrak{a}}N^*(\mathrm{T}_2 \underset{\mathrm{T}}{-} \mathrm{T}_1)).$$

The algorithm ${}_{\mathfrak{a}}\rho$ is a metric function both in the set $(c_{4,1} \in \mathrm{T})$ and in the set $(c_{4,1} \in {}_{\mathfrak{k}}\mathrm{T})$ (for given $\mathfrak{k}$). The list

$$\text{Ч}_4,\ (c_{4,1} \in \mathrm{T}),\ {}_{\mathfrak{a}}\rho, \underset{\mathrm{T}}{+}, \underset{\mathrm{T}}{\cdot}, 0$$

will be denoted by $R_{\mathfrak{a}}$. The list

$$\text{Ч}_4,\ (c_{4,1} \in {}_{\mathfrak{k}}\mathrm{T}),\ {}_{\mathfrak{a}}\rho,\ \underset{\mathrm{T}}{+},\ \underset{\mathrm{T}}{\cdot},\ {}_{\mathfrak{k}}0$$

will be denoted by $R_{\mathfrak{k},\mathfrak{a}}$.

It is not difficult to verify that R_α and $R_{\mathfrak{k},\alpha}$ are normed spaces. Moreover, R_2 and $R_{\mathfrak{k},2}$ are Hilbert spaces. The algorithm for computing the norm in the spaces R_α and $R_{\mathfrak{k},\alpha}$ coincides with the function ${}_\alpha N^*$.

Remark. The spaces R_α and $R_{\mathfrak{k},\alpha}$ are defined for the case where α is a rational number. The definition can be extended to the case where α is a real duplex satisfying the condition $\alpha \geq 1$. We have limited ourselves to the case of rational numbers only because we have described the operation of raising the absolute value of a duplex to a power only for the case where the exponent is a rational number.

13.2. Let $\mathfrak{k}$ be a positive integer. The standard normed *FR*-completion of the space $R_{\mathfrak{k},\alpha}$ will be denoted by $\mathfrak{E}_{\mathfrak{k},\alpha}$.

From 12.4.5 it follows that $\mathfrak{E}_{\mathfrak{k},2}$ is a Hilbert space. It is natural to consider this complete normed space as a constructive analogue of the concept of $\mathfrak{k}$-dimensional Euclidean space introduced in classical mathematics.

As a second constructive analogue of the concept of $\mathfrak{k}$-dimensional Euclidean space it is natural to consider the constructive metric space defined in the following manner.

The $\mathfrak{k}$-terms of σ-systems of real duplexes will be called words of type ${}_\mathfrak{k}Д$. The operation of adding words of type ${}_\mathfrak{k}Д$ (denoted by the letter $\mathfrak{S}$) and the operation of multiplying a word of type ${}_\mathfrak{k}Д$ by a real duplex (denoted by the letter $\mathfrak{T}$) are carried out component-wise. As metric function we take the algorithm δ in the alphabet $Ч_4^{sa}$ such that, for any words $c_{4,1}$ and $c_{4,2}$ of type ${}_\mathfrak{k}Д$,

$$\delta(c_{4,1} \square c_{4,2}) \simeq \left(\sum_{i=1}^{\mathfrak{k}} ([c_{4,2}]_i^\sigma - [c_{4,1}]_i^\sigma)^2 \right)^{1/2}.$$

One can prove that the list

$$Ч_4, \ (c_{4,1} \in {}_\mathfrak{k}Д), \ \delta, \ \mathfrak{S}, \ \mathfrak{T}, \ 0\sigma 0\sigma \ldots 0\sigma 0 \qquad (1)$$

(in the last word the symbol 0 occurs $\mathfrak{k}$ times) is a complete Hilbert space and this space is linearly isometric to the space $\mathfrak{E}_{\mathfrak{k},2}$.

The space (1) will be denoted by $\overline{\mathfrak{E}}_{\mathfrak{k},2}$.

13.3. The standard normed *FR*-completion of the space R_α will be denoted by l_α. It is natural to consider this complete normed space as a constructive analogue of the space which in classical mathematics has the same designation: the space of real sequences summable to the αth power.

Remark. A second constructive analogue of the latter space, obtained by a more faithful copying of the corresponding definition in classical mathematics, has a rather complicated definition. The points of this constructive space are words of the form $P\chi Q$, where χ is a new partitioning sign and P, Q are words in the alphabet $Ч_0$ such that $\langle P\rangle_3 \in (\text{Н} \to Д)_3$, $\langle Q\rangle_0 \in (\text{Н} \to \text{Н})_0$, and $\langle Q\rangle_0$ is a regulator of convergence in itself of the algorithm $\mathfrak{U}$ of type $(\text{Н} \to Д)_3$ such that, for every n,

$$\mathfrak{U}(n) \simeq \left(\sum_{i=0}^{n} M(\langle P\rangle_3(i))^{\alpha}\right)^{1:\alpha}.$$

If as words of the space to be defined we take not words of the kind just described but rather words of the form $P\chi$ such that for sequences of duplexes $\mathfrak{U}$ a regulator of convergence in itself is potentially realizable, then we obtain only a seminormed space and this space is only weakly linearly isometric to the space l_α.

From 12.4.5 it follows that l_2 is a complete Hilbert space.

13.4. Here we shall construct a locally bounded linear functional in l_2 which is not a normed functional, and a closed linear subset of the space l_2 which does not coincide with the carrier of the space l_2 and which is at the same time not a full subset of the space l_2.

We denote by the letter S the algorithm of E. Specker described in the proof of Theorem 8.3.1. We have

$$\forall k\,(0 \leqslant S(k) \leqslant S(k+1) < 1), \tag{1}$$

$$\forall z \neg (z \underline{\lim}_E S). \tag{2}$$

We construct an algorithm β of type $(\text{Н} \to Д)_3$ such that

$$\beta(0) = S(0), \quad \forall n\,(\beta(n+1) = (S(n+1)^2 - S(n)^2)^{1/2}).$$

We have

$$\sum_{i=0}^{n} \beta(i)^2 = S(n)^2.$$

We construct an algorithm Ω_0 in the alphabet $Ч_4^{sa}$ such that, for any word T_1 of type T,

$$\Omega_0(\text{T}_1) \simeq \sum_{i=0}^{H} \gamma_{i+1} \cdot \beta(i),$$

where

$$H \leftrightharpoons L_\tau(\text{T}_1) - 1, \quad \gamma_j \leftrightharpoons [\text{T}_1]_j^\tau \quad (j = 1, \ldots, L_\tau(\text{T}_1)).$$

It is easily seen that Ω_0 is a linear functional in the space R_2. Moreover, for any point T_1 of the space R_2,

$$M(\Omega_0(\text{T}_1)) \leqslant \left(\sum_{i=0}^{H} \gamma_{i+1}^2\right)^{1/2} \cdot \left(\sum_{i=1}^{H} \beta(i)^2\right)^{1/2} = N(\text{T}_1) \cdot S(H) < N(\text{T}_1), \tag{3}$$

where N is the algorithm for computing the norm in R_2. Hence Ω_0 is a locally bounded functional in R_2.

Applying to Ω_0 and the number 1 the standard algorithm for extending 1-ary Lipschitz operators, we obtain a linear locally bounded functional in l_2. Let us denote it by the letter Ω. Let us assume that Ω is a normed functional and that z is a real duplex such that (z norm Ω). Then for any point X of the space l_2 we have

$$M(\Omega(X)) \leqslant z \cdot \bar{N}(X), \tag{4}$$

where $\bar{N}$ is the algorithm for computing the norm in the space l_2.

It is not hard to construct an algorithm ξ such that, for any positive integer n and any real duplexes $Д_1, \cdots, Д_n$, the word $\xi(Д_1 \square \cdots \square Д_n)$ is an FR-construct in the space R_2 such that

$$\Omega(\xi(Д_1 \square \ldots \square Д_n)) = \sum_{i=0}^{n-1} Д_{i+1} \cdot \beta(i), \tag{5}$$

$$\bar{N}(\xi(Д_1 \square \ldots \square Д_n)) = \left(\sum_{i=0}^{n-1} Д_{i+1}^2\right)^{1/2}. \tag{6}$$

Let k be any natural number. We introduce the notation

$$\Gamma_k \leftrightharpoons \xi(\beta(0) \square \ldots \square \beta(k)).$$

On the basis of (5) and (6) we have

$$\Omega(\Gamma_k) = \sum_{i=1}^{k} \beta(i)^2 = S(k)^2, \quad \bar{N}(\Gamma_k) = \left(\sum_{i=0}^{k} \beta(i)^2\right)^{1/2} = S(k). \tag{7}$$

Substituting Γ_k for the variable X in (4) and using (7) and the fact that $\forall k\,(S(k)^2 = 0 \vee S(k)^2 > 0)$, we obtain

$$S(k)^2 \leqslant z \cdot S(k), \qquad S(k) \leqslant z. \tag{8}$$

On the other hand, since z is the norm of the functional Ω and since the set of all words of type T is dense in l_2, a word T_1 is potentially realizable such that

$$T_1 \underset{2P}{\neq} 0 \;\&\; M(\Omega(T_1)) : \bar{N}(T_1) > z - 2^{-k}. \tag{9}$$

From (9) and (3) it follows that

$$(z - 2^{-k}) \cdot \bar{N}(T_1) < M(\Omega(T_1)) \leqslant \bar{N}(T_1) \cdot S(L_\tau(T_1) - 1),$$

$$S(L_\tau(T_1) - 1) > z - 2^{-k}. \tag{10}$$

From (10), (1), and (8) it follows that

$$\exists m \forall n (n \geqslant m \supset z - 2^{-k} < S(n) \leqslant z).$$

Hence $(z \underline{\lim}_E S)$. But this contradicts (2). Therefore $\neg \exists z (z \underline{\text{norm}}\ \Omega)$, i.e. Ω is not a normed functional.

From the definition of the functional Ω_0 it follows that the set

$$\Omega(X) = 0 \tag{11}$$

does not coincide with the carrier of the space l_2. From 12.3.6 it follows that (11) is a closed linear subset of l_2. From 12.6.3 it follows that (11) is not a full subset of the space l_2.

§14. CONSTRUCTIVE ANALOGUE OF THE CONCEPT OF LEBESGUE MEASURABLE SET

For the rest of this book we shall use without explanation the terms and notation introduced in §7.4 and in the other subsections of §7.

14.1. Complexes will be called *words of type* K. We construct an algorithm mes_0 in the alphabet $Ч_4^{sa}$ transforming every complex K_1 into the rational number equal to the sum of the rational segments which are τ-terms of the word K_1. We construct an algorithm ρ_0 in the alphabet $Ч_4^{sa}$ such that, for any complexes K_1 and K_2,

$$\rho_0(\kappa_1 \square \kappa_2) \simeq \text{mes}_0(\kappa_1 \triangle \kappa_2).$$

14.1.1. *For any complexes* K_1 *and* K_2,

$$\text{mes}_0(\kappa_1) \geqslant 0, \tag{1}$$

$$(\kappa_1 \underset{\kappa}{\subseteq} \kappa_2) \supset \text{mes}_0(\kappa_1) \leqslant \text{mes}_0(\kappa_2), \tag{2}$$

$$\text{mes}_0(\kappa_1 \cup \kappa_2) \leqslant \text{mes}_0(\kappa_1) + \text{mes}_0(\kappa_2), \tag{3}$$

$$\kappa_1 \underset{\kappa}{\curlywedge} \kappa_2 \supset \text{mes}_0(\kappa_1 \cup \kappa_2) = \text{mes}_0(\kappa_1) + \text{mes}_0(\kappa_2), \tag{4}$$

$$\text{mes}_0(\kappa_1) \leqslant \text{mes}_0(\kappa_2) + \text{mes}_0(\kappa_1 \triangle \kappa_2), \tag{5}$$

$$M(\text{mes}_0(\kappa_1) - \text{mes}_0(\kappa_2)) \leqslant \rho_0(\kappa_1 \square \kappa_2). \tag{6}$$

Propositions (1) and (4) are obvious, (2) and (3) are proved by simple arguments, (5) follows from (2), (3) and the obvious relation

$$\kappa_1 \underset{\kappa}{\subseteq} \kappa_2 \cup (\kappa_1 \triangle \kappa_2),$$

and (6) follows from (5).

14.1.2. *For any* K_1, K_2 *and* K_3,

$$\rho_0(\kappa_1 \square \kappa_1) = 0, \tag{7}$$

$$\rho_0(\kappa_3 \square \kappa_1) \leqslant \rho_0(\kappa_1 \square \kappa_2) + \rho_0(\kappa_2 \square \kappa_3). \tag{8}$$

Proposition (7) is obvious, and (8) follows from 7.4.6, (2) and (3).

14.1.3. a) *The list*

$$Ч_4,\ (c_{4,1} \in \kappa),\ \rho_0 \tag{9}$$

is a metric space.

b) *The algorithm* mes_0 *is a 1-ary Lipschitz operator from the space* (9) *into the space of rational numbers (and therefore into the space of real duplexes) and* 1 *is a Lipschitz coefficient of this operator.*

c) *The algorithms* $\cup_K$, $\cap_K$, $\setminus_K$, Δ_K *are binary Lipschitz operators from the space* (9) *into the space* (9), *and* 1 *is a Lipschitz coefficient of each of these operators.*

Proposition a) follows from 14.1.2, proposition b) from (6), and proposition c) from 7.4.5, (2) and (3).

We introduce two new binary relations $\subseteq_{\rho_0}$ and $\curlywedge_{\rho_0}$. If K_1 and K_2 are complexes, then

$$\kappa_1 \underset{\rho_0}{\subseteq} \kappa_2 \leftrightharpoons \text{mes}_0(\kappa_1 \setminus \kappa_2) = 0,$$

$$\kappa_1 \underset{\rho_0}{\curlywedge} \kappa_2 \leftrightharpoons \text{mes}_0(\kappa_1 \cap \kappa_2) = 0.$$

It is obvious that, for any K_1 and K_2,

$$\kappa_1 \underset{\rho_0}{=} \kappa_2 \equiv (\kappa_1 \underset{\rho_0}{\subseteq} \kappa_2) \,\&\, (\kappa_2 \underset{\rho_0}{\subseteq} \kappa_1).$$

14.1.4. *For any* K_1, K_2, K_3 *and* K_4,

$$(\kappa_1 \underset{\rho_0}{\subseteq} \kappa_2) \supset \text{mes}_0(\kappa_1) \leqslant \text{mes}_0(\kappa_2), \tag{10}$$

$$\kappa_1 \underset{\rho_0}{=} \kappa_3 \,\&\, \kappa_2 \underset{\rho_0}{=} \kappa_4 \supset (\kappa_1 \underset{\rho_0}{\subseteq} \kappa_2 \equiv \kappa_3 \underset{\rho_0}{\subseteq} \kappa_4), \tag{11}$$

$$\kappa_1 \underset{\rho_0}{=} \kappa_3 \,\&\, \kappa_2 \underset{\rho_0}{=} \kappa_4 \supset (\kappa_1 \underset{\rho_0}{\curlywedge} \kappa_2 \equiv \kappa_3 \underset{\rho_0}{\curlywedge} \kappa_4), \tag{12}$$

$$\kappa_1 \underset{\rho_0}{\curlywedge} \kappa_2 \supset \text{mes}_0(\kappa_1 \cup \kappa_2) = \text{mes}_0(\kappa_1) + \text{mes}_0(\kappa_2). \tag{13}$$

This theorem is easily proved with the help of 14.1.3 b) and 14.1.3 c).

14.2. Let us construct the standard *FR*-completion of the space (9) and denote the resulting complete metric space by the letter И. We denote the metric function in И by the letter ρ. Points of the space И (i.e. *FR*-constructs in the space (9)) will be called *measurable FR-constructs*, or *measurable duplexes*, or *words of type* И. As a partitioning sign for the construction of measurable duplexes we shall use the symbol ①. Thus the alphabet of the space И is the alphabet $Ч_4 \cup \{①\}$. We shall denote this alphabet by $Ч_5$.

Applying to the algorithms mes_0, $\cup_К$, $\cap_К$, $\setminus_К$, $\Delta_К$, and the number 1 the appropriate standard algorithms for extending Lipschitz operators (see §10.4), we again obtain Lipschitz operators for which 1 is a Lipschitz coefficient in the corresponding dimensions. We shall denote the operators thus obtained by mes, $\cup_И$, $\cap_И$, $\setminus_И$, $\Delta_И$, respectively. The real duplex mes ($И_1$) will be called the *Lebesgue measure* of the measurable *FR*-construct $И_1$.

The algorithms $\cup_И$, $\cap_И$, $\setminus_И$, $\Delta_И$ will be called, respectively, the algorithms for constructing the union, intersection, difference, and symmetric difference of measurable duplexes. In those cases where there will be no cause for confusion, we shall use as designations of these algorithms the symbols $\cup$, $\cap$, $\setminus$, Δ, respectively.

We introduce binary relations $\subseteq_\rho$ and $\curlywedge_\rho$, setting, for any two measurable duplexes $И_1$ and $И_2$,

$$и_1 \underset{\rho}{\subseteq} и_2 \rightleftharpoons \mathrm{mes}\,(и_1 \setminus и_2) = 0,$$

$$и_1 \underset{\rho}{\curlywedge} и_2 \rightleftharpoons \mathrm{mes}\,(и_1 \cap и_2) = 0.$$

14.2.1. *Replacing in the formulations of Theorems* 14.1.1 *and* 14.1.4 *the expressions*

$$к_1,\ к_2,\ к_3,\ к_4,\ \mathrm{mes}_0,\ \rho_0,\ \underset{к}{\curlywedge},\ \underset{к}{\subseteq}$$

by the expressions

$$и_1,\ и_2,\ и_3,\ и_4,\ \mathrm{mes},\ \rho,\ \underset{\rho}{\curlywedge},\ \underset{\rho}{\subseteq},$$

respectively, we obtain true assertions. In addition, for any $И_1$ *and* $И_2$,

$$\rho\,(и_1 \square и_2) \underset{в}{=} \mathrm{mes}\,(и_1 \triangle и_2), \tag{14}$$

$$и_1 \triangle и_2 \underset{\rho}{=} (и_1 \setminus и_2) \cup (и_2 \setminus и_1), \tag{15}$$

$$(и_1 \underset{\rho}{=} и_2) \equiv (и_1 \underset{\rho}{\subseteq} и_2)\ \&\ (и_2 \underset{\rho}{\subseteq} и_1). \tag{16}$$

We shall not give the proof of this theorem here. We mention only that certain parts of the theorem are easily proved with the help of 9.4.1.

14.3. The concept of measurable *FR*-construct (measurable duplex) is a natural constructive analogue of the concept of Lebesgue measurable set of finite measure. The propositions α), β), γ) formulated below, and the remark concerning these propositions serve as justification for this point of view. Propositions α), β), and γ) are formulated on the basis of the concepts of classical mathematics and are proved by the logical methods of classical mathematics. In these propositions and in proposition δ) following them, the term "measurable set" is used as an abbreviation of the expression "subset of the set of all real numbers which is Lebesgue measurable and has finite measure", the expressions $\mathrm{mes}_L(U)$ and $\rho_L(V, W)$, where U, V, W are measurable sets, denote, respectively, the Lebesgue measure of the set U and the number

$$\mathrm{mes}_L((V \setminus W) \cup (W \setminus V)).$$

(Here the symbols $\cup$ and $\setminus$ denote, respectively, the set-theoretic operations of union and difference.) The remaining notation and terms are used in the sense customary in classical mathematics.

α) *For any measurable set* U *there is a sequence of measurable sets* $\{C_i\}_{i=1}^{\infty}$ *such that, first, for every* i, *the set* C_i *is a union of a finite number of intervals with rational end points, and, second,* $\rho_L(C_i, U) \to 0$ *as* $i \to \infty$.

β) *Let* $\{C_i\}_{i=1}^{\infty}$ *be a sequence of arbitrary measurable sets. In order that there be a measurable set* U *such that* $\rho_L(C_i, U) \to 0$ *as* $i \to \infty$, *it is necessary and sufficient that the sequence* $\{C_i\}_{i=1}^{\infty}$ *satisfy the Cauchy condition with respect to the metric function* ρ_L.

γ) *If measurable sets* U_1 *and* U_2 *are such that there exists a sequence of measurable sets* $\{C_i\}_{i=1}^{\infty}$ *for which* $\rho_L(C_i, U_1) \to 0$ *and* $\rho_L(C_i, U_2) \to 0$ *as* $i \to \infty$, *then*

$$\rho_L(U_1, U_2) = 0.$$

Remark. In classical mathematics the concept of measurable set is introduced on the basis of the general notion of set. However, in the theory of measure and the Lebesgue integral two measurable sets U_1 and U_2 are considered to be interchangeable not only when they are equal in the sense of the general definition of equality of sets but also when $\rho_L(U_1, U_2) = 0$.

For the justification of the naturalness of a definition formulated below we also mention the following theorem of the classical theory of measurable sets.

δ) *If* $\{C_i\}_{i=1}^{\infty}$ *is a sequence of measurable sets such that the sequence of numbers* $\{\text{mes}_L(\bigcup_{i=1}^{k} C_i)\}_{i=1}^{\infty}$ *is bounded above, then*:

δ_1) *the set* $\bigcup_{i=1}^{\infty} C_i$ *is measurable*;

δ_2) $\rho_L(\bigcup_{i=1}^{k} C_i, \bigcup_{i=1}^{\infty} C_i) \to 0$ *as* $k \to \infty$;

δ_3) *if a measurable set* U *is such that* $\rho_L(\bigcup_{i=1}^{k} C_i, U) \to 0$ *as* $k \to \infty$, *then* $\rho_L(\bigcup_{i=1}^{\infty} C_i, U) = 0$;

δ_4) mes_L *is a uniformly continuous function in the metric space of measurable sets, and therefore*

$$\text{mes}_L\left(\bigcup_{i=1}^{k} C_i\right) \to \text{mes}_L\left(\bigcup_{i=1}^{\infty} C_i\right) \quad \text{as} \quad k \to \infty;$$

moreover, if $\forall i(C_i \subseteq C_{i+1})$, *then*

$$\text{mes}_L(C_k) \to \text{mes}_L\left(\bigcup_{i=1}^{\infty} C_i\right) \quad \text{as} \quad k \to \infty,$$

and if $\forall ij(i \neq j \supset C_i \cap C_j = \Lambda)$, *then*

$$\sum_{i=1}^{k} \text{mes}_L(C_i) \to \text{mes}_L\left(\bigcup_{i=1}^{\infty} C_i\right) \quad \text{as} \quad k \to \infty.$$

Parts δ_2) and δ_3) of the last theorem suggest the following definition.

Let $\Phi_{5,1}$ be an algorithm in the alphabet $Ч_5^{sa}$ of type $(\text{Н} \to \text{Н})_5$ such that there is potentially realizable a real duplex z satisfying the condition

$$\forall k(\text{mes}(\breve{\Phi}_{5,1}(k)) \leqslant z).$$

Here and in the remainder of the text $\breve{\Phi}_{5,1}$ denotes the algorithm in the alphabet $Ч_5^{sa}$ such that

$$\breve{\Phi}_{5,1}(0) \simeq \Phi_{5,1}(0), \qquad \forall k(\breve{\Phi}_{5,1}(k+1) \simeq \breve{\Phi}_{5,1}(k) \underset{\text{И}}{\cup} \Phi_{5,1}(k+1)).$$

Let И_1 be a point of the space И. We shall say that И_1 is *the union of all measurable FR-constructs which are terms of the sequence* $\Phi_{5,1}$ if

$$0 \ \underline{\lim}_E \ G,$$

where G is the algorithm of type $(\text{Н} \to \text{Д})_3$ such that, for every k,

$$G(k) \simeq \rho(\text{И}_1 \square \breve{\Phi}_{5,1}(k)).$$

The next theorem follows immediately from §14.1 (6) and Theorem 10.4.10 b).

14.3.1. *The algorithm* mes *is a uniformly continuous function of type* $(\text{И} \to \text{Д})$ *in the metric space of measurable FR-constructs, and therefore, if* $\Phi_{5,1}$ *is a sequence of measurable FR-constructs and* И_1 *is a measurable FR-construct* *which is the union of all the terms of the sequence* $\Phi_{5,1}$, *then*

$$\mathrm{mes}\,(\text{И}_1)\ \underset{E}{\underline{\lim}}\ H,$$

where H *denotes the algorithm of type* $(\text{Н}\to\text{Д})_3$ *such that*

$$\forall k\,(H(k)\simeq \mathrm{mes}\,({}^{\smile}\Phi_{5,1}(k))).$$

Moreover, if $\forall i\,(\Phi_{5,1}(i)\subseteq_\rho \Phi_{5,1}(i+1))$, *then*

$$\mathrm{mes}\,(\text{И}_1)\ \underset{E}{\underline{\lim}}\ H_1,$$

where H_1 *is the algorithm of type* $(\text{Н}\to\text{Д})_3$ *such that*

$$\forall k\,(H_1(k)\simeq \mathrm{mes}\,(\Phi_{5,1}(k))),$$

and if

$$\forall ij\,(i\neq j\supset \Phi_{5,1}(i)\underset{\rho}{\perp}\Phi_{5,1}(j)),$$

then

$$\mathrm{mes}\,(\text{И}_1)\ \underset{E}{\underline{\lim}}\ H_2,$$

where H_2 *is the algorithm of type* $(\text{Н}\to\text{Д})_3$ *such that*

$$\forall k\,(H_2(k)\simeq \sum_{i=0}^{k}\mathrm{mes}\,(\Phi_{5,1}(k))).$$

Now we shall go into an essential difference between the theory of measurable *FR*-constructs and the classical theory of Lebesgue measurable sets.

The following assertion can be considered the natural translation into constructive mathematics of part δ_1) of Theorem δ): for any sequence of measurable *FR*-constructs $\Phi_{5,1}$ such that

$$\exists z\forall k\,(\mathrm{mes}\,({}^{\smile}\Phi_{5,1}(k))\leqslant z),$$

there is a potentially realizable measurable *FR*-construct И_1 which is the union of all the terms of the sequence $\Phi_{5,1}$. However, the assertion is refutable by a concrete example. In addition, we shall now prove the following theorem.

14.3.2. a) *One can construct an algorithm* $\Phi_{5,2}$ *of type* $(\text{Н}\to\text{К})_5$ *such that, for every* i,

$$\Phi_{5,2}(i)\underset{\text{к}}{\subseteq}\Phi_{5,2}(i+1)\ \&\ \mathrm{mes}_0(\Phi_{5,2}(i))<1$$

and at the same time there is no measurable FR-construct which is the union of all the terms of the sequence $\Phi_{5,2}$.

b) *One can construct an algorithm* $\Phi_{5,3}$ *of type* $(\text{Н}\to\text{К})_5$ *such that, for any* i *and* j,

$$(i\neq j\supset \Phi_{5,3}(i)\underset{\text{к}}{\perp}\Phi_{5,3}(j))\ \&\ \mathrm{mes}\,({}^{\smile}\Phi_{5,3}(i))<1,$$

and at the same time there is no measurable FR-construct which is the union of all the terms of the sequence $\Phi_{5,3}$.

Proof. We denote by S the algorithm of E. Specker described in the proof of Theorem 8.3.1. One can assume that $S(0) > 0$. We construct algorithms $\mathfrak{A}$ and $\mathfrak{B}$ in the alphabet $Ч_5^{sa}$ such that, for every n,

$$\mathfrak{A}(n) \mathrel{\overline{\smash{=}}} 0 \triangledown S(n), \qquad \mathfrak{B}(0) \mathrel{\overline{\smash{=}}} 0 \triangledown S(0),$$

$$\mathfrak{B}(n+1) \mathrel{\overline{\smash{=}}} \begin{cases} S(n) \triangledown S(n+1), & \text{if } S(n) < S(n+1), \\ \Lambda, & \text{if } S(n) \underset{P}{=} S(n+1). \end{cases}$$

It is obvious that $\mathfrak{A}$ and $\mathfrak{B}$ are algorithms of type $(\text{H} \rightarrow \text{K})_5$. Moreover, for any i and j,

$$\mathfrak{A}(i) \underset{K}{\subseteq} \mathfrak{A}(i+1), \qquad \text{mes}_0(\mathfrak{A}(i)) = S(i) < 1,$$

$$i \neq j \supset \mathfrak{B}(i) \underset{K}{\curlywedge} \mathfrak{B}(j), \qquad \text{mes}_0(\sim\mathfrak{B}(i)) = S(i) < 1.$$

If $И_1$ is a measurable FR-construct which is the union of all the terms of the sequence $\mathfrak{A}$ (sequence $\mathfrak{B}$), then on the basis of 14.3.1 we have

$$\text{mes}\,(И_1)\ \underline{\lim}_E\, S.$$

Hence $\exists z(z\ \underline{\lim}_E\ S)$. But this contradicts one of the properties of the algorithm S. Hence there can be no measurable FR-construct which is the union of all terms of the sequence $\mathfrak{A}$ (respectively, of the sequence $\mathfrak{B}$). The theorem is proved.

Thus part δ_1) of Theorem δ) does not carry over to constructive mathematics. Parts δ_2) and δ_3) of Theorem δ) play a guiding role in the definition of the relation "$И_1$ is the union of all the terms of the sequence $\Phi_{5,1}$". Theorem 14.3.1 can be considered as a constructive analogue of part δ_4).

14.4. Let $\mathfrak{k}$ be a natural number greater than 1. As a constructive analogue of the concept of Lebesgue measurable subset of $\mathfrak{k}$-dimensional Euclidean space (having in mind measurable subsets of finite measure), it is natural to take the concept of FR-construct in the metric space of all $\mathfrak{k}$-complexes. Here by $\mathfrak{k}$-complexes we mean words of the form $I_1 \tau I_2 \tau \cdots \tau I_m$, where m is any positive integer and $I_1, I_2, \cdots, I_m$ are pairwise disjoint "cubes" in the space $R_{\mathfrak{k},2}$, the dimensions of which can vary from 1 to $\mathfrak{k}$. We shall not explain the meaning of the term "cube" which we have used here, assuming that the hint given by the usual meaning of the term will suffice for the reader. In the definition of the relation of disjointness for "cubes" it is convenient to assume that every "cube", as a set of elements, is associated with a set which is open with respect to the linear carrier of the given "cube" in the space $R_{\mathfrak{t},2}$. In view of the fact that points of the space $R_{\mathfrak{t},2}$ are τ-systems of rational numbers, the condition characterizing the concept of "$\mathfrak{t}$-complex" is algorithmically verifiable.

The remaining steps in the construction of the theory imitate the presentation in §§14.1–14.3.

14.5. In classical mathematics the concept of measurable set is introduced on the basis of the general concept of set. At the same time, the concept of measurable FR-construct is a concept of a completely different kind. It is not subsumed under the concept of set used in constructive mathematics (see [3], §7). However, one can connect measurable FR-constructs in a natural way with certain sets, and, thanks to this, one can extend in a natural way the algorithm for computing measure to those sets. Let us consider some examples.

Let x and y be real duplexes such that $x \leq y$. With the segment $x \mathbin{\underline{\nabla}} y$ we associate a certain measurable FR-construct. First, we construct an algorithm $\mathfrak{F}$ in the alphabet $Ч_4^{sa}$ such that

$$\forall k (\mathscr{F}(k) \simeq \underbrace{\Upsilon_\uparrow(x)}(k) \nabla \underbrace{\Upsilon_\downarrow(y)}(k)),$$

and an algorithm G in the alphabet $Ч_0^{sa}$ such that

$$\forall k (G(k) = k + 2).$$

It is easily seen that the word $\{\mathscr{F}\} \oplus \{G\}$ is a measurable FR-construct and $\mathrm{mes}(\{\mathfrak{F}\} \oplus \{G\}) = y - x$. We associate this measurable FR-construct both with the segment $x \mathbin{\underline{\nabla}} y$ and with the set of $Д$-points of this segment.

If $x < y$, then the word $x \nabla y$ is an interval. With this interval and also with the set of $Д$-points of this interval, we associate the same measurable FR-construct. But in certain cases it is convenient to replace it by another measurable FR-construct, equal (in the space $И$) to the one constructed above and for which all terms of the sequence of complexes are contained in the interval $x \nabla y$.

By a *constructive Jordan curve* in the space $\mathfrak{E}_{2,2}$ (see §13.2) we mean any word of the form $S_1 * S_2$, where S_1 and S_2 are complete ciphers of uniformly continuous functions of type $(Д \to Д)$ satisfying the following conditions: first, $f(1) = f(0)$ and $g(1) = g(0)$, where $f \leftrightharpoons \underbrace{S_1}_{\pi}$ and $g \leftrightharpoons \underbrace{S_2}_{\pi}$ (the letter π denotes the ordinal number of the alphabet in which complete ciphers of uniformly continuous functions of type $(Д \to Д)$ are constructed), and second, for any points x, y of the segment $0 \mathbin{\underline{\nabla}} 1$ such that $0 < M(x - y) < 1$, the distance in the space $\mathfrak{E}_{2,2}$ between the points $f(x) \sigma g(x)$ and $f(y) \sigma g(y)$ is positive.

With every Jordan curve one can connect in a natural fashion a certain set: the set of points of the space $\overline{\mathfrak{E}}_{2,2}$ lying inside the given Jordan curve. (We shall not formulate the corresponding definition, since we shall limit ourselves below only to some remarks about a connected problem.) We shall call this set the *interior* of the given Jordan curve.

The problem arises about associating with every Jordan curve an *FR*-construct in the metric space of 2-complexes which it would be natural to consider as a presentation of an algorithm for the approximate representation to any given degree of accuracy of the interior of the given Jordan curve by means of 2-complexes. We shall not consider this problem here. We note only that in those cases where the Jordan curve turns out to be "sufficiently nice" (for example, in the case where the Jordan curve can, for every k, be covered by a finite number of rectangles, the sum of the areas of which is less than 2^{-k}), the problem can be solved without difficulty.

§15. CONSTRUCTIVE ANALOGUE OF THE CONCEPT OF A FUNCTION SUMMABLE TO A GIVEN POWER. CONSTRUCTIVE LEBESGUE INTEGRAL

15.1. We shall say that a word $c_{4,1}$ in the alphabet $Ч_4$ is a *graduated frame*, and also that it is a *word of type* σ, if $c_{4,1}$ is a σ-pair of words such that the word $[c_{4,1}]_1^\sigma$ is a complex (cf. §7.4), the word $[c_{4,1}]_2^\sigma$ is a τ-system of rational numbers, and $L_\tau([c_{4,1}]_1^\sigma) = L_\tau([c_{4,1}]_2^\sigma)$. In other words, the word $c_{4,1}$ is a graduated frame (word of type σ) if it has the form

$$Q_1\tau Q_2\tau\ldots\tau Q_{\mathfrak{k}}\sigma R_1\tau R_2\tau\ldots\tau R_{\mathfrak{k}}, \tag{1}$$

where $\mathfrak{k}$ is a natural number, Q_i is a rational segment, and R_i is a rational number $(i = 1, 2, \cdots, \mathfrak{k})$. Moreover, Q_i precedes Q_j if $i < j$. The case $\mathfrak{k} = 0$ is not excluded. Therefore the single-letter word σ is, by definition, a graduated frame.

Let us construct an algorithm $\mathfrak{B}$ of type $(\sigma \to c_0)_4$ such that, for any word σ_1 of type σ and any rational number a,

$$\langle\mathfrak{B}(\sigma_1)\rangle_2(a) \doteq \begin{cases} R_i, & \text{if } a \text{ belongs to } Q_i\ (i=1, 2,\ldots, \mathfrak{k}),\\ 0, & \text{if } a \text{ does not belong to any of the segments } Q_1, Q_2,\ldots, Q_{\mathfrak{k}}.\end{cases}$$

Here it is assumed that the word σ_1 is represented in the form (1).

For any word $\mathfrak{б}_1$, the algorithm $\langle \mathfrak{B}(\mathfrak{б}_1)\rangle_2$ is a function of type $(\mathfrak{p} \to \mathfrak{p})$. The function $\langle \mathfrak{B}(\mathfrak{б}_1)\rangle_2$ will be called the *functional interpretation* of the graduated frame $\mathfrak{б}_1$.

If $c_{4,1}$ is a graduated frame, then the complex $[c_{4,1}]_1^{\sigma}$ will be called the *supporting complex* of the word $c_{4,1}$. We shall denote by the letter $\mathfrak{K}$ the algorithm in the alphabet $Ч_4^{sa}$ transforming every graduated frame into the supporting complex of this frame. We have

$$\forall \mathfrak{б}_1 (\mathscr{K}(\mathfrak{б}_1) \doteq [\mathfrak{б}_1]_1^{\sigma}).$$

Now we introduce an operation of addition of graduated frames, an operation of multiplication of a graduated frame by graduated frames, an operation of multiplication of a graduated frame by a rational number, and an operation of constructing the absolute value of a graduated frame.

The operation of addition (multiplication) of graduated frames is a normal algorithm in the alphabet $Ч_4^{sa}$ equivalent with respect to $Ч_4$ to the following intuitively given algorithm. If the initially given object is the word $\mathfrak{б}_1 \square \mathfrak{б}_2$, then, first of all, we construct the union of the complexes $\mathfrak{K}(\mathfrak{б}_1)$ and $\mathfrak{K}(\mathfrak{б}_2)$. Then, for every rational segment I which is a τ-term of the complex $\mathfrak{K}(\mathfrak{б}_1) \cup \mathfrak{K}(\mathfrak{б}_2)$, we compute the sum (respectively, product) of the rational numbers $\langle \mathfrak{B}(\mathfrak{б}_1)\rangle_2(\gamma_I)$ and $\langle \mathfrak{B}(\mathfrak{б}_2)\rangle_2(\gamma_I)$, where γ_I denotes the middle of the segment I. If the index of the segment I among all τ-terms of the complex $\mathfrak{K}(\mathfrak{б}_1) \cup \mathfrak{K}(\mathfrak{б}_2)$ is equal to m, then we denote the resulting rational number by H_m. Finally, we construct the word

$$(\mathscr{K}(\mathfrak{б}_1) \cup \mathscr{K}(\mathfrak{б}_2)) \sigma H_1 \tau H_2 \tau \ldots \tau H_{\mathfrak{l}}, \tag{2}$$

where $\mathfrak{l}$ is the natural number equal to the number of τ-terms of the word $(\mathfrak{K}(\mathfrak{б}_1) \cup \mathfrak{K}(\mathfrak{б}_2))$. The word (2) is taken to be the result of applying the operation of addition (respectively, multiplication) to the word $\mathfrak{б}_1 \square \mathfrak{б}_2$.

The operation of multiplying a graduated frame by a rational number is a normal algorithm in the alphabet $Ч_4^{sa}$ transforming any word of the form $a \square \mathfrak{б}_1$, where $\mathfrak{б}_1$ is a graduated frame and a is a rational number, into the word

$$Q_1 \tau Q_2 \tau \ldots \tau Q_{\mathfrak{l}} \sigma (a \cdot R_1) \tau (a \cdot R_2) \tau \ldots \tau (a \cdot R_{\mathfrak{l}}).$$

Here we are assuming that the word $\mathfrak{б}_1$ is represented in the form (1).

The operation of constructing the absolute value of a graduated frame is a normal algorithm in the alphabet $Ч_4^{sa}$ transforming any $\mathfrak{б}_1$ into the word

$$Q_1 \tau Q_2 \tau \ldots \tau Q_{\mathfrak{l}} \sigma M(R_1) \tau M(R_2) \tau \ldots \tau M(R_{\mathfrak{l}}).$$

The operations of adding graduated frames, multiplying a graduated frame by graduated frames, multiplying a graduated frame by a rational number, constructing the absolute value of a graduated frame, and subtracting one graduated frame from another are to be denoted, respectively, by the expressions

$$\underset{б}{+},\ \underset{б}{\times},\ \underset{б}{\cdot},\ \underset{б}{M},\ \underset{б}{-}.$$

In the sequel the letter $\mathfrak{a}$ will denote a fixed rational number satisfying the condition $\mathfrak{a} \geq 1$. We construct an algorithm ${}_{\mathfrak{a}}N^*$ in the alphabet $Ч_4^{sa}$ such that, for any word $б_1$,

$$ {}_{\mathfrak{a}}N^*(б_1) \simeq \left(\sum_{i=1}^{\mathfrak{k}} M(R_i)^{\mathfrak{a}} \cdot \mathrm{mes}_0(Q_i) \right)^{1:\mathfrak{a}}. $$

Here it is assumed that the word $б_1$ is represented in the form (1). In other words, it is assumed that

$$\mathfrak{k} \leftrightharpoons L_\tau(\mathscr{K}(б_1)),$$

$$Q_i \leftrightharpoons [\mathscr{K}(б_1)]_i^\tau, \quad R_i \leftrightharpoons [[б_1]_2^\sigma]_i^\tau \quad (i = 1, 2, \ldots, \mathfrak{k}).$$

Let us also construct an algorithm $\int_0$ in the alphabet $Ч_4^{sa}$ such that, for any $б_1$,

$$\int_0(б_1) \simeq \sum_{i=1}^{\mathfrak{k}} R_i \cdot \mathrm{mes}_0(Q_i).$$

The rational number $\int_0(б_1)$ is called the *integral* of the graduated frame $б_1$.

For graduated frames the Hölder-Minkowski inequalities hold:

$$\int_0 (M(б_1 \underset{б}{\times} б_2)) \leqslant {}_{\mathfrak{a}}N^*(б_1) \cdot {}_{\mathfrak{b}}N^*(б_2), \tag{3}$$

where $\mathfrak{a} > 1$ and $\mathfrak{b} = \mathfrak{a} : (\mathfrak{a} - 1)$;

$$ {}_{\mathfrak{a}}N^*(б_1 \underset{б}{+} б_2) \leqslant {}_{\mathfrak{a}}N^*(б_1) + {}_{\mathfrak{a}}N^*(б_2). \tag{4}$$

It is easily seen that the algorithm ${}_{\mathfrak{a}}N^*$ satisfies conditions 12.1 (*). We construct an algorithm ${}_{\mathfrak{a}}\rho$ in the alphabet $Ч_4^{sa}$ such that, for any words $б_1$ and $б_2$,

$$ {}_{\mathfrak{a}}\rho(б_1 \square б_2) \simeq {}_{\mathfrak{a}}N^*(б_2 \underset{б}{-} б_1). \tag{5}$$

${}_{\mathfrak{a}}\rho$ is a metric function in the set $(c_{4,1} \in б)$. It is not hard to prove that the list

$$Ч_4,\ (c_{4,1} \in б),\ {}_{\mathfrak{a}}\rho,\ \underset{б}{+},\ \underset{б}{\cdot},\ \sigma$$

is a normed space. We denote this space by $B_{\mathfrak{a}}$. The algorithm for computing the norm in B_α coincides with the function ${}_\alpha N^*$. This algorithm will be denoted by ${}_\alpha N$.

It is easy to see that B_2 is a Hilbert space.

Let x and y be real duplexes such that $x < y$. We shall say that a graduated frame σ_1 is *imbedded* in the segment $x \underline{\nabla} y$ if all τ-terms of the complex $\mathfrak{K}(\sigma_1)$ are contained in $x \underline{\nabla} y$.

In the sequel the letters $\mathfrak{x}$ and $\mathfrak{y}$ will denote fixed real duplexes satisfying the condition $\mathfrak{x} < \mathfrak{y}$. Graduated frames imbedded in the segment $\mathfrak{x} \underline{\nabla} \mathfrak{y}$ will be called *words of type* σ'.

The normed subspace of the space B_α, induced by the space B_α in the set $(c_{4,1} \in \sigma')$, will be denoted by $B_\alpha(\mathfrak{x}, \mathfrak{y})$. It is evident that $B_2(\mathfrak{x}, \mathfrak{y})$ is a Hilbert space.

15.1.1. *For any graduated frames* σ_1, σ_2 *and any rational number* a,

$$\int_0 (\sigma_1 \underset{\text{б}}{+} \sigma_2) = \int_0 (\sigma_1) \underset{\text{в}}{+} \int_0 (\sigma_2), \tag{6}$$

$$\int_0 (a \underset{\text{б}}{\cdot} \sigma_1) = a \underset{\text{в}}{\cdot} \int_0 (\sigma_1), \tag{7}$$

$$\underset{\text{в}}{M}\left(\int_0 (\sigma_1)\right) \leqslant \int_0 (\underset{\text{б}}{M}(\sigma_1)) = {}_1N(\sigma_1), \tag{8}$$

$${}_1N(\sigma_1) \leqslant \text{mes}_0(\mathcal{K}(\sigma_1))^{(\mathfrak{a}-1):\mathfrak{a}} \cdot {}_\mathfrak{a}N(\sigma_1), \tag{9}$$

$${}_\mathfrak{a}N(M(\sigma_1)) = {}_\mathfrak{a}N(\sigma_1). \tag{10}$$

Proposition (9) follows from (3). The remaining assertions are proved by elementary arguments.

15.1.2. *For any graduated frame* σ_1 *imbedded in* $\mathfrak{x} \underline{\nabla} \mathfrak{y}$,

$${}_1N(\sigma_1) \leqslant (\mathfrak{y} - \mathfrak{x})^{(\mathfrak{a}-1):\mathfrak{a}} \cdot {}_\mathfrak{a}N(\sigma_1). \tag{11}$$

This proposition follows from (9).

Let us denote by Ξ the algorithm in the alphabet Ч_4^{sa} such that, for any graduated frame σ_1,

$$\Xi(\sigma_1) \doteq \max(C_1 \square \ldots \square C_\mathfrak{q}),$$

where

$$\mathfrak{q} \leftrightharpoons L_\tau(\mathcal{K}(\sigma_1)), \quad C_j \leftrightharpoons M([[\sigma_1]_2^{\mathfrak{z}}]_j^\tau) \quad (j = 1, \ldots, \mathfrak{q}).$$

It is easy to prove (on the basis of the definition of the algorithm ${}_\alpha N$) the following proposition.

15.1.3. *For any graduated frames* $\mathfrak{б}_1$ *and* $\mathfrak{б}_2$,

$${}_{\alpha}N(\mathfrak{б}_1 \underset{\mathfrak{б}}{\times} \mathfrak{б}_2) \leqslant \Xi(\mathfrak{б}_1) \cdot {}_{\alpha}N(\mathfrak{б}_2).$$

Let K_1 be any complex. By the *characteristic frame* of the complex K_1 we mean the word $K_1\sigma 1\tau\cdots\tau 1$ (1 occurs $\mathfrak{k}$ times to the right of σ), where $\mathfrak{k}$ is the number of τ-terms of the complex K_1. We denote by χ_0 the algorithm in the alphabet $Ч_4^{sa}$ transfoming any complex K_1 into the characteristic frame of this complex.

The following theorem is easily proved.

15.1.4. *For any complexes* K_1 *and* K_2,

$$\int_0 (\chi_0(\kappa_1)) = \text{mes}_0(\kappa_1), \tag{12}$$

$$\kappa_1 \underset{\rho_0}{\curlywedge} \kappa_2 \equiv \chi_0(\kappa_1 \cup \kappa_2) \underset{\alpha^\rho}{=} \chi_0(\kappa_1) + \chi_0(\kappa_2), \tag{13}$$

$$\chi_0(\kappa_1 \triangle \kappa_2) \underset{\alpha^\rho}{=} M(\chi_0(\kappa_1) - \chi_0(\kappa_2)), \tag{14}$$

$$\rho_0(\kappa_1 \square \kappa_2) = \text{mes}_0(\kappa_1 \triangle \kappa_2) = \int_0 (M(\chi_0(\kappa_1) - \chi_0(\kappa_2))), \tag{15}$$

$${}_{\alpha}\rho(\chi_0(\kappa_1) \square \chi_0(\kappa_2)) = \rho_0(\kappa_1 \square \kappa_2)^{1:\alpha}, \tag{16}$$

$${}_{\alpha}N(\chi_0(\kappa_1)) = \text{mes}_0(\kappa_1)^{1:\alpha}. \tag{17}$$

Here ρ_0 is the metric function in the space of complexes (see §14.1).

15.2. The standard normed FR-completion of the space B_α [the space $B_\alpha(\mathfrak{x}, \mathfrak{y})$] will be denoted by $\mathfrak{L}_\alpha$ (respectively, by $\mathfrak{L}_\alpha(\mathfrak{x}, \mathfrak{y})$). Points of the space $\mathfrak{L}_1$ (that is, FR-constructs in the space B_1) will be called *summable FR-constructs* (*summable duplexes*), as well as *words of type* Л. Points of the space $\mathfrak{L}_\alpha(\mathfrak{x}, \mathfrak{y})$ (that is, FR-constructs in the space $B_\alpha(\mathfrak{x}, \mathfrak{y})$) will be called *FR-constructs* (*duplexes*) *summable to the* αth *power* in the segment $\mathfrak{x} \veebar \mathfrak{y}$, as well as *words of type* Л′.

As a new partitioning sign to be used in the construction of FR-constructs in the spaces B_α and $B_\alpha(\mathfrak{x}, \mathfrak{y})$, we introduce the symbol $\oplus$. We also introduce the notation

$$Ч_6 \rightleftharpoons Ч_4 \cup \{\oplus\}, \quad Ч_7 \rightleftharpoons Ч_5 \cup \{\oplus\}.$$

Points of the spaces $\mathfrak{L}_\alpha$ and $\mathfrak{L}_\alpha(\mathfrak{x}, \mathfrak{y})$ are words in the alphabet $Ч_6$.

The metric function in the spaces $\mathfrak{L}_\alpha$ and $\mathfrak{L}_\alpha(\mathfrak{x}, \mathfrak{y})$ will be denoted by ${}_\alpha\bar{\rho}$, and the algorithm computing the norm in these spaces will be denoted by ${}_\alpha\bar{N}$.

From (10) it follows that the algorithm M_σ is a Lipschitz operator from B_α into $\mathfrak{L}_\alpha$ and from $B_\alpha(\mathfrak{x}, \mathfrak{y})$ into $\mathfrak{L}_\alpha(\mathfrak{x}, \mathfrak{y})$, where 1 is a Lipschitz coefficient of this operator. Hence one can construct an extension of the operator M_σ to the spaces $\mathfrak{L}_\alpha$ and $\mathfrak{L}_\alpha(\mathfrak{x}, \mathfrak{y})$.

It can happen that the algorithms obtained as a result of the standard extension to the spaces $\mathfrak{L}_\alpha$ and $\mathfrak{L}_\alpha(\mathfrak{x}, \mathfrak{y})$ of the operators $+_\sigma, \cdot_\sigma, -_\sigma, M_\sigma$, considered together with the corresponding Lipschitz coefficients, have different schemas for different values of α. However, these differences can be eliminated. In fact, the Lipschitz coefficients of the indicated operators used in the construction of the standard extensions do not depend on α, and, thanks to this, also not dependent on α is, for example, the regulator of convergence in itself of the sum of two fundamental sequences of type $(\mathrm{H} \to \mathrm{K})_4$, constructed in the standard way from the regulators of convergence in itself of the sequences being added.

From what has been said it is clear that, starting from $+_\sigma$, one can construct an algorithm, applicable to every meaningful word in the alphabet $Ч_6$, which is an extension of the algorithm $+_\sigma$ to each of the indicated spaces. We denote this algorithm by $+_Л$. Repeating what has just been said, but with respect to the algorithms $\cdot_\sigma, -_\sigma, M_\sigma$, we introduce algorithms $\cdot_Л, -_Л, M_Л$ which are extensions, respectively, of the algorithms $\cdot_\sigma, -_\sigma, M_\sigma$ to each of the indicated spaces. The problem of extending the operation $\times_\sigma$ will be considered separately.

Instead of $+_Л, -_Л, \cdot_Л, M_Л, \times_Л$ we shall use the simpler notation $+, -, \cdot$, $M, \times$ if this does not lead to ambiguity.

From 15.1.1 it follows that the algorithm $\int_0$ is a linear locally bounded operator from B_1 into E and that 1 is a Lipschitz coefficient of this operator (E denotes the normed space of all real duplexes). From 15.1.1 and 15.1.2 it follows that $\int_0$ is a linear locally bounded operator from $B_\alpha(\mathfrak{x}, \mathfrak{y})$ into E and that $(\mathfrak{y} - \mathfrak{x})^{(\alpha-1):\alpha}$ is a Lipschitz coefficient of this operator. Considering the space B_1 and applying to the algorithm $\int_0$ and the number 1 the algorithm $\mathfrak{Z}_1^*$ for the standard extension of 1-ary Lipschitz operators, we obtain a linear Lipschitz operator from $\mathfrak{L}_1$ into E, and 1 is a Lipschitz coefficient of this operator. The resulting operator will be denoted by $\int$. Considering the space $B_\alpha(\mathfrak{x}, \mathfrak{y})$ and applying to the algorithm $\int_0$ and the real duplex $(\mathfrak{y} - \mathfrak{x})^{(\alpha-1):\alpha}$ the algorithm $\mathfrak{Z}_1^*$, we obtain a linear Lipschitz operator from $\mathfrak{L}_\alpha(\mathfrak{x}, \mathfrak{y})$ into E, and $(\mathfrak{y} - \mathfrak{x})^{(\alpha-1):\alpha}$

is a Lipschitz coefficient of this operator. The resulting operator will be denoted by ${}_{\alpha}\int$. The operators $\int$ and ${}_{\alpha}\int$ are called *Lebesgue integrals.*[1)]

As justification for the recognition of the concepts and operators introduced above as natural constructive analogues of the similarly named concepts and operators of classical mathematics we can use the well-known theorems of classical mathematics about the denseness of the set of step functions (with a finite number of steps) in the normed space of functions summable to a given power, and about the uniform continuity of the Lebesgue integral, considered as a functional in this normed space.

About the connections between the spaces $\mathfrak{L}_1$ and $\mathfrak{L}_{\alpha}(\mathfrak{x}, \mathfrak{y})$ and between the operators $\int$ and ${}_{\alpha}\int$, one can say the following. From (11) it is easily deducible that every sequence of points of the space $B_{\alpha}(\mathfrak{x}, \mathfrak{y})$ which is a fundamental sequence with respect to the metric function ${}_{\alpha}\rho$ is also a fundamental sequence with respect to ${}_{1}\rho$. (If $\alpha > 1$, then the converse is of course false.) However, if $(\mathfrak{y} - \mathfrak{x}) > 1$ then one cannot assert that every algorithm of type $(\mathrm{H} \to \mathrm{H})_0$ which is a regulator of convergence with respect to the metric ${}_{\alpha}\rho$ of a given sequence of points of the space $B_{\alpha}(\mathfrak{x}, \mathfrak{y})$ is also a regulator of convergence with respect to the metric ${}_{1}\rho$. Hence, if $(\mathfrak{y} - \mathfrak{x}) > 1$, then one cannot assert that every point of the space $\mathfrak{L}_{\alpha}(\mathfrak{x}, \mathfrak{y})$ is also a point of the space $\mathfrak{L}_1$.

However, from what has been said above it follows that for every point of the space $\mathfrak{L}_{\alpha}(\mathfrak{x}, \mathfrak{y})$ one can construct a point, equal to it in $\mathfrak{L}_{\alpha}(\mathfrak{x}, \mathfrak{y})$ (differing from the given point only in the part of the word which is a transcription of the regulator of convergence), belonging to the space $\mathfrak{L}_1$. In addition, if $c_{6,1}$ is both a point of the space $\mathfrak{L}_{\alpha}(\mathfrak{x}, \mathfrak{y})$ and a point of the space $\mathfrak{L}_1$, then $\int(c_{6,1}) =_{\mathrm{B}} {}_{\alpha}\int(c_{6,1})$. However, the real duplexes $\int(c_{6,1})$ and ${}_{\alpha}\int(c_{6,1})$ may graphically differ from each other in view of the difference in the constructions of the algorithms $\int$ and ${}_{\alpha}\int$. It is important to emphasize that the algorithm ${}_{\alpha}\int$ is applicable to any point of the space $\mathfrak{L}_{\alpha}(\mathfrak{x}, \mathfrak{y})$, whether or not this point belongs to the space $\mathfrak{L}_1$.

---

1) For F-constructs in the space B_1 (in the space $B_{\alpha}(\mathfrak{x}, \mathfrak{y})$) a Lebesgue integral is also definable; however, in this case, the algorithm $\mathcal{H}$ figuring in the remark after 10.4.5 (respectively, the algorithm Ψ figuring in the remark after 10.4.6) serves as the tool for constructing the appropriate algorithm. It is intended in these references that one takes as $\mathfrak{M}$ the metric space of all rational numbers. With the help of the algorithm $\mathcal{H}$ one also defines a Lebesgue measure for F-constructs in the space И. The results of applying the algorithms for integration and computation of the measure to appropriate F-constructs are real F-numbers. (See [23].)

Some of the inconvenience arising in connection with the facts mentioned above can be eliminated by introducing in B_α a new norm, equal to the sum (or maximum) of the functions ${}_1N^*$ and ${}_\alpha N^*$. However we shall not go over to a new norm in order not to weaken the analogy with the corresponding theories of classical mathematics.

One can define in a natural way an operation of raising the absolute value of a point of the space $\mathfrak{L}_\alpha(\mathfrak{x}, \mathfrak{y})$ to a power with exponent α. We shall not formulate here the appropriate definition, but in order to be able to state one equation below we shall agree to denote by $M_\Lambda(\Lambda_1')^\alpha$ the result of raising the absolute value of the point Λ_1' to the power α. The operation in question is such that the following proposition turns out to be true.

If Λ_1' is a point of the space $\mathfrak{L}_\alpha(\mathfrak{x}, \mathfrak{y})$, then $M(\Lambda_1')^\alpha$ is a point of the space $\mathfrak{L}_1(\mathfrak{x}, \mathfrak{y})$.

The following theorem is easily deduced from what has been said above about the operators M_Λ, $\int$, and ${}_\alpha\int$, from (8), (10) and Theorem 9.4.1.

15.2.1. *For any point* Λ_1 *of the space* $\mathfrak{L}_1$ *and any point* Λ_1' *of the space* $\mathfrak{L}_\alpha(\mathfrak{x}, \mathfrak{y})$,

$$
\begin{aligned}
&{}_1\bar{N}(\Lambda_1)=\int(\underset{\Lambda}{M}(\Lambda_1)), && {}_\alpha\bar{N}(\Lambda_1')=\left(\int(\underset{\Lambda}{M}(\Lambda_1')^\alpha)\right)^{1:\alpha},\\
&{}_1\bar{N}(\underset{\Lambda}{M}(\Lambda_1))={}_1\bar{N}(\Lambda_1), && {}_\alpha\bar{N}(\underset{\Lambda}{M}(\Lambda_1'))={}_\alpha\bar{N}(\Lambda_1'),\\
&\underset{B}{M}\left(\int(\Lambda_1)\right)\leqslant\int(\underset{\Lambda}{M}(\Lambda_1)), && \underset{B}{M}\left({}_\alpha\!\int(\Lambda_1')\right)\leqslant{}_\alpha\!\int(\underset{\Lambda}{M}(\Lambda_1')).
\end{aligned}
$$

The second equation requires a separate proof, which we shall not give here.

From §15.1 (16) it follows that χ_0 is a uniformly continuous operator from the metric space of complexes into the metric space B_α, and therefore into the complete metric space $\mathfrak{L}_\alpha$. Simultaneously, χ_0 is a uniformly continuous operator from the metric space of complexes imbedded in the segment $\mathfrak{x} \nabla \mathfrak{y}$ into the space $B_\alpha(\mathfrak{x}, \mathfrak{y})$, and therefore into the complete space $\mathfrak{L}_\alpha(\mathfrak{x}, \mathfrak{y})$. As a regulator of uniform continuity of the operator χ_0 we can use the algorithm $\mathfrak{R}_\alpha$ of type $(\mathrm{H}\rightarrow \mathrm{H})_0$ transforming any natural number k into the natural number which is one greater than the integral part of the product of k and α. In fact, from the obvious inequality $k \cdot \alpha < \mathfrak{R}_\alpha(k)$ it follows that

$$\forall ak\,(M(a)<2^{-\mathfrak{R}_\alpha(k)} \supset M(a)^{1:\alpha}<2^{-k}).$$

Applying to the word $\{\chi_0\}\boxed{1}\{\mathfrak{R}_\alpha\}$, which is a complete cipher of a uniformly continuous 1-ary operator, the standard algorithm $\mathfrak{Z}_1$ for extending complete ciphers (see §10.4), we obtain an operator ${}_\alpha\chi$ mapping the space И into $\mathfrak{L}_\alpha$. At the same time, ${}_\alpha\chi$ maps the space $\text{И}(\mathfrak{x}, \mathfrak{y})$, which is obtained as a result of the *FR*-completion of the space of complexes imbedded in the segment $\mathfrak{x} \underline{\nabla} \mathfrak{y}$, into the space $\mathfrak{L}_\alpha(\mathfrak{x}, \mathfrak{y})$. [Points of the space $\text{И}(\mathfrak{x}, \mathfrak{y})$ will be called *words of type* И′.] If И_1 is a point of the space И (point of the space $\text{И}(\mathfrak{x}, \mathfrak{y})$), then ${}_\alpha\chi(\text{И}_1)$ will be called the *characteristic representative* of И_1 in the space $\mathfrak{L}_\alpha$ (respectively, in the space $\mathfrak{L}_\alpha(\mathfrak{x}, \mathfrak{y})$).

15.2.2. *For any measurable FR-constructs* И_1 *and* И_2,

$$ {}_\alpha\!\int ({}_\alpha\chi(\text{и}_1)) = \text{mes}(\text{и}_1), \tag{1}$$

$$ \text{и}_1 \underset{\rho}{\curlywedge} \text{и}_2 \equiv {}_\alpha\chi(\text{и}_1 \cup \text{и}_2) \underset{\alpha\bar{\rho}}{=} {}_\alpha\chi(\text{и}_1) \cup {}_\alpha\chi(\text{и}_2), \tag{2}$$

$$ {}_\alpha\chi(\text{и}_1 \triangle \text{и}_2) \underset{\alpha\bar{\rho}}{=} M({}_\alpha\chi(\text{и}_1) - {}_\alpha\chi(\text{и}_2)), \tag{3}$$

$$ \rho(\text{и}_1 \square \text{и}_2) = \text{mes}(\text{и}_1 \triangle \text{и}_2) = {}_\alpha\!\int (M({}_\alpha\chi(\text{и}_1) \dot{-} {}_\alpha\chi(\text{и}_2))), \tag{4}$$

$$ {}_\alpha\bar{\rho}({}_\alpha\chi(\text{и}_1) \square {}_\alpha\chi(\text{и}_2)) = \rho(\text{и}_1 \square \text{и}_2)^{1:\alpha}, \tag{5}$$

$$ {}_\alpha\bar{N}({}_\alpha\chi(\text{и}_1)) = \text{mes}(\text{и}_1)^{1:\alpha}. \tag{6}$$

Here ρ *is the metric function in the space* И. *In* (1) *and* (4), *if* $\alpha > 1$, *it is assumed that* И_1 *and* И_2 *are imbedded in the segment* $\mathfrak{x} \underline{\nabla} \mathfrak{y}$.

This theorem follows from 15.1.4 and 9.4.1.

Now we shall define an operation of multiplication of a point of the space $\mathfrak{L}_\alpha$ by another point which is a characteristic representative in $\mathfrak{L}_\alpha$ of some measurable *FR*-construct. (The multiplication operation can be defined under less stringent limitations on the type of the second point, but for our immediate purposes it suffices to consider only the indicated case.) To begin with, we shall obtain some estimates.

Let $\text{c}_{6,1}$ be any point of the space $\mathfrak{L}_\alpha$ and И_1 any measurable *FR*-construct. We introduce the notation

$$ U_\alpha \leftrightharpoons \underline{\text{c}_{6,1}}_{\,6}(\alpha), \quad V_\alpha \leftrightharpoons \underline{{}_\alpha\chi(\text{и}_1)}_{\,6}(\alpha), $$

$$ H_\alpha \leftrightharpoons \overline{\text{c}_{6,1}}^{\,6}(\alpha), \quad W_\alpha \leftrightharpoons \underline{\text{c}_{6,1}}_{\,6}(H_{\alpha+2}). $$

Here α is any variable of type H. We note that, for every k,

$$\underbrace{{}_{\alpha}\chi(\text{И}_1)}_{6}\,(k) \doteq \chi_0(\underbrace{\text{И}_1}_{5}\,(k)).$$

We construct an algorithm Q of type $(\mathrm{H} \to \mathrm{H})_0$ such that, for every k,

$$Q(k) \doteq \max(H_{k+2} \,\square\, \overbrace{{}_{\alpha}\chi(\text{И}_1)}^{6}\,(T_k + k + 1)),$$

where $T_k \leftrightharpoons \mu_j(\Xi_j(W_k) \leq 2^j)$ and Ξ is the algorithm occurring in 15.1.3.

Let k, m, n be natural numbers such that $m, n \geq Q(k)$. Then

$$\begin{aligned} {}_{\alpha}N((U_m \times V_m) - (U_n \times V_n)) &\leqslant {}_{\alpha}N(U_m \times (V_m - V_n)) \\ + {}_{\alpha}N(V_n \times (U_m - U_n)) &\leqslant {}_{\alpha}N(W_k \times (V_m - V_n)) \\ + {}_{\alpha}N((U_m - W_k) \times (V_m - V_n)) &+ {}_{\alpha}N(U_m - U_n) \\ \leqslant \Xi(W_k) \cdot {}_{\alpha}N(V_m - V_n) &+ {}_{\alpha}N(U_m - W_k) \\ + {}_{\alpha}N(U_m - U_n) < 2^{T_k} \cdot 2^{-(T_k+k+1)} &+ 2^{-(k+2)} + 2^{-(k+2)} = 2^{-k}. \end{aligned}$$

We denote by the letter P the algorithm in the alphabet Ч_4^{sa} such that, for every k,

$$P(k) \doteq U_k \times V_k.$$

We have

$$\forall kmn\,(m, n \geqslant Q(k) \supset {}_{\alpha}N(P(m) - P(n)) < 2^{-k}).$$

Hence the word $\{P\} \oplus \{Q\}$ is a point of the space $\mathfrak{L}_{\alpha}$. The algorithms P and Q can be constructed from $c_{6,1}$ and ${}_{\alpha}\chi(\text{И}_1)$ by means of certain algorithms the description of which can be formed without difficulty. Using what has been said, let us construct an algorithm in the alphabet Ч_6^{sa} transforming every word of the form $c_{6,1} \,\square\, {}_{\alpha}\chi(\text{И}_1)$, where $c_{6,1}$ is a point of the space $\mathfrak{L}_{\alpha}$ and И_1 is a point of the space И, into the word $\{P\} \oplus \{Q\}$. The algorithm so constructed shall be denoted by $\times_{\text{Л}}$. Instead of the expression $\times_{\text{Л}}(c_{6,1} \,\square\, {}_{\alpha}\chi(\text{И}_1))$ we shall often use the expression $(c_{6,1} \times {}_{\alpha}\chi(\text{И}_1))$.

Let us note that, if $c_{6,1}$ is a point of the space $\mathfrak{L}_{\alpha}(\mathfrak{x}, \mathfrak{y})$ and И_1 is a point of the space И, then $(c_{6,1} \times {}_{\alpha}\chi(\text{И}_1))$ is a point of the space $\mathfrak{L}_{\alpha}(\mathfrak{x}, \mathfrak{y})$.

Let $c_{6,1}$ be a point of the spaces $\mathfrak{L}_1$ or $\mathfrak{L}_{\alpha}(\mathfrak{x}, \mathfrak{y})$ and let И_1 be a measurable *FR*-construct. By the *integral of the FR-construct* $c_{6,1}$ *on the measurable FR-construct* И_1 we shall mean $\int(c_{6,1} \times {}_1\chi(\text{И}_1))$ in the case where $c_{6,1}$ is a point of the space $\mathfrak{L}_1$ and ${}_{\alpha}\!\int(c_{6,1} \times {}_{\alpha}\chi(\text{И}_1))$ in the case where $c_{6,1}$ is a point of the space $\mathfrak{L}_{\alpha}(\mathfrak{x}, \mathfrak{y})$. Instead of the expressions $\int(c_{6,1} \times {}_1\chi(\text{И}_1))$ and

$_{\mathfrak{a}}\int(c_{6,1} \times {}_{\mathfrak{a}}\chi(И_1))$ we shall use the expressions

$$\int_{И_1}(c_{6,1}), \quad {}_{\mathfrak{a}}\int_{И_1}(c_{6,1}).$$

In §14.5 we associated a certain measurable *FR*-construct with each Д-segment (Д-interval) $c_{4,1}$. Let us denote the algorithm realizing this association by ξ. By the *integral on the* Д-*segment* (Д-*interval*) $c_{4,1}$ it is natural to mean the integral on the measurable *FR*-construct $\xi(c_{4,1})$.

Summable *FR*-constructs are not constructive functions in the sense of A. A. Markov. However, we can operate with certain local characteristics of such constructs, which are in certain respects similar to values of constructive functions at individual points. Here we have in mind the average integral value of summable *FR*-constructs on all Д-intervals. If $\mathfrak{x}$ and $\mathfrak{y}$ are any real duplexes such that $\mathfrak{x} < \mathfrak{y}$, $Л_1$ is a point of the space $\mathfrak{L}_1$, and $Л_1'$ is a point of the space $\mathfrak{L}_{\mathfrak{a}}(\mathfrak{x}, \mathfrak{y})$, then by the average integral value on the interval $\mathfrak{x} \nabla \mathfrak{y}$ of the summable *FR*-construct $Л_1$ [of the *FR*-construct $Л_1'$ summable to the $\mathfrak{a}$th power in the segment $\mathfrak{x} \underline{\nabla} \mathfrak{y}$] we mean the real duplex $(\mathfrak{y} - \mathfrak{x})^{-1} \cdot \int_{\xi(\mathfrak{x}\nabla\mathfrak{y})}(Л_1)$ [respectively, $(\mathfrak{y} - \mathfrak{x})^{-1} \cdot {}_{\mathfrak{a}}\int_{\xi(\mathfrak{x}\nabla\mathfrak{y})}(Л_1')$].

15.2.3. *For any point* $Л_1$ *of the space* $\mathfrak{L}_1$, *any point* $Л_1'$ *of the space* $\mathfrak{L}_{\mathfrak{a}}(\mathfrak{x}, \mathfrak{y})$, *any points* $И_1, И_2$ *of the space* $\mathfrak{И}$, *and any points* $И_1', И_2'$ *of the space* $\mathfrak{И}(\mathfrak{x}, \mathfrak{y})$,

$$И_1 \curlywedge И_2 \supset \int_{И_1 \cup И_2}(Л_1) = \int_{И_1}(Л_1) + \int_{И_2}(Л_1),$$

$$И_1 \curlywedge И_2 \supset {}_{\mathfrak{a}}\int_{И_1 \cup И_2}(Л_1') = {}_{\mathfrak{a}}\int_{И_1}(Л_1') + {}_{\mathfrak{a}}\int_{И_2}(Л_1'),$$

$$(И_1 \underset{\mathfrak{p}}{\subseteq} И_2) \supset \int_{И_1}(M(Л_1)) \leqslant \int_{И_2}(M(Л_2)),$$

$$(И_1 \underset{\mathfrak{p}}{\subseteq} И_2) \supset {}_{\mathfrak{a}}\int_{И_1}(M(Л_1')) \leqslant {}_{\mathfrak{a}}\int_{И_2}(M(Л_1')).$$

This theorem is easily derived from 15.2.2.

15.2.4. *One can construct algorithms* $\Phi_{6,1}$ *and* $\Phi_{6,2}$ *in the alphabet* $Ч_6^{sa}$ *such that, for any point* $Л_1$ *of the space* $\mathfrak{L}_1$, *any point* $Л_1'$ *of the space*

$\mathfrak{L}_{\mathfrak{a}}(\mathfrak{x}, \mathfrak{y})$, *any point* $И_1$ *of the space* $И$, *any point* $И_1'$ *of the space* $И(\mathfrak{x}, \mathfrak{y})$, *and any natural number* k,

$$\int\limits_{и_1} (M(\lambda_1)) \leqslant \Phi_{6,1}(\lambda_1 \square k) \cdot \mathrm{mes}(и_1) + 2^{-(k+1)}, \tag{7}$$

$$_{\mathfrak{a}}\int\limits_{и_1'} (M(\lambda_1')) \leqslant \Phi_{6,2}(\lambda_1' \square k) \cdot \mathrm{mes}(и_1')^{1:\mathfrak{a}} + 2^{-(k+1)}. \tag{8}$$

Proof. Let $Л_1'$ be a point of the space $\mathfrak{L}_{\mathfrak{a}}(\mathfrak{x}, \mathfrak{y})$, $И_1'$ a point of the space $И(\mathfrak{x}, \mathfrak{y})$, and k a natural number. We have

$$_{\mathfrak{a}}\int\limits_{и_1'} (M(\lambda_1')) = {}_{\mathfrak{a}}\int (M(\lambda_1') \times {}_{\mathfrak{a}}\chi(и_1')) = {}_{\mathfrak{a}}\int (M(\lambda_1' \times {}_{\mathfrak{a}}\chi(и_1'))).$$

We introduce the notation

$$I \leftrightharpoons {}_{\mathfrak{a}}\int\limits_{и_1'} (M(\lambda_1')), \quad P \leftrightharpoons (\mathfrak{y} - \mathfrak{x})^{(\mathfrak{a}-1):\mathfrak{a}}$$

$$F_\alpha \leftrightharpoons \underbrace{\lambda_1'}_{6}(\alpha), \quad G_\alpha \leftrightharpoons \underbrace{{}_{\mathfrak{a}}\chi(и_1')}_{6}(\alpha),$$

$$\xi \leftrightharpoons \mu_j(\underline{P}(\bar{P}(0)) + 1 < 2^j),$$

$$T_\alpha \leftrightharpoons \overbrace{\lambda_1'}^{6}(\alpha + \xi), \quad S_\alpha \leftrightharpoons \underbrace{\lambda_1'}_{6}(T_{\alpha+2}).$$

Here α is any variable of type H. We note that

$$G_\alpha = \chi_0(\underbrace{и_1'}_{5}(\alpha)).$$

Let l be any natural number. We have

$$\underline{I}(l) = \int_0 (M(F_l \times G_l)) \leqslant P \cdot {}_{\mathfrak{a}}N(F_l \times G_l)$$

$$\leqslant P \cdot {}_{\mathfrak{a}}N(S_k \times G_l) + P \cdot {}_{\mathfrak{a}}N((F_l - S_k) \times G_l)$$

$$\leqslant P \cdot \Xi(S_k) \cdot {}_{\mathfrak{a}}N(G_l) + P \cdot {}_{\mathfrak{a}}N(F_l - S_k)$$

$$= P \cdot \Xi(S_k) \cdot \mathrm{mes}_0(\underbrace{и_1'}_{5}(l))^{1:\mathfrak{a}} + P \cdot {}_{\mathfrak{a}}N(F_l - S_k).$$

We introduce the notation

$$\gamma_k \leftrightharpoons \mu_j(\Xi(S_k) \leqslant 2^j).$$

We have

$$P \cdot \Xi(S_k) \leqslant 2^{\xi + \gamma_k}.$$

It is not hard to construct a natural number $\mathfrak{r}$ such that

$$l \geqslant \mathfrak{r} \supset \mathrm{mes}_0 (\underset{5}{\underbrace{\text{и}'_1}} (l))^{1:\mathfrak{a}} \leqslant \mathrm{mes}\,(\text{и}'_1)^{1:\mathfrak{a}} + 2^{-(\xi+\gamma_k+k+3)}.$$

In addition, if $l \geq T_{k+2}$, then

$$P \cdot {}_{\mathfrak{a}}N(F_l - S_k) < 2^{-(k+2)}.$$

Hence, if $l \geq \max\,(\mathfrak{r} \,\square\, T_{k+2})$, then

$$\underline{I}(l) < P \cdot \Xi(S_k) \cdot \mathrm{mes}\,(\text{и}'_1)^{1:\mathfrak{a}} + 2^{-(k+3)} + 2^{-(k+2)}.$$

Hence

$$\exists n \forall l (l \geqslant n \supset \underline{I}(l) < P \cdot \Xi(S_k) \cdot \mathrm{mes}\,(\text{и}'_1)^{1:\mathfrak{a}} + 3 \cdot 2^{-(k+3)}).$$

Therefore

$$I \leqslant P \cdot \Xi(S_k) \cdot \mathrm{mes}\,(\text{и}'_1)^{1:\mathfrak{a}} + 3 \cdot 2^{-(k+3)} < P \cdot \Xi(S_k) \cdot \mathrm{mes}\,(\text{и}'_1)^{1:\mathfrak{a}} + 2^{-(k+1)}.$$

We construct an algorithm ${}_{\mathfrak{a}}\mathfrak{P}$ in the alphabet $Ч_6^{\mathrm{sa}}$ such that, for any point $Л'_1$ of the space $\mathfrak{L}_{\mathfrak{a}}(\mathfrak{x}, \mathfrak{y})$ and for any natural number k,

$${}_{\mathfrak{a}}\mathfrak{P}(\lambda'_1 \,\square\, k) \simeq P \cdot \Xi(S_k).$$

The algorithm ${}_{\mathfrak{a}}\mathfrak{P}$ is the desired one: it satisfies condition (8). The second part of the theorem has been proved.

The proof of the first part is similar to the proof of the special case of the second part of the theorem where $\mathfrak{a} = 1$ (in this case $P = 1$).

In the formulation of the following theorem the expression ${}_{\mathfrak{a}}\mathfrak{P}$ has the same meaning as in the proof of Theorem 15.2.4. The letter $\mathfrak{P}$ will denote the algorithm ${}_1\mathfrak{P}$.

15.2.5. *For any point $Л_1$ of the space $\mathfrak{L}_1$, any point $Л'_1$ of the space $\mathfrak{L}_{\mathfrak{a}}(\mathfrak{x}, \mathfrak{y})$, any points $И_1$ and $И_2$ of the space $И$, any points $И'_1$ and $И'_2$ of the space $И(\mathfrak{x}, \mathfrak{y})$, and any natural number k,*

1) $$M\Big(\int_{\text{и}_1} (\lambda_1)\Big) < \mathfrak{P}(\lambda_1 \,\square\, k) \cdot \mathrm{mes}\,(\text{и}_1) + 2^{-(k+1)},$$

and therefore one can construct an algorithm $\Phi_{6,3}$ of type $(ЛИ \to И)_6$ such that, for any $Л_1$, $И_1$, and k,

$$\mathrm{mes}\,(\text{и}_1) < 2^{-\Phi_{6\,3}(\lambda_1 \square k)} \supset M\Big(\int_{\text{и}_1} (\lambda_1)\Big) < 2^{-k};$$

2) $$M\Big({}_{\mathfrak{a}}\!\int_{\text{и}'_1} (\lambda'_1)\Big) \leqslant {}_{\mathfrak{a}}\mathfrak{P}(\lambda'_1 \,\square\, k) \cdot \mathrm{mes}\,(\text{и}'_1)^{1:\mathfrak{a}} + 2^{-(k+1)},$$

and therefore one can construct an algorithm $\Phi_{6,4}$ *of type* $(Л'\mathrm{H} \to \mathrm{H})_6$ *such that, for any point* $Л_1'$ *of the space* $\mathfrak{L}_\alpha(\mathfrak{x}, \mathfrak{y})$, *any point* $И_1'$ *of the space* $И(\mathfrak{x}, \mathfrak{y})$, *and any natural number* k,

$$\operatorname{mes}(и_1') < 2^{-\Phi_{6,4}(\lambda_1' \square k)} \supset M\Big(\int_{и_1'} (\lambda_1')\Big) < 2^{-k};$$

3) $$M\Big(\int_{и_1} (\lambda_1) - \int_{и_2} (\lambda_1)\Big) < \mathfrak{P}(\lambda_1 \square k) \cdot \rho(и_1 \square и_2) + 2^{-(k+1)}$$

and thus for every $Л_1$ *the integral* $\int_{И_1}(Л_1)$, *considered as an operator from* $И$ *into* E, *is a uniformly continuous function in the metric space* $И$;

4) $$M\Big({}_{\alpha}\int_{и_1'} (\lambda_1') - {}_{\alpha}\int_{и_2'} (\lambda_1')\Big) < {}_{\alpha}\mathfrak{P}(\lambda_1' \square k) \cdot \rho(и_1' \square и_2')^{1:\alpha} + 2^{-(k+1)}$$

and thus for any point $Л_1'$ *of the space* $\mathfrak{L}_\alpha(\mathfrak{x}, \mathfrak{y})$, *the integral* $\int_{И_1'}(Л_1')$, *considered as an operator from* $И(\mathfrak{x}, \mathfrak{y})$ *into* E, *is a uniformly continuous function in the metric space* $И(\mathfrak{x}, \mathfrak{y})$.

This theorem follows from the last two parts of Theorem 15.2.1, from part (3) of Theorem 15.2.2, and from Theorem 15.2.4.

15.2.6. *If* $\Phi_{5,1}$ *is a sequence of points of the space* $И$, $И_1$ *is a point of the space* $И$ *which is the union of all terms of the sequence* $\Phi_{5,1}$ (*cf.* §14.3), *and* $Л_1$ *is a point of the space* $\mathfrak{L}_1$, *then*

$$\int_{и_1} (\lambda_1) \ \underline{\lim}_E \mathfrak{H}, \tag{9}$$

where $\mathfrak{H}$ *is the algorithm of type* $(\mathrm{H} \to Д)_3$ *such that, for every* k,

$$\mathfrak{H}(k) \simeq \int_{\breve{\Phi}_{5,1}(k)} (\lambda_1).$$

(*The notation* $\breve{\Phi}_{5,1}$ *was introduced in* §14.3.) *Moreover, if*

$$\forall i \,(\Phi_{5,1}(i) \subseteq_{\rho} \Phi_{5,1}(i+1)),$$

then

$$\int_{и_1} (\lambda_1) \ \underline{\lim}_E \mathfrak{H}_1, \tag{10}$$

where $\mathfrak{H}_1$ *is the algorithm of type* $(\mathrm{H} \to Д)_3$ *such that, for every* k,

$$\mathfrak{H}_1(k) \simeq \int_{\Phi_{5,1}(k)} (\lambda_1),$$

and if

$$\forall ij\,(i \neq j \supset \Phi_{5,1}(i) \underset{\rho}{\curlywedge} \Phi_{5,1}(j)),$$

then

$$\int\limits_{И_1} (Л_1)\ \underline{\lim}_E\, \mathfrak{H}_2, \tag{11}$$

where $\mathfrak{H}_2$ *is the algorithm of type* $(Н \to Д)_3$ *such that, for every* k,

$$\mathfrak{H}_2(k) \simeq \sum_{i=0}^{k} \int\limits_{\Phi_{5,1}(i)} (Л_1).$$

(The letter ρ *denotes the metric function in the space* $И$.)

15.2.7. *If* $\Phi_{5,1}$ *is a sequence of points of the space* $И(\mathfrak{x}, \mathfrak{y})$, $И_1$ *is a point of the space* $И(\mathfrak{x}, \mathfrak{y})$ *which is the union of all the terms of the sequence* $\Phi_{5,1}$, *and* $Л_1'$ *is a point of the space* $\mathfrak{L}_a(\mathfrak{x}, \mathfrak{y})$, *then, replacing everywhere in the text of Theorem* 15.2.6, *beginning with* (9), *the group of symbols* $\int(Л_1)$ *by the group of symbols* ${}_a\!\int(Л_1')$, *we obtain a true proposition.*

Theorems 15.2.6 and 15.2.7 are corollaries of Theorem 15.2.5.

Remark. In Theorems 15.2.6 and 15.2.7 it is assumed that $И_1$ is a measurable FR-construct which is the union of all terms of the sequence $\Phi_{5,1}$. In classical mathematics the theorems analogous to Theorems 15.2.6 and 15.2.7 usually are formulated in such a way that the assumption analogous to the one mentioned above does not occur in them, but the union of all terms of the given sequence of measurable sets is referred to as the result of applying to the given sequence the operation of the union of measurable sets. From 14.3.2 it follows that these theorems of classical mathematics do not carry over in their customary formulation to constructive mathematics.

15.3. From the fact that the operator $\int$ (the operator ${}_a\!\int$) is a uniformly continuous operator in the space $\mathfrak{L}_1$ (respectively, in the space $\mathfrak{L}_a(\mathfrak{x}, \mathfrak{y})$) the following theorem is an immediate consequence.

15.3.1. a) *If* $\Phi_{6,1}$ *is a sequence of points of the space* $\mathfrak{L}_1$, $Л_1$ *is a point of the space* $\mathfrak{L}_1$, *and* $Л_1\ \underline{\lim}_{\mathfrak{L}_1} \Phi_{6,1}$, *then*

$$\int (Л_1)\ \underline{\lim}_E\, \mathfrak{D}_1,$$

where $\mathfrak{D}_1$ *is the algorithm of type* $(Н \to Д)_3$ *such that*

$$\forall k\,(\mathfrak{D}_1(k) \simeq \int(\Phi_{6,1}(k))).$$

b) *If* $\Phi_{6,2}$ *is a sequence of points of the space* $\mathfrak{L}_a(\mathfrak{x}, \mathfrak{y})$, $Л_1'$ *is a point of the space* $\mathfrak{L}_{\mathfrak{a}}(\mathfrak{x}, \mathfrak{y})$, *and* $\Lambda_1' \ \underline{\lim}_{\mathfrak{L}_{\mathfrak{a}}(\mathfrak{x},\mathfrak{y})} \Phi_{6,2}$, *then*

$$\forall k (\mathfrak{D}_2(k) \simeq {}_{\mathfrak{a}}\!\int (\Phi_{6,2}(k))).$$

where $\mathfrak{D}_2$ *is the algorithm of type* $(\mathrm{H} \to \mathrm{Д})_3$ *such that*

$${}_{\mathfrak{a}}\!\int (\Lambda_1') \ \underline{\lim}_E \ \mathfrak{D}_2.$$

Theorem 15.3.1 is a "trivial" theorem about passage to the limit under the symbol for the Lebesgue integral. Below we shall formulate another theorem about passage to the limit under the integral sign. As a preliminary, we introduce some definitions.

For points of the space $\mathfrak{L}_1$ we introduce order relations $\leq_{\Lambda}$ and $<_{\Lambda}$. Let Λ_1 and Λ_2 be points of the space $\mathfrak{L}_1$. We shall say that the point Λ_1 is *majorized* by the point Λ_2, and we shall write $\Lambda_1 \leq_{\Lambda} \Lambda_2$, if $\Lambda_2 - \Lambda_1 \ {}_{1\bar{\rho}}\!= M(\Lambda_2 - \Lambda_1)$. We shall say that the point Λ_1 is *strongly majorized* by the point Λ_2, and we shall write $\Lambda_1 <_{\Lambda} \Lambda_2$, if $\Lambda_1 \leq_{\Lambda} \Lambda_2$ and ${}_1\bar{\rho}(\Lambda_1 \,\square\, \Lambda_2) > 0$.

It is easily seen that the relations just introduced are transitive.

15.3.2. *For any points* Λ_1 *and* Λ_2 *of the space* $\mathfrak{L}_1$,

$$\Lambda_1 \underset{\Lambda}{\leqslant} \Lambda_2 \ \& \ \Lambda_2 \underset{\Lambda}{\leqslant} \Lambda_1 \supset \Lambda_1 \underset{1\bar{\rho}}{=} \Lambda_2,$$

$$\Lambda_1 \underset{\Lambda}{\leqslant} \Lambda_2 \supset \int (\Lambda_1) \underset{\mathrm{B}}{\leqslant} \int (\Lambda_2),$$

$$\Lambda_1 \underset{\Lambda}{<} \Lambda_2 \supset \int (\Lambda_1) \underset{\mathrm{B}}{<} \int (\Lambda_2).$$

This theorem is proved by elementary arguments .

Now we shall formulate a second theorem about passage to the limit under the integral sign.

15.3.3. *If* $\Phi_{6,1}$ *is a sequence of points of the space* $\mathfrak{L}_1$ *such that* $\forall k (\Phi_{6,1}(k) \leq_{\Lambda} \Phi_{6,1}(k+1))$, *and if* $\exists z (z \ \underline{\lim}_E \ \mathfrak{D}_1)$, *where* $\mathfrak{D}_1$ *is the algorithm figuring in* 15.3.1, *then a point* Λ_1 *of the space* $\mathfrak{L}_1$ *is potentially realizable such that* $(\Lambda_1 \ \underline{\lim}_{\mathfrak{L}_1} \Phi_{6,1})$ *and* $(\int(\Lambda_1) \ \underline{\lim}_E \ \mathfrak{D}_1)$. *Moreover, the assertion remains true if we replace everywhere the space* $\mathfrak{L}_1$ *by the space* $\mathfrak{L}_1(\mathfrak{x}, \mathfrak{y})$.

Proof. Let $\Phi_{6,1}$ be a sequence of points of the space $\mathfrak{L}_1$ such that

$$\forall k (\Phi_{6,1}(k) \underset{\Lambda}{\leqslant} \Phi_{6,1}(k+1)) \ \& \ \exists z (z \ \underline{\lim}_E \ \mathfrak{D}_1).$$

Then, for any m and l,

$$ {}_1\bar{\rho}(\Phi_{6,1}(m) \square \Phi_{6,1}(m+l)) = \int (\underset{\Lambda}{M}(\Phi_{6,1}(m+l) - \Phi_{6,1}(m)) $$

$$ = \int (\Phi_{6,1}(m+l) - \Phi_{6,1}(m)) = \underset{B}{M}\left(\int (\Phi_{6,1}(m+l)) - \int (\Phi_{6,1}(m))\right) $$

$$ = \underset{B}{M}(\mathfrak{D}_1(m+l) - \mathfrak{D}_1(m)). $$

Hence every regulator of convergence in itself of the sequence $\mathfrak{D}_1$ in the space E is a regulator of convergence in itself of the sequence $\Phi_{6,1}$ in the space $\mathfrak{L}_1$. The rest is obvious.

Remark. In Theorem 15.3.3 it is assumed that $\exists z(z\ \underline{\lim}_E\ \mathfrak{D}_1)$. In classical mathematics the theorem similar to 15.3.3 is formulated differently in this respect: instead of an assumption similar to the one mentioned, an assumption occurs about the boundedness above of the sequence of real numbers obtained by term-by-term integration of the given sequence of functions. The following theorem shows that, in such a formulation, the indicated theorem of classical mathematics does not carry over to constructive mathematics.

15.3.4. *One can construct a sequence* $\Phi_{6,1}$ *of points of the space* $\mathfrak{L}_1(0,1)$ *such that, first,*

$$ \forall k(\Phi_{6,1}(k) \underset{\Lambda}{\leqslant} \Phi_{6,1}(k+1)), $$

second,

$$ \forall k\left(\int (\Phi_{6,1}(k)) < 1\right) $$

and third, there is no point $Л_1$ *of the space* $\mathfrak{L}_1(0, 1)$ *such that*

$$ (\Lambda_1\ \underline{\lim}_{\mathfrak{L}_1(0,1)} \Phi_{6,1}). $$

Proof. We construct an algorithm $\mathfrak{H}$ in the alphabet $Ч_6^{sa}$ such that, for every k,

$$ \mathfrak{H}(k) \doteq 0 \nabla 1 \sigma S(k), $$

where S is Specker's algorithm. The algorithm $\mathfrak{H}$ is an algorithm of type $(\text{Н} \to \text{Б})_6$, and moreover,

$$ \forall k(\mathscr{K}(\mathfrak{H}(k)) \doteq 0 \nabla 1). $$

Hence $\mathfrak{H}$ is a sequence of points of the space $\mathfrak{L}_1(0, 1)$. It is obvious that

$$ \forall k(\mathfrak{H}(k) \underset{\Lambda}{\leqslant} \mathfrak{H}(k+1)). $$

Further, for every k,

$$ \int (\mathfrak{H}(k)) = S(k) < 1. $$

There is no real duplex which is a limit of the sequence S. From this fact and from 15.3.1 it follows that there is no point of the space $\mathfrak{L}_1(0, 1)$ which is a limit in this space of the sequence $\mathfrak{H}$.

15.4. A constructive analogue of the classical concept of a measurable function defined on a segment can be introduced in the following manner.

Let σ_1 and σ_2 be two graduated frames, where σ_2 satisfies the condition

$$\forall i\,(i \leqslant L_\tau(\mathscr{K}(\sigma_2)) \supset [[\sigma_2]_2^\sigma]_i^\tau \neq 0).$$

For such graduated frames one can define in a natural way the operation of dividing the first frame by the second. The description of this operation is obtained by replacing in the description of the operation of multiplication of graduated frames the operation of multiplication of rational numbers by the operation of dividing one rational number by another. We denote the operation of division of graduated frames by $:_\sigma$.

We denote by I the algorithm in the alphabet $Ч_4^{sa}$ such that, for any σ_1, the word $I(\sigma_1)$ is a graduated frame and

$$\mathscr{K}(I(\sigma_1)) \doteq \mathscr{K}(\sigma_1), \quad [[I(\sigma_1)]_2^\sigma]_i^\tau = [[\sigma_1]_2^\sigma]_i^\tau \underset{p}{+} 1 \quad (i = 1, 2, \ldots, L_\tau(\mathscr{K}(\sigma_1))).$$

We construct the algorithm $_*\rho$ in the alphabet $Ч_4^{sa}$ such that, for any graduated frames σ_1 and σ_2 imbedded in $\mathfrak{x} \underline{\nabla} \mathfrak{y}$,

$$_*\rho(\sigma_1 \square \sigma_2) \doteq \int (M(\sigma_2 - \sigma_1) : I(M(\sigma_2 - \sigma_1))).$$

It is known that $_*\rho$ is a metric function in the set of all graduated frames imbedded in $\mathfrak{x} \underline{\nabla} \mathfrak{y}$. We denote the corresponding metric space by $\mathfrak{M}(\mathfrak{x}, \mathfrak{y})$. FR-constructs in $\mathfrak{M}(\mathfrak{x}, \mathfrak{y})$ will be called *FR-constructs functionally measurable in the segment* $\mathfrak{x} \underline{\nabla} \mathfrak{y}$. The standard FR-completion of the space $\mathfrak{M}(\mathfrak{x}, \mathfrak{y})$ will be called the *metric space of FR-constructs functionally measurable in the segment* $\mathfrak{x} \underline{\nabla} \mathfrak{y}$.

In classical mathematics one proves that the set of step functions (with a finite number of steps) is dense in the metric space of measurable functions defined on the segment. This theorem provides justification for considering the concept of FR-construct functionally measurable in the segment $\mathfrak{x} \underline{\nabla} \mathfrak{y}$ as a natural constructive analogue of the classical concept of measurable function defined on the segment.

For any graduated frames σ_1 and σ_2 imbedded in $\mathfrak{x} \underline{\nabla} \mathfrak{y}$,

$$_*\rho(\sigma_1 \square \sigma_2) \leqslant \int (M(\sigma_2 - \sigma_1)) = {}_1N(\sigma_2 - \sigma_1) \leqslant (\mathfrak{y} - \mathfrak{x})^{(\mathfrak{a}-1):\mathfrak{a}} \cdot {}_\mathfrak{a}N(\sigma_2 - \sigma_1).$$

From this we immediately obtain the following theorem.

15.4.1. a) *Every point of the space* $\mathfrak{L}_1(\mathfrak{x}, \mathfrak{y})$ *is an FR-construct functionally measurable in the segment* $\mathfrak{x} \underline{\nabla} \mathfrak{y}$.

b) *One can exhibit an algorithm which, for any point of the space* $\mathfrak{L}_a(\mathfrak{x}, \mathfrak{y})$, *constructs a point, equal to it in this space, which is an FR-construct functionally measurable in the segment* $\mathfrak{x} \underline{\nabla} \mathfrak{y}$.

15.5. The concept of FR-construct summable to a given power is essentially different from the concept of constructive function of type ($Д \dashrightarrow Д$). However, certain constructive functions of type ($Д \dashrightarrow Д$), supplemented by appropriate information, can be associated in a natural way with FR-constructs summable to a given power, and, thanks to this, the integration operation can be extended to such functions. From this point of view we shall consider here complete ciphers of uniformly continuous functions (see §9.3).

We shall use here the definitions and notation introduced in §9.3 relative to the case where the metric space $E[\mathfrak{x} \underline{\nabla} \mathfrak{y}]$ plays the role of $\mathfrak{M}$ (that is, the metric space induced by the space E in the set of points of the segment $\mathfrak{x} \underline{\nabla} \mathfrak{y}$), E plays the role of $\widetilde{\mathfrak{M}}$, 1 plays the role of $\mathfrak{k}$, and 3 plays the role of η and $\mathfrak{n}$. Points of the segment $\mathfrak{x} \underline{\nabla} \mathfrak{y}$ will be called *words of type* $Д'$.

Let $c_{4,1}$ be an arbitrary π-word (see §11.4) having the form 11.4 (1). With this π-word we associate the graduated frame

$$R_1 \nabla R_2 \tau R_2 \nabla R_3 \tau \ldots \tau R_{\mathfrak{k}-1} \nabla R_{\mathfrak{k}} \sigma B_1 \tau B_2 \tau \ldots \tau B_{\mathfrak{k}-1},$$

where $B_j \leftrightharpoons (R_{\mathfrak{k}+j} \dotplus R_{\mathfrak{k}+j+1}) : 2$, for $j = 1, 2, \cdots, k-1$. We shall denote by the letter $\mathfrak{R}$ the algorithm in the alphabet $Ч_4^{sa}$ realizing this correspondence.

In the proof of Theorem 11.4.1 there was constructed an algorithm $\mathfrak{F}$ transforming every word of the form $t_{\pi,1} \square k$, where $t_{\pi,1}$ is a complete cipher of a uniformly continuous function in the space $E[\mathfrak{x} \underline{\nabla} \mathfrak{y}]$ and k is a natural number, into a π-word $\mathfrak{F}(t_{\pi,1} \square k)$ imbedded in the segment $\mathfrak{x} \underline{\nabla} \mathfrak{y}$ and such that

$$\rho^*(t_{\pi,1} \square \mathfrak{B}(\mathfrak{F}(t_{\pi,1} \square k))) < 2^{-k}.$$

(The notation used here was introduced in §11.4.)

Let us note the following property of the algorithm $\mathfrak{F}$. As the value of the variable k increases without limit, the first and last τ-terms of the word $[\mathfrak{F}(t_{\pi,1} \square k)]_1^{\sigma}$ have $\mathfrak{x}$ and $\mathfrak{y}$, respectively, as their limits.

We introduce the notation

$$Q \leftrightharpoons \mu_j(\underline{H}(\overline{H}(0)) \dotplus 1 \leqslant 2^j),$$

where $H \leftrightharpoons (\mathfrak{y} - \mathfrak{x})^{1:\mathfrak{a}}$. It is not difficult to prove that, for any k, m and n, if m, $n \geq Q + k + 2$, then

$$_{\mathfrak{a}}N(\mathfrak{K}(\mathfrak{F}(t_{\pi,1} \square m)) - \mathfrak{K}(\mathfrak{F}(t_{\pi,1} \square n))) < 2^{-k}.$$

Hence the algorithm $\mathfrak{T}$, transforming (for given $t_{\pi,1}$) every natural number m into the word $\mathfrak{K}(\mathfrak{F}(t_{\pi,1} \square m))$, is a sequence of points of the space $B_{\mathfrak{a}}(\mathfrak{x}, \mathfrak{y})$, where one of the regulators of convergence in itself of the sequence $\mathfrak{T}$ in this space is the algorithm $\mathfrak{S}$ transforming every natural number k into $(q + k + 2)$. We denote by $_{\mathfrak{a}}\mathfrak{A}$ the algorithm transforming every complete cipher of a function uniformly continuous in the space $E[\mathfrak{x} \underline{\nabla} \mathfrak{y}]$ into the word

$$\{\mathfrak{T}\} \oplus \{\mathfrak{S}\}.$$

($\mathfrak{T}$ and $\mathfrak{S}$ are constructed with respect to the initially given complete cipher.)

The algorithm $_{\mathfrak{a}}\mathfrak{A}$ transforms any word $t_{\pi,1}$ of the kind indicated above into a point of the space $\mathfrak{L}_{\mathfrak{a}}(\mathfrak{x}, \mathfrak{y})$.

If $t_{\pi,1}$ is a complete cipher of a function uniformly continuous in the space $E[\mathfrak{x} \underline{\nabla} \mathfrak{y}]$, then by the *integral* of this complete cipher in the space $\mathfrak{L}_{\mathfrak{a}}(\mathfrak{x}, \mathfrak{y})$ we shall mean the real duplex $_{\mathfrak{a}}\int(_{\mathfrak{a}}\mathfrak{A}(t_{\pi,1}))$.

Polynomials with real duplexes as coefficients are (if we consider them only on the space $E[\mathfrak{x} \underline{\nabla} \mathfrak{y}]$) Lipschitz functions. Fixing an algorithm which associates with every such polynomial one of its Lipschitz coefficients, we easily obtain an algorithm which, for every polynomial, constructs a complete cipher of the corresponding uniformly continuous function. Constructing the composition of the latter algorithm and the algorithm $_{\mathfrak{a}}\mathfrak{A}$, we obtain an algorithm transforming every polynomial of the kind considered here into some point of the space $\mathfrak{L}_{\mathfrak{a}}(\mathfrak{x}, \mathfrak{y})$. By the integral of the given polynomial in the space $\mathfrak{L}_{\mathfrak{a}}(\mathfrak{x}, \mathfrak{y})$ we mean the integral computed for that point of the space $\mathfrak{L}_{\mathfrak{a}}(\mathfrak{x}, \mathfrak{y})$ which is associated with the polynomial by the algorithm just described.

§16. CONSTRUCTIVE ANALOGUES OF THE CONCEPT OF ABSOLUTELY CONTINUOUS FUNCTION AND OF SOME OTHER CONCEPTS OF CLASSICAL MATHEMATICS

Here the letters $\mathfrak{a}$, $\mathfrak{x}$ and $\mathfrak{y}$ will have the same meaning as in §15.

16.1. Π-words will also be called *words of type* Π. In addition, Π-words imbedded in the segment $\mathfrak{x} \underline{\nabla} \mathfrak{y}$ will also be called *words of type* Π'.

Let us denote by N_1^*, Var_0 and N_2^* the algorithms in the alphabet Ч_4^{sa} such that, for any word Π'_1 of type Π',

$$N_1^*(\pi'_1) \simeq \max(M(H_1)\square \ldots \square M(H_{\mathfrak{k}})),$$

$$\mathrm{Var}_0(\pi'_1) \simeq \sum_{i=1}^{\mathfrak{k}-1} M(H_{i+1} - H_i),$$

$$N_2^*(\pi'_1) \simeq M(H_1) + \mathrm{Var}_0(\pi'_1),$$

where

$$\mathfrak{k} \leftrightharpoons L_\tau([\pi'_1]_2^\sigma), \quad H_i \leftrightharpoons [[\pi'_1]_2^\sigma]_i^\tau \quad (i = 1, 2, \ldots, \mathfrak{k}).$$

For words of type Π one can define in the obvious way operations of addition, multiplication by rational numbers, and subtraction.

We denote these operations by $+_\Pi, \cdot_\Pi, -_\Pi$, respectively. It is easily seen that N_1^* and N_2^* satisfy conditions 12.1 (*). We construct algorithms ρ_1 and ρ_2 of type $(\Pi'\Pi' \to \mathfrak{D})_4$ such that, for any Π'_1 and Π'_2,

$$\rho_1(\pi'_1 \square \pi'_2) \simeq N_1^*(\pi'_2 \underset{\pi}{-} \pi'_1),$$

$$\rho_2(\pi'_1 \square \pi'_2) \simeq N_2^*(\pi'_2 \underset{\pi}{-} \pi'_1).$$

Let us fix a rational number $\mathfrak{b}$ belonging to the interval $\mathfrak{x} \nabla \mathfrak{y}$, and we denote by ξ the word $\mathfrak{b}\sigma 0$. It is easily seen that the list

$$Ч_4, \quad (c_{4,1} \in \pi'), \quad \rho_1, \quad \underset{\pi}{+}, \quad \underset{\pi}{\cdot}, \quad \xi,$$

denoted below by C_*, and the list

$$Ч_4, \quad (c_{4,1} \in \pi'), \ \rho_2, \ \underset{\pi}{+}, \ \underset{\pi}{\cdot}, \ \xi,$$

denoted below by $\mathfrak{A}$, are normed spaces. The algorithms computing the norms in these spaces will be denoted, respectively, by N_1 and N_2. It is obvious that, for any Π'_1,

$$N_1(\pi'_1) \leqslant N_2(\pi'_1), \tag{1}$$

$$\mathrm{Var}_0(\pi'_1) \leqslant N_2(\pi'_1). \tag{2}$$

We denote by $\overline{C}_*$ the standard normed FR-completion of the space C_*, and by $\overline{\mathfrak{A}}$ the standard normed FR-completion of $\mathfrak{A}$. The algorithms for computing the norms in these spaces will be denoted, respectively, by $\overline{N}_1$ and $\overline{N}_2$. The algorithm obtained by applying to Var_0 and 1 the algorithm for the standard extension of 1-ary Lipschitz operators will be denoted by Var. Points of the space $\overline{\mathfrak{A}}$ will be called *absolutely continuous FR-constructs* in the segment $\mathfrak{x} \nabla \mathfrak{y}$, and also *words of type* a.

The theorem of classical mathematics about the denseness of the set of polygonal functions in the normed space of absolutely continuous functions justifies us in considering the concept of absolutely continuous FR-construct as a natural constructive analogue of the concept of absolutely continuous function.

Points of the space $\overline{C}_*$ will be called *uniformly continuous FR-constructs* in the segment $\mathfrak{x} \nabla \mathfrak{y}$. The space $\overline{C}_*$ is linearly isometric to the space of complete ciphers of functions uniformly continuous in $E[\mathfrak{x} \nabla \mathfrak{y}]$. A linear isometric mapping of the indicated space of complete ciphers into the space $\overline{C}_*$ is easily constructed on the basis of 11.4.1. The construction of the inverse mapping is based on the obvious possibility of constructing, for every point z of the segment $\mathfrak{x} \nabla \mathfrak{y}$, the limit of the sequence of real duplexes obtained from the sequence of polygonal functions corresponding to the given uniformly continuous FR-construct by computing the value of these functions at the point z. It is easy to construct for a given construct of the type under consideration a regulator of uniform continuity of the function obtained in the indicated manner.

Corresponding to this intuitive characterization of the inverse mapping, we construct and fix a normal algorithm $\mathfrak{G}$ transforming every point of the space $\overline{C}_*$ into a complete cipher of a function uniformly continuous in $E[\mathfrak{x} \nabla \mathfrak{y}]$. If X is a point of the space $\overline{C}_*$, Δ_1' a point of the segment $\mathfrak{x} \nabla \mathfrak{y}$, and Π the index of the alphabet used for the construction of complete ciphers of functions uniformly continuous in $E[\mathfrak{x} \nabla \mathfrak{y}]$, then the real duplex $\underline{\mathfrak{G}(X)}_{\pi}(\Delta_1')$ will be called the *value* of the uniformly continuous FR-construct X at the point Δ_1', and will be abbreviated by $\check{X}(\Delta_1')$. The expression $\check{X}$ will denote the algorithm $\underline{\mathfrak{G}(X)}_{\pi}$.

From (1) it follows that every point of the space $\overline{\mathfrak{A}}$ is also a point of the space $\overline{C}_*$. Hence, for any point a_1 of the space $\overline{\mathfrak{A}}$ and any point Δ_1' of the segment $\mathfrak{x} \nabla \mathfrak{y}$, the expression $\check{\mathrm{a}}_1(\Delta_1')$ has meaning and signifies the value of the FR-construct a_1 at the point Δ_1'.

From (1), (2), and the definition of the algorithm N_2^* the next proposition follows.

16.1.1. *For any point* a_1 *of the space* $\overline{\mathfrak{A}}$,

$$\overline{N}_1(\mathrm{a}_1) \leqslant \overline{N}_2(\mathrm{a}_1), \quad \mathrm{Var}(\mathrm{a}_1) \leqslant \overline{N}_2(\mathrm{a}_1),$$

$$\overline{N}_2(\mathrm{a}_1) = M(\check{\mathrm{a}}_1(\mathfrak{x})) + \mathrm{Var}(\mathrm{a}_1). \tag{3}$$

Let us denote by $\mathfrak{A}_0$ the linear normed space induced by the space $\mathfrak{A}$ of the set of words given by the condition

$$(c_{4,1} \in \pi' \,\&\, [[c_{4,1}]_2^\sigma]_1^\tau = 0).$$
$$\mathrm{p}$$

If Π_1' is a point of the space $\mathfrak{A}_0$, then

$$N_2(\pi_1') = \mathrm{Var}_0(\pi_1').$$

The standard normed FR-completion of the space $\mathfrak{A}_0$ will be denoted by $\overline{\mathfrak{A}}_0$. The space $\overline{\mathfrak{A}}_0$ is a subspace of the space $\overline{\mathfrak{A}}$. The following proposition is obvious.

16.1.2. *If* a_1 *is a point of the space* $\overline{\mathfrak{A}}_0$, *then*

$$\overline{N}_2(\mathrm{a}_1) = \mathrm{Var}(\mathrm{a}_1).$$

Now we shall define for points of the space $\overline{\mathfrak{A}}$ an operation of computing the derivative. If a word Π_1' of type Π' has the form

$$R_1\tau R_2\tau \ldots \tau R_{\mathfrak{k}}\sigma R_{\mathfrak{k}+1}\tau R_{\mathfrak{k}+2}\tau \ldots \tau R_{\mathfrak{k}+\mathfrak{k}},$$

where $\mathfrak{k}$ is some natural number, $R_i \in \underline{\mathrm{rat}}$ $(i = 1, 2, \cdots, \mathfrak{k} + \mathfrak{k})$, and $R_1 < R_2 < \cdots < R_{\mathfrak{k}}$, then by the derivative word of the word Π_1' we shall mean the word

$$Q_1\tau Q_2\tau \ldots \tau Q_{\mathfrak{k}-1}\sigma P_1\tau P_2\tau \ldots \tau P_{\mathfrak{k}-1},$$

where

$$Q_i \leftrightharpoons R_i \nabla R_{i+1},$$

$$P_i \leftrightharpoons (R_{\mathfrak{k}+i+1} - R_{\mathfrak{k}+i}) : (R_{i+1} - R_i) \quad (i = 1, 2, \ldots, \mathfrak{k} - 1).$$

We denote by D_0 the algorithm transforming every word of type Π' into its derivative word.

16.1.3. *For any word* Π_1' *of type* Π', *the word* $D_0(\Pi_1')$ *is a graduated frame imbedded in the segment* $\mathfrak{x} \underline{\nabla} \mathfrak{y}$, *and*

$$_1N(D_0(\pi_1')) = {}_1\!\int (M(D_0(\pi_1'))) = \mathrm{Var}_0(\pi_1'). \tag{4}$$

Here $_1N$ *is the algorithm for computing the norm in the space* B_1.

The first part of Proposition 16.1.3 is obvious, and the second part is proved by actually computing the second and third terms of the triple equation (4).

It is easily established that D_0 is a linear mapping of $\mathfrak{A}$ into $B_1(\mathfrak{x}, \mathfrak{y})$.

The next proposition follows from (4), (2), and the definition of the algorithm N_2^*.

16.1.4. *For any word* Π_1' *of type* Π',

$$_1N(D_0(\pi_1')) \leqslant N_2(\pi_1'), \tag{5}$$

$$[[\Pi'_1]^{\sigma}_{\mathfrak{a}}]^{\tau}_1 = 0 \supset {}_1N(D_0(\Pi'_1)) = N_2(\Pi'_1). \qquad (6)$$

From (5) it follows that D_0 is a 1-ary Lipschitz operator mapping the space $\mathfrak{A}$ into the space $B_1(\mathfrak{x}, \mathfrak{y})$, and the number 1 is a Lipschitz coefficient of this operator. From (6) it follows that D_0 is a linear isometric mapping of the space $\mathfrak{A}_0$ into the space $B_1(\mathfrak{x}, \mathfrak{y})$.

Applying to the algorithm D_0 and the number 1 the standard algorithm for extending 1-ary Lipschitz operators, we obtain an algorithm mapping the space $\overline{\mathfrak{A}}$ into the space $\mathfrak{L}_1(\mathfrak{x}, \mathfrak{y})$. We denote this algorithm by D and shall call it the *algorithm for computing the derivative of absolutely continuous FR-constructs.* We have

16.1.5. *For any word* $\mathfrak{a}_1$ *of type* $\mathfrak{a}$,

$${}_1\overline{N}(D(\mathfrak{a}_1)) = {}_1\!\int (M(D(\mathfrak{a}_1))) = \mathrm{Var}\,(\mathfrak{a}_1) \leqslant \overline{N}_2(\mathfrak{a}_1).$$

Moreover, if $\mathfrak{a}_1$ *is a point of the space* $\overline{\mathfrak{A}}_0$, *then*

$${}_1\overline{N}(D(\mathfrak{a}_1)) = \overline{N}_2(\mathfrak{a}_1).$$

This theorem follows from 9.4.1, 16.1.3, 16.1.1, and 16.1.2.

Now we define for points of the space $\mathfrak{L}_1(\mathfrak{x}, \mathfrak{y})$ an operation for constructing an antiderivative construct.

Let σ'_1 be any word of type σ'. We construct the complex $\mathfrak{K}(\sigma'_1)$ and write down without repetition and in increasing order all left and right end points of the rational segments which are the τ-terms of the complex $\mathfrak{K}(\sigma'_1)$. Then, between every two adjacent terms of the list so obtained, we insert the letter τ. As a result we obtain a word of the form

$$R_1 \tau R_2 \tau \ldots \tau R_{\mathfrak{k}},$$

where $\mathfrak{k}$ is some natural number and $R_1, R_2, \cdots, R_{\mathfrak{k}}$ are rational numbers. For every i, $1 \leq i \leq \mathfrak{k}$, we compute the integral of the graduated frame which is obtained by multiplying the graduated frame σ'_1 by the characteristic frame of the one-termed complex $R_1 \nabla R_i$. The resulting rational number is denoted by $R_{\mathfrak{k}+i}$. The word

$$R_1 \tau R_2 \tau \ldots \tau R_{\mathfrak{k}} \sigma R_{\mathfrak{k}+1} \tau R_{\mathfrak{k}+2} \tau \ldots \tau R_{\mathfrak{k}+\mathfrak{k}} \qquad (7)$$

is a word of type Π'. In addition, it is obvious that it is a point of the space $\mathfrak{A}_0$.

The word (7) is called the *antiderivative* Π*-word for the graduated frame* σ'_1. The algorithm transforming every word σ'_1 of type σ' into the antiderivative Π-word for σ'_1 is denoted by $\underset{\sim}{\int}_0$. It is easily established that $\underset{\sim}{\int}_0$ is a linear mapping of $B_1(\mathfrak{x}, \mathfrak{y})$ into $\mathfrak{A}_0$.

16.1.6. *For any word* σ_1' *of type* σ',

$$D_0\left(\underset{\sim}{\int}_0(\sigma_1')\right) \underset{1\rho}{=} \sigma_1', \tag{8}$$

$$N_2\left(\underset{\sim}{\int}_0(\sigma_1')\right) = \mathrm{Var}_0\left(\underset{\sim}{\int}_0(\sigma_1')\right) = {}_1\!\int_0(M(\sigma_1')) = {}_1N(\sigma_1'). \tag{9}$$

16.1.7. *For any word* Π_1' *belonging to the space* $\mathfrak{A}_0$,

$$\underset{\sim}{\int}_0(D_0(\pi_1')) \underset{\rho_2}{=} \pi_1'. \tag{10}$$

Theorems 16.1.6 and 16.1.7 are proved by simple computations.

The following theorem is an immediate corollary of Theorems 16.1.4, 16.1.6, and 16.1.7.

16.1.8. *The algorithm* D_0 *is a linear isometric mapping of the space* $\mathfrak{A}_0$ *onto the space* $B_1(\mathfrak{x}, \mathfrak{y})$. *The algorithm* $\underset{\sim}{\int}_0$ *is a linear isometric mapping of* $B_1(\mathfrak{x}, \mathfrak{y})$ *onto* $\mathfrak{A}_0$. *Moreover,* $\underset{\sim}{\int}_0$ *and* D_0 *are mutually inverse operators.*

From (9) it follows that $\underset{\sim}{\int}_0$ is a 1-ary Lipschitz operator mapping $B_1(\mathfrak{x}, \mathfrak{y})$ into $\mathfrak{A}_0$, and the number 1 is a Lipschitz coefficient of this operator. Applying to the algorithm $\underset{\sim}{\int}_0$ and the number 1 the standard algorithm for extending 1-ary Lipschitz operators, we obtain an algorithm mapping the space $\mathfrak{L}_1(\mathfrak{x}, \mathfrak{y})$ into $\overline{\mathfrak{A}}_0$. We denote this algorithm by $\underset{\sim}{\int}$ and call it the *algorithm forming the antiderivative construct for points of the space* $\mathfrak{L}_1(\mathfrak{x}, \mathfrak{y})$.

The next theorem follows from 9.4.1, 16.1.6, and 16.1.7.

16.1.9. *For any point* Λ' *of the space* $\mathfrak{L}_1(\mathfrak{x}, \mathfrak{y})$ *and any point* a_1 *of the space* $\overline{\mathfrak{A}}_0$,

$$D\left(\underset{\sim}{\int}(\lambda_1')\right) \underset{1\bar\rho}{=} \lambda_1', \qquad \underset{\sim}{\int}(D(\mathrm{a}_1)) \underset{\bar\rho_2}{=} \mathrm{a}_1,$$

$$\bar N_2\left(\underset{\sim}{\int}(\lambda_1')\right) = \mathrm{Var}\left(\underset{\sim}{\int}(\lambda_1')\right) = {}_1\!\underset{\sim}{\int}(M(\lambda_1')) = {}_1\bar N(\lambda_1').$$

Here $\bar\rho_2$ *is the metric function in the space* $\overline{\mathfrak{A}}$.

From 16.1.5 and 16.1.9 we immediately obtain the following theorem.

16.1.10. *The algorithm* D *is a linear isometric mapping of the space* $\overline{\mathfrak{A}}_0$ *onto the space* $\mathfrak{L}_1(\mathfrak{x}, \mathfrak{y})$. *The algorithm* $\underset{\sim}{\int}$ *is a linear isometric mapping of*

$\mathfrak{L}_1(\mathfrak{x}, \mathfrak{y})$ *onto* $\overline{\mathfrak{A}}_0$. *Moreover,* $\underset{\sim}{\int}$ *and* D *are mutually inverse operators.*

16.2. Below we shall formulate without proof some theorems analogous to corresponding theorems of classical mathematical analysis.

16.2.1. *If* a_1 *and* a_2 *are points of the space* $\overline{\mathfrak{A}}$ *such that* $D(a_1) \underset{1\rho}{=} D(a_2)$, *then, for any point* z *belonging to the segment* $\mathfrak{x} \nabla \mathfrak{y}$,

$$\breve{a}_2(z) \underset{B}{=} \breve{a}_1(z) + (\breve{a}_2(\mathfrak{x}) - \breve{a}_1(\mathfrak{x})).$$

16.2.2. *If* Λ'_1 *is a point of the space* $\mathfrak{L}_1(\mathfrak{x}, \mathfrak{y})$ *and* x, y *are points of the segment* $\mathfrak{x} \nabla \mathfrak{y}$ *such that* $x < y$, *then*

$$\underset{x \nabla y}{{}_1\!\int} (\Lambda'_1) = \check{H}(y) - \check{H}(x), \tag{11}$$

where $H \leftrightharpoons \underset{\sim}{\int}(\Lambda'_1)$.

This proposition, which is the Newton-Leibnitz Theorem, is proved first (with the help of simple computations based on the definition of the algorithm $\underset{\sim}{\int}$) for the case where x and y are rational numbers and Λ'_1 is a graduated frame. The transition to the general case is based on the uniformly continuous dependence of the left and right sides of equation (11) on Λ'_1, x and y.

The next theorem corresponds to the rule of "integration by parts". For this theorem it is necessary to introduce an operation of multiplication of an *FR*-construct, summable in the segment $\mathfrak{x} \nabla \mathfrak{y}$, by absolutely continuous *FR*-constructs. We shall not construct this operation in detail here, but shall limit ourselves only to an intuitive description.

As a new symbol to be used for the construction of absolutely continuous *FR*-constructs, we introduce the symbol @, and we introduce the alphabets $Ч_8$, $Ч_9$, $Ч_{10}$, and $Ч_{11}$:

$$Ч_8 \leftrightharpoons Ч_4 \cup \{@\}, \qquad Ч_9 \leftrightharpoons Ч_5 \cup \{@\},$$

$$Ч_{10} \leftrightharpoons Ч_6 \cup \{@\}, \qquad Ч_{11} \leftrightharpoons Ч_7 \cup \{@\}.$$

Absolutely continuous *FR*-constructs are words in the alphabet $Ч_8$.

In §15.5 we introduced an algorithm $\mathfrak{K}$ transforming every Π-word Π_1 into a certain graduated frame $\mathfrak{K}(\Pi_1)$. If a_1 is a point of the space $\overline{\mathfrak{A}}$, then the algorithm in the alphabet $Ч_4^{sa}$ transforming every n into the word $\mathfrak{K}(\underline{a_1}_8(n))$, is a sequence of points of the space $B_{\mathfrak{a}}(\mathfrak{x}, \mathfrak{y})$. Simple estimates present us with the opportunity of constructing from a_1, $\mathfrak{x}$ and $\mathfrak{y}$ a regulator of convergence in itself of this sequence in the space $B_{\mathfrak{a}}(\mathfrak{x}, \mathfrak{y})$. On the basis of these considerations, we can construct in an obvious way an algorithm ${}_{\mathfrak{a}}\mathfrak{B}$ in the alphabet Ч^{sa}_{10} transforming every point of the space $\overline{\mathfrak{A}}$ into a point of the space $\mathfrak{L}_{\mathfrak{a}}(\mathfrak{x}, \mathfrak{y})$. The word ${}_{\mathfrak{a}}\mathfrak{B}(a_1)$ will be called the *characteristic representative* of the absolutely continuous *FR*-construct a_1 in the space $\mathfrak{L}_{\mathfrak{a}}(\mathfrak{x}, \mathfrak{y})$.

For what follows we note that it is not hard to construct an algorithm η transforming any point a_1 of the space $\overline{\mathfrak{A}}$ into a rational number $\eta(a_1)$ such that

$$\forall n\,(\Xi\,(\mathfrak{K}\,(\underbrace{a_1}_{8}\,(n)))\leqslant\eta\,(a_1)),$$

where Ξ is the algorithm introduced in §15.1.

In §15.2 we defined an operation of multiplication of a point of the space $\mathfrak{L}_{\mathfrak{a}}$ by another point which is a characteristic representative in $\mathfrak{L}_{\mathfrak{a}}$ of some measurable *FR*-construct. This definition was preceded by some estimates. By analogy with them, one can develop estimates for the case of a sequence of graduated frames given by an algorithm transforming every n into the word

$$\underbrace{\Lambda_1'}_{6}\,(n)\underset{6}{\times}\mathfrak{K}\,(\underbrace{a_1}_{8}\,(n)),$$

where Λ_1' is a point of the space $\mathfrak{L}_{\mathfrak{a}}(\mathfrak{x}, \mathfrak{y})$ and a_1 is a point of the space $\overline{\mathfrak{A}}$. In these estimates one uses in an essential way the number $\eta(a_1)$. On the basis of these estimates, one constructs a regulator of convergence in itself of the given sequence of graduated frames in $\mathfrak{L}_{\mathfrak{a}}(\mathfrak{x}, \mathfrak{y})$. As a result we arrive (in obvious fashion) at a definition of an operation of multiplication of one point of the space $\mathfrak{L}_{\mathfrak{a}}(\mathfrak{x}, \mathfrak{y})$ by another point which is a characteristic representative in $\mathfrak{L}_{\mathfrak{a}}(\mathfrak{x}, \mathfrak{y})$ of an absolutely continuous *FR*-construct. We denote this operation by the symbol $\times_{\Lambda}$. If Λ_1' is a point of the space $\mathfrak{L}_{\mathfrak{a}}(\mathfrak{x}, \mathfrak{y})$ and a_1 is a point of the space $\overline{\mathfrak{A}}$, then as a notation for the expression $\times_{\Lambda}(\Lambda_1' \,\square\, {}_{\mathfrak{a}}\mathfrak{B}(a_1))$ we shall employ the expression $(\Lambda_1' \times {}_{\mathfrak{a}}\mathfrak{B}(a_1))$.

We note that everything said above about the operation of multiplication can be extended to the case where, instead of absolutely continuous *FR*-constructs, we deal with uniformly continuous *FR*-constructs.

Now we can formulate two variations of the rule of "integration by parts".

16.2.3. *Let x and y be real duplexes such that $\mathfrak{x} \leq x < y \leq \mathfrak{y}$. Then:*

1) *for any points a_1 and a_2 of the space $\overline{\mathfrak{A}}$,*

$$\underset{x \nabla y}{{}_1\!\int}(D\,(a_1)\times{}_1\mathfrak{B}\,(a_2))+\underset{x \nabla y}{{}_1\!\int}(D\,(a_2)\times{}_1\mathfrak{B}\,(a_1))=\check{a}_1\,(y)\cdot\check{a}_2\,(y)-\check{a}_1\,(x)\cdot\check{a}_2\,(x);$$

2) *for any points* Λ_1' *and* Λ_2' *of the space* $\mathfrak{L}_1(\mathfrak{x}, \mathfrak{y})$,

$$\underset{x\nabla y}{{}_1\int} (\lambda_1' \times {}_1\mathfrak{B}(H_2)) + \underset{x\nabla y}{{}_1\int} (\lambda_2' \times {}_1\mathfrak{B}(H_1)) = \check{H}_1(y)\cdot\check{H}_2(y) - \check{H}_1(x)\cdot\check{H}_2(x),$$

where

$$H_1 \leftrightharpoons \underset{\sim}{\int}(\lambda_1'), \quad H_2 \leftrightharpoons \underset{\sim}{\int}(\lambda_2').$$

16.3. Here the letters $\mathfrak{x}$ and $\mathfrak{y}$ will be used in the same sense as in preceding sections of this chapter. We shall denote the metric space $E[\mathfrak{x} \nabla \mathfrak{y}]$ by the letter $\mathfrak{M}$.

Every σ-system of rational numbers will be called a polynomial frame, and also a word of type Ю. We denote by $\mathfrak{Q}$ an algorithm of type $(Ю \to c_0)_4$ such that, for any word $Ю_1$ and any real duplex z,

$$\langle \mathfrak{Q}(Ю_1)\rangle_3(z) \simeq Q_1 + Q_2\cdot z + Q_3\cdot z^2 + \ldots + Q_{\mathfrak{k}}\cdot z^{\mathfrak{k}-1},$$

where $\mathfrak{k} \leftrightharpoons L_\sigma(Ю_1)$, $Q_j \leftrightharpoons [Ю]_j^\sigma$ $(j = 1, 2, \cdots, \mathfrak{k})$. The algorithm $\langle \mathfrak{Q}(Ю_1)\rangle_3$ will be called the polynomial *interpretation* of the word $Ю_1$.

For any word $Ю_1$, the algorithm $\langle \mathfrak{Q}(Ю_1)\rangle_3$, considered as a 1-ary operator from the space $\mathfrak{M}$ into the space E, is a Lipschitz function. Based on this, we construct an algorithm $\mathfrak{R}$ of type $(Ю \to c_0)_4$ transforming every word $Ю_1$ into the transcription of a regulator of uniform continuity of the function $\langle \mathfrak{Q}(Ю_1)\rangle_3$ in the space $\mathfrak{M}$. After this, we construct an algorithm $\mathfrak{C}$ transforming every word $Ю_1$ into the word $\mathfrak{Q}(Ю_1) \boxed{7} \mathfrak{R}(Ю_1)$, which is a complete cipher of a 1-ary uniformly continuous function in the space $\mathfrak{M}$. Finally, we construct an algorithm $M_Ю$ transforming every word $Ю_1$ into the word $M_{c.c}(\mathfrak{C}(Ю_1))$ (see §11.3). The word $M_Ю(Ю_1)$ will be called the *modulus* of the word $Ю_1$. The modulus of any word of type Ю is a complete cipher of a uniformly continuous function in the space $\mathfrak{M}$.

The composition of the algorithms $\mathfrak{C}$ and ${}_1\mathfrak{A}$ (see §15.5), denoted below by the letter $\mathfrak{D}$, transforms every word $Ю_1$ of type Ю into the point ${}_1\mathfrak{A}(\mathfrak{C}(Ю_1))$ of the space $\mathfrak{L}_1(\mathfrak{x}, \mathfrak{y})$. The point $\mathfrak{D}(Ю_1)$ will be called the *characteristic representative* of the word $Ю_1$ in the space $\mathfrak{L}_1(\mathfrak{x}, \mathfrak{y})$.

We now introduce two algorithms in the alphabet Ч_4^{sa}: an addition algorithm for words of type Ю (denoted by $+_Ю$) and an algorithm for multiplying words of type Ю by rational numbers (denoted by $\cdot_Ю$). A characterization of these algorithms is obtained from the characterization of the corresponding algorithms for words of type Т (see §13.1) as a result of replacing the letters Т and τ by the letters Ю and σ, respectively. In the usual way we construct a subtraction algorithm (denoted by $-_{Ю}$).

We introduce an algorithm $D_0^{(1)}$ in the alphabet $Ч_4^{sa}$ which is characterized in the following manner: if the word Ю$_1$ is represented in the form

$$Q_1\sigma Q_2\sigma \ldots \sigma Q_{\mathfrak{k}},$$

where $\mathfrak{k}$ is a positive integer and $Q_1, Q_2, \cdots, Q_{\mathfrak{k}}$ are rational numbers, then the word $D_0^{(1)}$ (Ю$_1$) has the form

$$Q_2\sigma(2 \cdot Q_3)\sigma(3 \cdot Q_4)\sigma\ldots\sigma((\mathfrak{k}-1) \cdot Q_{\mathfrak{k}}),$$

if $\mathfrak{k} > 1$, and $D_0^{(1)}$ (Ю$_1$) $\doteqdot 0$ if $\mathfrak{k} = 1$.

The word $D_0^{(1)}$(Ю$_1$) will be called the *derivative word* of the word Ю$_1$.

We denote by $D_0^{(2)}, D_0^{(3)}, \cdots$ the algorithms in the alphabet $Ч_4^{sa}$ such that, for every m, beginning with 1, the algorithm $D_0^{(m+1)}$ is the composition of the algorithms $D_0^{(m)}$ and $D_0^{(1)}$. We shall also use the expression $D_0^{(0)}$, treating it as a designation of the identity algorithm in the alphabet $Ч_4^{sa}$. We have

$$\forall m ю_1 (D_0^{(m+1)}(ю_1) \doteqdot D_0^{(1)}(D_0^{(m)}(ю_1))).$$

Now we fix some natural number, denoted in what follows by the letter $\mathfrak{l}$, and we construct algorithms ${}_{\mathfrak{l}}N_{\mathrm{I}}^*$ and ${}_{\mathfrak{l}}N_{\mathrm{II}}^*$ in the alphabet $Ч_4^{sa}$ such that, for any word Ю$_1$,

$${}_{\mathfrak{l}}N_{\mathrm{I}}^*(ю_1) \simeq \max(U_0 \square U_1 \square \ldots \square U_{\mathfrak{l}}),$$

$${}_{\mathfrak{l}}N_{\mathrm{II}}^*(ю_1) \simeq \max(V_0 \square V_1 \square \ldots \square V_{\mathfrak{l}}),$$

where

$$\left.\begin{aligned} U_i &\leftrightharpoons \sup_{\mathfrak{M}}(\underset{ю}{M}(D_0^{(i)}(ю_1))), \\ V_i &\leftrightharpoons {}_1\!\int(\underset{\lambda}{M}(\mathfrak{D}(D_0^{(i)}(ю_1)))). \end{aligned}\right\} \quad i = 0, 1, 2, \ldots, \mathfrak{l}.$$

$M_{Д}$ is the algorithm introduced in §15.2.

The algorithms ${}_{\mathfrak{l}}N_{\mathrm{I}}^*$ and ${}_{\mathfrak{l}}N_{\mathrm{II}}^*$ satisfy conditions 12.1 (*). We construct algorithms ${}_{\mathfrak{l}}\rho_{\mathrm{I}}$ and ${}_{\mathfrak{l}}\rho_{\mathrm{II}}$ of type (ЮЮ → Д)$_4$ such that, for any Ю$_1$ and Ю$_2$,

$${}_{\mathfrak{l}}\rho_{\mathrm{I}}(ю_1 \square ю_2) \simeq {}_{\mathfrak{l}}N_{\mathrm{I}}^*(ю_2 \underset{ю}{-} ю_1),$$

$${}_{\mathfrak{l}}\rho_{\mathrm{II}}(ю_1 \square ю_2) \simeq {}_{\mathfrak{l}}N_{\mathrm{II}}^*(ю_2 \underset{ю}{-} ю_1).$$

One can prove that the list

$$\text{Ч}_4,\ (\text{c}_{4,1} \in \text{ю}),\quad {}_{\mathfrak{l}}\rho_{\text{I}},\ \underset{\text{ю}}{+},\ \underset{\text{ю}}{\cdot},\ 0,$$

denoted below by $C^{(\mathfrak{l})}$, and the list

$$\text{Ч}_4,\ (\text{c}_{4,1} \in \text{ю}),\quad {}_{\mathfrak{l}}\rho_{\text{II}},\ \underset{\text{ю}}{+},\ \underset{\text{ю}}{\cdot},\ 0,$$

denoted below by $S^{(\mathfrak{l})}$, are normed spaces. The algorithms for computing the norms in these spaces will be denoted, respectively, by ${}_{\mathfrak{l}}N_{\text{I}}$ and ${}_{\mathfrak{l}}N_{\text{II}}$.

It is obvious that, for any ю_1 and for any i not exceeding $\mathfrak{l}$,

$$_{(\mathfrak{l}-i)}N_{\text{I}}(D_0^{(i)}(\text{ю}_1)) \leqslant {}_{\mathfrak{l}}N_{\text{I}}(\text{ю}_1), \tag{1}$$

$$_{(\mathfrak{l}-i)}N_{\text{II}}(D_0^{(i)}(\text{ю}_1)) \leqslant {}_{\mathfrak{l}}N_{\text{II}}(\text{ю}_1). \tag{2}$$

We remark also that $D_0^{(i)}$ is a linear mapping of the space $C^{(\mathfrak{l})}$ into $C^{(\mathfrak{l}-i)}$ and a linear mapping of the spaces $S^{(\mathfrak{l})}$ into $S^{(\mathfrak{l}-i)}$.

We denote by $\overline{C^{(\mathfrak{l})}}$ the standard normed FR-completion of the space $C^{(\mathfrak{l})}$, and by $\overline{S^{(\mathfrak{l})}}$ the standard normed FR-completion of the space $S^{(\mathfrak{l})}$.

Points of the space $\overline{C^{(\mathfrak{l})}}$ will be called *FR-constructs uniformly differentiable* $\mathfrak{l}$ *times* in the segment $\mathfrak{x} \underline{\nabla} \mathfrak{y}$. Points of the space $\overline{S^{(\mathfrak{l})}}$ will be called *FR-constructs generally differentiable* (*in the sense of S. L. Sobolev*) $\mathfrak{l}$ *times* in the segment $\mathfrak{x} \underline{\nabla} \mathfrak{y}$. Well-known theorems of classical mathematics testify to the fact that it is natural to consider these concepts as constructive analogues of the similarly named concepts of classical mathematics.

Let i be a natural number not exceeding $\mathfrak{l}$. From (1) it follows that $D_0^{(i)}$ is a Lipschitz operator from the space $C^{(\mathfrak{l})}$ into the space $C^{(\mathfrak{l}-i)}$ (and therefore into the space $\overline{C^{(\mathfrak{l}-i)}}$) and the number 1 is a Lipschitz coefficient of this operator. Applying to $D_0^{(i)}$ and 1 the algorithm for the standard extension of 1-ary Lipschitz operators, we obtain a linear Lipschitz operator mapping $\overline{C^{(\mathfrak{l})}}$ into $\overline{C^{(\mathfrak{l}-i)}}$. We denote this operator by $D^{(i)}$. It is natural to call it the *operator for constructing the derivative of order* i in the space $\overline{C^{(\mathfrak{l})}}$.

One can associate in a natural way with every point of the space $\overline{C^{(0)}}$ a certain complete cipher of a 1-ary uniformly continuous function in the space $\mathfrak{M}$. This correspondence is based on the obvious possibility of constructing, for every point z of the segment $\mathfrak{x} \underline{\nabla} \mathfrak{y}$, the limit of the sequence of real duplexes obtained from the sequence of polynomial functions associated with the given point of the space $\overline{C^{(0)}}$ by computing the value of these functions at the point z.

For a given point of the space $\overline{C^{(0)}}$ one can easily construct a regulator of uniform continuity of the function of type $(Д' \to Д)$ obtained in the indicated way.

Starting from this association of complete ciphers of uniformly continuous functions with points of the space $\overline{C^{(0)}}$, we can (in the same way as in the case of the space $\overline{\mathfrak{A}}$) introduce an algorithm for computing the value of any point of the space $\overline{C^{(0)}}$ at any point of the segment $\mathfrak{x} \nabla \mathfrak{y}$.

We shall assume that, for the construction of points of the spaces $\overline{C^{(0)}}$, $\overline{C^{(1)}}, \dots, \overline{C^{(\mathfrak{l})}}$, we have chosen one and the same alphabet, denoted below by $Ч_{12}$. Under this assumption the next proposition follows from the properties of the algorithm $\mathfrak{l} N_{\mathrm{I}}^*$.

16.3.1. *For any natural numbers n and m, if $m < n$, then every point of the space $\overline{C^{(n)}}$ is a point of the space $\overline{C^{(m)}}$. In particular, for every n, every point of the space $\overline{C^{(n)}}$ is a point of the space $\overline{C^{(0)}}$.*

Proposition 16.3.1 permits us to compute, for any n, the value of any point of the space $\overline{C^{(n)}}$ at any point of the segment $\mathfrak{x} \nabla \mathfrak{y}$. In particular, if X is a point of the space $\overline{C^{(\mathfrak{l})}}$ and i is a natural number not exceeding $\mathfrak{l}$, then we can compute the value of the FR-construct $D^{(i)}(X)$, which is a point of the space $\overline{C^{(\mathfrak{l}-i)}}$, at any point of the segment $\mathfrak{x} \nabla \mathfrak{y}$.

The variant of the differential calculus obtained on the basis of the definitions formulated above has many features in common with the theory of R. L. Goodstein, about which we spoke in §0.13. However, Goodstein's theory also has essential differences from this variant. It cannot be subsumed under the general scheme of the completion of constructive metric spaces.

Another variant of the differential calculus is obtained in the case where the operation of constructing derivatives of various orders is defined with respect to constructive objects introduced in a suitable way on the basis of the concept of a function of type $(Д \to Д)$ (or of type $(Д' \to Д)$). This variant is formally much closer to the traditional construction of the differential calculus. However, we shall not go into this any further.

Let i be a natural number not exceeding $\mathfrak{l}$. From (2) it follows that $D_0^{(i)}$ is a Lipschitz operator from the space $S^{(\mathfrak{l})}$ into the space $S^{(\mathfrak{l}-i)}$ (and therefore into the space $\overline{S^{(\mathfrak{l}-i)}}$), with the number 1 as a Lipschitz coefficient of this operator. Applying to $D_0^{(i)}$ and 1 the algorithm for the standard extension of 1-ary Lipschitz operators, we obtain a linear Lipschitz operator mapping $\overline{S^{(\mathfrak{l})}}$ into $\overline{S^{(\mathfrak{l}-i)}}$. We denote this operator by $D_*^{(i)}$. It is natural to call it the *operator for constructing the generalized derivative of order i* in the space $\overline{S^{(\mathfrak{l})}}$.

We shall assume that, for the construction of points of the spaces $\overline{S^{(0)}}$, $\overline{S^{(1)}}, \dots, \overline{S^{(\mathfrak{l})}}$, we have chosen one and the same alphabet, denoted below by Ч_{13}. We also introduce an alphabet Ч_{14}, equal to the union of the alphabets Ч_{13} and Ч_6.

Let Y be a point of the space $\overline{S^{(0)}}$. Then for every n the word $\mathfrak{D}(\underline{Y}_{12}(n))$ is a point of the space $\mathfrak{L}_1(\mathfrak{x}, \mathfrak{y})$. Simple estimates show that the algorithm $\mathfrak{D}$ is a linear isometric mapping of the space $\overline{S^{(0)}}$ into the space $\mathfrak{L}_1(\mathfrak{x}, \mathfrak{y})$. Hence, for any k, m and n, if $m, n \geq \overline{Y}^{12}(k)$, then

$$ {}_1\overline{N}(\mathfrak{D}(\underline{Y}_{12}(m)) - \mathfrak{D}(\underline{Y}_{12}(n))) = {}_0N_{\text{II}}(\underline{Y}_{12}(m) - \underline{Y}_{12}(n)) < 2^{-k}. $$

Hence the word $H \circledcirc \{\overline{Y}^{12}\}$, where H is the transcription of the algorithm in the alphabet Ч_6^{sa} which is the composition of the algorithms $\underline{Y}_{12}$ and $\mathfrak{D}$, is an FR-construct in the space $\mathfrak{L}_1(\mathfrak{x}, \mathfrak{y})$. The limit of this FR-construct in the complete space $\mathfrak{L}_1(\mathfrak{x}, \mathfrak{y})$ will be called the *characteristic representative* of the word Y in the space $\mathfrak{L}_1(\mathfrak{x}, \mathfrak{y})$. The algorithm in the alphabet $\text{Ч}_{14}^{\text{sa}}$ transforming any point Y of the space $\overline{S^{(0)}}$ into the word which is the characteristic representative of Y in the space $\mathfrak{L}_1(\mathfrak{x}, \mathfrak{y})$ will be denoted by $\overline{\mathfrak{D}}$.

By the integral of the point Y on the segment $\mathfrak{x} \underline{\nabla} \mathfrak{y}$ we shall mean ${}_1\int(\overline{\mathfrak{D}}(Y))$. If $x \nabla y$ is an interval contained in the segment $\mathfrak{x} \underline{\nabla} \mathfrak{y}$, then by the *average integral value* of the point Y on the interval $x \nabla y$ we shall mean the average integral value on this interval of the summable FR-construct $\overline{\mathfrak{D}}(Y)$.

The next proposition follows from the properties of the algorithm ${}_{\mathfrak{l}}N_{\text{II}}^*$.

16.3.2. *For any natural numbers m and n, if $m < n$, then every point of the space $\overline{S^{(n)}}$ is a point of the space $\overline{S^{(m)}}$. In particular, for every n, every point of the space $\overline{S^{(n)}}$ is a point of the space $\overline{S^{(0)}}$.*

Proposition 16.3.2 permits us to compute, for any n, the integral of any point of the space $\overline{S^{(n)}}$ on the segment $\mathfrak{x} \underline{\nabla} \mathfrak{y}$ and the average integral value of any point of the space $\overline{S^{(n)}}$ on any interval contained in $\mathfrak{x} \underline{\nabla} \mathfrak{y}$. In particular, if Y is a point of the space $\overline{S^{(\mathfrak{l})}}$ and i is a natural number not exceeding $\mathfrak{l}$, then we are able to compute the integral of the FR-construct $D_{+}^{(i)}(Y)$, which is a point of the space $S^{(\mathfrak{k}-i)}$, on the segment $\mathfrak{x} \underline{\nabla} \mathfrak{y}$, and also to compute the average integral value of this FR-construct on any interval contained in $\mathfrak{x} \underline{\nabla} \mathfrak{y}$.

16.4. In contemporary mathematics a great role is played by the concepts of multimetric space and multinormed space, which are generalizations of the concepts of metric and normed spaces. It is not difficult to introduce constructive analogues of these concepts. Following the same plan which was used above for the presentation of the foundations of the theory of constructive metric and normed spaces, one can present the foundations of the theory of constructive multimetric and multinormed spaces.

Important roles in this theory are played by the concepts of F-construct and FR-construct in the given space. However, these concepts have more complicated definitions than in the theory of constructive metric spaces. The complication arises from the fact that, for the definition of these concepts, it is necessary, generally speaking, to start not from constructive sequences of points of the space but from constructive mappings into the given space from a suitably chosen partially ordered set.

Based on the concept of constructive multinormed space, one can introduce natural constructive analogues of the concept of generalized function in the sense of Sobolev-Schwartz and of other concepts dealt with in contemporary functional analysis and connected with the term "generalized function". As a guide in the formulation of the corresponding definitions one can use well-known approximational variants of the definitions of the indicated concepts of classical mathematics.

A constructive analogue of the concept of linear topological space can be introduced by means of a certain generalization and modification of the concept of constructive multimetric space.

A more detailed consideration of these concepts of constructive mathematics is not among the tasks of this book.

APPENDIX

ON CRITICISM OF CLASSICAL MATHEMATICS

This appendix is an extension of §0.5, in which the basic content of the criticism of classical mathematics set forth by Brouwer, Weyl, Markov and some other mathematicians was briefly described. The general formulation in §0.5 is lacking in precision and concreteness. This appendix is devoted to a consideration, more detailed and more concrete than in §0.5, of the situation which has stimulated criticism with respect to the foundations of classical mathematics. Here we shall try to present a summary of the most important aspects of the critical analysis of classical mathematics carried out by Brouwer, Weyl, Hilbert, Markov, and other mathematicians, and we shall also attempt a detailed presentation of some components of this critical analysis.

I. First of all, we shall go into some aspects of the processes involved on the formulation of mathematical concepts.

In the formulation of mathematical concepts mental acts of various kinds are carried out. Let us note certain kinds of such mental acts.

1) Mental acts of "pure" abstraction. These mental acts consist in the conceptual selection of certain properties out of all the properties applicable to all the objects included at the given moment in our field of attention, and, with respect to the existence or nonexistence of any other properties, our consciousness remains completely indifferent.

If we associate with the chosen properties some terms not being used for other purposes, then we obtain some general concepts.

2) Mental acts of idealization. These acts consist of the generation by our imagination of certain ideas or concepts, considered by our consciousness as objects of study endowed by our imagination not only with those properties which were selected by acts of "pure" abstraction with respect to the objects forming the initial material for the given mental operations, but also with conceptual properties which are completely absent from the initial objects or which reflect properties of the initial objects in a considerably distorted form.

3) Multi-stage levels of various acts of "pure" abstraction and acts of idealization. At every stage of the mental processes of this kind, as initial objects for acts of "pure" abstraction and acts of idealization one uses not only objects which are the initial material in the whole chain of mental operations but also concepts and ideas which have been formed at preceding stages.

Mental acts of the kinds mentioned above are acts of abstraction.[1)]

The presence of acts of idealization in almost all the processes of formation of mathematical concepts is the result of the tendency of people, in studying new objects or new connections between certain objects or, speaking more generally, in studying new situations, to look for support from previously accumulated knowledge and previously developed tools relating to different initially given objects. The complexity of the situation being studied often forces people to look for conceptual support by acts of imagination which bring our presentation of the situation under study closer to a situation which has been previously studied and for which there exists some (sometimes only partial or remote) resemblance to the given situation and for which a sufficiently simple apparatus has been worked out. Often it is necessary to proceed in this way simply because no other realizable possibility is found to be successful.

If in the course of studying some situation we succeed in finding an idealization which permits us to solve a certain problem with the required precision, then this idealization may be fixed and turned into a tradition, to which people automatically turn even in those cases where it is necessary to consider problems of new kinds or to meet more strenuous requirements in the formulation and solution of problems of the initial type. The attractive aspect of such traditions is the development of and familiarity with a certain apparatus. This attractive aspect explains the fact that many such traditions do not encounter opposition for a long time. One of these traditional idealizations is the abstraction of actual infinity.

II. The systematic application in contemporary mathematics of the abstraction of actual infinity and of ideas generated by this abstraction can explain to a considerable extent the tendency to rely, in various mathematical considerations, on those methods of thought which are customary for people with academic background, and which classical logic puts at our disposal.

---

1) Sometimes by abstractions we mean only mental acts of "pure" abstraction. In this appendix the term "abstraction" will be used in a much wider sense, including the mental acts of the kinds mentioned above. This interpretation of the term "abstraction" has many precedents in the application of this term in the literature devoted to the foundations of mathematics.

It was remarked above that in acts of idealization our imagination generates ideas and concepts in which are combined, first, properties chosen by acts of "pure" abstraction in the study of certain objects, and, second, those conceptual properties which distort the picture of our knowledge about the original situation and become objects of study only as a result of a conceptual approximation of the situation of interest to us with a situation which has already been studied, and which are produced so that one may try to use, even partially, some previously worked out apparatus.

After an idea or concept arising as a result of an act of idealization enters into the fabric of mathematical theory, mathematicians usually forget the mechanism of the origin of the given idea or concept and fail to notice the difference between properties of the first kind and of the second kind. Properties of both kinds become in equal measure the initial basis for new acts of abstraction for processes of logical inference. As a result of new acts of idealization generated on this basis, new ideas or concepts arise in which it is even more difficult to separate properties which can be considered satisfactory reflections of properties of the initial objects lying at the base of the formation of the whole chain of ideas and concepts being considered from those properties which are only products of a method. This indefiniteness grows still larger in the transition to higher levels of the processes of abstraction occurring in mathematics.

An analogous situation exists when we consider processes of logical deduction. In such processes we use properties of the second kind with the same right as properties of the first kind. In addition, in applying a rule of inference, mathematicians proceed from the belief that the rule being applied is admissible in the cases being considered. However, the justification for the admissibility of rules of inference includes within itself not only acts of "pure" abstraction but also acts of idealization, in many cases even multi-staged acts.

Hence every logical inference places before us a series of problems. In what way can one interpret the proposition obtained as a result of the given logical inference, i.e. in what way can one transform this proposition into a proposition about the initial objects which serve as a basis of the formation of the whole chain of ideas and concepts being considered? If a concrete condition suggests to us some interpretation, then the problem arises: should one consider the proposition obtained as a result of the given logical inference a satisfactory reflection of the properties of the initial objects and the connections between them? Does it not happen that the essential use of various acts of idealization of various conceptual properties and situations on the way between the initial objects and the given result of logical inference so radically isolates the conceptual processes in our consciousness from the initial situation that the final proposition resulting from the given logical inference gives a substantially distorted idea of the initial objects?

No general recipes for answering these questions exist. However, it is necessary to note the following.

The difficulty mentioned above of returning from ideas, concepts, and arguments to the initial objects which serve as a basis for the formation of the whole chain of ideas and concepts of the given theory always arises when acts of idealization are involved in the process of forming ideas and concepts. But this difficulty of restoration can occur in essentially different ways in different cases; it varies in dependence on the type of idealization used, on the nature of the level of the idealization, and on those aspects of the given theory which are of interest to us in the given case. In some cases the restoration can be realized much more easily than in others. (Intuitively speaking, in some cases mathematical concepts and arguments are significantly more "tangible" than in others.) In some cases logical inferences, considered together with some way of interpreting statements, give a much greater basis for recognizing their cognitive value than in other cases. Idealizations used in mathematics turn out to be nonuniform with respect to the point of view of interest to us now.

An important circumstance inducing criticism with respect to the foundations of classical mathematics is the fact that the abstraction of actual infinity and the ideas and concepts raised on its basis are very remote idealizations, i.e. idealizations for which the connection between the ideas, concepts and arguments, on the one hand, and the real objects forming the initial material for the whole chain of acts of abstraction under consideration, on the other hand, in many cases turns out to be very indirect and vague, or even do not exist at all. The difficulty of returning from the ideas, concepts and arguments, in the formation of which the abstraction of actual infinity has taken part, to the initial real objects and the connections between them turns out in many cases to be very considerable.

III. In classical mathematics a fundamental role is played by the general concept of set. This concept is not connected with the fixing of some definite method for individually describing those objects which are covered by this concept.

It is well known that the general concept of set is not definable in terms of simpler concepts (it is clarified only by means of some examples) and the methods of working with this concept are introduced on the basis of the system of ideas generated by the abstraction of actual infinity. The initial material for the formation of the general concept of set consists in the first place of various collections of real objects. (When we apply the expression "collection of real objects" we have in mind that the objects of which the collection consists are conceptually chosen from the surrounding environment by means of direct exhibition or by means of a clear characterization of their type, that the objects occurring in the collection exist simultaneously and steadily during some interval of time, and that they clearly differ from one another.)

It is necessary to emphasize that the experimental investigation of nature has not given any example of an infinite collection of real objects (see [10]). However, in the classical theory of sets, there occur as objects of study not only finite sets but also concepts with which are connected ideas about collections for which the process of counting never at any step exhausts all their elements, and with which the term "infinite set" is connected. Therefore reference to collections of real objects existing in nature as the source of the formation of the general concept of set is insufficient as an explanation of the mechanism for forming this concept.

Everyday experience and constructive human activity bring us together not only with objects existing in nature at that given interval of time but also with processes of construction of some new objects. Here we have in mind processes of construction carried out by both people and mechanisms.

For a long time mathematicians have used certain methods of introducing general concepts which cover not only objects existing in nature but also possible results of processes of construction. If we choose and fix some finite sequence of initial objects and some finite sequence of constructive operations, and we introduce some new term (denoted by the latter T), then we obtain all the necessary ingredients for a genetic definition (more concretely, for a constructive definition) of a new concept. Every object covered by this new concept receives the name "object of type T". Objects of type T are called possible (more precisely, potentially realizable[1]) results of the processes of construction realized by a

1) This term will be explained below.

sequential performance of constructive operations occurring in the fixed finite sequence. It is assumed that, before each step of the construction process, the next constructive operation can be chosen arbitrarily from among those constructive operations which serve as a basis of the given definition and the description of which permits their application to any results of the process obtained at preceding steps or to any initial objects.

It is possible (and in many cases also necessary) to introduce constructive definitions of a more general form, namely definitions in which one fixes: 1) a finite sequence of initial objects; 2) a finite sequence of constructive operations; 3) a term for the defined concept; and, in addition, 4) some condition clearly formulated in a suitable language. As objects of the defined type we count in this case those possible (potentially realizable) results of constructive processes, based on the given finite sequence of constructive operations, which satisfy the given condition.

If some general concept is introduced by means of a definition of one of the two types just mentioned, then in constructive mathematics one connects with the definition of this general concept (more precisely, with the text of the definition, along with which one assumes a definite method of interpretation) the name "set of objects of such-and-such a type".[1)] In constructive mathematics the term "sets" is connected with individually given objects, each of which is a definition, written in a suitable precise language, of constructive objects of a concrete type. Applying the term "set" in this sense we can state that there is no justification for considering all elements of the given set as existing simultaneously. It can happen that at a given moment some elements of the set have already been constructed. We are justified for talking about these elements as if they exist simultaneously. But there can be only a finite number of such elements. Therefore, generally speaking, elements of a set are determined only as possible objects, and we are able to investigate them only on the basis of given constructive operations and a given selecting condition. One can sat that a general concept covering not only existing but also possible objects arises only as a result of fixing a

---

1) We remark that the concepts "natural number", "integer", "rational number" can be introduced by definitions of the first type (§1). The definitions of these concepts are, respectively, the set of natural numbers, the set of integers, and the set of rational numbers.

As examples of concepts introduced by definitions of the second type, one can cite the concepts of real F-number and real FR-number (§3.5). The definitions of these concepts are, respectively, the set of real F-numbers and the set of real FR-numbers.

finite sequence of constructive operations and a selecting condition.[1] In other words, a set of the type just considered arises only as a result of fixing a finite sequence of constructive operations and a selecting condition. This fact underlines the exceptional role of the individual presentation of sets in the problem of the "tangibility" of mathematical concepts.

Both in classical and constructive mathematics, in considering objects characterized by definitions of the types described above, one assumes a certain idealization, called the abstraction of potential realizability (see [1]). It consists of the conceptual assumption that, in carrying out constructive operations on constructive objects, there do not arise obstructions of a material nature, caused by a limitation of the constructive possibilities of men and machines in space and time, by limited resources, etc. Applying this idealization, we treat as objects of study not only those objects which already exist or can be constructed in a really possible number of steps, but also imagined objects the construction of which, on the basis of the given constructive operations, could be realized if, in carrying out the given operations, no obstructions of a material nature arose. As a name for this realizability (stipulated by the indicated assumption) of construction one uses the term "potential realizability" (see [1]).

Applying the abstraction of potential realizability and starting, for example, from the definition of natural numbers, we arrive at the idea of potential infinity, i.e. at the idea of the possibility of extending the sequence of natural numbers endlessly. In this sense one can say that the set of natural numbers is potentially infinite.

From what has been said it follows that, using as objects of study only collections of real objects, we do not go beyond the concept of "finite set", and using as objects of study finite sequences of constructive operations and processes of construction realizable on their basis and applying the abstraction of potential realizability, we do go beyond the concept of "finite set" and we arrive at the concept of potentially infinite sets, but we do not all reach that idea with which the term "infinite set" is understood to be connected in classical mathematics. Classical mathematics does not give any indication as to how one can connect the idea used by it and denoted by this term with any real objects (collections

---

1) One can assume that a selecting condition figures in every constructive definition. Those definitions which do not include a selecting condition can be supplemented by a condition expressing the equality of an object with itself.

of real objects and finite sequences of constructive operations are not adequate for this purpose). In every case it is indisputable that this idea arises in the mind of every mathematician thanks to an act of idealization which is essentially different from the abstraction of potential realizability.

IV. Constructive mathematics limits itself to the consideration of sets individually given by one of the two methods indicated above.[1] Classical mathematics does not limit itself in this way and extends the sequence of ideas and concepts to be studied by introducing another idealization, called the abstraction of actual infinity.

This idealization can be characterized in the following manner. 1) Considering any fixed finite sequence of constructive operations, we begin by imagining as not only potentially realizable but as actually carried out all possible processes of construction admitted by the given finite sequence of constructive operations, and we conceive all the results of these operations as existing simultaneously. 2) We conceptually equate this imaginary picture with the situation with which we have to deal in considering collections of real objects, and, in particular, we begin to reason about the imaginary "collections" of all these results in the same way that we reason about collections of real objects, i.e. by the methods of classical logic. 3) We begin to conceive of these imaginary collections as existing independently of the finite sequence of constructive operations. 4) After this we give our imagination even greater scope and begin to conceive of infinite collections of simultaneously existing objects not connected with any constructive operations even by their "origin", meeting expressions of mental processes only in the introduction of certain axioms and the development of the process of logical deduction on the basis of classical logic; moreover, we disregard the problem of the possibility of a clear semantics which would permit us to connect the concepts and arguments of such a formal-deductive theory[2] with any real or potentially realizable objects or processes.

In classical mathematics not only the general concept of set but also the concept of subset of a given set is not connected with the fixing by any definite methods of an individual presentation of those objects which are covered by this

---

1) Here we have in mind suitably precise formulations of these methods (see [3, §7]).

2) In such a formal-deductive theory the general concept of set and the concepts based upon it figure only as terms, and the ideas (imaginary pictures) connected with these terms in the process of forming the theory (in the choice of the axioms and the apparatus of logical deduction) lie outside the theory itself.

concept. The same is true when, as the set about whose subsets we are talking, a set occurs which has a simple constructive presentation (for example, the set of all natural numbers, the set of all rational numbers, etc.). The concept of a mapping of one set into another and its special case, the concept of a sequence of elements of a given set, are also not connected with the fixing by any definite methods of an individual presentation of the objects covered by these concepts.

The nonconstructive concepts of subset, mapping, and sequence of elements do not contain any "tangible" initial objects for their contensive interpretation.[1)] The difficulty, caused by this situation, of interpreting the indicated concepts carries over also to those concepts which are defined in terms of them. In particular, these difficulties carry over to the concept of real number in the sense of Dedekind, at the basis of which lies the nonconstructive concept of subset of the set of rational numbers, and to the concept of real number in the sense of Meray-Cantor, at the basis of which lies the nonconstructive concept of a sequence of rational numbers.

V. In applying mathematics to science, engineering and other domains of human activity the concept of real number usually figures as a means of expressing concrete information about physical or other quantities, determined by indication of methods for matching objects or processes of certain types with given standards of measurement. However, there is a significant gap between these practical assignments of the concept of real number, on the one hand, and the content of this concept, as well as the theory of this concept, on the other hand. (Here we have in mind the concept of real number which is used in classical mathematics.) This gap can be described in the following way.

In mathematics there are no means for expressing concrete information about physical quantities other than groups of symbols introduced by means of constructive definitions. Therefore, in mathematics, only constructive objects can be considered as possible carriers of concrete information about physical quantities. However, in classical mathematics the theory of real numbers is constructed not as a theory of constructive objects of a certain type, intended for the expression of concrete information about physical quantities, but rather as a theory the objects of which are certain ideas formed in the imagination of mathematicians as a result of complicated processes of idealization. On the path between the

---

1) What has been said above about the general concept of set extends (with suitable changes in details) to these nonconstructive concepts.

processes of measurement of physical quantities and those ideas which are connected with the term "real number" lies the abstraction of actual infinity.

VI. If we are to speak not about ideas originating in the imagination of mathematicians but about mathematical tools, then one can state that the assumption of the abstraction of actual infinity as a method of thought means the assumption without any limitation of the tools of logical deduction of classical logic. However, it is well known that among the propositions deducible by means of these logical tools there are some which are false from the point of view of the construction intepretation of propositions. (see below; see [3, §4.5]). In this sense the tools of logical deduction furnished by classical logic are not suitable in those theories in which the objects of investigation are constructive objects and the study of these objects is carried out by taking into account their method of definition.

From what has been said it follows that theorems about real numbers deducible in classical mathematical analysis are not statements directly concerning real or potentially realizable objects. In particular, there is no foundation for assuming that every theorem of the form "There exists a real number α satisfying condition S" permits an interpretation in the form of a statement about the existence or potential realizability of a constructive object falling under the concept "real number" and satisfying condition S.

For many theorems of the classical theory of real numbers one can find similarly formulated assertions which are formulable and provable within the scope of constructive mathematics. These constructive analogues of theorems of the classical theory of real numbers give a clearer opportunity for translation into assertions about physical or other quantities. The existence of constructive analogues of many theorems of this theory explains the fact that in spite of everything said above about the classical theory of real numbers, some theorems of this theory make it possible to answer, with a definiteness satisfying certain practical requirements, certain problems about physical or other quantities.

At the same time, for some theorems of the classical theory of real numbers which play an important role in this theory, it is necessary to state that among those assertions which are formulable within constructive mathematics and which have formulations close to the formulations of the given theorems of classical mathematics one cannot discover an assertion provable in constructive mathematics.

From what has been said it follows that the problem of interpreting the theorems of the classical theory of real numbers meets considerable difficulty, having its source in the nonconstructive concept of real number used in classical mathematics. The difficulty of interpretation connected with the concept of real number induces difficulties in all the superstructures based on this concept, and are supplemented in these superstructures by new difficulties caused by the idealizations which are introduced in the conceptual formation of these superstructures.

Very great difficulty of the type just considered is caused by the general concept of transfinite number (not connected in classical mathematics with the fixing of any definite methods for the individual presentation of the objects covered by this concept) and the idea of the method of transfinite induction based upon this concept.

Concepts with which considerable difficulty of interpretation is connected often form the basis for entire branches of classical mathematics. One can exhibit a large number of examples of such concepts. We shall limit ourselves to the examples cited above.

VII. An assertion of the form "There exist an object α_1 of type $P_1, \cdots,$ and an object α_k of type P_k such that condition S is fulfilled" is customarily called an existence assertion. In classical mathematics there occur various kinds of proofs of existence assertions. These include proofs which contain methods for constructing certain constructive objects satisfying the condition which figures in the given existence assertion. At the same time, there also occur proofs which are strictly regulated by the rules of inference of classical logic but do not give any means for obtaining some constructive and therefore concretely defined objects satisfying the given condition. In classical mathematics proofs of the second kind are considered completely acceptable. However, in spite of this, even in the presence of proofs of the second kind, considerable attention is given to searching for proofs of the first kind. For any existence theorem, the construction of a proof of the first kind is often considered to be a result of considerably greater value than the construction of a proof of the second kind.

This point of view on the relation between proofs of the first and second kinds is expressed in a particularly clear way when one considers existence assertions closely connected with applied mathematics. This point of view and the considerable attention to constructive objects connected with it are results of extensive experience in the application of mathematics in science and engineering. This experience testifies to the fact that constructive objects are the most "tangible" and the most adaptable for the interpretation of parts of classical mathematics.

However, in classical mathematics constructive objects are considered on a par with nonconstructive objects. Most often they are considered as concrete representations of some general concept the definition of which is not connected with the fixing of some definite methods for individually presenting the objects covered by this concept and, thanks to this freedom, permits us to assume that, in addition to constructive objects, this concept also covers some other objects. The root property of constructive objects, consisting of the fact that they are by definition potentially realizable results of constructive processes, is completely disregarded in classical mathematics. This disregard shows itself, in particular, in the fact that in all reasoning, including that in which constructive objects occur, the rules of inference of classical logic are applied without limitation.

The original source of the apparatus of logical deduction of classical logic is elementary logic, which has to do with the processes of thought arising under certain "elementary" conditions. These conditions are characterized by the following features.

1) The objects of study are invariable and form a fixed finite collection.[1)]

2) For every given initial concept one can form a two-valued characteristic table selecting those objects of the given collection which belong to the given concept.

3) For every given initial relation one can form a two-valued characteristic table selecting those ordered groups of objects the terms of which are in the given relation.

For statements formulated with respect to the indicated conditions there is a precise semantics, subconsciously applied by people in appropriate cases in everyday practice for many thousands of years, but formulated clearly and in systematic form only at the end of the nineteenth century. The existence of a precise semantics gives us the opportunity of putting in a clear form and solving in an affirmative sense the problem of justifying, under the initially given conditions indicated above, the rules and methods of logical deduction of elementary

---

1) We have in mind, of course, not absolute invariability but invariability only in a chosen interval of time of those aspects of the objects of study which are of interest in the given investigation and only to that degree of precision which suffices for the stated purpose of the given study.

logic.[1] It has been established that upon fulfillment of the conditions indicated above, every statement derivable by the methods which are placed at our disposal by the apparatus of logical deduction of elementary logic, including in derivations some true statements as initial statements or without inclusion of such additional initially given statements, are true statements.[2] This justification of the apparatus of logical deduction reveals the cognitive meaning of the processes of logical deduction which flow from the initially given conditions indicated above on the basis of the apparatus of elementary logic.

In the course of the historical development of the apparatus of logical deduction belonging to elementary logic, a displacement into a mathematical theory having to do with the concept of infinite set automatically occurred. This process of automatic displacement of the apparatus of elementary logic into a considerably more complex condition represents an even more remote idealization. This idealization is one of the chief aspects of the abstraction of actual infinity. Applying this idealization, we agree in the case of infinite sets of objects of study to permit (without any justification) the methods of logical deduction worked out for perfectly concrete initially given objects: for the case where we have a finite domain of objects of study and where all the conditions which were called "elementary" above are fulfilled. Hence we have agreed to treat every situation in the case of an infinite domain of objects of study as completely analogous to the situation which holds under the "elementary" conditions described above.

There is no justification for asserting a priori that the apparatus of logical deduction worked out for certain initially given objects will be suitable for other initially given objects. This observation supports, in particular, those mathematical theories in which the objects of study are constructive objects and the starting point for the investigation of these objects is the root property of constructive objects mentioned above.

VIII. It is well known that the interpretation of mathematical statements about

---

1) Here we have in mind the contemporary apparatus of logical deduction of elementary logic. This apparatus has been formed gradually in the course of the history of human thought. Until the rise of mathematical logic, it was formed mainly in a heuristic way. The rise of mathematical logic was to a considerable degree a process of making precise, partially revising, and significantly extending the previously formed parts of this apparatus on the basis of the precise semantics mentioned above.

2) We remark that, upon fulfillment of the conditions indicated above, justification is obtained, in particular, for the law of the excluded middle.

constructive objects, based on the root property of constructive objects and on the so-called constructive interpretation of mathematical propositions (see [3])[1] reveals the inadmissibility of certain rules of inference of classical logic. The rules of inference which we have in mind here can lead to false statements. Not all mathematical propositions about constructive objects provable by means of the rules of classical logic (i.e. by means of those rules of inference which are considered in classical mathematics to be completely admissible) can be considered as true under the interpretation of propositions which starts from the root property mentioned above of constructive objects. From what has been said it follows that classical mathematics as a whole and classical mathematical analysis in particular are not adapted to the exposure of those connections between constructive objects for which the root property mentioned above of these objects is essential.

Evidence of this unsuitability is manifold. Let us go into some of this evidence. The first manifestation is the fact that the consideration of constructive objects and nonconstructive concepts on a par generates a situation in which it is difficult to distinguish the theorems about constructive objects provable (even by means of classical logic) without drawing upon nonconstructive concepts. But now we turn out attention to another aspect of the matter, namely to the practical consequences which are caused by the use of the complete range of logical methods of classical logic.

Let us assume that we are given a constructive problem which presupposes some constructive initially given objects [for example, words in some alphabet, algorithm schemas (programs for computing machines), etc.] and consists of finding a method of constructing, for arbitrary admissible values of the initially given objects, some constructive objects satisfying a definite condition formulated in terms of constructive mathematics. Let us further assume that mathematicians, in trying to solve this problem, in their investigation subconsciously limit their field of attention only to constructive objects, but are inclined to believe that, for the problems of interest to them, the type of theorem provable by means of classical logic plays a satisfactory guiding role. Let us pose the question: in this situation what role do theorems of this type actually play?

---

1) One of the fundamental principles of the constructive interpretation of mathematical propositions is that every assertion about the existence of a constructive object satisfying a given condition is understood, in complete accord with the root property of constructive objects, as an assertion about the potential realizability of the construction of a constructive object satisfying the given condition.

A mathematician, having before him the indicated problem and at the same time some theorem provable by means of classical logic and asserting the existence of the required constructive objects for arbitrary admissible initially given objects, finds himself in essentially the same situation as when he did not have this theorem at his disposal. Desiring to actually use this theorem for the formulation of the required method, he is compelled to find a constructive proof, that is, he must prove (if this is possible) some proposition of constructive mathematics. If, not finding a constructive proof, he nevertheless regards the theorem as an encouraging stimulus for continuing his attempts to solve the problem, it can happen that he thus directs his mind along an absolutely hopeless path—the problem can turn out to be theoretically unsolvable, in spite of the existence of a suitable theorem of classical mathematics.

As an example of a problem for which just this situation occurs one can cite the problem of finding, for the concrete algorithmically given nondecreasing and bounded above sequence S of rational numbers constructed by E. Specker and described in §8.3.1, an algorithm (program for a computing machine with unbounded memory) which, for any natural number n, computes a subscript beginning with which the terms of the sequence are separated from each other by a distance less than 2^{-n}. Such an algorithm is impossible (see Theorem 8.3.1). At the same time, using a proof by "contradiction", we can deduce (for example, with the help of the corollary of §8.3.2) a theorem of classical mathematics (about constructive objects) which asserts that, for every n, there exists the required subscript.

One can exhibit a large number of examples of similar situations. A situation of a similar kind may arise, for example, in connection with theorems for the logical derivation of which one uses without any limitation proofs by "contradiction" or the law of the excluded middle. However, the cited logical methods of classical logic form only part of the "sources of nonconstructivity", only part of the obstacle on the way to the creation of a faithful picture telling us for which required constructive objects there are algorithms constructing (computing) them in terms of such-and-such initially given constructive objects, and for which there are no such algorithms.

IX. An obstacle of another kind, another "source of nonconstructivity" in mathematics, is connected with the widely practiced transition in classical mathematics from any assertion of the form

(*) "For any object α of type P, there exists an object β of type Q which is in the relation Γ to α"

to the assertion

(**) "There exists an operation ϕ associating with every object α of type P an object $\phi(\alpha)$ of type Q which is in the relation Γ to α".

Here Γ is a binary predicate; we shall assume that this predicate is invariant with respect to replacement of any pair of admissible objects by an equal pair (in the sense of equality of pairs induced by the relations of equality introduced for objects of type P and objects of type Q) and that, for any admissible value of the second argument, it is single-valued (up to equality of objects of type Q) in the first argument. Under these conditions the transition from (*) to (**) is often accompanied in classical mathematics by a transition from the predicate variant of the theory connected with the predicate to an operator variant in which there occurs an operation Φ replacing in a certain sense (together with the equality relation for objects of type Q) the predicate Γ. For the purposes of computational mathematics the operator variant is preferred, for obvious reasons. Mathematics offers many examples of the preference for such operator variants of theories.

The case where the proposition (*) cannot be proved by the methods of constructive mathematics does not require discussion— "nonconstructivity" is already present. Let us consider now the case where (*) is a proposition about constructive objects provable within constructive mathematics. In considering (*) and (**) as propositions of constructive mathematics it is necessary to think of the words "exists" and "operation" as being replaced by the words "is potentially realizable" and "algorithm", respectively.

In many cases the constructive reformulation of proposition (*) shows that it is an assertion about the realizability of an algorithm of a more complicated kind than that which is spoken about in proposition (**) (see [3, §8]). Hence the semantics of constructive logic and the corresponding apparatus of logical deduction does not always permit the transition to (**). In the case where the verification of the condition characterizing the concept "object of type P" includes within itself a non-algorithmizable search for a solution of some constructive task, proposition (**) can turn out to be refutable (see for example, Theorem 3.7.3 and the accompanying remark), and then the operator variant of the theory in the form suggested by (**) is impossible. However, in similar cases, one nevertheless succeeds in finding operator variants of theories of constructive mathematics, but they acquire a more complex form: as initially given objects for the algorithm Φ associated with the predicate Γ it is necessary to consider not individual objects of type P but rather systems of objects, each of which consists of some object H of type P (or a transcription of such an object) and additional objects carrying certain information about some solution of the constructive problem arising in the justification of the assertion "H is an object of type P".

The introduction into constructive mathematics of real FR-numbers, FR-constructs of various types, complete ciphers of uniformly continuous operators, metric spaces with a fixed algorithm for passage to the limit or with a fixed algorithm for constructing nets, etc. (see the main text of this paper), along with real F-numbers, F-constructs of appropriate kinds, uniformly continuous operators, metric spaces, etc., is dictated, in particular, by the tendency to have available, along with predicate variants of certain theories, also (and even preferably) operator variants, even at the expense of the introduction of objects of more complex kinds than in the corresponding theories of classical mathematics.

The transition, carried out in classical mathematics without any limitations, from predicate variants of the construction of theories to operator variants (on the basis of the transition from (*) to (**)) often produces mathematical theories for which the attempt to interpret the symbol for the operator Φ associated with the predicate Γ as a symbol for an algorithm applicable to all objects of type P and such that, for any object α of type P, the object $\Phi(\alpha)$ is in the relation Γ to α, immediately leads to confusion, in view of the impossibility of an algorithm with those properties. In similar cases in classical mathematics, in the transition to the operator variant, a change takes place in the type of the objects which can be considered as suitable initially given objects for the algorithm associated with the predicate Γ in the transition from the predicate to the operator variant of the theory admissible within constructive mathematics. Such a change leads to a certain disorientation of a mathematician dealing with the corresponding theory of classical mathematics, for example, in the light of the requirements of computational mathematics, the more so as, under the conditions of the multi-level character of contemporary mathematics, it is not always easy to discover the type of initially given objects for which a constructively justifiable operator variant of the theory is possible.

What has been said above is illustrated by the following example. In the classical theory of real numbers, one introduces a binary predicate "the real number q is the limit of the sequence of real numbers f" and one proves a theorem of the form (*), where the roles of α, β, P, Q, and Γ are played, respectively, by f, q, "fundamental sequence of real numbers", "real number", and "is the limit of". The transition to (**) is considered as the justification for the introduction of the operation lim of passage to the limit. Replacing in this theorem of the form (*) the concepts of classical mathematics by the corresponding concepts of constructive mathematics (with the concept "real number" we associate the concept "real F-number"), we obtain a proposition provable by the methods of constructive logic (see Theorem 10.5.3). However, the proposition ot the form (**) obtained by such a replacement is refutable and therefore the attempt to interpret the symbol lim (with the types of initially given objects borrowed from classical mathematics) as the symbol for an algorithm leads to obvious misunderstandings. An analysis of the proof of the constructive variant of the theorem of the form (*) just considered shows (see the proof of Theorem 10.4.5 and the remark after §10.4.6) that, as a basis for the operator construction of the theory of limits of sequences of real F-numbers, one can set an algorithm for which the initially given objects are pairs of the following form: the first term of a pair is a transcription of any fundamental sequence of real F-numbers, and the second term is the transcription of any algorithm transforming any natural number n into the transcription of a regulator of convergence in itself of the sequence of rational numbers which is based on the nth term of the sequence of F-numbers the transcription of which is the first term of the given pair (the terminology is explained in §3).

One can exhibit a large number of different examples of this kind from various branches of mathematics. We note that the kinds of "sources of nonconstructivity" in mathematics are not exhausted by the types considered above.

In constructive mathematics (in contradistinction to classical mathematics) the predicate variant and the operator variant of the construction of a theory are precisely delineated. Moreover, it is often necessary to carry out the transition from the first to the second variant by methods more complicated than in the corresponding theory of classical mathematics, but, in return, the possibility of changes in the types of relations between constructive objects is excluded. Thus, constructive mathematical analysis is a theory in which various mathematical phenomena are considered with more careful and more complete regard for the requirements of computational mathematics than in classical mathematical analysis.

BIBLIOGRAPHY

[1] A. A. Markov, *The theory of algorithms*, Trudy Mat. Inst. Steklov. 42 (1954); English transl., Israel Program for Scientific Translations, Jerusalem, 1961. MR **17**, 1038; MR **24** #A2527.

[2] A. N. Kolmogorov and V. A. Uspenskiĭ, *On the definition of an algorithm*, Uspehi Mat. Nauk 13 (1958), no. 4 (82), 3–38; English transl., Amer. Math. Soc. Transl. (2) **29** (1963), 217–245. MR **20** #5735.

[3] N. A. Šanin, *On the constructive interpretation of mathematical judgements*, Trudy Mat. Inst. Steklov. 52 (1958), 226–311; English transl., Amer. Math. Soc. Transl. (2) **23** (1963), 109–189. MR **21** #2.

[4] ______, *On an algorithm for the constructive reformulation of mathematical propositions*, Z. Math. Logik Grundlagen Math. **4** (1958), 293–303. (Russian) MR **21** #5566.

[5] H. Weyl, *Das Kontinuum*, Leipzig, 1918.

[6] ______, *On the philosophy of mathematics*. Collection, Russian transl., OGIZ, Moscow, 1934.

[7] A. Heyting, *Les fondaments des mathématiques. Intuitionism. Théorie de la démonstration*, Paris, 1955.

[8] A. A. Markov, *On constructive functions*, Trudy Mat. Inst. Steklov. 52 (1958), 315–348; English transl., Amer. Math. Soc. Transl. (2) **29** (1963), 163–195. MR **20** #5131.

[9] ______, *On the continuity of constructive functions*, Uspehi Mat. Nauk 9 (1954), no. 3 (61), 226–229. (Russian) MR **16**, 436.

[10] D. Hilbert, "On the infinite", Suppl. VIII in *Grundlagen der Geometrie*, Leipzig, 1899; 8th ed., Teubner, Stuttgart, 1956; Russian transl., OGIZ, Moscow, 1948; English transl., The Open Court, La Salle, Ill., 1959. MR **18**, 227; MR **22** #7011.

[11] S. C. Kleene, *On the interpretation of intuitionistic number theory*, J. Symbolic Logic 10 (1945), 109–124. MR **7**, 406.

[12] P. Lorenzen, *Einführung in die operative Logik und Mathematik*, Die Grundlehren der mathematischen Wissenschaften, Band 78, Springer-Verlag, Berlin, 1955; new ed., 1967. MR **17**, 223.

[13] A. M. Turing, *On computable numbers, with an application to the Entscheidungsproblem*, Proc. London Math. Soc. (2) 42 (1937), 230–265.

[14] ______, *A correction*, Proc. London Math. Soc. (2) 43 (1937), 544–546.

[15] E. Specker, *Nicht konstruktiv beweisbare Sätze der Analysis*, J. Symbolic Logic **14** (1949), 145–158. MR **11**, 151.

[16] G. S. Ceĭtin, *Algorithmic operators in constructive metric spaces*, Trudy Mat. Inst. Steklov. 67 (1962), 295–361; English transl., Amer. Math. Soc. Transl. (2) 64 (1967), 1–80. MR **27** #2406.

[17] ______, *Mean-value theorems in constructive analysis*, Trudy Mat. Inst. Steklov. 67 (1962), 362–384. (Russian) MR 27 #2407.

[18] I. D. Zaslavskiĭ, *Some properties of constructive real numbers and constructive functions*, Trudy Mat. Inst. Steklov. 67 (1962), 385–457; English transl., Amer. Math. Soc. Transl. (2) 57 (1966), 1–84. MR **27** #3519.

[19] I. D. Zaslavskiĭ and G. S. Ceĭtin, *Singular coverings and properties of constructive functions connected with them*, Trudy Mat. Inst. Steklov. 67 (1962), 458–502. (Russian) MR **27** #2408.

[20] R. L. Goodstein, *Mean value theorems in recursive function theory.* I: *Differential mean value theorems*, Proc. London Math. Soc. (2) **52** (1950), 81–106. MR **12**, 664.

[21] ______, *Constructive formalism. Essays on the foundations of mathematics*, University College, Leicester, 1951. MR **14**, 123.

[22] ______, *Function theory in an axiom-free equation calculus*, Proc. London Math. Soc. (2) **48** (1945), 401–434. MR **8**, 245.

[23] N. A. Šanin, *Some problems of mathematical analysis in the light of constructive logic*, Z. Math. Logik Grundlagen Math. **2** (1956), 27–36. (Russian) MR **18**, 2.

[24] ______, *On linear constructive functionals in a constructive Hilbert space*, Z. Math. Logik Grundlagen Math. 5 (1959), 1–8. (Russian) MR **21** #5573.

[25] G. Gentzen, *Untersuchungen über das logische Schliessen*, I, II, Math. Z. **39** (1934), 176–210, 405–431.

[26] E. Post, *Formal reductions of the general combinatorial decision problem,* Amer. J. Math. 65 (1943), 197–215. MR 4, 209.

[27] ______, *Recursively enumerable sets of positive integers and their decision problems,* Bull. Amer. Math. Soc. 50 (1944), 284–316. MR 6, 29.

[28] S. C. Kleene, *Introduction to metamathematics,* Van Nostrand, New York, 1952; Russian transl., IL, Moscow, 1957. MR 14, 525; MR 19, 2.

[29] V. K. Detlovs, *The equivalence of normal algorithms and recursive functions,* Trudy Mat. Inst. Steklov. 52 (1958), 75–139; English transl., Amer. Math. Soc. Transl. (2) 23 (1963), 15–81. MR 21 #5.

[30] È. S. Orlovskiĭ, *Some problems in the theory of algorithms,* Trudy Mat. Inst. Steklov. 52 (1958), 140–171. (Russian) MR 20 #6357.

[31] N. A. Šanin, *On constructive mathematical analysis,* Proc. Third All-Union Math. Congress, Vol. II, 1956, pp. 69–70. (Russian)